MAGILL'S
SURVEY
OF
SCIENCE

MAGILL'S SURVEY OF SCIENCE

LIFE SCIENCE SERIES

Volume 2
411-894

Central Metabolism Regulation—Eukaryotic Transcriptional Control

Edited by

FRANK N. MAGILL

Consulting Editor
LAURA L. MAYS HOOPES

SALEM PRESS

Pasadena, California   Englewood Cliffs, New Jersey

∞ The paper used in these volumes conforms to the
American National Standard for Permanence of Paper
for Printed Library Materials, Z39.48-1984.

Library of Congress Cataloging-in-Publication Data
Magill's survey of science. Life science series/edited by
Frank N. Magill, consulting editor, Laura L. Mays Hoopes.
   p. cm.
   Includes bibliographical references.
   Includes index.
   1. Life sciences. I. Magill, Frank Northen, 1907-
QH307.2.M34 1991   90-19102
574—dc20   CIP
ISBN 0-89356-612-8 (set)
ISBN 0-89356-614-4 (volume 2)

PRINTED IN THE UNITED STATES OF AMERICA

CONTENTS

LIFE SCIENCE

MAGILL'S
SURVEY
OF
SCIENCE

CENTRAL METABOLISM REGULATION

Type of life science: Biochemistry
Other fields of study: Animal physiology, genetic regulation in eukaryotes, genetic regulation in prokaryotes, and microbiology

All chemical reactions in the body are organized into metabolic pathways, and virtually all the metabolic pathways interconnect. All metabolic pathways eventually lead, directly or indirectly, to the reactions that involve the breakdown and synthesis of glucose, one of the key sources of energy for all cells in the body.

Principal terms

CENTRAL METABOLISM: the metabolic reactions that are involved in the regulation of glucose metabolism

GLUCAGON: a hormone produced by the alpha cells in the pancreas; one key function of glucagon is to stimulate the process of glycogenolysis in the liver

GLUCONEOGENESIS: the wide variety of reactions that the body can use to make glucose from molecules other than carbohydrates

GLYCOGEN: a very large carbohydrate that serves as the main form of glucose storage in the body; glycogen consists of a long chain of glucose molecules hooked end to end

GLYCOGENESIS: the chemical reactions that result in the synthesis of glycogen from glucose; glycogenesis takes place primarily in the liver and in muscle

GLYCOGENOLYSIS: the chemical reactions that result in the breakdown of glycogen into glucose; the process is stimulated in the liver by glucagon

INSULIN: a hormone produced by the beta cells of the pancreas; one key function of insulin is to stimulate all cells in the body, especially those in the liver, to take up glucose from the blood

KREBS CYCLE: the major metabolic pathway that uses products of glycolysis, producing a large amount of energy; also known as the tricarboxylic acid (TCA) cycle and the citric acid cycle

METABOLISM: a general term for all the chemical reactions that take place in the body

Summary of the Phenomenon

An organism's metabolism includes all the chemical reactions necessary to support life. Included in these are the reactions that keep an organism alive on a day-to-day basis as well as those processes that support growth and reproduction. All the chemical reactions in the body are organized into metabolic pathways. Each metabolic pathway consists of a sequence of related reactions. The product of each reaction is used as the starting material for the next reaction in the sequence.

Virtually all the metabolic pathways interconnect. A single chemical compound may be either the product or the starting material for one or more different reactions, with each reaction leading to a different metabolic pathway. These reactions are something like a major freeway interchange, with many roads meeting in one place. Each road, in turn, leads to one or more other roads. Similarly, metabolic pathways form a network much like that diagrammed by a road map.

All metabolic pathways eventually lead, either directly or indirectly, to the chemical reactions that involve the breakdown and synthesis of a simple sugar called glucose. Glucose is one of the most important and most carefully managed chemicals in the body. The metabolism of glucose is one of the key sources of energy for all cells in the body. For some organs, such as the brain, glucose is the only source of energy that can be used. Maintaining a level of glucose in the blood that is neither too low nor too high is therefore critical to the survival of the organism. It is so important that several major organs work together to control the amount of glucose present. When there is too much glucose available, such as right after a meal, the body changes the glucose into a storage form. Several hours after eating, however, when the level of glucose falls below adequate levels, the body uses its store of glucose to return to a more acceptable level. The goal is always to keep a relatively constant level of glucose in the blood.

The metabolic reactions that control the level of glucose are thus central to the stability of metabolism, and therefore of the individual. These are the reactions that lead to the specific pathway known as glycolysis. Glycolysis is the pathway by which glucose is metabolized to produce energy. In the presence of oxygen, a major connecting pathway leads from the reactions of glycolysis to a metabolic pathway called the Krebs cycle, which is also known as the tricarboxylic acid cycle (TCA cycle) and the citric acid cycle. The Krebs cycle is the most efficient way the body has to obtain cellular energy.

The main source of glucose is the food an individual eats. When the body takes in more glucose than it needs, the amount of glucose in the blood increases. The increase in glucose is sensed by special cells in the pancreas called beta cells, which release the hormone insulin. Insulin stimulates all organs in the body, but especially the liver and muscle tissue, to take up glucose from the bloodstream.

Insulin has another major effect. It stimulates the liver and muscle tissues to start a series of chemical reactions that convert the excess glucose into a storage chemical called glycogen. Glycogen is made up of a long chain of glucose molecules hooked end to end. Glycogen is thus a polysaccharide ("poly" means many, and "saccharide" means sugar). This process of storing glucose as glycogen involves a series of chemical reactions that together are called glycogenesis ("glycos" means sugar, or sweet, and "genesis" means birth, or origin). The reactions of the glycogenesis pathway and the enzymes involved in this process were worked out by the biochemist Luis Leloir and his colleagues in 1957.

Glycogenesis takes place primarily in the liver and in muscle, and storing glucose as glycogen is a very energy-efficient process. The amount of cellular energy used to put each molecule of glucose into "glycogen storage" plus the amount needed to take it out of storage add up to less than 5 percent of the total energy the cell could get from breaking down a single molecule of glucose. The overall efficiency of the process is therefore greater than 95 percent. By stimulating glycogenesis, insulin leads to a drop in blood glucose. As blood glucose drops, the beta cells in the pancreas stop releasing insulin.

Several hours after a meal, all the cells in the body have used glucose for energy. Gradually, the amount of glucose in the blood decreases. When this happens, the body responds with mechanisms to reverse the trend. When the amount of glucose in the blood drops below a certain "safe" level, this is sensed by alpha cells in the pancreas, which release a hormone called glucagon into the bloodstream. The overall effect of glucagon is exactly the opposite of insulin: Glucagon increases the amount of glucose in the blood.

One of the most important organs affected by glucagon is the liver. Glucagon acts on the liver to break down stored glycogen into glucose. The glucagon stimulates enzymes in the liver that function in breaking down glycogen through a series of reactions called glycogenolysis ("lysis" means to break). In glycogenolysis, the glucose molecules at the end of a glycogen molecule are split off, one by one, by an enzyme called liver phosphorylase. The glucose produced through glycogenolysis is then taken out of the liver into the bloodstream. As the amount of glucose in the blood goes up and returns to normal levels, the pancreas senses this increase and stops releasing glucagon.

The reactions of glycogenolysis are different from those of glycogenesis. That is, it is not a case of the same reactions going in the opposite direction, but of different chemical reactions, with different enzymes involved. When glucagon stimulates the liver cells, a group of enzymes called protein kinases are activated. Protein kinases have their effect by adding a phosphate atom to an enzyme. The process of addition of a phosphate to an enzyme is called phosphorylation. In the case of the liver phosphorylase, this phosphorylation is necessary for the enzyme to function properly.

The body can store enough glycogen in the liver to keep blood glucose levels stable for about twelve to twenty-four hours. In extreme situations, when all the glycogen is broken down, there is a third process, called gluconeogenesis, that the body is able to use. Gluconeogenesis, which literally means "new birth of glucose," includes all the reactions by which glucose can be made from molecules other than carbohydrates. For example, when fats are broken down, one of the products is glycerol. The glycerol molecule can eventually be used to make glucose.

In a healthy individual who is on a balanced diet, there is a limited amount of protein breakdown every day; however, most of the glucose the body uses is derived from carbohydrates or, indirectly, from fat metabolism. In times of extreme starvation, proteins are broken down into amino acids. The amino acids are then chemically modified by an enzyme, and they are used in a set of chemical reactions that result in the formation of glucose.

Gluconeogenesis takes place primarily in the liver and, to some degree, in the kidneys. The process is regulated by sensors in the brain, which detect a drop below a certain level of the concentration of glucose in the bloodstream. The sensors send a signal to the pituitary, a small gland about the size of a lima bean found at the base of the brain. When the pituitary senses a constant low level of blood glucose, it releases a hormone called corticotropin. Corticotropin, in turn, stimulates the adrenal gland to secrete a group of hormones called glucocorticoids. One of the many functions of glucocorticoids is to signal cells to break down proteins into amino acids. The amino acids are released into the bloodstream and taken to the liver. The liver is the main organ in the body involved in changing amino acids into glucose.

Another hormone that is involved in the process of gluconeogenesis is thyroxine, which is made in the thyroid gland. It is one of the key hormones that regulate the metabolic rate. One of the effects of thyroxine is to trigger the breakdown of proteins and fats to their constituents; for example, proteins are broken down into amino acids, and fats are broken down into glycerol, which is used to make glucose via gluconeogenesis, and fatty acids.

Breaking down protein for energy is a last resort used by the body only in an emergency. Gluconeogenesis is chemically a very expensive process for the body in terms of the cellular energy. The body uses it because there are some organs, such as the brain, that cannot use anything other than glucose as a source of energy. Others, such as the heart, begin malfunctioning if deprived of glucose for any length of time. It is obviously in the best interests of the body to keep organs such as the heart and the brain in as prime a functioning condition as possible. Chemical mechanisms such as gluconeogenesis have thus evolved to ensure the organism's continued survival.

Methods of Study

The precise regulation of central metabolic reactions is essential to the survival of the organism. The control of these central pathways represents a complex interaction of physiological, cellular, biochemical, and genetic controls. Reaching an understanding of how these pathways are controlled has necessitated the interaction of scientists from many different disciplines of the life sciences. To study the effects of the various hormones on metabolism, physiologists have injected hormones into experimental animals and examined the effects on blood glucose and on overall metabolic rate. Physiologists have also used surgery to remove the pancreas, thyroid, adrenal, and pituitary glands and analyzed the effects of the removal on metabolic rate.

Using the techniques of protein purification, biochemists have purified all the enzymes involved in the various reactions involving glucose metabolism. Having the pure enzymes has allowed scientists to re-create these chemical reactions and study how each individual reaction is controlled. Molecular biologists have studied how the genes that code for the enzymes and hormones that regulate metabolism are themselves controlled. The last half of the twentieth century has witnessed a tremendous surge in understanding how this important process works. The significance of these advances is even greater when one considers that all of these chemical reactions take place in cells that measure less than 0.1 millimeter in diameter.

Context

Glucose is the only fuel used to any significant degree by some cells in the body, and it is the major fuel used by the brain. For example, red blood cells, the lens of the eye, the cornea of the eye, and some portions of the kidney all depend on glucose as their primary source of energy. It is absolutely critical that the body be able to maintain very careful control of the levels of glucose.

One of the most significant features of these central reactions that regulate glucose is that they are found in all living things, from bacteria to humans. In terms of evaluation, these reactions have supported life virtually since its inception: These metabolic pathways have not changed significantly since the first living creatures appeared. This is the reason they are so fundamental to the survival of the individual. Any genetic mutations or physiological defects that cause a change in these reactions can be deadly.

One of the best-known diseases related to glucose metabolism is diabetes mellitus. In diabetes mellitus, there is a drop in the amount of insulin produced by the pancreas. With less insulin, the liver takes up less glucose. This leads to a large increase in blood glucose. Although it is not known what causes diabetes, scientists believe that heredity plays a role. Diabetes mellitus can be treated by insulin injections as well as by careful management of food intake; however, it is still a very serious condition that must be taken seriously by anyone affected. In some individuals, the glycogenolysis enzymes are absent or defective. When this happens, the glycogen cannot be broken down readily when glucose is needed. One of the results of this condition is an enlarged liver; large amounts of glycogen are continually stored without being broken down, and swelling results.

There are some ways, in addition to disease, that glucose metabolism can be altered. For example, ethanol, the alcohol found in alcoholic beverages, can inhibit glucose metabolism in the liver. This can lead to a reduction in the overall amount of glucose to the body and—most important—to the brain.

Bibliography

Alberts, Bruce, Dennis Bray, Julian Lewis, Martin Raff, Keith Roberts, and James D. Watson. *Molecular Biology of the Cell*. 2d ed. New York: Garland, 1989. Although this advanced molecular biology text requires an understanding of college-level biology, it contains two good sections summarizing the concept of central metabolism. There is an excellent schematic diagram (on page 81) that demonstrates the intricacies of the metabolic pathways and their convergence on a few key reactions.

Arms, Karen, and Pamela S. Camp. *Biology*. 3d ed. Philadelphia: Saunders College

Publishing, 1987. A good introductory college-level textbook. Chapter 42, "Animal Hormones and Chemical Regulation," includes a good summary of the key hormones involved in metabolic regulation. Contains end-of-chapter objectives, self-quizzes, and questions for discussion.

Devlin, Thomas M., ed. *Textbook of Biochemistry with Clinical Correlations.* 2d ed. New York: John Wiley & Sons, 1986. This is a readable clinical biochemistry textbook. The advanced high school student as well as college undergraduates should find it helpful. Chapter 7, "Carbohydrate Metabolism I: Major Metabolic Pathways and Their Control," covers glycolysis, glycogenesis, glycogenolysis, and gluconeogenesis in detail.

Guyton, A. C. *Textbook of Medical Physiology.* 7th ed. Philadelphia: W. B. Saunders, 1986. This is one of the best medical physiology textbooks available. Although it is written for advanced students, it is extremely readable and very easy to understand. Most of the necessary basic information is provided in the text. Unit 12, "Metabolism and Temperature Regulation," and unit 13, "Endocrinology and Reproduction," contain a total of thirteen chapters ranging from basic carbohydrate metabolism to temperature, temperature regulation, and the regulation of feeding. The emphasis is on human physiology.

Purves, William K., and Gordon H. Orians. *Life: The Science of Biology.* 2d ed. Sunderland, Mass.: Sinauer Associates, 1987. A useful introductory college-level text. Chapter 26, "Animal Hormones," contains good summaries of the actions of the key animal hormones. Although college level, this text will also be useful for the high school student.

Stryer, Lubert. *Biochemistry.* 3d ed. New York: W. H. Freeman, 1988. This is one of the most comprehensive general biochemistry textbooks available. Although this is intended for the advanced college student, it is quite readable. The excellent color diagrams provide good illustrative material. Chapter 18 includes a complete discussion on gluconeogenesis. Chapter 19 covers the reactions of glycogen metabolism in detail.

Alina C. Lopo

Cross-References

Allosteric Regulation and Covalent Modification, 65; ATP and Other Energetic Molecules, 134; Catabolism of Fats and Proteins, 337; Digestion Regulation, 650; Endocrine Functions of the Pancreas, 787; Endocrinology of the Adrenal Glands, 800; Endocrinology of the Pituitary Gland, 807; Endocrinology of the Thyroid and Parathyroid Glands, 814; Glycolysis and Fermentation, 1219; The Krebs Cycle, 1520; Metabolic Pathways, 1691; Metabolic Rates, 1699.

CHEMICAL ELEMENTS OF LIVING SYSTEMS

Type of life science: Biochemistry
Other fields of study: Botany, invertebrate biology, and zoology

Chemical elements are the basic building blocks of all matter and the basis for all structures of life. By studying uptake, usage, and effect of these elements in living systems, scientists are able to identify and attempt to understand their complex interactions.

Principal terms
ANALYSIS: the investigation of a sample to discover its chemical identity (qualitative analysis), or how much (quantitative analysis) of the material is present
ATOM: the smallest particle that is involved in a chemical combination
BOND: a link holding two atoms together; electronic structure of the bonded atoms differs from that of the original atoms; energy is required to break such a link
ELEMENT: a pure substance that cannot be decomposed by a chemical change
PERIODIC TABLE: the listing of elements by their atomic number, in a manner which describes the periodic nature of their properties

Summary of the Phenomenon

All matter, living and nonliving, is composed of atoms. The chemistry of living systems involves making and breaking links, or bonds, between these atoms and does not affect the atoms themselves. An atom may be regarded as a very dense and tiny nucleus, which contains protons (which are positively charged) and neutrons; surrounding each nucleus is a diffuse area that contains electrons—minutely small, negatively charged particles. The amount of space that the nucleus occupies compared to the space that the electrons occupy is extremely small. If the nucleus could be expanded to 1 meter in diameter, the closest electron would be more than 50 kilometers from it.

Each atom has the same number of protons and electrons and, since their charges cancel, there is no overall charge. The number of neutrons is approximately equal to the number of protons, but this may vary. Atoms are classified into types, or elements, by the number of protons (called the atomic number) they possess. An element consists of atoms which have the same atomic number. For example, all atoms of hydrogen have one proton; all atoms of the element iron have fifty-six protons. Elements may be regarded as fundamental units of matter, defined by the number of protons. Each element has different physical and chemical characteristics. These properties can be predicted if the atomic number of the element is known. For example, the element oxygen, atomic number 8, is a clear colorless gas, while the element silver, atomic number 47, is a metallic solid.

When atoms combine, materials are formed that may not resemble the starting elements. When carbon and chlorine combine, for example, they form the molecule carbon tetrachloride, the pungent-smelling cleaning fluid used in dry cleaning. This material bears little resemblance to carbon, the element found in diamond and graphite. Neither does it resemble chlorine, the element that is often used to disinfect swimming pools and is recognized by its sharp smell. There are elements with atomic numbers that range from 1 to 109. Of these, about ninety are found naturally, while the remaining elements are artificially prepared using nuclear science techniques. The name assigned to an individual element depends on when and where the element was discovered. Ancient man recognized nine elements: seven metals and two nonmetals. Some elements were named after mythological figures. Thorium was named for the Norse god of war, Thor, since the element was first discovered in a Norwegian mineral. Other elements are named for celestial bodies (for example, uranium, for Uranus) or colors (rubidium, Latin for dark red). More recently, elements have been named for people: curium (for Marie Curie, the French discoverer of radioactivity) or einsteinium (for Albert Einstein, the German physicist).

Geographical locations have also been used to name elements—for example, californium or germanium. Indeed, the name used for a particular element sometimes depends on where one lives. In 1964, a Russian group reported the production of the element with atomic number 104 and named it khrushchevium (for Nikita Khrushchev, the Soviet premier from 1955 to 1964). At the same time, an American group produced the same element; they named it rutherfordium, for Ernest Rutherford, the New Zealander who made significant contribution to science's understanding of the structure of the atom. Elements heavier than plutonium (atomic number 94) are not found in nature and must be produced artificially. No element that does not occur naturally is important in sustaining life. Even of the naturally occurring elements, very few are essential to life.

The element that is most fundamental to life is probably carbon, since all plant and animal life is based upon it. Elemental carbon is found in diamond, graphite (pencil "lead"), coal, and charcoal. In living systems, however, carbon is always combined with other elements, such as hydrogen, nitrogen, and oxygen. Carbon-containing materials are called organic. Carbon makes up 18.5 percent of human body weight. The compound formed from one atom of carbon and two atoms of oxygen, carbon dioxide, is the major waste product of the body and is formed from foods—which all contain carbon. In addition, carbon dioxide serves as a basic raw material for plants in the process of photosynthesis.

Hydrogen, the smallest atom, is a gas. Combined with other elements, hydrogen constitutes 9.5 percent of body weight. It is found combined with oxygen in water and in most organic materials. Nitrogen is a gas which makes up 80 percent of the atmosphere. It is found combined with organic molecules in living systems. It represents 3.5 percent of the weight of a human. Nitrogen is found in amino acids, basic building blocks of biological systems. Oxygen is the most abundant element on earth, making up about 20 percent of the atmosphere. Oxygen is found combined with hydrogen (in water) and with organic molecules. Oxygen is the only element that can be used by the body in its elemental form: It is taken in and used in the process of respiration. Oxygen makes up the largest proportion of the body's mass at 65 percent.

These four elements—carbon, hydrogen, nitrogen, and oxygen—make up about 96 percent of body mass. In addition to these elements, phosphorus and sulfur are present in all living things. Phosphorus is an important component of the genes (the material responsible for passing information from generation to generation) and of brain and nervous system tissue. In addition, phosphorus is needed for energy utilization in the body. Phosphorus makes up about 1 percent of the weight of the human body. The daily requirement for phosphorus can be met from meat, poultry, fish, and whole grains. Sulfur, a yellow element, is found combined with many organic molecules and is an important structural feature of these materials. Sulfur forms less than 1 percent of the body's weight.

Carbon, hydrogen, nitrogen, oxygen, phosphorus, and sulfur are essential for life and are found in many chemical substances in humans and other living systems. A number of other elements are essential for growth and good health. They are the "macrominerals": calcium, sodium, chlorine, potassium, and magnesium. These five elements are needed in relatively large amounts every day (more than one-third of a gram). Calcium is essential for healthy teeth and bones. It regulates the activities of muscles and nerves and is important in blood clotting. The daily calcium requirement may be met by eating milk products, green vegetables, citrus fruits, and beans. Sodium is essential for water balance in the body and is often taken into the body as salt (sodium chloride). Chlorine is also essential for water balance and, when combined with hydrogen, forms hydrochloric acid, the material responsible for digestion of food in the stomach. It, too, is supplied to the body from salt. Potassium is an element similar to sodium and, like sodium, is involved in electrical balance and transmission in living systems. Potassium is found in tomatoes, citrus fruit, and bananas. Magnesium is necessary for enzyme activity. Enzymes control and aid almost all chemical reactions that occur in the body. Magnesium is found in green leafy vegetables.

Another group of elements is needed for healthy life, but they are necessary in much smaller daily amounts: only a few milligrams. These chemicals are known as the trace elements and include arsenic, chromium, cobalt, copper, fluorine, iodine, iron, manganese, molybdenum, nickel, selenium, silicon, tin, and vanadium. The biological purpose of some of these elements is not known, although many have been linked to enzyme function.

Some trace elements, however, have well-known chemistry in the body. Iron is vital for the transport of oxygen in blood hemoglobin. Men need 10 milligrams each day, while women require 18 milligrams. Liver is the richest source of dietary iron. Cooking in cast-iron cookware adds considerable amounts of iron to the human diet. The tendency in recent years to move away from the use of cast-iron cookware has been linked to an increased incidence of conditions, such as anemia, caused by iron deficiency. Iodine is necessary for correct thyroid gland function. Fluorine is essential for healthy teeth and bones. Indeed, many states add fluorine to their drinking water to supplement dietary sources. Many elements are common to different life-forms, whereas some are specific to a particular species or living system. Vanadium and boron are essential to some plants, although their function is not well understood. Tin is necessary for rats, while nickel is essential for healthy chickens.

Silicon provides an interesting example of an extremely common element (making up 20 percent of the earth's crust) whose role in many organisms is not well understood. An exception to this is the use of silicon by diatoms, unicellular algae that form a glassy protective coating of silica. The silicon is metabolized from silicates in seawater. Evidence of millions of these marine creatures is found in rock deposits with glassy characteristics known as diatomaceous earth. It has been known for many years that in many types of animals and plants a diet deficient in silicon is harmful and ultimately deadly. Evidence indicates that, unlike other essential elements, there are no known biochemical sites (these are often protein-based) for silicon. It has been postulated that silicon is necessary for the animal or plant to exclude toxic aluminum. Thus, although not essential itself, the protection that silicon provides is in some way vital for the survival of the organism.

Methods of Study

By the late eighteenth century, approximately thirty elements were known. Scientists of this period faced considerable difficulty identifying the elemental composition of the materials they studied. These difficulties were addressed by the work of Antoine-Laurent Lavoisier. (Lavoisier, the French chemist widely considered to be a founder of modern chemistry, came to an untimely end when he was guillotined in 1794 during the French Revolution.) His studies on the combustion of organic compounds led to the nineteenth century work of Justus von Liebig, a German chemist. Liebig's method applied the principle that organic compounds containing carbon and hydrogen, in contact with hot copper oxide, react with oxygen to give gaseous products, carbon dioxide, and steam. These products can be trapped and accurately weighed to give their elemental composition. Oxygen cannot be directly measured, but if the material is known to contain only carbon, hydrogen, and oxygen, then its oxygen content may be calculated. Jean Dumas, the French scientist, introduced a similar process in 1830 for nitrogen analysis. Fritz Pregl, the Austrian researcher, refined the process to allow analysis on very small samples; for this work Pregl received the 1923 Nobel Prize in Chemistry. This method is still used today and is often required as final proof of the identity of a new compound.

As with Liebig's method, most procedures to measure the amount of an element present in a biological sample are based on the destruction of the sample. Most analytical methods fall broadly into two categories: more traditional means, using laboratory bench procedures (often referred to as "wet" methods), and instrument-based experiments using more sophisticated equipment. Choice of method depends on a range of criteria: how accurate the results need to be, how quickly the results are needed, in what form the sample exists, and what equipment and chemicals are available. For example, if a patient comes into the hospital with symptoms of arsenic poisoning (nausea, vomiting, weakness, and diarrhea), there is a choice of techniques. The Gutzeit test is a simple wet test using sulfuric acid, zinc, and silver nitrate on the patient's urine. This test is rapid and is accurate enough to allow physicians to administer treatment almost immediately. This is particularly important in the case of arsenic poisoning, since the medication used to treat this problem, dimercaprol, is most effective if administered within twenty-four hours of exposure. A more accurate method to determine arsenic poisoning is atomic absorption spectroscopy. This procedure may be used on a range of samples, including blood, urine, hair, and nails, and is the definitive test for arsenic levels. The technique is based on the fact that free atoms will, when suitable energy is shown upon them, absorb some of that energy. The amount of energy absorbed can be related to the amount of a specific atom in the sample.

For many biological samples, the levels of specific molecules are more important than the elemental composition. Techniques to quantitate elements are well established, but the field of measuring specific molecules, such as drugs, pharmaceuticals, and toxic materials, is an area of continuing and vital research. Many techniques for routine analysis and screenings, particularly in medical fields, are highly automated. Some instruments commonly found in hospitals and clinical laboratories can run twenty tests on a sample and provide a detailed chemical analysis within thirty minutes.

Context

In addition to the elements that make up a necessary part of normal life, unusually high levels of essential—and sometimes of unwanted—elements are being found in living systems. Modern agriculture has done much to improve world production of food, and new techniques have provided higher yields. High-impact farming, however, using large quantities of chemical nutrients, pesticides, and fungicides, as practiced in the United States and the West, has come under considerable criticism. One problem is that some of these materials can leach out of the soil and into water supplies, where the cumulative effects may be undesirable. The three key elements added to soils to aid healthy plant growth are nitrogen, potassium, and phosphorus. Nitrogen is usually introduced as ammonium salts or nitrates. Many plants can absorb nitrates directly, but ammonium salts are converted to more accessible forms by the plants. High levels of these nitrogen-containing materials in water supplies have caused health problems in the United States and Great Britain.

Two trace metals that have significant toxicity and have received considerable interest from the press are lead and mercury. Lead was once used extensively as an "anti-knocking" agent in gasoline. Studies have shown that lead density in living tissue can be related to traffic flow patterns: The greater the density of traffic, the higher the incidence of lead poisoning. The introduction of lead-free additives for gasoline has helped alleviate this concern; however, this is not the only source of lead. Many occupations, such as mining and welding, expose workers to lead. In the southern United States, moonshine whiskey is a significant source of lead poisoning. Potentially toxic levels of lead have been found in moonshine, as a result of the lead solder used to connect the stills and the old lead radiators that are often used as condensers.

Prior to the industrial revolution, an average person had 2 milligrams of lead in his system. In industrialized nations, this value is now 250 milligrams. Lead poisoning leads to a variety of medical conditions affecting the abdomen, the blood, and the nervous system. Tetraethyl lead, the gasoline additive, can cause euphoria, nervousness, insomnia, hallucinations, convulsions, and psychosis.

Mercury, another heavy metal recognized as toxic, causes a range of medical conditions, affecting many parts of the body and mental function. Large quantities of mercury are used in dental offices, since it has been used as a component in tooth fillings; some up to 10 percent of dental offices have been found to have excess levels of mercury vapor. Mercury is also widely used in industry, and some occupations became infamous for the illness of their workers. Lewis Carroll's Mad Hatter, from *Alice in Wonderland*, may be based on observation. In the Victorian era, it was the fashion for men to wear tall hats; mercury compounds were used in the pressing process to achieve the necessary stiffness in the fabric. Thus, hatters inhaled large doses of mercury vapor. Since many of the disorders of mercury poisoning affect mental function, mad hatters apparently were not that unusual an occurrence.

It is easy to forget, when considering individual elements and molecules, the amazingly complex systems on which life is based. Each atom and molecule interacts with billions of other atoms, either directly or indirectly. Although scientists are beginning to acquire an understanding of some of the simplest of these links, understanding is far from complete.

Bibliography

Bernstein, Ruth, and Stephen Bernstein. *Biology: The Study of Life*. New York: Harcourt Brace Jovanovich, 1982. Provides a basic introduction to the science of biology, with detailed introductory chapters on chemistry. Also covers chemical control systems and organization for survival, including defense against the environment.

Emsley, John. *The Elements*. Oxford, England: Clarendon Press, 1989. Contains a complete listing of the physical and chemical properties of all elements. A good, useful source.

Griffith, H. Winter. *Complete Guide to Medical Tests*. Tucson, Ariz.: Fisher Books, 1988. A detailed description of clinical diagnostic tests for the nonspecialist.

Guerlac, Henry. *Lavoisier—The Crucial Year: The Background and Origin of His First Experiments on Combustion in 1772*. Ithaca, N.Y.: Cornell University Press,

1961. A specific biography covering Lavoisier's most important work, in the light of the revolution in chemistry that his studies caused.

Kaufman, Peter B., and Michael L. Evans. *Plants: Their Biology and Importance.* New York: Harper & Row, 1989. A detailed introduction to botany. The text discusses structure, genetics, major groups (such as viruses, prokaryotes, fungi, algae), development, and ecology. A college-level introductory course.

McMurray, John. *Organic Chemistry.* Pacific Grove, Calif.: Brooks/Cole, 1988. A more technical introduction to the structure, reactions, and activity of organic compounds. The emphasis is on the chemistry, although some biological and medical examples are used to illustrate the concepts.

Ucko, David A. *Living Chemistry.* New York: Academic Press, 1986. A general introduction to basic chemical principles in terms of the chemistry of life. Examples related to humans are used throughout.

Wyngaarden, James B., and Lloyd H. Smith, Jr., eds. *Cecil Textbook of Medicine.* Philadelphia: W. B. Saunders, 1985. A comprehensive and highly technical text that is widely regarded as the standard for medicine. Each section is written by an expert in that field. Specific references are included.

Susan J. Mole

Cross-References

Biochemical Pathway Analysis, 163; Intermediates, Monomers, and Polymers, 1452; The Definition of Life, 1564; Nucleic Acid Structure, 1987; Nutrition and Metabolic Diversity in Microbes, 2001; Prebiotic Evolution in the Laboratory, 2170; Protein Phosphorylation, 2257; Proteins, 2272; Thermodynamics in Biology, 2625; Water in Living Cells, 2702.

CHLOROPLAST REACTION SITES

Type of life science: Photosynthesis
Other fields of study: Biochemistry, biophysics, botany, and plant physiology

The chloroplast is the cellular organelle found in plants which carries on photosynthesis. Photosynthesis is the process by which plants take in carbon dioxide and convert it to carbohydrate, which is utilized by other organisms for energy.

Principal terms

ADENOSINE TRIPHOSPHATE (ATP) SYNTHETASE: a complex found in the thylakoid membrane which helps to convert light energy into chemical energy in the form of ATP

GRANA (*sing.* GRANUM): the stacks of thylakoid membranes that are found in the chloroplast and that function in the light reactions of photosynthesis

MEMBRANE: a thin layer of tissue, composed of lipids (fats) and proteins, that acts as a barrier to the movement of molecules

ORGANELLE: a membrane-bound compartment inside the cell with a specific function; a chloroplast is an organelle for photosynthesis

pH: a measure of the extent to which a solution is acid or basic; the pH scale goes from 0 to 14, with 1 being acid, 7 neutral, and 14 basic

PHOTOSYSTEM: location of pigment molecules in the thylakoid membranes, where the light-absorbing reactions of photosynthesis take place

STROMA: the fluid surrounding the thylakoid membranes, where the sugars and carbohydrates of photosynthesis are produced

THYLAKOIDS: membrane-bound sacs found in the chloroplast, some of which are organized into grana; the site where sunlight energy is captured in photosynthesis

Summary of the Phenomenon

The chloroplast is a cellular organelle found in algae and higher plants, where the process of photosynthesis occurs. Photosynthesis converts sunlight energy into chemical energy, which can be used to convert carbon dioxide into sugars and carbohydrates. It is through photosynthesis that carbohydrates initially enter the food chain that supports other organisms.

The chloroplasts are cellular organelles bounded by two lipid membrane bilayers. It is speculated that chloroplasts descended from prokaryotic organisms (organisms consisting of a cell or cells lacking membrane-bound nuclei). They may have become engulfed within a prokaryotic cell, finally forming a beneficial relationship for both the chloroplast and the prokaryotic cell. This theory is supported by the fact that chloroplasts contain their own deoxyribonucleic acid (DNA), ribonucleic acid

(RNA), and ribosomes, which are prokaryotic in nature. Chloroplasts also have the capacity for their own protein synthesis. They are relatively large organelles, on the order of 5 to 20 micrometers in diameter. A typical photosynthetic cell can contain 20 to 40 chloroplasts per cell.

The structure of the chloroplast participates in the function of the chloroplast in photosynthesis. The chloroplast is surrounded by two individual lipid bilayer membranes, separated by an intermembrane space. The outer membrane is more permeable to small molecules than is the inner membrane. The inner membrane bilayer contains protein molecules that aid in the transport of molecules in and out of the chloroplast. The chloroplast contains an additional internal membrane system that is not connected to the inner and outer membranes. This internal membrane system is organized into thylakoids, which appear as flattened sacs in electron micrographs. The thylakoids are arranged in stacks called grana. The thylakoids may also travel from stack to stack, in which case they are referred to as stroma thylakoids. The thylakoids surround the thylakoid space, which is a water-filled, or aqueous, compartment. The area surrounding the thylakoids and contained by the two lipid bilayers is called the stroma. It contains the soluble proteins, starch grains, DNA, RNA, amino acids, sugars, and lipid droplets.

The main function of the chloroplast is in photosynthesis. The process of photosynthesis can be broken down into two reaction sequences: light reactions and dark reactions. The light reactions of photosynthesis convert sunlight into chemical energy and occur in or on both sides of the thylakoid membranes. The dark reactions utilize the chemical energy formed in the light reactions and convert carbon dioxide into sugars and carbohydrates. The dark reactions occur in the stroma of the chloroplast.

The light reactions of photosynthesis occur on the thylakoid membranes. There are five complexes associated with the light reactions of photosynthesis: two photosystems, the light-harvesting chlorophyll-protein (LHCP) complexes, the electron transport carriers, and the adenosine triphosphate (ATP) synthetase coupling factor.

The first of these complexes are the photosystems. These complexes contain pigments, which are molecules that absorb light. The primary pigment in the chloroplast is chlorophyll (both chlorophyll a and chlorophyll b), which gives the leaves their characteristic green color. Chlorophyll a is a dark green, while chlorophyll b is a yellow-green. Chlorophyll absorbs primarily blue and red light, and it is blue and red light that drive the light reactions of photosynthesis. Other pigments that are found in the thylakoids are the carotenoids. The carotenoids, which are various colors of yellow and orange, are accessory pigments that absorb light that chlorophyll cannot absorb. This additional absorption of light increases the energy that can be used for photosynthesis. The carotenoids then transfer the captured light energy to the chlorophyll molecules.

Both the chlorophylls and the carotenoids are lipid-soluble molecules, enabling them to be anchored in the thylakoid membranes. Chlorophyll has a long hydrophobic (or "water-fearing") tail to anchor the molecule in the membrane. The carotenoids are relatively long chains of carbon and hydrogen atoms (or hydrocarbons). These pigments are assembled into complexes containing between two hundred and three hundred pigment molecules and proteins. In the assemblages, there is a special chlorophyll a molecule called the reaction center. The reaction center and the accessory chlorophyll and carotenoid molecules collectively are called photosystems. These photosystems are found in the thylakoid membranes.

Two types of photosystem are known in higher plants, photosystem I and photosystem II. The reaction center of photosystem I contains a chlorophyll a molecule that absorbs red light at a wavelength of 700 nanometers (10^{-9} meters) and is called P700. The reaction center of photosystem II contains a chlorophyll a molecule that absorbs red light at a wavelength of 680 nanometers and is called P680. These photosystems are distributed throughout the thylakoid membranes, photosystem I being found primarily in the curved and unstacked regions of the thylakoid membranes. Photosystem II is found in the stacked regions of the thylakoid grana membranes.

There is another complex associated with the photosystems, the light-harvesting chlorophyll-protein (LHCP) complex. The LHCP contains both chlorophyll a and b pigment molecules. The LHCP functions in absorbing sunlight energy and transferring it to either photosystem reaction center, thus distributing the energy for maximum efficiency for photosynthesis.

The next complex aids in energy flow between the two photosystems. Energy is transferred from photosystem II to photosystem I via the electron transport chain. The electron transport chain is located in the thylakoid membrane and associated with the surface of the membranes. When sunlight energy is absorbed at the reaction center of P680, electrons are boosted in energy and lost from the chlorophyll a reaction center. The electron is then captured by the primary acceptor, which is the start of the electron transport chain. The next molecule is called plastoquinone (PQ), a lipid-soluble molecule, which takes the electrons from the primary acceptor. Electrons then flow from PQ through a cytochrome molecule in the thylakoid membranes of plastocyanin (PC). Plastocyanin is found on the inner surface of the thylakoid space and transfers the electrons to the reaction center of photosystem I. Electrons then are boosted in energy by the absorption of sunlight at the reaction center (P700) to another series of electron carriers, starting with a primary acceptor. This primary acceptor then transfers the electrons to ferredoxin (FD), which is associated on the stroma side of the thylakoid membranes. Ferredoxin transfers the electrons to nicotinamide adenine dinucleotide phosphate (NADP) reductase and ultimately NADP to form NADPH in the stroma. The NADPH is then used in the dark reactions of photosynthesis.

As electrons flow from the P680 reaction center to the P700 reaction center via the electron transport chain, hydrogen ions are shuttled across the thylakoid membrane from the stroma to the thylakoid space by the electron carrier PQ. This action creates a hydrogen ion (pH) gradient from the thylakoid space, which has an acidic pH of 4.5, to the stroma, which has a basic pH of 8.0.

The last major complex in the thylakoid membrane, the ATP synthetase, utilizes the pH gradient. The ATP synthetase is located in the unstacked and curved regions of the thylakoid membranes and has two major protein components. The first component spans the thylakoid membrane and acts as a pore which enables hydrogen ions to flow from the thylakoid space to the stroma. The other component, which looks like a knob, is on the stroma surface of the thylakoid membrane attached to the membrane component. It is here that the production of ATP occurs.

The ATP and NADPH produced by the light reactions of photosynthesis are then utilized in the dark reactions of photosynthesis. It can be noticed that the production of both ATP and NADPH occurs on the stroma side of the thylakoid membranes. The dark reactions, better known as the Calvin-Benson cycle, also occur in the stroma of the chloroplast. All the associated enzymes which catalyze the reactions of the Calvin-Benson cycle are found in the stroma. It is this series of reactions that requires the energy from the sunlight to produce the sugars and carbohydrates.

There are other reactions occurring in the stroma. One is the production of starch. This reaction occurs when excess sugars produced by photosynthesis cannot be transferred out of the chloroplast to other regions of the plant as fast as production. Another series of reactions found in the chloroplast are nitrogen and sulfur reactions. The chloroplast, through a series of reactions, produces a form of nitrogen and sulfur used by the plant. The ATP and NADPH produced by the light reactions of photosynthesis are used in the nitrogen and sulfur reactions.

Methods of Study

The process of photosynthesis has been studied for centuries, and the equation for photosynthesis has been known since the early 1800's. First, given the chloroplast's large size, its structure could be studied by light microscopy. Utilization of the light microscope noted that the chloroplasts were the green part of the leaf. The use of the light microscope has enabled researchers to find that chloroplasts also contain starch as a storage product. The limitations of light microscopy, however, did not allow the fine, detailed structure of the chloroplast to be observed.

Further microscopic research had to wait for the invention of the electron microscope. Photosynthetic plant cells are killed, fixed into plastic, sectioned, and then examined using the transmission electron microscope (TEM). The TEM has enabled researchers to examine the fine detail of the chloroplast, such as the thylakoid membranes and the granal stacks.

Chloroplasts can be isolated from photosynthetic cells by cellular fractionation. Cells are ground up in a blender and then centrifuged at relatively low speed. This process separates the chloroplasts from the other, lighter cellular organelles. Once the chloroplasts are isolated, many types of different experiments can be performed on them. They can, moreover, be used to study the location of the protein complexes in the thylakoid membranes. This process uses the TEM and a technique called freeze-fraction replication. Cells are rapidly frozen using liquid nitrogen (at

−200 degrees Celsius). A sharp knife edge is then allowed to strike the tissue, splitting the tissue into two pieces. The tissue is then stained with heavy metals, and the replica is viewed in the TEM. Use of this technique has enabled researchers to locate the protein complexes in the thylakoid membranes.

Further research has used a combination of TEM and isolated chloroplasts. First, chloroplasts are isolated by cellular fractionation techniques; then they burst open to release the thylakoid membranes. Detergents are used because the exposed portions of the membrane will break away from the other regions of the thylakoids. Once the different portions of thylakoid membranes are isolated, the proteins that are found in each region can be separated by gel electrophoresis. This technique separates proteins by molecular weight and allows researchers to determine that the curved regions of the thylakoid membranes contain more of the photosystem I complexes and that the stacked regions contain more of photosystem II and LHCP complexes. These findings can be verified using the TEM and a technique called immunocytochemical localization. The protein complexes of the membranes are tagged with other molecules that show their location.

Research on the pigments found in chloroplasts can be performed by isolating the chloroplast and then breaking the chloroplasts open to release the pigments. The pigments are then separated from one another by chromatography, a process that separates the pigments by their solubility in different solvents. Once the pigments are isolated, absorption spectrums, which show which colors of light the pigments absorb, can be generated for the different pigments found in chloroplasts.

The study of the dark reactions has been easier than the study of the light reactions because the process of the dark reactions takes place in the stroma and the enzymes that carry out the conversion of carbon dioxide to sugars are soluble in water. Melvin Calvin and his associates worked out the steps of the dark reaction in the 1950's. They used radioactive carbon dioxide and followed the path as the carbon dioxide was converted into sugars.

Context

Understanding the location of the reactions in the chloroplast is essential to understanding the process of photosynthesis. This fundamental process, which utilizes carbon dioxide and water to produce sugars, carbohydrates, and oxygen, forms the basis for life. A complete understanding of the light and dark reactions of photosynthesis requires that scientists understand how the structure and function is related in the chloroplast.

The overall goal is to produce plants that have higher rates of photosynthesis, which will make it possible to design crops that have a higher productivity and, thus, will yield more food to society. Plant breeders for many years have successfully bred plants to increase crop yield, but by understanding the underlying processes, they may be able to improve plants even more.

One area in which information on the location of chloroplast reaction sites has been helpful has been with use of herbicides. Herbicides are chemicals that are harmful to weeds. Weeds, which are growing with crops, use the fertilizer and water that are essential to crops. This competition for water and fertilizer by weeds and crops will, in the long run, reduce crop yield. Some herbicides kill weeds by inhibiting photosynthesis. Herbicides (simazine and atrazine) that affect photosynthesis usually do so by blocking electron transport from photosystem II to photosystem I. Other herbicides (paraquat) accept electrons from photosystem I and destroy the thylakoid membranes and other cellular membranes. These herbicides do, however, present problems: They are effective in low doses and are harmful to animals, including humans; some weedy species, moreover, have become resistant to them.

Biotechnology may be able to overcome such problems. Usage of molecular-genetic techniques could allow investigators to modify genes, making it possible to replace genes in crop plants with genes that would increase photosynthesis (and thus crop yields) or genes that would increase resistance to herbicides. Other benefits of such genetic engineering include targeted killing of weeds (not crop plants) and resistance to disease and insects.

Bibliography

Arms, Karen, and Pamela S. Camp. *Biology: A Journey into Life*. 3d ed. Philadelphia: W. B. Saunders, 1987. An introductory college textbook for the nonbiology major. Chapter 8, "Photosynthesis," covers the process of photosynthesis and the location of the reactions inside the chloroplast, using many colorful diagrams and electron micrographs. Glossary. Suitable for a high school student.

Campbell, Neil. *Biology*. Menlo Park, Calif.: Benjamin/Cummings, 1987. An introductory college textbook, well written for the biology major but easily understood by the high school student. Chapter 7, "A Tour of the Cell," covers chloroplasts and their structure. This well-illustrated chapter also contains essays on methods of studying cells. Chapter 10, "Photosynthesis," clearly discusses the structure and function of chloroplasts in the process of photosynthesis. Glossary and helpful diagrams.

Jensen, Richard G. "Biochemistry of the Chloroplast." In *The Plant Cell*, edited by N. E. Tolbert. New York: Academic Press, 1980. A comprehensive treatment of the biochemical reactions taking place in the chloroplast. The focus is on the process of carbon dioxide fixation in chloroplasts. Other processes occurring in the chloroplast are also explained.

Karp, Gerald. *Cell Biology*. 2d ed. New York: McGraw-Hill, 1984. An excellent book on the structure of the chloroplast, especially Chapter 9, "Photosynthesis and the Chloroplast," and chapter 20, "Methods in Cell Biology." More advanced, but still accessible to the general reader. Full references at the end of each chapter point the way toward more advanced study.

Miller, Kenneth R. "The Photosynthetic Membrane." *Scientific American* 241 (October, 1979): 102-113. The article describes the role of the photosynthetic membrane in photosynthesis, explaining why and how the membrane functions. Electron micrographs help clarify this slightly advanced discussion.

Ting, Irwin P. *Plant Physiology*. Reading, Mass.: Addison-Wesley, 1982. A comprehensive treatment of plant physiology, reviewing cell structure and photosynthesis. Chapter 15 covers the primary processes of photosynthesis; chapter 16, carbon metabolism. A more advanced book than most introductory textbooks.

Lonnie J. Guralnick

Cross-References

The Calvin-Benson Cycle, 316; Chloroplasts and Other Plastids, 431; Chromatographic Analysis of Chloroplast Pigments, 453; Electron Microscopy, 744; Electron Transport and Oxidative Phosphorylation, 751; Photosynthetic Light Absorption, 2073; Photosynthetic Light Reactions, 2080; Subcellular Fractionation Using Centrifugation, 2552.

CHLOROPLASTS AND OTHER PLASTIDS

Type of life science: Cell biology (cytology)
Other fields of study: Botany, photosynthesis, plant anatomy, and plant physiology

Plastids are a group of organelles found in plants and have a number of specialized functions. Chloroplasts, one type of plastid, are especially important in plants because it is in these organelles that photosynthesis takes place.

Principal terms

AMYLOPLAST: a plastid containing extensive starch deposits resulting in the organelle being considerably denser than the cytoplasm of the cell in which it resides

CHLOROPHYLL: a light-harvesting pigment located in chloroplasts, which can absorb and channel light energy

CHLOROPLAST: a plastid containing all the necessary cellular constituents for the physiological process of photosynthesis

CHROMOPLAST: plastids that do not contain chlorophyll but instead have a high carotenoid content

DARK REACTION: the portion of photosynthesis which incorporates carbon dioxide into starch in the stroma of the chloroplast

ETIOPLASTS: the name given to plastids in development between a proplastid and chloroplast, common in plants which have not been exposed to the light

GRANA: stacks of thylakoid membranes within chloroplasts, which are associated with the harvesting of light energy

LIGHT REACTION: the photosynthetic system which, using light energy, splits a water molecule and traps the energy in the form of ATP and $NADPH_2$ occurring in the thylakoid membrane of chloroplasts

PROPLASTID: an undifferentiated plastid with no specialized function

STROMA: the fluid inside the chloroplasts surrounding the thylakoids, the region in which the dark reaction of photosynthesis occurs

THYLAKOIDS: membranes containing the photosynthetic machinery used in the light reaction of photosynthesis

Summary of the Phenomenon

Plastids are organelles found only in plants and eukaryotic algae cells. Plastids contain a two-unit membrane system and their own deoxyribonucleic acid (DNA) and ribosomes. The genetically autonomous nature of plastids has led many scientists to believe that plastids originated from free-living prokaryotes which became associated with primitive eukaryote cells. This theory is supported by the observation that plastids are capable of their own protein synthesis and have numerous genes in common with those found in cyanobacteria, a prokaryote capable of photosynthesis. Although plastids share a common evolutionary heritage and structure, plastids are involved in a diverse number of separate plant functions, appear at distinct developmental stages in plants, and are concentrated in different locations throughout the plant body.

All plastids have a common origin from an undifferentiated organelle called a proplastid. Typically, a proplastid will be nonpigmented and contain only a few small starch granules. Higher numbers (ten to forty per cell) of proplastids are concentrated in nondifferentiated tissues such as the root and shoot meristem. The maturation of proplastids will lead to the development of numerous types of plastids with specialized functions. These plastids are separated based on their morphology and the chemical constituents of the organelle.

Plastids that contain large deposits of starch and are devoid of any pigmentation are called amyloplasts. Amyloplasts are important as starch-storing organelles and gravity detectors of plants. They are located in storage tissues such as cotyledons, tubers, or the endosperm of seeds. When a seed germinates, the starch that has been sequestered in amyloplasts is mobilized to provide energy for embryo growth and differentiation. Amyloplasts are also found in the columella cells (eight to ten per cell) of the root cap, where they are denser than the cytoplasm in these cells. Because they are denser, the amyloplasts in the root cap will always sediment toward the bottom of the cell or the portion of the cell closest to the origin of the gravity force. The movement of the amyloplasts enables the plant to recognize their orientation within a gravity field.

Chromoplasts are plastids that have little chlorophyll (a light-harvesting plant pigment) but a large abundance of the plant pigments, or carotenoids, which give these organelles their characteristic orange, red, and yellow colors. These plastids are usually derived from aging chloroplasts. Chromoplasts are not, however, capable of photosynthesis, as the photosynthetic membrane has been replaced by a membrane rich in carotenoids and devoid of any organized photosynthesis complexes.

Chromoplasts can be further divided into five types. Globular chromoplasts contain one homogenous concentration of carotenoid. Flower petals contain numerous globular chromoplasts, which give them their characteristic colors. A second type is the membranous chromoplast, which contains numerous concentric membranes packed with carotenoids. This chromoplast is less frequently observed but is dominant in daffodil petals. Chromoplasts found in the skin or peels of some fruits which possess many carotenoid-containing fibers are referred to as tubulous chromoplasts. The reticulo-tubular type contains a network of branched tubules and is also common in some fruit skins. Plastids with carotenoids organized into crystalline structures are the fifth type of chromoplast. These crystalline chromoplasts are particularly abundant throughout tomatoes.

Although chromoplasts are usually viewed as the final stage of an aging chloroplast, many chromoplasts do have specific functions in plants. The turning of leaves in the fall is a signal of a developmental change in leaves (loss of chlorophyll or the end of a season) resulting from an increase in the number of chromoplasts as chloroplasts are converted into chromoplast in leaves. Also, the bright color of petals and sepals may attract pollinators, while the color of fruits may attract birds and animals to consume the fruits and assist in seed dispersal.

Etioplasts do not commonly occur in plants, but they do appear when plants are grown in the dark. They occur naturally in the primary leaves (cotyledons) of germinating seedlings before they emerge from the soil into the light. Thus, etioplasts are usually viewed as a developmental stage preceding the formation of chloroplasts. These plastids share many of the proteins found in chloroplasts but lack significant amounts of chlorophyll and carotenoids. An inner membrane such as that occurring in the chloroplast is lacking. In its place are structures called prolamellar bodies which are large quasicrystalline structures. The prolamellar body is the precursor of the lamellae in chloroplasts. Etioplasts do not have any known function in plants.

The majority of research on plastids is concerned with chloroplasts. These plastids are responsible for trapping and utilizing the energy of light. Chloroplasts can be found throughout plants but are in especially high concentrations in leaves. Few, if any, chloroplasts are found in roots. Within leaves, chloroplasts are often found in great abundance in palasade and mesophyll cells. These cells are arranged within leaves to maximize the exposure of chloroplasts to light. Indeed, the orientation of chloroplasts within the leaf cells can be altered, maximizing the exposure of chloroplasts to light.

Chloroplasts, like all plastids, are surrounded by a double-unit membrane. Internally, chloroplasts are divided into two systems. A flattened membranous system consists of thylakoids, and the remaining embedding matrix is termed the stroma. The thylakoid system consists of stacks of disk-shaped thylakoids called grana and single flattened thylakoid membranes called fret membranes. The open space between the thylakoids is referred to as the loculus.

The name "chloroplast" is derived from the fact that heavy concentrations of chlorophyll are present in these organelles. The chlorophyll molecule is unique in that its structure allows for the absorption and rapid transfer of light energy. This harnessing of the energy of light to power the numerous metabolic events occurring within plant cells is referred to as photosynthesis. Photosynthesis can be divided into two separate reactions: The light reaction involves capturing light energy and then converting that energy into a chemical currency which can be used to pay for running various metabolic events. The dark reaction stores the light energy by coupling carbons from carbon dioxide to form larger carbon chains, such as starch.

The light reaction is composed of two photosystems, referred to as photosystem I and photosystem II. Both these complexes contain the light-harvesting pigments chlorophyll a and beta carotene. All the light energy absorbed by these pigments is channeled to the reaction center of the photosystem. In the case of photosystem I, this is the P680 reaction center; for photosystem II, the P700 reaction center. The chemical environment of photosystem I is slightly different from that of photosystem II. The difference in the environment of the two photosystems allows them to absorb slightly different wavelengths of light, enabling the plant to harvest a greater amount of light energy. In addition to the two photosystems, there is a third light-absorbing pigment system, referred to as the light-harvesting complex. The function of this complex is to absorb light energy and then transfer it to either photosystem I or photosystem II. The two photosystems and the light-harvesting complex cooperate together to use the energy of light to transfer electrons from water to a molecule referred to as $NADP^+$. Photosystem II will catalyze the splitting of a water molecule, and the energy liberated with this action in conjunction with the light energy absorbed by photosystem I transforms $NADP^+$ into the energy currency molecule NADPH.

At first glance, however, the location of photosystems I and II in chloroplasts does not suggest that these two photosystems are capable of this type of collaboration. Fret membranes contain primarily photosystem I reaction centers, and the grana contain principally photosystem II reaction centers. Thus, the two are physically separated. This problem is overcome by two sets of mobile electron carriers called plastocyanin and plastoquinones. These two groups serve to couple the two photosystems together. Plastocyanins move within the thylakoid membrane channels, while the plastoquinones carry energy laterally within the thylakoid membranes.

A final component of thylakoid membranes within chloroplasts is the ATPase, or coupling factor complex. This complex is responsible for producing the energy currency adenosine triphosphate (ATP) in a process referred to as photophosphorylation. Coupling factor is composed of a circular headpiece that is attached to the stroma side of the thylakoid membrane and a stalk that extends across the fret membrane to the inside of the fret membrane. ATP is produced during photophosphorylation as a result of the buildup of hydrogen ions on the inside of the thylakoid membrane. As the hydrogen ions move from the inside of the thylakoids to the stroma, they provide the energy to produce an ATP molecule, much as water flowing through the waterwheel of a gristmill powers the movement of the gristwheel.

The dark reaction of photosynthesis occurs only in the stroma of the chloroplast. The dark reaction utilizes the energy compounds (ATP and NADPH) produced in the light reaction to produce sugars and ultimately the energy storage compound starch by linking six carbon dioxide molecules together. The assembly of the carbon dioxide molecules into the sugars is catalyzed by numerous enzymes found within the stroma of the chloroplast; however, the enzyme ribulose-1,5-bisphosphate (RuBP) regulates the initial fixation of the carbon dioxide. The fixation of carbon dioxide into starch allows for the storage of high-energy compounds in plants, which can later be broken down to release energy to fuel cellular metabolic events, much as in the case of adipose (fat) tissue in humans.

The acquisition by chloroplasts of light energy to create the high-energy storage compound starch is a complex process completely enclosed within the chloroplasts of plant cells. It requires the coordination of numerous photochemical and biochemical reactions compartmentalized within a single chloroplast. Light energy is trapped, through excitation of electrons, in a light-harvesting complex and both photosystems I and II. The light-harvesting complex contributes energy to both photosystems I and II. Photosystem II, located in the granum of the chloroplast, uses the energy of the absorbed light to split a water molecule, releasing a highly energetic electron. This electron is rapidly conveyed to the photosystem I complex in the fret membrane of the chloroplast by the mobile electron carriers plastocyanin and plastoquinone. The energy conveyed by the electron, in conjunction with additional light energy absorbed by photosystem I, powers the formation of the energy currency molecule NADPH. This reaction also creates chemical conditions favorable for the formation of ATP. The NADPH and ATP produced in the thylakoid membrane of the chloroplast during the light reaction is then used to power the fixation of carbon dioxide into starch in the stroma of the chloroplast.

Methods of Study

Early studies on plastid morphology and the location of plastids within the plant body were conducted using low-power light microscopy. Indeed, one of the first characteristics identified in living plant tissues was the leaf chloroplast. Early plant scientists could separate plastids based on their size, structural appearance, and color. Proplastids and etioplasts lacked any pigmentation and appeared very similar, except that etioplasts were larger and more ellipsoidal in appearance. Amyloplasts lacked pigmentation but could be easily discerned by the glistening appearance of the large starch granules. Green chloroplasts were separated from the variously pigmented orange, red, and yellow chromoplasts. The pigments in these plastids were later determined using a spectrophotometer. A spectrophotometer measures the amount of a specific wavelength of light as it passes through a sample. Since different pigments absorb different wavelengths of light, the absorption of a specific wavelength indicates the presence of a particular class of pigment. In this manner, the quantity and quality of pigments present in a plastid can be determined.

Technological advances in microscopy led to more detailed observations of plastid structure. These observations, in conjunction with biochemical analysis, have presented the modern-day scientist with a good understanding of both the compartmentalization and photosynthetic machinery present in chloroplast. The more detailed structural studies on chloroplast structure have been conducted using a transmission electron microscope. This instrument enables a researcher to observe subcellular structures. The basic concept behind a transmission electron microscope is the detection of electrons as they pass through a tissue sample. The tissues are usually coated with some type of heavy metal, which blocks the passage of the electrons. Thus, where the tissue or membrane of an organelle is located, electrons do not freely penetrate. If the electrons are deflected, they do not reach the photographic paper, which in turn remains unexposed, creating a dark image. This technique was used to visualize the first photosynthetic unit and the thylakoid membranes of chloroplasts.

One of the more elegant studies on the structural compartmentalization of chloroplast dealt with the identification and localization of photosystems I and II in thylakoid membranes. This experiment used a method of electron microscopy referred to as freeze-fracturing. In this method, the tissue of a specimen is rapidly frozen in liquid nitrogen and then broken or fractured along the longitudinal axis of the specimen. This method allows for the examination of the tissue in several planes and as close to living conditions as possible. When freeze-fractured chloroplasts were examined with an electron microscope, it was noted that the inside and outside of thylakoid membranes exhibited two different contours and contained bumps thought to be associated with one of the two photosystems. The inside was given the label ES_u, while the outside was labeled the PF_s. When mutant chloroplasts lacking photosystem II were compared with normal chloroplasts, the bumps on the ES_u side of the thylakoid membrane were lacking especially in the grana region of the thylakoid membrane, indicating that photosystem II was inside the thylakoid membrane and concentrated in the granum stacks of chloroplasts.

In another series of experiments, the location of bumps on chloroplast membranes in a mutant lacking photosystem I was compared with that in a normal chloroplast. In these studies, the ES_u face still contained bumps; however, the PF_s side had fewer bumps, especially in the unstacked region of the fret membranes. Thus, these studies indicated that photosystem I was associated with the outside of the thylakoid membrane and in larger concentrations within the fret membranes.

Other experiments have been performed using antibodies to the various proteins involved in both photosynthesis and chloroplast structure. These antibodies are produced within the immune systems of animals and can readily distinguish and bind to specific proteins. A second antibody, coupled with a heavy metal, which can recognize and bind to the first antibody, is added for visualization with the transmission electron microscope. Where the second antibody rests, a dark point will appear on the electron transmission picture, indicating the presence of the protein that the first antibody specifically recognized. This sort of study has been used to identify the location of many of the proteins and photosynthetic complexes involved in chloroplast function.

Context

Studies on plastid development and structure are basic to attaining an understanding of how plants function and the developmental stages through which plants pass as they mature. This information is both important to the understanding of plant sciences and essential to applied use in agricultural and horticultural sciences.

Amyloplasts play an important role in both seed germination and the response of plants to gravity. An increase in the number of amyloplasts within seeds may indicate a greater potential for seed germination and continued development. By increasing the number of amyloplasts and therefore the amount of starch stored in seeds, scientists might someday be able to increase the longevity of seed storage before seeds become nonviable. The role of amyloplasts in the response of plants to gravity has become an increasingly important issue, as a permanently manned space station becomes more feasible. Such a space station would require plants both as a food source and as a source of oxygen. Thus, a better understanding of the role of amyloplasts in gravity perception may enable researchers to engineer ultragravisensitive plants capable of detecting small gravitational fields such as those which might exist in a space station environment.

An increased understanding of the basis for developmental changes in plastids, which occur from early embryogenesis (seeds) to the death of a plant, may also help to prolong the reproductive life span of many plants. An understanding of the mechanisms behind the development of proplastids in the seed embryo, to the etioplast apparent in the young emerging seed, and finally to the chloroplasts in the mature plant might help plant scientists understand how to increase the number of chloroplasts and thus the amount of photosynthesis an individual plant could conduct. Also, by studying the mechanism through which chloroplasts are converted into chromoplasts, it may be possible to slow the aging and death of some plant species. These developmental markers of plastid maturation may also be quite useful to scientists interested in studying plant aging and fruit development.

Intricate studies on chloroplast structure and the arrangement of photosynthetic machinery within chloroplasts may in the future reap important benefits to humankind. By understanding how all the various components of the photosynthesis machine function and are arranged in chloroplasts, scientists may, through either plant breeding or biotechnology, be able to alter the structure of chloroplasts, increasing the efficiency with which plants utilize the energy of light and making it possible, for example, to grow crops in areas of the world that have heretofore been unsuitable to crop plants, or increase crop yields in areas of the world that are already being intensively cultivated.

Bibliography

Anderson, Jan. "The Architecture of Photosynthetic Membranes: Lateral and Transverse Organization." *Trends in Biochemical Sciences* 8 (August, 1982): 288-292. A detailed review article on the components of photosystem I and photosystem II. Includes an interesting diagram comparing photosynthesis to a summer resort. An article with a considerable amount of terminology but understandable at both the beginning undergraduate and advanced high school levels.

Campbell, Neil A. *Biology.* 2d ed. Menlo Park, Calif.: Benjamin/Cummings, 1990. A clearly written, well-illustrated text for either an advanced high school student or a beginning college student. Chapter 10, "Photosynthesis," presents and expands upon many of the principles of photosynthesis, including chloroplast structure and function. Numerous schematics make this textbook particularly useful to the beginning biology student.

Esau, Katherine. *Anatomy of Seed Plants.* 2d ed. New York: John Wiley & Sons, 1977. One of the best plant anatomy texts available, written at the college undergraduate level. Chapter 3, "The Cell," presents a general discussion of plastid differentiation and an overview of photosynthesis. Also in chapter 3 is a brief discussion of the evolutionary origin of plastids, with concentration on chloroplasts. Numerous light micrographs of plastids are reprinted.

Giese, Arthur. *Cell Physiology.* 5th ed. Philadelphia: W. B. Saunders, 1979. A comprehensive college text on the form and function of organelles within cells, especially good for relating the structure of chloroplasts to their photosynthetic function. This text has numerous electron micrographs of chloroplast membranes, as well as a brief explanation of the technique of electron microscopy and freeze-fracturing.

Rost, Thomas, Michael Barbour, Robert Thornton, Elliot Weier, and Ralph Stocking. *Botany: A Brief Introduction to Plant Biology.* 2d ed. New York: John Wiley & Sons, 1984. An easy-to-understand and well-illustrated high-school-level text, specifically dealing with plant science. Presents a general explanation of photosynthesis and chloroplast structure, particularly well suited to beginning students, if lacking some detail.

Salisbury, Frank, and Cleon Ross. *Plant Physiology.* 3d ed. Belmont, Calif.: Wadsworth, 1985. An advanced undergraduate-level text that provides a detailed treatment of the light and dark reactions of photosynthesis. Contains numerous references to primary literature dealing with photosynthesis, as well as numerous references to current journal articles. Some background in plant sciences should be attained before using this text.

Starr, Cecie, and Ralph Taggart. *Biology: The Unity and Diversity of Life.* 2d ed. Belmont, Calif.: Wadsworth, 1981. This text can be used by both the layperson and the beginning undergraduate. Particular attention should be given to chapter 19, "Plant Cells, Tissues, and Systems," which discusses, in a general format, plastid structures and photosynthesis, and chapter 21, "Origins and Patterns of Adaptation," which presents the case for the evolutionary origin of plastids in eukaryotes.

Charles L. Stinemetz

Cross-References

Anaerobic Photosynthesis, 87; The Calvin-Benson Cycle, 316; Chloroplast Reaction Sites, 424; Chromatographic Analysis of Chloroplast Pigments, 453; Photorespiration, 2059; Photosynthetic Light Absorption, 2073; Photosynthetic Light Reactions, 2080.

LOWER CHORDATES

Type of life science: Systematics (taxonomy)
Other fields of study: Animal anatomy, animal physiology, evolutionary biology, and zoology

Lower chordates are those members of the phylum Chordata other than the vertebrates. They are small marine organisms, chiefly of interest for the light that they shed on the history of vertebrate development.

Principal terms

CHORDATA: a phylum of organisms characterized by the presence of a notochord, a dorsal nerve cord, and gill slits

DEUTEROSTOMES: echinoderms, hemichordates, and chordates, a group linked by features of cell development including retention of the blastopore as anus

LOWER CHORDATES: a group within the Chordata that shows chordate characteristics in the larvae but is separated from vertebrates by the lack of a skeleton

NEOTENY: a process by which larval features are retained into the reproductive adult stage

NOTOCHORD: a flexible stiffening rod found in primitive chordates

PROTOSTOMES: annelids, mollusks, flatworms, and arthropods, a group linked by features of cell development including retention of the blastopore as the mouth

Summary of the Phenomenon

The phylum Chordata is chiefly of interest because it includes the human taxonomic group, the vertebrates. Yet the phylum also includes a number of lesser-known groups, termed the lower chordates. Chordates as a whole are characterized by the presence of a longitudinal cartilaginous stiffening rod (the notochord), a single tubular dorsal nerve cord, and perforations in the pharynx comparable to gill slits. The subphylum that includes humans, the Vertebrata, is further characterized by the presence of a bony skeleton that forms an internal support and protects vital structures such as the spine and brain. In land-dwelling vertebrates, gill slits are present only in the embryonic stages. The other two subphyla currently included within the Chordata and making up the lower chordates are the Urochordata, or tunicates, and the Cephalochordata, all of which are small marine organisms. In the past, an additional group, the Hemichordata (acorn worms and pterobranchs), were also considered chordates. They possess a dorsal nerve cord and gill slits but do not have a notochord; they are now placed in a separate phylum, although they are considered to be closely related to chordates. In addition, a group of fossil organisms with echinoderm affinities have been interpreted as chordates and given the name Calcichordata. Most specialists on this group (generally known as mitrates) consider them to be echinoderms, however, as their chordate affinities are based entirely on soft-part reconstructions.

The largest group of lower chordates, containing about thirteen hundred species, is the Urochordata. These organisms, commonly called tunicates, little resemble chordates in their adult form: Only the tadpolelike larval stage possesses distinct chordate characters. Three classes are recognized—the Ascidiacea, Thaliacea, and Larvacea—and of these the most common and typical tunicates are the ascideans, or sea squirts.

Adult sea squirts are sessile (attached to the ocean bottom) marine organisms commonly found in coastal waters worldwide. They are sack-shaped, range from a few millimeters to a few centimeters in length, and have two siphons, inhalent and exhalent, extending from the upper surface. The outer part of the body is called the tunic. This is a protective structure made of proteins and polysaccharides, which is often quite thick and may vary from a soft, delicate consistency to one that is tough and similar to cartilage. Within the tunic, much of the space is taken up by the pharynx (an expanded part of the digestive tube), which has small perforations in its wall, creating a net. Small hairlike structures called cilia create currents that pull water in through the inhalent siphon. The water then passes through the openings in the wall of the pharynx into the atrium (the surrounding cavity), and from there it passes out through the exhalent siphon. Food particles are trapped on the pharynx wall by a mucus sheet, which moves constantly to the midline of the pharynx and then posteriorly to the gut, where digestion takes place. This is a very effective system, and it can filter out particles only 1 to 2 micrometers in diameter, although the diatoms on which sea squirts normally feed are closer to 200 micrometers in diameter.

Sea squirt larvae, unlike the adults, are tadpole-shaped and mobile. They are generally very small and are mobile for only a few hours before settling and becoming sessile adults. The tail of the larva has a notochord, which acts in much the same way as the vertebral column of vertebrates. As it is flexible but of a fixed length, it will not shorten when muscles on either side contract; it thus makes them antagonistic, bending the tail from side to side. Above the notochord is a dorsal nerve cord that swells anteriorly into a light detector and an organ sensitive to tilting. The larvae tend to swim down and away from light—behavior that takes them to sites such as overhanging rock faces that are suitable adult habitats.

The Thaliacea and Larvacea are both planktonic (that is, they float near the surface of the ocean). The Thaliacea, or salps, are colonial forms that may reach 2 meters in length. Their inhalent and exhalent siphons are at opposite ends of the body, and water is pumped through by rhythmic muscular contractions. This class has no tadpolelike larvae, but instead develops directly into the adult form. The Larvacea do develop from larvae, but they retain the tail as a permanent organ. Water is filtered through a mucus sheet in the pharynx as in other tunicates, but in this group the entire animal is surrounded by a delicate gelatinous "house" that is probably homologous to the sea squirt's tunic. The house has mesh at the inhalent and exhalent openings that helps to concentrate food particles; this concentrate is then passed through the mucus sheet, and food particles are trapped. The house is continually shed and replaced, probably to counteract clogging of the filters, and may not last more than a few hours.

The subphylum Cephalochordata includes only about twenty species of two genera of organisms that are often referred to as amphioxus. These are small, fusiform, and rather fishlike organisms up to 7 centimeters long that live in sandy and shelly bottoms in shallow coastal waters. They burrow head down in coarse sediments and can filter-feed even when buried by filtering the water that penetrates between grains.

In cephalochordates, the notochord extends almost to the snout. This is further forward than in fishes, and it may aid in burrowing by stiffening the snout. The swimming muscles are arranged in myomeres (muscle segments) down the body and are similar to those found in fish, though simpler in shape. A hollow dorsal nerve cord runs above the notochord and is enclosed in a tube of collagen fibers that enclose the cord in a way similar to the vertebrae in fish. There is no anterior swelling of the nerve cord that might be comparable to the brain in vertebrates. The nerve cord, however, sends a ventral motor nerve and a dorsal sensory nerve to each myomere, an arrangement identical to that found in vertebrates. As it is in the urochordates, the pharynx is pierced by numerous slits, and food particles are trapped by a mucus sheet that moves across them and back to the gut. The blood system is more complex, however, and is similar in general arrangement to that of fish, although there is no heart; blood is propelled by pulsations of some of the vessels.

The cephalochordates and urochordates are particularly interesting for what they suggest about vertebrate origins. Although in the past it has been suggested that vertebrates evolved from various invertebrate groups such as annelids (segmented worms) or cephalopods (squids and octopus), it is now recognized that fundamental patterns of development distinguish chordates and echinoderms from mollusks and advanced segmented invertebrates. These differences involve the way in which cells divide and the relative potential of the cells.

In mollusks and annelids, spiral cleavage results in cells that are nested between one another in successive rows. They are also determinate—that is, the fate of each cell is predetermined, so that the removal of one results in the developmental failure of part of the organism. In chordates and echinoderms, however, the cells are directly above one another in layers (radial cleavage), and if a cell is removed, adjacent cells will compensate for its loss (indeterminate cleavage). In both groups, cells initially form a ball, termed the blastula, and cells at one end grow in to form a second layer of tissue, the endoderm, which forms the lining of the gut. The external layer, or ectoderm, forms the outer surface of the body. In the mollusk-annelid group, the opening in the blastula (the blastopore) is retained as the mouth, while in the echinoderms and chordates it becomes the anus.

Despite the fact that this information points to a close relationship between echinoderms and chordates, there are too many differences for them to make convincing vertebrate ancestors. The larvae are similar to those of lower chordates, but the adults are quite different. The same can be said for hemichordates, although they are probably more closely related to chordates than echinoderms are. Adult urochordates are also too specialized to be suitable candidates for the vertebrate ancestor, and the same can be said of cephalochordates, although amphioxus does show many vertebratelike features. It is currently accepted that the echinoderms, hemichordates, and lower chordates must have diverged from vertebrate ancestors no later than the lower Cambrian period (about 550 million years ago). This is substantiated by the presence of a fossil cephalochordate in the Burgess shale, which is middle Cambrian in age.

It has been suggested that the lower chordates show how the vertebrate ancestor may have arisen by a process of neoteny or pedogenesis, in which larval characteristics may be retained in the adult. Sexual development is accelerated, and the development of other organ systems is arrested, so that the nonreproductive larvae of the ancestor become the reproductive adults of the descendant. In this case, a notochord and tail muscles are found in sea squirt larvae but not in the adults; however, they are retained in the Larvacea. Further retention of larval features could have given rise to cephalochordates and, by a further step, to vertebrates.

Methods of Study

Lower chordates, small marine organisms, are often difficult to study because of their size and delicacy. The gelatinous covering of the Larvacea, for example, is so easily damaged as to be almost impossible to observe. Many modern techniques, however, have been developed to aid in the study of organisms such as these. Cinematography is used in studies of movement, and high-speed photography is particularly useful; the film can then be shown at a much slower speed to enable detailed analyses of complex movements. Electromyography can also be used to trace muscular action, as it follows the electrical changes that take place in muscles when they are active. The lower chordates are all filter feeders, and it is possible to carry out experiments that show how effective they are at removing small particles from the water. Sea squirts can be placed in a dish containing a suspension of colloidal graphite, and their filtering ability can be seen as a function of the rate at which the water clears. In addition, the size of particles can be varied to show how efficient the filtering apparatus is; this has shown that sea squirts can remove particles as small as 1 to 2 micrometers in diameter, although the diatoms on which they normally feed are closer to 200 micrometers in diameter.

Fossil lower chordates are extremely rare; however, a probable cephalochordate, *Pikaia*, is known from the Burgess shale of British Columbia, which is dated as middle Cambrian (530 million years ago). The Burgess shale contains a variety of soft-bodied organisms preserved as films of carbon on the bedding surfaces. Study is difficult because the material is compressed and because it is the same color (black) as the rock that contains it. Specimens can be prepared by picking rock away with needles. Details can then be studied by observing the specimens under low-angle light, which picks out differences in reflectivity of the rock surfaces and carbon films, or by immersing specimens in water or alcohol, which also enhances differences between the fossil and the surrounding rock.

These techniques make it possible to determine which characters are important in determining relationships within the lower chordates. Studies on relationships rely heavily on a methodology called phylogenetic systematics, or cladistics. In this taxonomic method (taxonomy is the study of interrelationships), only advanced characters shared between species (termed synapomorphies) are used to develop a picture of relationship. These relationships are expressed as branching diagrams termed cladograms (*Klados* is Greek for branch), hence the name cladistics. Studies using this technique have advanced understanding of the relationship between lower chordates and the vertebrates. The picture is by no means clear, however, and much still waits to be done.

Context

The lower chordates are of particular interest for the light that they shed on the way in which the group to which humans belong, the vertebrates, may have developed and when this may have occurred. Vertebrates differ from lower chordates in possessing both an internal skeleton and a brain; however, there is only limited fossil record of the earliest members of the group. The earliest known vertebrates are fish that are found in rocks of the Ordovician period (450 million years ago) in Australia, South America, and North America. These animals had an external bony armor, but knowledge of both their external appearance and their internal anatomy is restricted by poor fossil preservation. It is clear, however, that these animals were already relatively advanced and, hence, that a fairly long period of vertebrate development is not represented in the fossil record. As the lower chordates are the nearest relatives of the vertebrates, they can provide some information on how this development may have taken place.

It has been suggested that the process of neoteny, or pedogenesis, might explain the development of vertebrates. In this process, development of adult characters is retarded, and the organism reaches sexual maturity while still in the larval stage. This process may already have operated in the lower chordates, as the urochordates show chordate characters in the tadpolelike larval stage only, whereas the more advanced cephalochordates retain the chordate characters in the fishlike adult stage. It is fairly easy to see, therefore, how a continuation of this process could lead, by fairly small morphological changes, to organisms similar to the larvae of modern lampreys, jawless fish that represent the most primitive modern vertebrates.

It is clear, however, that vertebrates did not evolve directly from cephalochordate ancestors. Although the modern cephalochordate amphioxus shows many features that one would expect to find in a vertebrate ancestor, it also has a number of basic differences that are inconsistent with a position on the direct evolutionary lineage of the vertebrates. In particular, the presence of a notochord extending to the anterior end of the rostrum and the lack of a clearly differentiated head make cephalochordates unlikely ancestors of organisms with large brains. It seems more likely, therefore, that both vertebrates and cephalochordates represent divergent lineages from a common ancestor, probably of urochordate type. The presence of the fossil cephalochordate *Pikaia* in rocks of Middle Cambrian age (530 million years ago) indicates that the division had already taken place then and that the first vertebrates must have been present some time in the early Cambrian period.

Bibliography

Alexander, R. McNeill. *The Chordates*. 2d ed. New York: Cambridge University Press, 1981. A general review of the entire phylum, covering both fossil and modern representatives. The second chapter deals entirely with lower chordates, providing a very useful review of their anatomy and relationships. Suitable for high school and college students.

Barrington, E. J. W. *The Biology of the Hemichordata and Protochordata*. Edinburgh: Oliver and Boyd, 1965. Although this is not a recent text, the study of these organisms has not moved fast enough to make it obsolete. There is a particularly good section on life habits and development. Suitable for college students.

Margulis, Lynn, and Karlene V. Schwartz. *Five Kingdoms*. 2d ed. New York: W. H. Freeman, 1988. This text covers all known phyla, devoting only two or three pages to each; it therefore provides only an overview. It has sections on hemichordates and chordates and is very valuable in placing them in context. Suitable for the general reader and the college student.

Orr, R. T. *Vertebrate Biology*. 5th ed. Philadelphia: Saunders College Publishing, 1982. A general text at the high school/college level. Covers lower chordates as part of an initial section on vertebrate ancestry.

Pough, F. H., J. B. Heiser, and W. N. McFarland. *Vertebrate Life*. 3d ed. New York: Macmillan, 1989. An excellent text, particularly in its use of cladistic taxonomy throughout. Deals with lower chordates in discussion of vertebrate ancestry in chapter 2. Suitable for college students.

Young, John Z. *The Life of Vertebrates*. 3d ed. New York: Oxford University Press, 1981. A revised version of a classic text. The cephalochordates are dealt with as part of chordate classification in chapter 2. Chapter 3 covers the hemichordates and tunicates as part of a discussion of the origin of chordates from filter-feeding organisms. Suitable for college students.

David K. Elliott

Cross-References

Circulatory Systems of Invertebrates, 476; Evolution: A Historical Perspective, 903; Extinction, 953; Higher Invertebrate Animals, 1475; Lower Invertebrate Animals, 1483; Muscle Anatomy in Invertebrates, 1814; Neoteny and Other Heterochronic Effects, 1885.

CHROMATIN STRUCTURE FOR ACTIVE GENES

Type of life science: Genetic regulation in eukaryotes
Other fields of study: Biochemistry, cell biology (cytology), genetics, and molecular biology

Within a eukaryotic organism, each cell type contains a specific set of genes that are actively producing messenger RNA while the rest of its genes remain inactive. One clue to understanding the genetic signals that indicate certain genes are to be active may lie in the changes to chromatin structure around many active genes.

Principal terms

CHROMATIN: an inclusive term referring to DNA and the proteins that bind to it, located in the nucleus of eukaryotic cells

DEOXYRIBONUCLEIC ACID (DNA): the molecule that carries the genetic information; some sequences of nucleotides, which form DNA, act as a code to direct the synthesis of proteins

DNASE I SENSITIVITY: the phenomenon whereby certain regions of DNA within chromatin are more susceptible to degradation by enzymes

GENE: the specific sequence of nucleotides in a DNA molecule that acts as a code to direct the synthesis of a specific protein

METHYLATION: the addition of a group of atoms (a carbon and three hydrogens) to another molecule; it changes the chemical properties of that molecule

RESTRICTION ENDONUCLEASE: an enzyme that responds to a specific, short sequence of nucleotides within a DNA molecule by binding to that sequence and breaking the DNA strands near the sequence

Summary of the Phenomenon

One of the most intriguing questions that biologists address is how a fertilized egg can develop into an organism as complex as a human being. Clearly, that fertilized egg carries the genetic blueprint that directs the development of the organism. Soon after fertilization, the egg divides into two cells, each of which then divides into two more, and so the process continues. As each cell divides, a complete copy of the genetic blueprint is passed to each daughter cell until the organism, composed of millions of such daughter cells, is complete. Whereas the first few cells of the embryo are very much alike in their structure and function, groups of cells in the adult are very different from one another. These different types of cells use different parts of the genetic blueprint.

The structure and function of a particular cell is determined primarily by the proteins present in that cell. Each different cell type contains a different group of proteins. Some proteins are present in virtually all cells, while some proteins are found only in very specific cells. For example, hemoglobin, the protein that carries oxygen in the blood, is found only in red blood cells. Similarly, pepsin, a digestive enzyme, is produced specifically by cells lining the stomach. The proteins each cell makes are determined by information contained in the genetic blueprint acquired from the fertilized egg.

The DNA molecules within the chromosomes serve as the cell's genetic blueprint. Information is stored in the DNA molecule in the sequence of the four nucleotides adenine (A), guanine (G), cytosine (C), and thymine (T), much the way information in a language is stored in a sequence of letters. Certain groups of letters in a specific sequence make up a unit of information, a word. In like manner, certain groups of nucleotides in a specific sequence make up a unit of information known as a gene. Genes must go through a two-step process before their information means anything to the cell. First, the information must be converted into messenger RNA (mRNA) in a process called transcription. Then, the mRNA's information is converted into a protein in the process of translation. Since the function of each cell is determined by the specific proteins it contains, and since genes carry the information for making these proteins, the function of the cell ultimately relies on which genes are active. Thus, cells are different from one another mainly on the basis of differences in active and inactive genes. The DNA, which contains a cell's genes, is organized into chromosomes. Chromosomes consist of long, compacted molecules of DNA associated with proteins. Most eukaryotic cells have many chromosomes. Chromatin is a general term that refers to all the DNA and its associated protein within a cell nucleus. Therefore, genes exist in the form of chromatin. Often, genes are separated from one another by sequences of nucleotides that are meaningless with respect to coding for proteins. In fact, much of the DNA between genes may be useless. Certain regions of DNA, however, especially those that lie close to the beginning of genes, have very important functions related to the activity of the genes.

Molecular geneticists reason that the key to understanding how an organism develops lies in understanding what controls, or regulates, the activation and inactivation of genes. Several scientific models of eukaryotic gene regulation have been proposed. Any such model must account for activating and inactivating specific groups of genes during the development of an organism within the structure of chromatin. It must also account for the ability of adult cells to pass on their specific program of gene activity to daughter cells. Most of the proposed models are based on observations of chromatin structure and on experience with prokaryotic genetics and suggest that regulatory proteins interact with specific control regions on or near genes to activate or inactivate those genes. One may predict from the models that when the regulatory proteins change genes from active states to inactive states, or vice versa, chromatin structure around those genes should also change. The changes in chromatin structure could occur prior to the change in activity, in which case chromatin structure may play a direct regulatory role, or chromatin structure could change as an indirect result of the change in gene activity. In either case, identifying changes in chromatin structure will help to clarify the mechanisms of gene regulation. In the 1970's, armed with the new tools and techniques of molecular biology, scientists began to look for differences in the structure of chromatin surrounding active and inactive genes. They discovered two important differences. One involved a chemical modification of the nucleotides of DNA and the other involved the exposure of DNA to the actions of certain proteins.

One important difference between active and inactive genes is with regard to a chemical modification of the nucleotide cytosine in and around genes. From 2 to 7 percent of the cytosine in mammalian DNA contains an extra methyl group (a carbon with three hydrogens attached by covalent bonds). This methylation occurs primarily when a cytosine is attached to the phosphate group of guanine. Since DNA is double-stranded and cytosine always bonds to guanine on the opposite strand, both strands contain this CG pair, and the cytosine is usually methylated on both strands. It is not known when CG groups are first methylated. Once methylated, however, the methylation pattern can easily be transmitted to daughter cells following replication. After DNA replicates, each new molecule consists of one original parental strand bound to one newly synthesized strand. If the parental strand contains a methylated CG group, then an enzyme known as a maintenance methylase could recognize the methylated cytosine on the parental strand and methylate the corresponding cytosine on the new daughter strand. Therefore, methylated CG groups would remain completely methylated, and nonmethylated groups would remain nonmethylated. If this pattern of methylation is important to gene regulation, the parental pattern of gene regulation would now be passed to the daughter cells, satisfying one of the requirements listed above for an appropriate model.

Scientific evidence suggests that methylation may be very important in gene regulation. Scientists have discovered that when many genes are active, they contain fewer methylated cytosines than their inactive counterparts. Some of the first studies that showed a correlation between undermethylation and gene activity looked at the genes that produce hemoglobin. Each hemoglobin molecule contains two alpha globin and two beta globin protein chains. Additionally, in humans for example, different globins appear in the embryo, the fetus, and the adult. Since each globin (embryonic beta globin, fetal alpha globin, and more) is encoded by a different gene, at each stage of development of the human two globin genes must be active in hemoglobin-producing cells—one alpha and one beta—while the rest of the globin genes may remain inactive. As development proceeds, the active genes switch to inactivity, while inactive genes become active. These genes need only be active in maturing red blood cells and are inactive in cells not destined to become red blood cells.

Studying the globin gene system, molecular biologists have shown that relatively few CG groups in and around globin genes are methylated in cells producing globin. In contrast, the same groups are highly methylated in sperm cells and other cells not producing globin. Since these early studies, similar results have been obtained by studying a variety of vertebrates (including rabbits, mice, chickens, and toads) and a variety of genes (such as those for antibodies, albumin, growth hormone, and muscle proteins). In fact, under the special circumstance in female mammalian cells where an entire chromosome (one of the two X chromosomes) is inactive, the active chromosome is undermethylated in comparison to the inactive chromosome. In most cases, active genes are undermethylated. With all the evidence in vertebrates correlating changes in methylation and gene activity, methylation's importance as a major regulatory mechanism is still controversial. One of the most highly studied eukaryotic organisms, the fruit fly, *Drosophila melanogaster*, contains few, if any, methylated nucleotides. Yet, its genes still undergo developmental and tissue-specific changes in activity.

The second difference in chromatin structure around active genes was also discovered by studying the state of globin genes in different types of cells. DNase I is an enzyme that attacks and degrades DNA. DNase I is considered nonspecific in that it indiscriminately reacts anywhere along a DNA strand with little regard to the sequence of nucleotides. When chromatin from cells producing globin was digested with small amounts of DNase I, the active globin genes were much more sensitive to digestion than globin genes that were not active. Active genes are said to be DNase I sensitive. Such a result would be expected if the chromatin around an active gene were more loosely associated with the chromatin proteins.

In an extension of these studies, it was found that decreasing the amount of DNase I still resulted further in preferential digestion of DNA in regions just in front of active genes—regions that scientists believe are important for the binding of regulatory proteins. Because of the increased sensitivity to digestion, these regions are said to be DNase I hypersensitive. Similar sites which are sensitive to digestion by DNase I and many other nucleases have been identified in genes that are specifically expressed, such as the globin genes, as well as in genes that are generally expressed in all cells, such as the histone genes. (Histones are the major proteins in chromatin.)

As with undermethylation, it is not clear whether DNase I hypersensitivity is critical in establishing the activity of a gene or is simply an easily detected phenomenon that results from a gene's activity. The importance of DNase I hypersensitive regions is indicated by the isolation of proteins which bind these sites. Proteins that bind globin-hypersensitive regions are present in nuclei of cells with active globin genes but not in other cells. In any case, the identification of both undermethylated and DNase hypersensitive regions of active genes has played an important role in identifying nucleotide sequences in DNA surrounding active genes, which may function to the regulation of gene activity.

Methods of Study

Differences in methylation in specific DNA sequences was first identified using restriction endonucleases. Restriction endonucleases recognize a specific sequence of nucleotides (usually four or six) in DNA and break the double-stranded molecule at that location. The ability of a restriction endonuclease to recognize a sequence may depend on whether a cytosine within that sequence is methylated. For example, the two enzymes known as MspI and HpaII both recognize and break DNA at the sequence . . . CCGG. . . . Yet, if the cytosine next to the guanine is methylated (. . . CmCGG . . .), only MspI will break the DNA. The methylation prohibits HpaII from recognizing this sequence. Since this sequence may occur fairly frequently in a cell's DNA, digestion with the enzyme will break the DNA into many fragments. DNA that is highly methylated will break into more, smaller fragments if digested with MspI than if digested with HpaII; whereas DNA that is undermethylated will be broken into more similar-size fragments by digestion with each enzyme.

Different sizes of DNA fragments resulting from restriction endonuclease digestion are separated by a technique known as gel electrophoresis. In gel electrophoresis, DNA samples are placed in a slot near the top of a thin, horizontal gel. The gel is submersed in a solution that will conduct electricity, and an electric current is applied. Since DNA molecules carry a negative charge, the electric current attracts the molecules toward the positive pole of the current. Smaller DNA fragments can slip through the viscous gel easily, while large DNA fragments move more slowly. After a period of time, the electric current is removed, and the DNA is observed by staining with a fluorescent dye and visualizing it under an ultraviolet lamp.

Other techniques can then be used to identify specific genes, such as globin genes. If one has isolated, or cloned, the globin gene, the cloned DNA can be synthesized using radioactive nucleotides. This radioactive, cloned DNA can then be reacted with the DNA fragments separated by gel electrophoresis to determine which fragments contain the globin gene by techniques known as Southern blot and hybridization. In Southern blotting (named in honor of the scientist who developed the technique, E. M. Southern), the double-stranded DNA in the gel is soaked in sodium hydroxide to make it single-stranded and is then transferred, or blotted, to a solid support, a special filter paper. When this filter paper is soaked at the correct temperature in a solution containing the radioactive, cloned DNA, the radioactive DNA will bind specifically to DNA on the paper with the same sequence of nucleotides. The location of the gene containing fragments on the filter paper is determined by exposing the paper to X-ray film in the dark (autoradiography). The radioactivity will cause a dark spot to form on the film, which can be seen after the film is developed. Using these techniques, scientists showed that genes isolated from cells in which they are active are broken into similar-size fragments by the restriction endonucleases MspI and HpaII. Yet, when the DNA was isolated from cells in which that gene was not active, the gene fragments produced by MspI were smaller than the fragments produced by HpaII. Therefore, genes are more highly methylated in their inactive state and undermethylated in their active state.

Other experiments tell more about the functional relationship of methylation and gene activity. The chemical 5-azacytidine is a potent demethylating agent. When this chemical is added to cells growing in culture, certain genes that were previously

inactive become active. Similarly, if a cloned gene that is not methylated is introduced into cultured cells, the gene becomes active. If that cloned gene is methylated
before it is introduced into cells, however, it remains inactive in the cells.

Identification of DNase I hypersensitive sites is based also on the techniques of
Southern blot and hybridization. First, cell nuclei are carefully isolated so as not to
disrupt the chromatin structure. Then, DNase I is added and allowed to proceed
until less than 10 percent of the DNA is degraded. (Degraded DNA becomes soluble
in acid. Therefore, the amount of acid-soluble DNA is monitored to determine the
amount that has been degraded.) Next, the DNA is purified and broken into fragments using restriction endonucleases. The fragments are separated by gel electrophoresis, Southern blotted to filter paper, and hybridized with a radioactive,
cloned fragment. The sizes of the fragments are compared with fragments that
result when DNA is not digested with DNase I. By comparing experiments using
different restriction enzymes and different radioactive fragments, the location and
size of DNase I hypersensitive regions becomes apparent.

The methods for identifying undermethylated and DNase I sensitive regions of
chromatin rely on fragmentation of DNA with restriction endonucleases and identification of specific fragments using Southern blot and hybridization techniques.
Scientists have altered the regions on isolated, cloned genes and placed them back
into cells to confirm that these regions actually affect gene activity. Finally, proteins
that may function in regulating gene activity by binding to DNA in these regions
have been isolated from cells in which the genes are active.

Context

Biology is the study of life. Many biologists believe that the best way to understand how living organisms survive is by studying the way molecules function in
cells. These people are biochemists, geneticists, and molecular biologists. The
molecules that do most of the work in a cell and that distinguish one cell from
another are the proteins. The only way a cell makes proteins is by accessing the
information contained within the genes of its DNA. Therefore, molecular biologists
are interested in determining how certain genes become accessible, or active, while
other genes remain inactive. They have discovered that active genes tend to be
undermethylated and more susceptible to degradation by the enzyme DNase I.
These discoveries have led to the identification of specific nucleotide sequences in
DNA that act as signals for various other components functioning in gene activity
and of proteins that bind to some of these nucleotides. Ultimately, scientists hope to
unravel the great mystery of how thousands of different genes are regulated in the
many different cells of a complex organism.

These discoveries have provided the joy of knowing the fundamental nature of
how cells function, but there are also practical applications to this knowledge.
Foremost is the ability to prevent disease. Many vaccines are produced by manipulating genes in a test tube and placing them into cultured cells, where they become
active. These genes produce the substances, antigens, to which the human immune

system makes antibodies. In turn, the antibodies provide resistance to disease. Without the knowledge of how to activate genes in cultured cells, humankind would still be susceptible to many dangerous diseases.

An important group of diseases that are virtually impossible to cure by traditional means are genetic diseases. Genetic diseases are caused by defective genes acquired from one's parents. They often result from inappropriate activity of a certain gene, either too little activity or too much activity. By combining the knowledge of the structure of active genes and the techniques of genetic engineering, it may be possible to correct genetic defects in human beings. Finally, cancer is a disease thought to be caused by changes in the activity of genes that regulate the growth of cells. With a greater understanding of how the activity of normal genes is regulated, biomedical scientists hope to find a way to control the activity of genes in malignant cells.

Bibliography

Adams, Roger, and Roy Burdon. *Molecular Biology of DNA Methylation*. New York: Springer-Verlag, 1985. Provides an advanced, yet understandable, analysis of many aspects of DNA methylation and its possible roles in the function of genes in both prokaryotes and eukaryotes. Includes an extensive list of scientific review articles on the subject.

Campbell, Neil A. *Biology*. 2d ed. Menlo Park, Calif.: Benjamin/Cummings, 1990. Several chapters provide clear discussion and excellent illustrations of general phenomena related to gene structure and activity. Chapter 18 "Control of Gene Expression and Development in Eukaryotes," expands many of the concepts introduced here, from chromatin structure to the globin gene family. A college-level text suitable for high school and lay readers. Includes glossary and lists for further reading.

Freifelder, David. *Essentials of Molecular Biology*. Boston: Jones and Bartlett, 1985. A condensed version of a comprehensive college text by the same author. Covers gene activity from the structure of DNA and proteins, through transcription and translation, to the regulation of eukaryotic gene expression. Well illustrated; intriguing problem sets for each chapter.

Kolata, Gina. "Fitting Methylation into Development." *Science* 228 (June 7, 1985): 1183-1184. An interesting historical account of the discovery of DNA methylation and the studies trying to identify its role in gene activity. Scientists discuss some of the controversy over the significance of DNA methylation.

_____. "Genes Regulated Through Chromatin Structure." *Science* 214 (November 13, 1981): 775-776. A historical look at some of the early research identifying DNase I sensitive and hypersensitive sites. Presents information on the organisms studied, the scientists directing the work, and their perspective on their research.

Scott, Andrew. *Vital Principles*. New York: Basil Blackwell, 1988. An excellent book for readers with little or no science background. Not directly related to methylation and DNase I sensitivity, however, presents the important concepts of biochemical processes in cells—proteins, genes, and energy to run chemical reactions.

Watson, James, Nancy Hopkins, Jeffrey Roberts, Joan Steitz, and Alan Weiner. *Molecular Biology of the Gene*. 4th ed., vol. 1. Menlo Park, Calif.: Benjamin/ Cummings, 1987. An easily readable, advanced college-level text written by leading scientists. Part 8, "The Functioning of Eukaryotic Chromosomes," provides a detailed look at chromatin structure and many features of eukaryotic genes that affect gene activity.

Gary J. Lindquester

Cross-References

Bioethics: Molecular Biological Decisions, 187; Chromosomes, 462; DNA Sequencing, 698; DNA's Molecular Structure, 706; Gel Electrophoresis and Blotting, 1082; Eukaryotic Gene Regulation, 1111; Genes and Nucleic Acids, 1134; Nucleic Acid Structure, 1987; Transcription of DNA to Form RNA, 2632; X Inactivation and the Lyon Hypothesis, 2721.

CHROMATOGRAPHIC ANALYSIS OF CHLOROPLAST PIGMENTS

Types of life science: Biochemistry and photosynthesis
Other field of study: Plant physiology

The brilliant green colors of plants are caused by a mixture of multicolored pigments housed within subcellular compartments called chloroplasts. The various colored pigments can be individually observed through a method called chromatography. As a separation tool, chromatography has played a key role in advancing many areas of modern biochemistry, including immunology, pharmacology, and protein chemistry.

Principal terms

CHLOROPLAST: a specialized subcellular structure of plant cells that contains the pigments actively involved in photosynthesis

CHROMATOGRAM: a graph, chart, strip of paper, or other permanent record of the separated compounds that results from using chromatography to analyze a mixture

CHROMATOGRAPHY: a method of separating the individual components of a mixture into isolated and, ideally, pure chemical forms by utilizing both a stationary and mobile phase

MOBILE PHASE: a liquid, gas, or other chemical agent that facilitates a chromatographic separation via movement across or through a stationary phase

NONBONDED INTERACTION: one of the properties of chemicals that can be used advantageously to achieve a good chromatographic separation; an interplay between chemical species that does not involve a chemical change

PHOTOSYNTHESIS: a complex series of biochemical reactions in which carbon dioxide and water are converted into sugar and oxygen; a food-producing event aided by the absorption of sunlight at photoreceptor sites found in plants and some microorganisms

PIGMENTS: colorful components of living systems that contain complex substructures made of proteins, metal ions, and other chemical groupings

RETENTION FACTOR: often written as R_f, this term is a ratio of the distance traveled by a component of a mixture as compared with the distance traveled by the mobile phase in chromatography

SOLVENT: a chemical that causes the dissolution (dissolving) of another substance; generally, the substance present in the greatest amount in a mixture—for example, in blood, water is the solvent

STATIONARY PHASE: generally a solid, or a liquid coated onto a solid, that does not travel, yet facilitates a separation by temporarily holding or trapping some component(s) of a mixture more strongly than other components

Summary of the Methodology

Chromatography is a method of separation that selectively removes some portions of a mixture over time. With this method, all components of a mixture can be fully isolated. If a chromatographic separation is well executed, no loss of the original chemical form or reactivity of the components will occur. This kind of recovery is important if further investigations or analyses are to be performed on the purified components.

Chromatography was first described in 1850 by a German chemist, Friedlieb Ferdinand Runge, whose work focused on the development of laboratory methods for testing dyes. He performed a simple experiment in which he separated the components of a dye mixture by spotting the dye solution onto blotting paper. Runge observed that as the color spot spread over the paper, different colors began to separate from the original spot. As the dye spread more, some pigments traveled further than others. In spite of the potential chemical applications of this effect, Runge did not investigate the effect any further or attempt to explain his findings.

Approximately ten years after Runge's observations were noted, another German chemist, F. Groppelsroder, described a similar event. He utilized strips of paper, one end of which was dipped into a colored solution. The colored pigments of the dye solution would travel up the paper at different rates, thus revealing constituent colors once again. This was the first performance of what today is called paper chromatography.

Nearly fifty years later, the person most often recognized as the founder of chromatographic science, Michael S. Tswett, made his historical contributions. The "founder of chromatography" seems an appropriate appellation, since Tswett was the first to explain the phenomenon and methods of this analytical tool. He named the method chromatography, based upon the combination of two Greek roots— *chroma*, meaning color, and *graphia*, meaning writing. "Color writing" is precisely what Tswett did as he extracted green pigments from plants, then ran the plant extract through a glass column (or cylinder) packed with crushed chalk (calcium carbonate). During this process, Tswett noticed that distinct zones of greens and yellows of varying hues appeared at different locations in the column. Tswett described the techniques of "color writing" to a group of fellow Russian botanists at a 1903 meeting held in Warsaw. In 1906, he published two papers on the topic of chromatography: One paper described the chromatographic method itself, while the other outlined practical applications of the method. Although Tswett recognized that chromatographic techniques could be used also to analyze the components of colorless mixtures, he did not investigate the possibilities of chromatographic applications beyond his original work. Nearly another fifty years would pass before chromatography would revolutionize the young sciences of biochemistry and petroleum chemistry.

Several overlapping aspects of the methods used by Runge, Groppelsroder, and Tswett should be noted. First, all three scientists had the good fortune to study colorful mixtures so that a mere glance of the eye could easily allow the progress of a separation to be monitored. Another common feature is that all three used a solid stationary phase combined with a mobile liquid phase to achieve isolation of the many chemicals found within one mixture.

An example of a naturally occurring chromatographic process can be seen in the way water is filtered as it seeps into the ground. Barring the presence of unnatural components of rain water, such as acids or pesticides, the water is cleansed as it slowly trickles down into the earth's crust. A slow journey allows natural filtering to occur so that selective particles settle apart from the water. The analogy to chromatography applies in that a rush of mobile phase over a stationary phase would result in a poor separation or purification. Conversely, a slow journey allows for competitive, nonbonded interactions to occur between individual components in the mixture and the stationary and mobile phases it travels in or over. This slow competition between traveling and stopping is essential to a chromatographer.

As might be correctly guessed, the time factor reaches a limit. Eventually, the time required for a perfect separation to occur versus the improved quality of the separation diverge. Choices must be made to determine what amount of time can produce a good, acceptable separation. For chromatography to be a useful method of analysis, the separation must be effectively achieved within a reasonable time frame. The method described below is a classical demonstration of chromatographic principles. In this method, techniques that allow plant pigments to be isolated are given. This method is similar to the work performed by Tswett.

Spinach leaves are an excellent tool for the identification of four pigments— chlorophyll a, chlorophyll b, carotene, and xanthophyll. If fresh spinach is used, the color pigments can be extracted from the leaves. There are several ways to do this. One is to heat torn spinach leaves gently in rubbing alcohol. The 70 percent isopropyl alcohol acts as the extracting solvent.

The stationary phase can be made by dipping strips of paper into a mixture of acetone and ligroin. These strips can be made from large coffee filters, thick paper towels, construction paper, or any white, solid, absorbent material. The preferred choice for the mobile phase is a mixture made of 10 percent acetone and 90 percent ligroin (petroleum ether).

The paper strip, with a dried spot of the plant extract upon it, can now be placed in a vertical position into a jar containing the mobile phase of acetone-ligroin. The bottom of the paper strip is carefully dipped into the pool of acetone-ligroin mixture. As the acetone-ligroin mobile phase comes into contact with the carefully placed strip, capillary action allows the liquid to travel up the strip against gravity.

The mobile phase has a migrating moisture line, or leading line of wetness, which is properly called the solvent front. As the solvent migrates up the strip, it eventually comes in contact with the pigment spot. As the solvent travels over the spot, some of the pigments will be swept along with the mobile phase; others will move slightly, if at all, from the original spot. As this traveling continues, some spinach pigments will begin to adhere to the paper more strongly than others. Yellow-green chlorophyll b is the first pigment to stop moving along with the mobile phase. One says that chlorophyll b is the first pigment to "elute" (separate) from the extract sample. The other pigments will continue to travel upward with the solvent. Because chlorophyll b elutes first, it has a greater nonbonded interaction with the chemical constituents of the paper strip than with the chemicals of the mobile phase. Chlorophyll b is a more polar (water-loving) pigment than the other pigments found in spinach extracts.

The next pigment to separate is blue-green chlorophyll a, followed by yellow-orange xanthophyll and, finally, the orange pigment of carotene. Because carotene is the last pigment to elute from the extract, it exhibits stronger nonbonded interactions with the acetone-ligroin mixture (mobile phase) than it does with the paper. This stronger, nonbonded interaction with the mobile phase indicates that carotene is the most nonpolar (water-fearing) pigment found in spinach chloroplasts.

Once the solvent front is about half an inch from the top of the paper strip, the strip should be carefully removed from the chamber. A pencil line must be drawn across the top of the strip immediately to indicate how far up the paper the mobile phase traveled. The paper strip is now referred to as a chromatogram.

The R_f value is a numerical constant that is unique for each of the four pigments identified in spinach. The ratio of the distance each pigment travels, as compared with the distance traveled by the mobile phase (from the start to finish lines), will be unique to that pigment alone. Thus, chlorophyll b will not switch places with carotene on the chromatogram because of the unique nonbonded interactions it has with the stationary and mobile phases. Carotene, which has a totally different chemical configuration, cannot mimic the interactions of chlorophyll b or any other pigment. For this reason, the R_f values determined by the method described above can be generated repeatedly by anyone using this method. This reproducibility of results is a helpful feature when analyzing plant pigments, or other mixtures, using chromatography.

Applications of the Method

As performed by Runge and Tswett, chromatography has evolved from the days of paper, chalk, and dyes into a sleek, computerized, and versatile instrumentation requiring expert training and a significantly larger budget.

The requirement that a sample be applied to a system comprising stationary and mobile phases offers chromatography many degrees of freedom. As such, great diversity as well as specificity can be achieved by switching the chemical composition of both phases. This flexibility spawned the development of specialized types of chromatography that have wide applications. Although each method is useful, generally one optimal method will be selected over the others in order to meet the needs of a particular problem.

In gas chromatography (GC), an inert gas, perhaps helium or nitrogen, flows through several feet of a packed and coiled column. The gas acts as the mobile phase by sweeping the sample through the column. The packing is often a solid material, but liquid-coated solid particles are also used. Aside from the worldwide use of GC methods to analyze samples drawn from oil wells, GC can also be used to analyze products of fermentation; to determine the amount of alcohol and flavorings in a cough syrup; to measure the quantity of a drug in a pharmaceutical tablet; to measure air quality; to determine if a car meets local auto emissions standards; or to determine what and how much of an insecticide may be present on a food crop.

Thin-layer chromatography (TLC) is useful in protein chemistry. The stationary phase of this method consists of thin gel applied to a plastic or glass plate (strip). Various gels can be used to coat the plate. Some coatings may be polar, while others may be nonpolar. TLC can be used to identify amino acids of proteins, to determine the sugar content of a fruit or cane crop, to identify the constituents of an over-the-counter analgesic, or to determine the success of a reaction in an organic or pharmaceutical synthesis.

Column chromatography also has useful applications in organic chemistry and pharmaceutical laboratories, as well as biochemical research laboratories. Separations can be performed to look for the amounts and types of vitamins in food or diet supplement tablets. Pigments, steroids, alkaloids, or carbohydrates all can be identified and measured using an appropriate column-chromatographic system.

High-pressure liquid chromatography (HPLC) can purify biologically important enzymes from living systems without destroying the biological activity of the enzyme. It can also test for the presence of illegal drugs in urine and blood samples. Forensics laboratories use HPLC to determine the presence of toxic chemical substances that can be used to identify victims and criminals. Public water treatment centers use HPLC to test for the presence of ions, or electrolytes, in a municipal water supply. If the detection of ions shows an unsafe concentration of a certain substance, public health officials can take appropriate actions to remedy the problem.

As for the paper chromatography pioneered by Michael Tswett, this early method now seems somewhat archaic when compared to modern chromatographic technology and instrumentation. While paper chromatography continues be a popular method for analysis of plant pigments, dyes, inks, and food colorings, it is largely used in academic settings to demonstrate the principles of chromatography.

Michael Tswett was a "chromatographic prophet." Nearly a century ago, he foresaw the great potential of "color writing." His work of the early twentieth century laid the foundations of a science that revolutionized analytical chemistry and fostered the maturation of biochemistry. Today, the usefulness, diversity, and multitude of applications of chromatographic analyses continues to grow.

Context

The chromatographic analysis of chloroplast pigments represents a uniting of two fields of study: separations science and photosynthesis. Historical accounts show that Tswett's chromatography of plant pigments prompted scientific investigations of photosynthesis—an all-important biochemical reaction. While photosynthesis and chlorophyll are now familiar terms, at the beginning of the twentieth century the correlation of plant pigments to their role as photosynthetic "machines" had not yet been discovered. Photosynthesis was not understood as a biochemical process at that time, although speculation of what chemical changes were involved had been proposed as early as the early nineteenth century. All life on earth relies upon the continuous growth and life-sustaining output of plants and microorganisms that are photosynthetically active. For that sole reason, investigation and complete comprehension of photosynthesis have been a prime target of biochemical research for centuries.

The analysis of plant pigments through simple or sophisticated chromatographic methods has been important to an increased understanding of phototropic life. These living organisms are capable of absorbing specific wavelengths of radiant energy from the sun and then converting that energy into stored food or chemical energy.

Chromatography has revealed that many different pigments, not only green ones, are simultaneously present in plants. Each pigment absorbs only certain energies from sunlight rather than absorbing all the incident light energy that falls upon it. Each pigment behaves as though it has a tiny "window" that allows only certain bands of solar energy to be harvested. These little bundles of energy are quantized, or set, amounts of energy, and they are unique for each different type of pigment. (White sunlight is actually composed of a broad range of energies, which can be seen as a rainbow of visible color or light when passed through a prism.)

Paper chromatography has allowed for the discovery of many specialized pigments, including at least five forms of chlorophyll; chlorophyll pigments are now known to include chlorophylls a through e. Also, many different forms of carotenes and xanthophylls exist. Surprisingly, paper chromatography reveals that red and yellow pigments are always present in green plants. Because of the high abundance of the green chlorophyll pigments, as compared with the bright red of carotenes or yellows of xanthophyll, only the dominant green hues are generally seen. The lush greens simply camouflage other color tones. In the fall, those trees that are deciduous show an annual loss of chlorophyll pigments, thereby revealing the brilliant foliage associated with an autumn forest.

Once pigments are separated from one another, they can be chemically characterized and further studied. Some of the terms used to describe individual pigments have Greek origins (*chloros* means green; *xanthos* means yellow). Carotene pigments combine to produce an overall orange color. A Latin term, *carota*, refers to the carrot vegetable; it is the word from which carotene is derived. Carotenes and xanthophylls have been discovered to be of similar chemical composition, with each being made of forty carbon atoms covalently bonded to one another. Different arrangements of these covalent bonds produce the different colors of red and orange.

Chromatography has not only aided scientists' comprehension of pigments as the initiators of photosynthesis; it has also allowed scientists the opportunity to trace the path that carbon atoms follow through every tiny increment of the photosynthetic process. Paper chromatography, coupled with radioisotopic studies of carbon-labeled (or radioactively tagged carbon atoms within) compounds, eventually led to the ability to describe the carbon-containing products of each minute step in the rather long and complicated series of reactions that constitute photosynthesis. Today, this pathway is called the carbon cycle. It helps to explain how carbon recycles itself through the life-death seasons experienced by living systems.

Ancient references to separation science (most notably, distillation) can be found in the Bible. Based upon the fact that different substances possess different boiling points, distillation is one of the earliest examples of a practical, everyday application of separations chemistry. Although it continues to be the most popular method of separation for the liquor industry, distillation cannot offer the degree of flexibility necessary for the separation of heat-sensitive materials, including most biologically important molecules. Many biochemical researchers consider modern chromatography to be the method of choice for analysis of biochemicals.

The deceptively simple work of Michael Tswett opened more avenues of research in the twentieth century than Tswett could have imagined. Many of the questions prompted by modern applications of chromatography in the analyses of living matter are still unanswered. The task of separating, purifying, and identifying the molecules that actually keep the "soup of life" living, regenerating, and replenished continues. "Color writing" holds numerous answers to those who continue to pursue the hidden messages locked within the chemistry of life.

Bibliography

Allamong, B., and T. Mertens. *Energy for Life: Photosynthesis and Respiration.* New York: John Wiley & Sons, 1976. A self-help book with clear learning objectives, chapter tests, and finals with correct responses available. It is not the most updated report on photosynthesis, but it has good basic information in the chapters addressing plant life and is appropriate for young adult readers.

Bassham, J. A. "The Path of Carbon in Photosynthesis." *Scientific American* 206 (June, 1962): 40, 88-100. Describes the paper chromatography method as coupled with radioisotope tracers. It is an excellent article of historical significance, as it gives an account of the surprise intermediate products, such as amino acids, fats, carbohydrates, and other compounds, made during photosynthesis. It is chemically intense, but the photographs of the chromatograms are worth scrutiny. Some sections are easily read, especially the introduction, "The Capture of Light," and "Chromatograms and Radiographs."

Braithwaite, A., and F. J. Smith. *Chromatographic Methods.* 4th ed. New York: Chapman and Hall, 1985. An excellent book that describes the many types of chromatography available today. Specific chapters deal with column chromatography, TLC, GC, HPLC, and combined techniques, such as mass spectroscopy and gas chromatography. The final chapter of the book provides model experiments in a cookbook style. This book is not overly technical, but it is more sophisticated than some references geared specifically to the beginner (such as the Tocci book cited below).

Clevenger, Sarah. "Flower Pigments." *Scientific American* 210 (June, 1964): 84-88. This article is a great resource to teachers because it offers options for pigments from nature that can be investigated. The reading gets technical in sections, but the introduction is quite accessible. The photographs show both one-dimensional and two-dimensional paper chromatograms, using methods that can be applied to the analysis of either plant leaf or petal extracts.

Crum, Lawrence E. *Classroom Activities and Experiments for Life Science*. West Nyack, N.Y.: Parker, 1974. This book is somewhat dated, but the basic information and suggested activities are worth investigating. Chapter 6, on plants, contains a description of affordable, fun experiments for the exploration of photosynthesis and growth. Teachers will find many resources listed for their reference in this highly readable resource; the step-by-step approach is concise.

Hamilton, R. J., Sheila Hamilton, and David Kealey. *Thin Layer Chromatography: Analytical Chemistry by Open Learning*. New York: John Wiley & Sons, 1987. An excellent, self-taught approach to TLC theory and methods. This book is not as difficult to read as the title may imply; much of the material is very clearly written.

Keeton, W., M. Dabney, and R. Zollinhofer. *Biology in the Laboratory*. New York: W. W. Norton, 1970. This is a simple, easy-to-follow book of activities with appropriate discussion sections that meet the needs of true novices. While it is not an outstanding book, it does do a good job of stating concepts very simply and concisely. Chapter 5, "Autotropic Nutrition," gives a short essay on photosynthesis and paper chromatography.

Levine, R. P. "The Mechanism of Photosynthesis." *Scientific American* 221 (December, 1969): 15, 58-64. This article requires some previous knowledge of the biochemistry of photosynthesis, as many chemical terms appear early in the article. What is attractive in this article is the attention given to the different pigments as photoreceptors. The article's introduction and first section, "The Absorption of Light Energy," can be managed without much chemistry background.

Morholt, E., P. Brandwein, and A. Joseph. *A Sourcebook for the Biological Sciences*. 2d ed. New York: Harcourt, Brace & World, 1966. This dated reference was designed as a resource for high school science teachers and is still very useful. The diagrams of paper chromatography (which in this case is applied to amino acid analysis) and column chromatograpy are accurate and clear. Contacts and sources of audiovisual support materials can be found toward the end of the text. The best features of the book, however, are its well-written presentations and step-by-step approach.

Tocci, Salvatore. *Biology for Young Scientists*. New York: Franklin Watts, 1987. This book contains excellent, brief descriptions of paper chromatography and photosynthesis. Chapter 4, "Photosynthesis and Respiration," makes particularly good reading for high school students.

Mary C. Fields

Cross-References

Anaerobic Photosynthesis, 87; Autoradiography and Subcellular Fractionation of Radioactive Tracer Molecules, 148; The Calvin-Benson Cycle, 316; Chloroplast Reaction Sites, 424; Chloroplasts and Other Plastids, 431; The Cytoplasm, 575; Gas Exchange in Plants, 1076; Leaf Anatomy, 1535; Leaf-Fall Regulation, 1542; Liquid Transport Systems in Plants, 1613; Photorespiration, 2059; Photosynthetic Light Absorption, 2073; Photosynthetic Light Reactions, 2080.

CHROMOSOMES

Types of life science: Cell biology (cytology) and genetics
Other fields of study: Biochemistry, genetic regulation in eukaryotes, and molecular
biology

Chromosomes are the subunits into which the hereditary material of all organisms is divided. The study of chromosomes and their molecular constituents has led to an understanding of the cellular and molecular basis of heredity, embryonic development, and many diseases of humans and other organisms.

Principal terms
CENTROMERE: the site on a chromosome in dividing cells at which tension is applied to separate the duplicated parts of the chromosome
CHROMATID: one of the two copies of a duplicated chromosome
CHROMATIN: a collective term describing all the DNA of the cell nucleus and its associated histone and nonhistone proteins
CHROMOSOME: a subdivision of the DNA of the cell nucleus, held in combination with histone and nonhistone proteins
DEOXYRIBONUCLEIC ACID (DNA): a molecule consisting of long chains of chemical subunits called nucleotides; the sequence of nucleotides encodes hereditary information
GENE: a unit of hereditary information—in molecular terms, a coding segment of a DNA molecule; most genes encode proteins
HISTONE: a structural protein associated with DNA in chromosomes; histones combine with DNA to form nucleosomes
NONHISTONE: a functional protein associated with DNA in chromosomes; most nonhistones are enzymes or proteins regulating gene activity
NUCLEOSOME: the fundamental unit of chromosome structure, consisting of two turns of DNA wrapped around a core of histones
TELOMERE: a specialized region at the tips of chromosomes necessary for chromosome duplication, chemical stability, and division

Summary of the Phenomenon

The deoxyribonucleic acid (DNA) of the cell nucleus acts as a molecular storage site for the information required to assemble proteins. DNA consists of long chains of subunits called nucleotides. Four different types of nucleotides occur in DNA; the sequences in which these nucleotides occur in DNA molecules spell out directions for the assembly of all cellular proteins.

In all animals, plants, fungi, and protozoa, the DNA of the nucleus, rather than existing as a single molecule, is subdivided into several to many individual, linear molecules. The total number of molecules is constant and characteristic of each species. Each of the individual DNA molecules, which may be as long as several centimeters, is a chromosome of the cell nucleus. In a chromosome, the DNA occurs in close association with two classes of proteins, the histone and nonhistone proteins. The three constitutents—DNA, histones, and nonhistones—collectively form what is known as the chromatin of the cell nucleus. DNA and the histone proteins occur in approximately equal quantities by weight in chromatin. The more variable nonhistone proteins are found in different cells in quantities ranging from as little as 20 percent to approximately the same as the DNA by weight.

DNA is the best known of the three molecular components of chromatin. X-ray diffraction and other methods have allowed DNA structure to be traced down to the positions of its individual atoms. While not as well characterized as DNA, the histones have all been identified and isolated, and their amino acid sequences are completely known in many organisms. Five different histone types are present in most organisms. The histones act in chromatin primarily as structural elements in chromatin.

Many of the nonhistone proteins have also been identified and completely sequenced. The proteins in this group have proved to be primarily functional rather than structural molecules. Some nonhistones act as enzymes involved in DNA duplication, or in the reactions that copy information from the DNA. Other nonhistones, perhaps the most important proteins of this group, regulate the individual coding segments of the DNA, the genes. In effect, the nonhistone proteins determine which of the many protein codes of the DNA are to be utilized in making proteins. Through this regulatory activity, the nonhistone proteins directly or indirectly control both embryonic development and the varied activities of cells in adult organisms.

The histone proteins combine with the DNA to form a fundamental structural unit that occurs in the nuclei of all organisms of the world except the bacteria and blue-green algae. In this structural unit, two each of four different histones assemble into a core particle that is roughly spherical in shape. Around this core, the DNA wraps through approximately two turns, much as a rope winds around a pulley. The DNA is held on the core particle by one molecule of the fifth histone type. One of these subunits, consisting of two turns of DNA wrapped around the histone core particle, is a nucleosome. Each nucleosome has an outside diameter of about 10 namometers. By way of comparison, the DNA molecule in naked form, with no attached proteins, is about 2 nanometers in diameter.

The long DNA molecules of chromosomes wrap around many thousands of nucleosome core particles in succession, producing a structure that appears in the electron microscope much like a series of beads on a string. Each nucleosome is separated from the next by a short length of DNA called the linker, which appears as the string in the beads-on-a-string image. The assembly of DNA and histones into nucleosomes packs the DNA into a stable superstructure in which the DNA occupies only about one-seventh of its fully extended length.

The present understanding of nucleosome structure is based on a hypothesis first proposed by Roger D. Kornberg in 1974. Kornberg's model integrated information from many sources, including his own experiments and the work of other investigators.

It is not considered likely that chromosomes are arranged in the cell as an extended chain of nucleosomes. X-ray diffraction studies of chromatin by A. T. Finch and A. Klug indicate that the chain of nucleosomes winds further into a tight coil, much like a door spring, called the solenoid or chromatin fiber. The solenoid coil is proposed by Finch and Klug to contain six to eight nucleosomes per turn and to have a total outside diameter of 34 nanometers. The DNA apparently remains wrapped into nucleosomes, and wound further into the solenoid coil at all times in the cell nucleus except during the instant its directions are being duplicated or copied. During duplication or copying, the DNA probably unwinds from both the solenoid coil and the nucleosomes and exists in fully extended form.

During the stage in which cells are actively growing in mass through the assembly of proteins and other molecules, the chromosomes are extended throughout the nucleus. Even with winding of the DNA into nucleosomes and coiling into solenoids, the chromosomes are still highly elongated fibers ranging from several to many millimeters in length. During periods of cell division, however, the chromosomes pack and coil into short, thick rods only a micron or so in length and less than a micron in diameter. It is only during division, when the chromosomes have packed down into compact rods, that they become thick enough to be visible in the light microscope.

Just before cell division, and before the chromosomes pack into thick rods, the DNA and proteins of each chromosome are duplicated. As a result, the chromosomes appear as double structures when they pack down in preparation for cell division. Each of the two parts of a duplicated chromosome is known as a chromatid. During division, the two chromatids of each chromosome are separated, and one is delivered to each of the two daughter cells resulting from the division. As a result, the daughter cells receive exactly the same numbers and kinds of chromosomes as the parent cell entering the division process.

While they are packed down into double rods awaiting division, the chromosomes have a typical structure that can be traced out in the light microscope. At some point along each of the chromosomes is a narrowed region known as the centromere or primary constriction. This region contains the site at which tension is applied to separate the chromatids during division. The parts of the chromosomes extending on either side of the centromere region are known as the chromosome arms. At the outermost tip of each chromosome arm is a specialized region known as the telomere (from Greek *telos*, meaning "end").

Telomeres do more than simply define the ends of chromosomes. Specialized DNA sequences occur in this region that are necessary for successful duplication of the chromosome ends in preparation for division. Telomeres are also necessary for the chemical stability of chromosomes. Broken chromosomes lacking telomeres are highly susceptible to enzymatic breakdown and readily interact chemically with other cellular molecules, including other chromosomes. Frequently, as a result of such interactions, chromosomes fuse into multiple structures that cannot be distributed correctly during division. Even without fusions with other chromosomes, chromosomes lacking telomeres are frequently lost entirely, so that one or both of the daughter cells receives an incomplete set.

The locations of the centromeres and telomeres and the lengths of the arms are characteristic for each chromosome of the set during division. Collectively, the morphology of the entire set of chromosomes forms what is known as the karyotype of a species. Although each chromosome of a karyotype is characteristic in structure, the locations of centromeres and telomeres and the lengths of the arms of many chromosomes are so similar that the chromosomes cannot be separately distinguished. This is true of many higher animals, including humans. Several staining techniques, however, produce banding patterns that are unique and standard for each chromosome. In one technique, for example, the chromosomes are treated very briefly with an enzyme that digests proteins. The digestion rearranges the chromatin fibers of the chromosome arms into a pattern of crossbands that is intensified by a blue stain much used in preparing chromosomes for light microscopy.

The banding patterns would be little more than a scientific curiosity except for the fact that, because the bands are characteristic and different for each chromosome, they allow each chromosome to be unambiguously identified. The banding patterns have made it possible to assign known genes to specific chromosomes in humans and many other mammals. The bands have also revealed that several human diseases result from a shift of segments from one chromosome to another, or from the loss or addition of chromosome segments. Shifts between chromosome segments have been implicated, for example, among the causes of several human cancers, including some leukemias. By means of the banding techniques, not only the fact that the shifts have occurred but also the precise regions involved in the shift can be determined.

Methods of Study

Chromosomes have been studied through several avenues of research, including morphological, chemical, and molecular approaches. Very early in the development of cell biology, before the beginning of this century, chromosomes were first identified in dividing cells under the light microscope. A variety of staining techniques were employed to color the chromosomes so that they could be seen more easily. The name "chromosome," which means "colored body," refers to the intense colors produced in chromosomes by these staining techniques. The chromosomes were suspected by early investigators of carrying hereditary information because they occur in constant numbers in each cell of a species and because they are duplicated and divided precisely during division. The hereditary function of the chromosomes was not demonstrated conclusively, however, until the early 1900's. At that time, experiments in the newly developed field of genetics, combined with micro-

Life Science

scopic studies, established that the units of heredity, the genes, are carried on the chromosomes.

Chemical studies of the chromosomes also began during the nineteenth century. In 1871, Johann Friedrich Miescher, a physician and physiological chemist, first isolated DNA in impure form from cell nuclei. Methods for purifying DNA acids were worked out by the late 1800's, and the structures of the major chemical constituents of DNA were identified. Later research, in the 1920's and 1930's, confirmed that DNA is located in the chromosomes, and many cell biologists began to suspect direct involvement of this substance in heredity. Finally, in the 1940's and 1950's, a series of experiments by Oswald Avery, Alfred D. Hershey, and Martha Chase confirmed that DNA provides the molecular basis of heredity. In 1953, James D. Watson and Francis H. C. Crick, using data obtained by the X-ray diffraction of extracted DNA samples, worked out the molecular structure of DNA. From this structure, Watson and Crick were able to predict how DNA is duplicated and how genetic information is encoded in DNA.

In the X-ray diffraction technique, which has been of central importance to studies of the molecular structure of chromosomes, a narrow beam of X rays is passed through a molecular specimen. The specimen must be in the form of a crystal or be packed into a highly ordered state resembling a crystal. Reflection from the regularly repeating patterns of atoms in the crystal or ordered specimen splits the X-ray beam into subparts, much as a beam of light is split by reflection from the facets of a diamond. The split X-ray beam produces a pattern of spots on a photographic plate. By measuring the distances and angles separating the spots on the plate, the distances separating the atoms and their positions in the specimen can be deduced.

The proteins of chromosomes were also first extracted chemically during the 1800's. The histones, which have highly characteristic chemical properties, were identified in 1884. The remaining proteins of the nucleus were simply designated as nonhistone proteins. During the 1960's and 1970's, electron microscopy, X-ray diffraction, and the results of several chemical techniques were used to work out the arrangement of the histones with DNA in nucleosomes. X-ray diffraction was also used to deduce the pattern in which chains of nucleosomes wind into the solenoid coil.

The nonhistone proteins have yielded to chemical analysis only relatively recently. The first proteins of this group to be definitely identified were the enzymes active in duplicating DNA and copying the genetic information for use in assembling proteins. This line of investigation, carried out by isolating the molecules and tracing their interaction in the test tube, began in the 1950's and 1960's and continues at an intensive pace today. The first nonhistone proteins responsible for genetic regulation were identified during the 1960's and 1970's; this work, which is among the most exciting and important endeavors of present-day cell and molecular biology, also continues at a rapid pace. Much of the research identifying regulatory nonhistone proteins is carried out by isolating particular genes and noting the effects of purified nonhistone proteins on the activity of the genes.

Many of the regulatory nonhistone proteins have been isolated by taking advantage of their ability to combine with the DNA of specific genes. In this approach, copies of the DNA of a gene are attached to the surface of a piece of filter paper. A preparation of nonhistone proteins is then poured over the paper. From the many proteins in the preparation, the nonhistones recognizing and binding the DNA of the gene are trapped by their attachment to the DNA on the filter paper. The paper is then washed to eliminate any unbound proteins. The trapped proteins are then released from the DNA and separately purified. Studies of the interactions of these proteins with their genes have begun to reveal how genes are regulated and controlled.

Context

Research on chromosomes has been among the most significant and far-reaching of all biological studies. As soon as chromosomes were identified as carriers of hereditary information, combined genetic and microscopic studies revealed that the development of individuals as male or female in humans and many other organisms depends on differences in the number or types of chromosomes in the two sexes. The chromosomes that differ in the two sexes are known as sex chromosomes.

The combined genetic and microscopic studies also revealed that many disabilities in humans and other organisms are caused by losses of chromosome parts or transfers of segments from one chromosome to another. Down syndrome, for example, which appears with distressing frequency among human births, is caused by the presence of an extra copy of one chromosome of the human set. Examination of cells removed from the fluid surrounding the embryo in the uterus can reveal whether the extra chromosome responsible for Down syndrome is present. Abnormalities in the numbers and kinds of sex chromosomes are also responsible for several important hereditary diseases. In more recent years, combined genetic and microscopic studies revealed the association of transfers of chromosome segments with the development of some forms of cancer. Scientists hope eventually to be able to counteract the effects of these chromosome deficiencies by introducing corrected copies of altered chromosomes or inactivating extra copies.

Examination of the chromosomes is also routinely used for more mundane purposes. In athletic contests, such as the Olympics, it is sometimes difficult to tell from appearances alone whether an individual should compete as a male or female. Determination of sex in such cases is routinely accomplished by examining the sex chromosomes in cells removed from the body. The cells are obtained by lightly scraping the inside of the mouth.

The molecular studies of chromosomes have also been of inestimable benefit to humankind and the development of science. The discovery of DNA structure by Watson and Crick is widely considered to be the most important single discovery in the history of biology. The discovery led directly to an understanding of how genetic information is encoded in DNA and how the information is duplicated and passed on in heredity. In more recent years, research in the molecular biology of chromosomes has revealed the molecular structure of genes and how they are regulated by the nonhistone proteins. Continued investigation in this area has already begun to reveal how genes work normally during embryonic development and abnormally in the production of hereditary defects and disease. With this molecular understanding, the means to correction of hereditary defects and diseases are almost certain to follow.

Bibliography

Alberts, Bruce, Dennis Bray, Julian Lewis, Martin Raff, Keith Roberts, and James D. Watson. *Molecular Biology of the Cell*. 2d ed. New York: Garland, 1989. Much of this book, written at the college level, describes the structure and function of chromosomes. The approach is highly molecular and includes many photographs and informative diagrams. Chapter 9, "The Cell Nucleus," is especially pertinent. An extensive bibliography of technical articles and books at an advanced level is included at the end of each chapter. One of the authors of the book, James D. Watson, is one of the discovers of DNA structure.

Croce, C. M., and G. Klein. "Chromosome Translocations and Human Cancer." *Scientific American* 252 (March, 1985): 44-50. Outlines research leading to the discovery that the transfer of segments between chromosomes is implicated in the development of some kinds of cancer. A number of the translocations responsible are illustrated in text and diagrams.

Darnell, James, Harvey Lodish, and David Baltimore. *Molecular Cell Biology*. New York: Scientific American Books, 1986. Much of this book is also devoted to the molecular structure and functions of chromosomes. The book is clearly written at the college level and contains many informative diagrams and photographs. An extensive bibliography of technical scientific articles is included.

Felsenfeld, Gary. "DNA." *Scientific American* 253 (October, 1985): 58-67. Describes DNA structure and how the molecule is packed into superstructures in the nucleus, including nucleosomes and the solenoid coil. The article also considers the relationship of DNA structures to genetic regulation. The article is illustrated with many informative diagrams.

Kornberg, Roger D., and A. Klug. "The Nucleosome." *Scientific American* 244 (February, 1981): 52-64. This article summarizes the discoveries and lines of research leading to the development of Kornberg's hypothesis for nucleosome structure, which has been completely supported by subsequent research. The confirming research includes the important X-ray diffraction studies carried out in Klug's laboratory.

Murray, Andrew W., and Jack W. Szostak. "Artificial Chromosomes." *Scientific American* 257 (November, 1987): 62-68. This article outlines the minimum molecular regions a DNA molecule must have in order to be duplicated and passed on in cell division. By adding these regions, which include centromeres and telomeres, to DNA molecules, the authors and others were able to create artificial chromosomes that were duplicated and passed on successfully in division in yeast cells.

Watson, James D. *The Double Helix*. New York: Atheneum, 1968. An entertaining and readable book that outlines the events leading to the discovery of DNA structure by Watson and Francis H. C. Crick. The book reveals as much about the way scientific research is conducted, and how scientists interact, as it does about the structure of DNA.

Stephen L. Wolfe

Cross-References

CILIA, FLAGELLA, BASAL BODIES, AND CENTRIOLES

Type of life science: Cell biology (cytology)
Other fields of study: Animal anatomy, biochemistry, biophysics, and microbiology

Cilia and flagella are tiny, hairlike structures on the surface of cells which provide either a means for their locomotion or a method by which fluids can be moved across them. Basal bodies and centrioles are intracellular structures which function as organizing centers for a class of large molecules known as microtubular proteins.

Principal terms

AXONEME: the central structural core of eukaryotic cilia or flagella, consisting of microtubule doublets

DYNEIN: a protein found at regular intervals on the A subfiber of microtubules in the axoneme of cilia and flagella; it forms connections to the B subfiber of adjacent microtubule doublets during the beating of cilia and flagella

MICROTUBULE: a cylindrical structure composed of tubulin proteins, found in the axoneme of eukaryotic cilia and flagella among other places in eukaryotic cells

POWER STROKE: the first part of the beat of a cilium, which produces the most movement of the surrounding fluid

RECOVERY STROKE: the second part of the beat of a cilium, which brings it back to its starting position

TUBULIN: the type of protein that makes up microtubules

Summary of the Phenomenon

Cilia and flagella are two organelles of essentially the same structure found on the surface of many different types of eukaryotic cells (cells that contain membrane-bound nuclei, which include all cells except bacteria and blue-green algae). The function of cilia and flagella is either to propel the cell through the medium in which it is found or to move that medium across the surface of the cell if it is part of a fixed tissue. Basal bodies and centrioles, which are believed to be identical in structure, are thought to function in the organization and assembly of the protein structures known as microtubules. Basal bodies and centrioles are usually located in a more interior position within the cytoplasm of cells.

Cilia and flagella were first observed by early microscopists such as Anton van Leeuwenhoek about three hundred years ago. As microscopes improved, accounts of the occurrence of cilia and flagella in many protozoans, invertebrates, and vertebrates were published. A few examples of cilia and flagella can also be found among the plants, algae, and fungi, although these are rare. The ciliates, the largest of the protistan subgroups, derive their name from, and are partially categorized by, the possession of cilia. Various species of the familiar *Paramecium* belong to this group. Another protistan subgroup, the flagellates, is defined by the presence of one or more flagella. Other cells that possess these structures include those in ciliated epithelium, a covering tissue found in many animals, and the spermatozoa of most animals and a few plants.

Although some variation exists, the structure of both cilia and flagella is so similar that describing one organelle will suffice for the other. One difference is that cilia are usually shorter than flagella. It is believed that cilia are a specialized class of flagella. Here, the word "cilium" will be used for the generalized organelle.

Cilia are cylindrical, with a diameter of approximately 0.25 micrometer and a length of up to several micrometers covered with an extension of the cell surface membrane, and they have an inner cylindrical bundle of microtubular proteins, referred to as the axoneme, extending the length of the organelle. The axoneme is surrounded by cytoplasm. Just beneath the surface of the cell the axoneme extends to the organelle known as a basal body. Each cilium is connected to a single basal body.

When seen in cross section through the transmission electron microscope (TEM), the microtubular proteins of the axoneme are arranged in a precise and, now, well-known pattern called the 9 plus 2 array. The numbers 9 and 2 refer to the number of pairs of microtubules, or microtubular doublets, which form the outer ring of the axoneme, and the single pair of microtubules in the center of the axoneme, respectively. The outer doublets are composed of two microtubules, the A subfiber and the B subfiber. Subunits, called protofilaments, made of the protein tubulin and arranged as a cylinder, form each of the subfibers. Subfibers A and B are fused together along their length, and two or three of the tubulin subunits are shared by each of the subfibers in the region of fusion. One way to visualize the entire axoneme is to picture a sheath of bamboo stalks with two in the center. Each of the nine pairs of stalks would be made of thirteen smaller stalks.

Groups of proteins, called dynein arms, occur at regular intervals along subfiber A. These molecules form pairs of arms that initiate short-lived bridges to the B subfiber of the adjacent doublet during beating of the cilium. The dynein proteins are enzymes that break down adenosine triphosphate (ATP) to make energy available for the beating of cilia.

Additional proteins in the axoneme connect the microtubule doublets to the central pair of microtubules like the spokes of a wheel. Proteins also form curved projections from the central pair and connections between adjacent outer doublets. More than 250 different proteins have been purified from axonemes, but the function of most of them is still unclear.

Experiments with isolated axonemes have demonstrated that the beating of cilia occurs when doublets of tubulin slide past one another as the cilia bend. The initial bending is known as the power stroke, and subsequent bending to return the organelle to the original position is called the recovery stroke. At rest, the dynein arms permanently attached to the A microtubule of each doublet are oriented downward toward the cilium base as they form bridges to the B microtubule. When ATP is added to the system, the dynein arms move to a position perpendicular to the

A microtubule, causing the two doublets to slide relative to each other. Upon completion of the stroke, dynein detaches from the B microtubule, is bent downward, and reattaches to the B microtubule. The next stroke can then begin.

The dynein arms on all doublets produce a force in the same direction, so, to prevent the resulting total forces from canceling, with a result of no movement, the doublets are divided into two functional groups. During the power stroke, doublets 1 through 4 act together, and doublets 5 through 9 slide against one another to straighten the cilium during the recovery stroke. Proteins in the axoneme which give the cross section a spokelike appearance seem to convert the sliding of the doublets into bending of the axoneme. During the power stroke, the commonest way in which the cilium moves is toward one side while bending only at the base. During the recovery stroke, the bending proceeds up the shaft to the tip as the cilium returns to its initial position.

Flagella move by undulations of the shaft from the base to the tip either in a single plane or in a cylindrical fashion. The mechanism of doublet sliding and the role of dynein are the same as for cilia.

Actual motion produced by cilia or flagella involves the movement of water by the structure. A cilium carries with it a small amount of water surrounding the shaft. It carries more water near the tip than near the cell surface. In effect, a cone of moving water is propelled during the power stroke. During the recovery stroke, the amount of water moved is less, because the cilium is bent more and lies closer to the cell surface. A net forward movement of water results.

Studies with *Paramecium* have shown that an influx of calcium ions across the cell membrane can act as a stimulus to initiate the beating of cilia. Changes in calcium ion concentration will cause the beat of cilia and flagella to reverse. Once a single cilium begins to move the water surrounding it, it interacts and moves water around neighboring cilia, which causes them to become hydrodynamically linked. They then move in synchrony. No internal coordination for the synchronous beating of cilia occurs.

Basal bodies are about 0.5 micrometer in length and are located at the base of the cilium or flagellum beneath the cell surface membrane. They consist of an outer ring of nine triplet microtubules. Near the ciliary base, thin protein filaments may connect the far end of each triplet to the cell membrane. The central pair of microtubules from the axoneme ends near the cell surface membrane; thus, the basal body has no central pair of microtubules.

Microtubules of the axoneme are synthesized and assembled by the basal body. Basal bodies are called microtubular organizing centers (MTOCs). Centrioles serve the function of forming the spindle apparatus, the structure in cells where chromosomes attach during mitosis, and were probably derived from the basal body of an ancestral flagellate. Centrioles usually are found in pairs at right angles to one another when not involved in spindle formation. Although basal bodies are necessary for development of cilia and flagella, these structures will continue to beat if they are severed from the basal body.

Methods of Study

Early studies of cilia, flagella, basal bodies, and centrioles were restricted to what could be seen through a light microscope. The first physiological studies of the functioning of cilia and flagella were done toward the end of the nineteenth century. Centrioles were observed as part of the mitotic spindle apparatus which is formed during nuclear and cell division by early microscopists interested in cellular reproduction.

At present, the principal methods of the study of the structure of these organelles involve the use of the TEM and the scanning electron microscope (SEM). Use of the former instrument allows visualization of the interior of cells and organelles; magnifications of greater than one million times are possible with the best microscopes. The SEM produces images of the surfaces of cells and therefore is most valuable for viewing cilia and flagella. Preparation of cells for viewing with TEM involves rapid fixation to preserve structures in death as they were moments before in life, embedding the cells in an epoxy resin or similar compound so that they may be cut into extremely thin slices, staining the slices, and viewing them. Preparation of cells for the SEM involves fixation and subsequent dehydration and coating so that their surface may be viewed.

A second method, called fracture, has also proved useful for both types of microscopy. Cells are quickly frozen in liquid nitrogen and then carefully fractured to reveal various surface and internal components. The arrangement of cilia and flagella on the surfaces of cells and the position of basal bodies and centrioles have all been determined by these methods. The detailed internal structure (called ultrastructure) of the axoneme, with its microtubules and other proteins, was determined mainly through the use of TEM, as was the ultrastructure of basal bodies and centrioles.

The types and amounts of the various proteins, such as tubulin, found in cilia, flagella, basal bodies, and centrioles, was determined by disrupting the cells and subjecting the contents to high-speed spinning called ultracentrifugation. Once the organelles were separated, they could be collected and treated chemically to release various proteins. These molecules were then subjected to a process known as electrophoresis. Here, the molecules are placed in a gel and exposed to an electric field of known intensity and polarity. Charges on the proteins cause them to migrate through the gel, depending upon their size and weight, toward either the plus or the minus pole of the electrophoresis unit. Similar proteins will be found in similar positions in the gel and can be collected for study.

The movement of cilia and flagella has long been studied by using cinephotography and, more recently, videotape cameras. These devices, attached to light microscopes, allow the determination of beat patterns in real time or in slow motion. Stroboscopes, units which use pulses of light flashing at about the same speed as the ciliary beat, have also been used with great success to visualize the movements in slow motion. These pictures can then be run forward or backward at any rate for careful analysis of beat patterns.

Context

Cilia and flagella provide one of the principal sources of locomotion in eukaryotic cells. Major groups of protozoa, the ciliates and flagellates, move using these organelles. Many species of flatworms and other tiny animals also use cilia for locomotion. The ciliates also use some of their cilia to bring food such as bacteria and algae down the oral groove to the cytostome, where it is taken inside the cell. The sponges use flagellated cell to move food-laden water into their pores and through their canal systems. Food particles and water are also driven across the gills of various mollusks and into their mouths. In mammals, including humans, mucus is moved up the trachea by cilia on epithelial cells. In a rare genetic disease, known to occur in human males, the arms of dynein are usually short or even absent. The X chromosome carries a mutation that causes abnormal dynein to be formed or prevents it from attaching to microtubules correctly. Cilia and flagella in these individuals cannot move. Therefore, spermatozoa are nonmotile, and dust and other particles cannot be cleared effectively from the upper respiratory tract, resulting in an increase in the number of ear infections, common colds, sinusitis, and bronchitis.

In human medicine, the spermatozoan flagellum and its movement, or lack of it, has been intensively studied because of the relationship of nonmotility or poor motility to male infertility. The action of various compounds encountered in the environment and of drugs used to control medical conditions such as cancer and hypertension on spermatozoan formation and motility is an area of much current interest and study.

Since centrioles form the spindle apparatus necessary for the movement of chromosomes during mitosis, much effort has been expended in an attempt to understand the role of the centriole in microtubule synthesis, especially in humans.

Bibliography

Lazarides, Elias, and J. P. Revel. "The Molecular Basis of Cell Movement." *Scientific American* 240 (May, 1979): 100-113. This article explains the principal chemical processes which occur during cell movement, including cilia and flagella. Excellent diagrams and clear explanations are presented for readers with little chemical background. The role of dynein is described, as well as the function of ATP.

Mitchell, Larry G., John A. Mutchmor, and Warren D. Dolphin. *Zoology*. Menlo Park, Calif.: Benjamin/Cummings, 1988. A very complete general text for beginning biology or zoology students. Marvelous diagrams and photographs and an easy-to-understand text make this book very useful. The role and occurrence of cilia and flagella in various animal groups are presented. A summary of the mechanisms of ciliary and flagellar movement and the roles of basal bodies and centrioles are given.

Prescott, D. M. *Cells: Principles of Molecular Structure and Function*. Boston: Jones and Bartlett, 1988. A comprehensive yet easy-to-understand introductory cell biology text. Clearly explains in detail the mechanisms of ciliary and flagellar movement. Excellent TEM and SEM photomicrographs of cilia, flagella, basal bodies, and centrioles are presented. The function and occurrence of basal bodies and centrioles are also covered in detail.

Satir, Peter. "How Cilia Move." *Scientific American* 231 (October, 1974): 44-52. A good general article describing the chemical and physical mechanisms involved in the movement of eukaryotic cilia. This article can be understood by the nonbiologist and nonchemist. The axoneme is especially well described. Illustrated.

Sleigh, M. A. *Cilia and Flagella*. London: Academic Press, 1974. The classic work on cilia, flagella, and basal bodies, edited by one of the experts in the field. The articles are somewhat technical, but anyone wanting a complete understanding of the topics involved should not miss this volume. Excellent diagrams and photomicrographs abound, as well as a history of study in this field.

_____. *Protozoa and Other Protists*. 2d ed. London: Edward Arnold, 1989. The second edition of another classic work by Sleigh. Describes in detail the role of cilia and flagella in the protists. A discussion of their evolutionary origins and significance is presented. An excellent summary of the structure and function of cilia and flagella is also included. Line drawings are numerous and easy to interpret. The text is somewhat technical but certainly worth the effort.

Yates, G. T. "How Microorganisms Move Through Water." *American Scientist* 74 (1986): 358-365. A good summary of the mechanims by which organisms move through water including the use of cilia and flagella. The physical problems are especially well treated. Clearly written, with useful illustrations.

Thomas R. Kozel

Cross-References

ATP and Other Energetic Molecules, 134; Electron Microscopy, 744; Gill, Trachea, and Lung Anatomy, 1212; The Mitotic Spindle Apparatus, 1760; Flagellar and Ciliary Motion, 1797; Protein Phosphorylation, 2257; Proteins, 2272; Protista, 2281; Thermodynamics in Biology, 2625.

CIRCULATORY SYSTEMS OF INVERTEBRATES

Type of life science: Animal anatomy
Other fields of study: Evolutionary biology, histology, invertebrate biology, and
systematics (taxonomy)

*Any circulatory system provides transport for materials required by cells that
cannot be supplied quickly or efficiently enough by diffusion. Invertebrates possess a
great variety of circulatory systems. Some are closed systems; some are open
systems.*

Principal terms
BLOOD: the fluid connective tissue within blood vessels that carries raw
materials to cells and carries products and wastes from them
BLOOD VESSELS: membranous tubes through which blood flows; arteries
carry blood from the heart, veins carry blood to the heart, and
capillaries are tiny vessels in which exchange takes place
CLOSED CIRCULATION: a circulatory pattern in which blood is always
contained within blood vessels
DIFFUSION: the process whereby a substance moves from an area of
greater concentration to one of lesser concentration, as through a cell
membrane
HEART: a discrete, localized pumping structure within the circulatory
system
HEMOLYMPH: the transport fluid of organisms with open circulation
systems in which there is no clear distinction between blood and
intercellular tissue fluid
LACUNAE: small spaces among tissue cells through which hemolymph
flows in open circulatory systems
OPEN CIRCULATION: a circulatory pattern in which the blood is not always
contained within blood vessels
SINUSES: larger spaces, thought to represent through channels, for
hemolymph in open circulatory systems, sometimes bound by
membranes
TRACHEAL SYSTEM: the respiratory system of insects and other terrestrial
invertebrates; it consists of numerous air-filled tubes with branches
extending into tiny channels in direct contact with body cells

Summary of the Phenomenon

Circulatory systems are necessary when the process of diffusion no longer provides an organism with sufficient gas, nutrients, and waste exchange with its
environment. Some invertebrate groups, such as sponges, coelenterates, and flatworms, have such thin body walls that diffusion can meet all their needs. For most

invertebrates, however, the distance from the organism's surface to the cells in the interior is too great for diffusion to support their metabolic requirements. A circulatory system is composed of three parts: the pump, the fluid that is pumped, and the vessels in which the fluid is transported. As in the design of invertebrate body plans, there is great diversity in the design of invertebrate circulatory systems.

The pump may be a simple tube lined by muscle fibers. Alternate contraction and relaxation of these muscles produces a peristaltic wave that pushes the blood along. The pump may be a heart: a localizable, discrete organ whose muscle layers are the primary generators of the power that propels blood through the blood vessels. The heart can be a simple muscular enlargement, or it can be complex and multichambered, depending on the evolutionary history and the needs of the organism. Some organisms may have more than one heart.

If the pumped fluid remains within the blood vessels, it is usually called blood. If it leaves the blood vessels to enter cavities surrounded by tissue cells with which it exchanges materials, it is called hemolymph. In the cavities (called lacunae if small and sinuses if large and lined with a membrane) blood mingles with intercellular fluid. Whatever it is called, the fluid is composed of water, solutes (such as salts, sugars, and other nutrients), and, in some cases, cells and formed elements. The blood may also contain a respiratory pigment that helps deliver oxygen to the cells.

Blood vessels may extend only a short distance from the heart or may provide a continuous path for the transport of blood. If the blood vessels are incomplete and blood is pumped from arteries into body spaces—sinuses and lacunae—it is an open circulatory system. If the blood vessels are continuous and the blood never leaves these circulatory channels, it is a closed circulatory system. These are generalized terms for convenience; there are actually many intermediate cases. Some open systems have membrane-lined sinuses and lacunae, and exchange takes place by diffusion just as it does in the tiniest vessels of closed systems. Blood vessels are categorized according to their function. Arteries carry blood away from the heart; veins carry blood back to the heart. Closed circulatory systems have tiny tubules, called capillaries, connecting small arteries to small veins. The exchange of materials between the tissue cells and the blood takes place only in the capillaries.

A few generalities based on physical principles indicate the rules guiding fluid transport. Organisms relying on diffusion alone to circulate nutrients and eliminate wastes are limited to certain shapes and sizes: They are often only two cell layers thick. Organisms using bulk transport of fluid, on the other hand, may be as complex and as differently shaped as plants and animals are.

A fluid transport system is any system in which internal fluid movement reduces diffusion distances—either between points within an organ or between a point within an organism and the external environment. While diffusion is always used for short-distance transport, bulk flow augments diffusion for any long-distance transport. Bulk flow requires a pump and a fluid that must come into intimate contact with tissues and the environment for efficient transfer. Either the tissue layers must be thin (as in open circulatory systems) or the vessels must have a small radius (as in a closed circulatory system). The circulatory fluid should spend the majority of its time in the transfer regions (sinuses and lacunae or capillaries) and not in transit.

Such transport systems use both large and small vessels. Large vessels move fluid from one exchange site to another, and small vessels allow diffusion at the exchange sites. The total cross-sectional area of the small vessels must exceed that of the large vessels so that the flow rate in small vessels will be less than the velocity in large vessels. High-speed pumps in large vessels are preferable to low-speed pumps in the small vessels. This means that accessory hearts are only used when the "cost" of operation is not a major factor or when the pump serves some additional functional role—as when active cephalopod mollusks, such as squid and octopods, use accessory hearts to ensure adequate blood flow through their gills.

Circulatory systems are traditionally divided into two categories. Closed systems are those in which the blood is always contained within distinct vessels and is physically separated from the organism's intercellular fluids. They are usually characteristic of organisms with high metabolic demands. High volumes and high pressures can be maintained in the closed vessels to aid transport and diffusion. Annelids, cephalopod mollusks, and vertebrates usually have closed circulatory systems.

Open systems are those which possess large, usually ill-defined, cavities (sinuses if bound by an endothelial layer, lacunae if not) and in which the blood is not physically separated from the intercellular fluids. Arthropods and noncephalopod mollusks have open systems.

Open circulatory systems are not always sluggish, low-pressure arrangements. Some spiders generate sufficient pressure in their open systems to use hydraulic pressure as a substitute for extensor muscles in their legs. In addition, capillaries often exist in open systems, particularly in areas such as the excretory organs and the cerebral ganglion. The major sinus in the foot of gastroped and bivalve mollusks is not a large, open cavity but a network of channels in a spongy tissue that function as capillaries. The lack of return vessels in these systems is usually a result of the fact that fluid simply has nowhere to go other than in the direction of low pressure: back to the heart. These volume constraints are sufficient to develop pressure, although this system is incompatible with high pressure and flow rates.

In the two major groups with open circulatory systems, arthropods and noncephalopod mollusks, the circulatory sinuses play an additional role: In bivalve and gastropod mollusks, the hemocoel (main body cavity) functions as a hydrostatic skeleton in locomotion and burrowing. In aquatic arthropods, it serves the same function during molting, when arthropods lose the support of the exoskeleton. In insects, the tracheal system has assumed the respiratory function, and the blood merely delivers nutrients and removes wastes. In large flying insects, the circulatory systems may also have the primary responsibility of removing heat to maintain thoracic temperatures.

To function effectively, the circulatory system must have a regular pattern of pressure increases that will push the blood along through the vessels. The heart-beats that accomplish this may be initiated and maintained by nerves, or they may be self-generated. If nerves initiate the contraction of the heartbeat, the heart is called neurogenic, meaning that nerve impulses generate the depolarization that results in the contraction of the heart's muscle cells. In these hearts, the heart muscle will not contract without a nerve impulse. Some species with neurogenic hearts are crustacea, horseshoe crabs, some spiders, and scorpions.

Heart muscles that continue to beat even when nervous connections are severed are called myogenic, meaning that the heart muscle contracts without external stimuli. Under these circumstances, the contraction of the muscles may occur at a different rate from that imposed by the nervous system when active. Myogenic hearts are found in mollusks and many insects.

All heart action must be modulated to respond to external and internal conditions, so even myogenic hearts usually receive some innervation. Modulation occurs through the mediation of nerves, hormones, or intrinsic controls in the heart. In the lobster, for example, nerves are crucial to maintaining the best rhythm and amplitude, but neurohormones released from a pericardial organ influence the heart action. Stretching the heart muscle, an intrinsic control, will also increase the vigor and rate of contraction.

In many cases, the structure of the heart and its suspensory ligaments contributes to the functioning of the circulatory system. Values at the openings (ostia) to the heart prevent backflow when the heart contracts. This pulls at the ligaments. Their elasticity pulls back the walls of the heart, creating low pressure that enables the heart to fill on relaxation. In effect, the heart sucks blood from veins to refill itself for the next contraction.

In many species, the contraction of body parts contributes to the circulation of blood. Arthropods have a rigid exoskeleton; contraction in one part pushes the blood into another segment. A quick flexion of the abdomen in American lobsters (an important locomotor movement) raises pressure in the abdomen and increases the rate of blood flow to the thorax and into the heart region.

All flow depends upon pressure differences, regardless of whether the circulatory system is open or closed, and there are two kinds of pressure. Background pressure is the pressure that prevails everywhere in the animal. Since pressure differences are responsible for flow, these pressure differences are imposed on the background pressure. If the body changes posture and increases background pressure, the blood pressure must similarly increase in order to maintain flows at the same level they were before the postural change. The blood-pressure gradient and the resistance to flow in the system affect blood flow. The low resistance in open circulatory systems probably permits relatively high rates of blood flow with relatively low pressure. The high blood-flow rate compensates for the low oxygen-carrying capacity of the blood.

Open and closed systems differ; neither is necessarily superior. The inherent weakness of the open circulatory system is that the peripheral blood flow cannot be as well controlled as that of closed circulatory systems. Yet the large sinuses are often subdivided, thereby providing discrete channels of flow, and the peripheral blood flow may be more regular than previously thought. Closed circulatory systems have a flow that is easily controlled. Flow through particular regions can be managed by using muscles to close off certain channels. Cardiac output can be distributed to meet tissue demands. In open systems, this is not possible after the blood leaves the major vessels, although muscle contractions and accessory hearts may influence peripheral flow. Whatever their patterns, the circulatory systems of invertebrates are adequately matched to their needs; they have enabled these creatures to survive and proliferate for millions of years.

Methods of Study

Methods used to study invertebrate circulatory systems are varied. One basic problem is that 95 percent of all animal species are invertebrates, and many of these creatures are not known and have never been studied. The larger, more common organisms that are easiest to study have been subjected to experimentation. Many invertebrates are difficult to maintain in the laboratory, but techniques to maintain them in good health are being developed and improved. Without these culture techniques, experimenters must use recently caught subjects whose condition is doubtful.

Most knowledge of invertebrate circulatory systems is anatomical. Even a common animal must be described so that a physiologist can apply appropriate techniques to study the functioning of the heart, vessels, and blood. Descriptions are usually derived from dissection and from microscopic study. These painstaking methods have been used on known species for centuries. Larger invertebrates, such as lobsters, crabs, clams, squids, and octopods, have been studied by techniques similar to those used in vertebrate circulation physiology. A heart can be exposed and either attached to a lever that can record its contractions or attached to an electronic force transducer, which can measure the strength of contraction.

The heart is large enough to be punctured for blood samples, and hemolymph can be withdrawn from the larger sinuses. These blood samples can be analyzed for the presence and activity of cells, respiratory pigments, nutrients, and wastes, using ordinary biochemical techniques. The development of microanalytic techniques in biochemistry allows the sampling of body fluids from small insects, worms, and rare organisms that might be damaged by taking larger samples.

In addition, force transducers can be placed along blood vessels and in hemocoels to determine the pressure exerted during flow. Electronic devices can monitor the flow rate by detecting cells or the passage of a dye or magnetic substance. Radioactive tracers can be injected and their path followed. All these less invasive techniques allow the animals to survive longer and to deliver data that can be more reliably interpreted because they are from a healthy subject. The use of fewer organisms in research and the survival of rare creatures are important both to the environment and to the development of a full understanding of these complex systems.

Context

Invertebrate circulatory systems occur in two plans, closed or open, and both styles of circulation have benefits for their users. Although open circulatory systems are usually thought to be sluggish and inefficient, they are not necessarily so. Active animals such as crustaceans and insects have open circulatory systems and metabolic rates (oxygen and nutrient demands) that equal those of the most active invertebrates, squids and octopods, which have closed circulatory systems.

Nemertean worms (Rhynchocoela) are a small group of inconspicuous and inconsequential worms that have an interesting circulatory system. These worms may reach 30 meters in length (although they are only a few millimeters wide), but they have a simple blood system. There may be two or three blood vessels, with connections between them, running the length of the body. The vessels have a layer of muscle in the walls. Contraction of these muscles and the main body muscles move blood—in any direction—along the vessels.

Annelids (wormlike animals) also have a closed circulatory system. The major blood vessel has pulsatile regions, often called hearts, which drive the blood forward. The pattern of blood vessels, including capillaries, is repeated in each segment of the animal, although most segments do not have "hearts." Accessory hearts occur in different segments, and the overall pattern of circulation varies greatly among species (and even within a single individual's many segments).

Arthropods and most mollusks have open circulatory systems; these invertebrates have a well-developed central heart. The heart pumps blood through an extensive arterial network, which may end in capillaries. The blood eventually leaves the blood vessels and enters lacunae. Diffusion of materials takes place in the capillaries or in the lacunae. Sinuses collect the blood for return to the heart. In these organisms, the blood follows an ill-defined path. Contractions of the body musculature affect the speed and volume of blood flow in any region.

The crustacean arthropods are a group having inactive members, which lack a heart and blood vessels entirely, and active members, which have a high level of circulatory system organization. The inactive members pump their body fluid through sinuses and lacunae using the pressure developed by muscle contraction. Decapod crustaceans, the familiar crabs, have a heart whose contraction drives blood into well-defined arteries; the return of blood to the heart from the veins occurs because of the elastic recoil of the ligaments suspending the heart in the pericardial cavity. Part of the beauty of this pattern is that only veins from the gills enter the pericardial cavity. Therefore, only oxygenated blood enters the heart and is pumped into the body. Therefore, although there may be body spaces in which flow is indeterminate, the important blood flows are well-controlled and can meet the needs of complex and active organisms.

Bibliography

LaBarbara, M., and S. Vogel. "The Design of Fluid Transport Systems in Organisms." *American Scientist* 70 (January/February, 1982): 54-60. This interesting article describes the few physical principles that point out generalities in the ways that liquids are transported in animals.

Mader, Sylvia. *Biology: Evolution, Diversity, and the Environment*. Dubuque, Iowa: Wm. C. Brown, 1987. In this clearly written text, basic ideas of the circulatory system are treated in a straightforward and interesting fashion.

Meglitsch, Paul. *Invertebrate Zoology*. 3d ed. New York: Oxford University Press, 1972. This well-known work describes all the invertebrate groups and the attributes of each. It discusses the effects of the interaction between physiology and environment on the evolution of organisms.

Purves, W. K., and G. H. Orians. *Life: The Science of Biology*. Sunderland, Mass.: Sinauer Associates, 1983. This is an excellently written text that integrates discussion of vertebrate and invertebrate circulatory systems so that they can be compared and contrasted effectively.

Schmidt-Nielsen, Knut. *Animal Physiology: Adaptation and Environment*. 2d ed. New York: Cambridge University Press, 1979. An excellent book that raises questions as it provides answers. Chapter 4 relates specifically to circulation in vertebrates and invertebrates, although the initial six chapters would all be of value in understanding the integration of transport needs and design.

Starr, Cecie, and Ralph Taggart. *Biology: The Unity and Diversity of Life*. Belmont, Calif.: Wadsworth, 1987. A clearly written text that provides a good summary of the basic types of invertebrate circulation patterns.

Judith O. Rebach

Cross-References

Lower Chordates, 439; Diffusion in Circulation, 621; Endocrine Functions of the Kidneys and Heart, 780; Gill, Trachea, and Lung Anatomy, 1212; Heart-Output and Blood-Flow Regulation, 1269; Higher Invertebrate Animals, 1475; Lower Invertebrate Animals, 1483; Muscle Anatomy in Invertebrates, 1814.

CIRCULATORY SYSTEMS OF VERTEBRATES

Type of life science: Animal physiology
Other fields of study: Animal anatomy, histology, and zoology

Vertebrates' circulatory systems consist of a closed system of blood vessels with a centrally placed heart, which receives oxygen-poor blood from the body and pumps it to the organs of respiration, where it is oxygenated and returned to the body's tissues. It is here that the oxygen and nutrients are unloaded and carbon dioxide and excretory products are picked up.

Principal terms
AORTA: the major arterial trunk, into which the left ventricle of the heart pumps its blood for transport to the body
ARTERIOLE: the finest branch of an artery
ARTERY: a blood channel with thick muscular walls which transports blood from the heart to various parts of the body
ATRIA: the two chambers of the heart, which receive venous blood from the body (via the right atrium) or oxygenated blood from the lungs (left atrium)
CAPILLARIES: the very fine vessels in various tissues, which connect arterioles with venules; it is here that the exchange between blood and the extracellular fluid takes place
CARDIAC OUTPUT: the amount of blood ejected by the left ventricle into the aorta per minute
DIASTOLE: relaxation (filling with blood) of the heart chambers
PACEMAKER: a specialized group of cardiac muscle cells in the right atrium which initiates the heartbeat; also called the sinoatrial node
SYSTOLE: contraction (emptying of blood) of the heart chambers
VALVES: a specialized, thickened groups of muscle cells in the heart chambers, major arterial trunks, arterioles, and veins which prevent backflow of blood
VEIN: a tubelike, elastic channel with thin walls enforced with smooth muscles and valves that transport oxygen-poor blood; veins start as fine venules in tissues connected with capillary beds
VENTRICLES: the right and left chambers of the heart, which pump blood, respectively, into pulmonary and systemic circulation

Summary of the Phenomenon

Cells, the units of the animal body, need a constant supply of blood. Blood effects the transport of important materials needed for metabolic, synthetic, and degradative activities, supplying energy and materials necessary for growth, repair of worn-out components of cells, reproductive activity, and other functions of the body. Among the many products that blood transports through a system of closed channels are oxygen, nutrients, metabolic wastes, heat, and hormones. The circulatory system links all tissues with one another and with the external environment to and from which many of these materials are transported.

Basically, the circulatory system of vertebrates consists of two parallel systems of blood vessels: One, the arterial system, actively transports blood and its constituents from a central pumping station, the heart; the other, the venous system, more or less passively brings the blood back to the heart. The two systems branch again and again until they ramify all tissues. In the extracellular space of tissues, the finest branches of each system, called arterioles and venules, are connected by means of a network of fine capillaries that allow the movement of blood in one direction, from arterial into the venous system, in which the valves prevent any backflow of blood. A head of pressure, generated in the heart, pumps the blood in this direction, facilitating the transport of substances as well as their movement and filtration out of the capillary membranes and into the extracellular fluid.

The simplest level of organization of the circulatory system of vertebrates is seen in fishes. The heart in fishes consists of two chambers, an atrium (auricle) and a ventricle. The oxygen-poor, carbon-dioxide-rich blood returning from the body via a system of veins is first received by an enlarged vein, the *sinus venosus*, prior to entering the atrium. The atrium empties its blood into the thick-walled, muscular ventricle, which then pumps it into an enlarged artery, the *conus arteriosus*. The blood then passes through a major arterial trunk, the ventral aorta, going directly to the gills. The arteries in gills branch profusely and are connected via capillaries with other arteries. In the capillary bed, the blood becomes oxygenated and provides nutrients to the tissue. The oxygenated blood then flows to the head and the rest of the body, and from there returns to the heart through the venous system.

In preparation for their journey to land, ancient aquatic vertebrates had to evolve lungs for aerial breathing and had to evolve a complementary circulatory system. As demands for oxygen for a terrestrial existence increased, greater blood pressure and a new way of oxygenating blood were in order. The atrium became divided into two, the right one receiving the deoxygenated blood returning from the body and the left one receiving the oxygenated blood from the lungs (which replaced gills). The deoxygenated blood, entering the right part of the single ventricle is pumped into the pulmonary artery, all the way to the lungs. The left part of the ventricle, receiving oxygenated blood from the left atrium, pumps it into the body. This three-chambered heart is present in amphibians and most reptiles. The oxygenated and deoxygenated bloods mix partially in the ventricle. In some amphibians, flaps and partial valves tend to prevent such mixing. Reptiles have a partition between the right and left parts of the ventricle which is complete in alligators, crocodiles, and turtles.

Latter reptiles, birds, and mammals developed four-chambered hearts. This complete division of the heart into two separate right and left pumps enables birds and mammals to achieve high speeds. One pumping circuit, the pulmonary, receives blood from the body and pumps it to the lungs; the other pumping circuit, the systemic, receives oxygen-rich blood from the lungs and pumps it into the systemic circulation. Valves within the heart prevent the blood from flowing through it in the opposite direction.

The contractile tissue of the heart consists of muscle cells that receive sympathetic and parasympathetic nerve impulses. The vertebrate heart is myogenic; that is, all of its muscle cells and fibers possess an inherent capacity to contract (electrically depolarize) rhythmically; however, all these fibers are under the control of a group of specialized heart muscle cells which have a lower threshold for depolarization than other heart muscle cells: the pacemaker. In fish, amphibians, and reptiles, the pacemaker is located in the wall of the *sinus venosus* (the first heart chamber before the atrium). In higher vertebrates, which lack a *sinus venosus*, the pacemaker is found in the wall of the atrium and is called the sinoatrial node. The wave of electrical depolarization initiated here is conducted through the atrioventricular node via a special group of fibers called the "Bundle of His" which branch out into the ventricular muscle. The depolarization enters and traverses the atrioventricular node only relatively slowly but spreads down the atrioventricular bundle and its branches much more rapidly than it could travel through ordinary ventricular muscle. This regulates the sequence of contraction of the heart chambers: The atria contract first and the ventricles later, each group of muscles contracting approximately in unison.

Since the pulmonary (right) circuit is much shorter than the systemic circuit, it contains less blood volume and offers less frictional resistance to blood flow; also, the right ventricle has muscular walls that are less thick than those of the left ventricle, which has to pump large volumes of blood to the entire body via the systemic circuit. After the two ventricles are completely filled (a condition referred to as diastole), they contract simultaneously (called systole). During systole, the maximum arterial pressure is generated; during diastole (just before systole), arterial pressure decreases to a minimum. In young adult humans, the aortic blood pressure fluctuates, averaging between 120 (systolic) and 80 (diastolic) millimeters of mercury. The pulmonary side of the heart contains the funnel-shaped valve between the atrium and the ventricle known as the atrioventricular valve, the right one having three flaps, or cusps (and hence named the tricuspid valve) and the left one (the bicuspid or mitral valve) having two. The free edges of these cusps hang down into the ventricular cavities and are anchored by tendonlike cords of connective tissue called *chordae tendinae*, each of which is attached to the ventricular wall by a lump called a papillary muscle. The pulmonary artery and the aorta originate at the base of the right and left ventricles, respectively, each having a semilunar valve at its origin. Each of these valves opens in the direction of the blood flow and prevents the backflow of blood. The ventricular contraction and the resulting turbulence in the blood produce the long, low-pitched "lub" sound that can be detected with a stethoscope. The sudden closure of the semilunar valves is similarly perceived to emit a relatively short, high-pitched "dup" sound.

The volume of blood that is pumped by the heart each minute is called the minute-volume. The human heart beats (contracts) about seventy times each minute (cardiac stroke rate), ejecting about 70 milliliters of blood per beat. This rate is altered by the body's activity and by the volume of blood returning to the heart from the veins each minute. If the venous blood volume is adequate, then increase in stroke rate can increase minute-volume. The increased stroke rate, however, involves a decrease in the ventricular filling time, and as a result, the ventricles do not fill completely. Thus, the stroke volume is decreased; at rapid heart rates, even the minute-volume may be decreased, so that it offsets the stroke rate. During systole, the ventricles do not empty completely. A small residual volume of blood (about 70 milliliters) remains in them. An increased venous return may cause more complete filling and emptying of the ventricles, thus increasing the cardiac output to as much as 25 liters per minute without changing the stroke rate.

The vessels at various points in the circulatory path differ anatomically and functionally. The great arteries have thick walls heavily infested with smooth muscle and contractile tissue to enable them to transport blood under pressure from the heart to peripheral tissues. The arteries become smaller and thinner-walled as they branch out toward the periphery. The systemic arteries deliver blood to the microcirculatory beds of the tissues and organs. These "capillary beds" consist of microscopic arterioles, capillaries, and venules. The contraction (vasoconstriction) and relaxation (vasodilation) of the smooth muscles in the terminal branches of the arteries play an important role in regulating blood flow in the capillary bed. Control of the arteriole muscles is mediated by sympathetic neurotransmitters, hormones, and local effects. From the arterioles, the blood enters the capillaries, minute vessels whose walls consist of a single layer of cells, facilitating transfer of oxygen and nutrients to the tissues and the loading of metabolic waste and carbon dioxide, all via the extracellular fluid. Their density depends on the need of the particular tissue for nutrients and oxygen. The capillaries drain into small, thin-walled but muscular vessels called venules, whence the blood begins its return to the heart through the veins. The veins have elastic walls but are without muscles. The venous vasculature serves as a reservoir, storing about 60 percent of the blood.

Methods of Study

Circulatory systems of vertebrates have been studied since ancient times through dissection and observation of animal and human cadavers: The heart can be cut open to examine its chambers and their structures, and the body wall can be cut open from the ventral side to expose the circulatory organs. Preserved, dissected animals, including fish, amphibians, reptiles, and mammals, are available from suppliers for students of anatomy who wish to conduct their own dissections. The venous systems of these animals are dyed blue and the arterial systems are dyed red. Plastic models of the circulatory system can be purchased for classroom use.

Blood pressure is of particular interest to physicians and patients and is measured by a sphygmomanometer, which consists of a rubber cuff attached to a rubber tube.

The cuff is placed around the patient's arm and air is pumped into it via the tube, increasing the pressure on the person's brachial artery until the artery is closed. When this pressure is slowly released, the initial pressure upon opening of the artery is recorded; this is the systolic blood pressure, the force with which the blood is pumped through the arteries. The pressure is recorded again, upon further reduction of cuff pressure, when the sound of the blood flow becomes faint and finally disappears; this is the diastolic blood pressure, which provides information about the resistance of the blood vessels.

Physicians are also interested in the rate of the heart beat, or the pulse. The pulse should be strongest near the heart and weakest as it disappears into the capillaries. The radial artery, at the wrist (base of the thumb), is commonly used to measure the pulse, although other arteries can be used as well. A clock is used to count the number of beats per minute at the pulse point. The pulse rate matches the heart rate, which in normal human adults is between seventy and ninety beats per minute. Variations from normal can exist, but the interval between beats, as well as the strength of each beat, should not vary. In a young adult, the difference between systolic and diastolic pressure (males average 120/80, females 110/70) is 40, which is called the "pulse pressure." The normal ratio of systolic to diastolic to pulse pressure is 3:2:1.

Measurements of blood pressure and pulse rate can be observed under different conditions to determine the health or pathology of a person: For example, a person's pulse rate and blood pressure, measured after increasing amounts of exercise, can reveal information about the condition of the arteries. The effects of age, weight, time of day, body posture, emotional state, drugs, hot or cold water, cigarette smoking, and many other conditions can also be determined.

The condition of the heart can be measured by placing electrodes on the body surface surrounding the heart. The heart's conducting current is measured and recorded as an electrocardiogram (ECG or EKG). In a normal ECG, the first small hump (the "P" wave) represents the current generated by the sinoatrial node and its conduction through the atria; the spike following this hump (the "qrs" wave) is generated by the stimulation of the atrioventricular node and the passage of the impulse through the ventricles; and the final hump (the "u" wave) represents the return of the ventricles to their resting state. The resulting measure of the heart's myogenicity (the regularity, or rhythmicity, of the heart's contractions), which can be modified by neuronal, hormonal, and other "intrinsic" influences, can provide life-saving information for doctors and their patients.

Scientists are also interested in microcirculation, or circulation at the capillary level. One can fasten a live frog on a frog board and observe the capillaries in the frog's foot web under a microscope. The movement of the red blood cells into the capillary is observed; it is slow and intermittent. The blood flow is regulated by the central nervous system (the vasomotor center in the medulla), as well as by local conditions (such as levels of carbon dioxide, acidity, histamine, temperature, and inflammation). One can then immerse the foot in hot or cold water and observe the resulting change in blood flow. Histamine can be applied to cause vasodilation, which can be controlled by epinephrine. Drops of dilute hydrochloric acid can be applied to the foot to cause vasodilation and inflammation.

Context

It is clear from the foregoing discussion that the heart and circulatory system are of vital importance to the health of an animal. Thousands of persons die or are seriously impaired each year as a result of heart attacks, strokes, and other heart and circulatory diseases. The human circulatory system can be maintained and strengthened by regular aerobic exercise, which strengthens the heart muscle. Exercise increases the cardiac output, the rate and depth of breathing, the amount of muscular "milking" action on the veins, and the contraction of smooth muscles in the veins. The latter three cause an increase in the amount of venous return of blood. Similarly, contraction of smooth muscles in arterial walls raises the blood pressure and the velocity or arterial blood flow and increases the work load on the heart. Thus, exercise raises the blood pressure and the flow of the arterial and venous blood at the time when skeletal muscles need more blood-borne nutrients and oxygen. Venous return increases at the time of increased cardiac output. Contraction of muscles (precapillary sphincters) in the walls of selected arterioles will shunt the blood to open arterioles without causing a change in arterial blood pressure. In addition, the number of open capillaries increases twenty- to fiftyfold in exercising muscles; hence, circulation in muscles not used during normal activity can be improved during exercise. The overall effect of regular exercise is to strengthen the heart muscles and increase the flow of blood to peripheral muscles and tissues, thus delivering more oxygen and nutrients, and removing more wastes, at a greater rate than normal. As a result, the health of all systems of the organism is improved, as are the chances for longer life.

Bibliography

Berne, R., and M. Levy. "The Cardiovascular System." In *Physiology*. St. Louis: Mosby, 1987. An advanced undergraduate textbook providing an introduction to controls over circulatory function. A good source of information on anatomical details and a good introduction to technical terms.

Curtis, Helena, and N. Sue Barnes. *Biology*. 4th ed. New York: Worth, 1983. An introductory biology text for college students. Chapter 36 provides a brief description of the circulatory system in humans.

Hill, Richard W., and Gordon Wyse. *Animal Physiology*. 2d ed. New York: Harper & Row, 1987. A textbook for advanced undergraduates. The chapter on circulation deals lucidly with the needs, evolution, and functioning of circulatory systems in animals. Covers all groups of invertebrate and vertebrate animals.

Johansen, K., and A. W. A. Martin. "Comparative Aspects of Vertebrate Circulatory Systems." In *Handbook of Physiology*, edited by W. F. Hamilton. Vol. 3, sec. 2, *Circulation*. Washington, D.C.: American Physiological Society, 1965. An advanced text that covers all aspects of vertebrate circulation from a comparative point of view.

Raven, P. H., and G. B. Johnson. *Biology.* St Louis: Mosby, 1989. An introductory biology text for college students. The chapter on circulation provides a good description of circulatory systems in animals, with helpful diagrams and illustrations. Good for the beginner.

Robinson, T. F., et al. "The Heart as a Suction Pump." *Scientific American* 254 (June, 1986): 84-91. An excellent introduction to the heart and its functioning, for high school students, college freshmen, and general readers. Provides basic information at a nontechnical level.

Vander, Arthur, James Sherman, and Dorothy Luciano. *Human Physiology.* 4th ed. New York: Harper & Row, 1985. A text for premedical and medical students. The chapter on circulation provides a complete account of the human circulatory system and its function. Although elaborate and designed for professionals, can be used by the general reader, in conjunction with the introductory material, for complete details on the topic.

M. A. Q. Khan

Cross-References

The Blood-Brain Barrier, 233; Blood Circuits, 248; Blood Components, 262; Blood Pressure, 270; Diffusion in Circulation, 621; Fluid Balance, 1017; Heart-Output and Blood-Flow Regulation, 1269; The Lymphatic System's Function, 1619; Muscle Anatomy in Vertebrates, 1822.

CLEAVAGE, GASTRULATION, AND NEURULATION

Type of life science: Developmental biology (embryology)
Other fields of study: Animal anatomy, animal physiology, cell biology (cytology), invertebrate biology, reproduction, and zoology

A single-celled zygote goes through the processes of cleavage, gastrulation, and neurulation to become a many-celled embryo. By learning about normal development, scientists are finding ways to prevent abnormal development.

Principal terms

ARCHENTERON: the primitive gut cavity formed by the invagination of the blastula; the cavity of the gastrula

BLASTULA: an early stage of an embryo which is shaped like a hollow ball in some animals and a small, flattened disc in others; contains a cavity called the blastocoele

CLEAVAGE: the process by which the fertilized egg undergoes a series of rapid cell divisions which result in the formation of a blastula

GASTRULATION: the transformation of a blastula into a three-layered embryo, the gastrula; initiated by invagination

GERM LAYERS: the embryonic layers of cells which develop in the gastrula: ectoderm, mesoderm, and endoderm

INVAGINATION: the turning of an external layer into the interior of the same structure; formation of archenteron

MORULA: a solid ball or mass of cells resulting from early cleavage divisions of the zygote

NEURULATION: the process by which the embryo develops a central nervous system; formation of a neural plate and subsequent closure of the plate to form a neural tube

NOTOCHORD: a fibrous rod in an embryo which gives support; a structure that will later be surrounded by vertebrae

ZYGOTE: the fertilized egg; the first cell of a new organism

Summary of the Phenomenon

A fertilized egg divides into many smaller cells, which then undergo rearrangement and differentiation to form the embryo of a new individual. The division of the one-celled zygote into smaller and smaller cells is called cleavage. The cellular rearrangement is known as gastrulation, and the proliferation and movement of cells into position to form the beginnings of the central nervous system is termed neurulation. The significance of these events lies in the fact that a single cell with genetic information from two parents is transformed into a multicellular structure with three germ layers that will give rise to all the organs and systems of the body.

After fertilization, the resultant zygote undergoes many rapid cell divisions. The cleavage process results in smaller and smaller cells, called blastomeres. The cell divisions are by mitosis, which produces identical chromosomes in each new cell. When between sixteen and thirty-two cells have been formed, the structure is called a morula. Early observers noted its resemblance to a mulberry and gave it the Latin name.

The morula stage is short-lived because, as soon as it is formed, processes are initiated that bring it to the next stage, known as the blastula. A cavity begins to form in the center of the morula as water flows in and pushes out the cells. The new cavity is called the blastocoele and the embryonic stage the blastula. Cleavage continues until the blastula consists of hundreds of cells but is still no larger than the original zygote. The blastula is the terminal cleavage structure. The egg, much larger than an average cell, has been fertilized and subdivided into hundreds of normal-sized cells. The blastomeres all appear to be similar to one another, but studies have shown that the individual cells are already destined for the tissues they will become.

The principles of cleavage are the same in all vertebrate groups, but the mechanics differ according to the amount of yolk in the egg. Eggs with large amounts of yolk undergo only partial cleavage, because the yolk retards the cytoplasmic division. In birds, reptiles, and many fishes, the yolk is so dense that the cytoplasm and nucleus are crowded into a small cap or disk on one side of the cell. The cleavage divisions all occur in this small area, resulting in a flattened blastula atop the large inert yolk.

Eggs with but a moderate amount of yolk, such as amphibian eggs, are able to cleave completely. Because division proceeds more slowly through the part of the cell where yolk has accumulated, the cleavage is uneven. The cells are formed more slowly on the yolky side and are larger and fewer in number. The blastocoele is smaller and displaced to the side, with less yolk. The side with smaller blastomeres will develop into the embryo and is called the animal hemisphere. The side containing larger amounts of yolk is called the vegetal hemisphere and will provide nutrients for the embryo.

Eggs with very little yolk undergo total and equal cleavage divisions. The blastula has a large, centrally located blastocoele, and blastomeres are uniform in size. Starfish and the primitive chordate amphioxus undergo this kind of cleavage. They are often used to demonstrate the successive cleavage stages which are more easily seen in the absence of yolk. Though mammalian eggs do not have large amounts of yolk, their development is similar to that of birds. The outer layer of cells of the morula develop into a membrane, called the trophoblast, that surrounds the embryo. The embryo forms from cells in the inner region known as the inner cell mass. A large, fluid-filled blastocoele forms within the trophoblast, giving rise to the term "blastocyst," for the mammalian blastula. The inner cell mass develops atop the blastocoele as the bird embryo on the yolk.

Gastrulation is the next process in embryonic development and consists of a series of cell migrations that result in cellular rearrangement. The final gastrula will have three embryonic germ layers destined to give rise to all body structures and systems.

The first step in gastrulation is an indenting or invagination in the blastula at a spot known as the dorsal lip. Cells begin to move over the lip and drop into the interior, forming the lining of a new cavity, the archenteron, or primitive gut. Continued inward movement of cells forms a middle layer between outer cells and inner ones which have dropped in through the opening, or blastopore. The three embryonic germ layers have now been formed, and they are called ecotoderm, mesoderm, and endoderm.

In animals with little egg yolk, such as the starfish, gastrulation begins when a few cells lose their adhesiveness and drop into the blastocoele. That causes a dent or depression in that area. Cells move in and deepen the depression, forming the archenteron. As the archenteron expands, the inner blastocoele shrinks and is finally obliterated. This process may be visualized as punching in the side of a hollow rubber ball with one's finger. The hole the finger makes is the blastopore; the new cavity formed by the hand represents the archenteron; and the original space inside the ball represents the blastocoele. The indentation forms two cell layers, and a third one is formed as cells continue to move in and take position between the inner and outer layers.

The outer ecotoderm is destined to become epidermis and nerve tissue. The inner endoderm will form digestive glands and the lining of the digestive and respiratory systems. The middle germ layer, the mesoderm, will give rise to bone, muscle, connective tissue, and the cardiovascular and urinary systems. Additional mesoderm forms a rodlike structure known as the notochord, which lies in the roof of the archenteron. The notochord is a distinctive characteristic of chordates and gives embryonic support. The mesoderm lateral to the notochord will segregate into paired masses known as somites, each with prospective skin, bone, and nerve segments.

Gastrulation in blastulas with moderate amounts of yolk, such as amphibians have, proceeds similarly, but the archenteron is displaced toward the animal hemisphere and is filled with yolk cells. The early stages are similar to those in starfish.

Gastrulation in birds and mammals is initiated in a manner different from that in starfish and amphibians, because of the discoidal configuration of the blastula. Both groups have incomplete cleavage with embryonic development on a disklike area on one side of the egg. The upper cells of the disk separate from the lower ones, forming two layers, the epiblast and the hypoblast. After the two layers are formed, a thickening occurs in one quadrant of the blastula and soon becomes noticeable as a distinct streak, the primitive streak. The streak becomes grooved, and cells from either side begin to migrate to the groove and sink down through it. The cells then move into position between the epiblast and hypoblast. The three embryonic germ layers have been formed.

The primitive groove in the gastrula is considered homologous to the blastopore in the starfish and amphibians. After the germ layers have been established, cells continue to move in to the new cavity, the archenteron, and form a mesodermal notochord in the roof of the archenteron.

Neurulation is the final stage of early embryonic development. Studies have shown that the notochord induces the neurulation process to begin. Cells just above the notochord are induced to proliferate and thicken, forming a neural plate. After the neural plate is formed, a buckling occurs in it, forming a depression known as the neural groove. Modern microscope techniques have revealed microfilaments and microtubules lying beneath the surface of the plate. Contraction of the microfilaments and elongation of microtubules appear to cause cell buckling and folding of the plate. The neural groove deepens at its cephalic end, and folds on either side continue to grow higher until they actually touch each other, forming an enclosed tube, the neural tube. At the same time that the neural tube is forming, the head is growing forward and tissue is folding beneath it so it projects forward free from the surface. Brain differentiation begins with the enlargement of the anterior end of the neural tube. The undilated caudal portion will give rise to the spinal cord. The brain forms several constrictions, so that three bulges appear. These will become the three embryonic brain divisions: the forebrain, the midbrain, and the hindbrain.

Upon completion of the three brain divisions, the embryo undergoes forward flexion of the forebrain and a lateral torsion so that the embryo comes to life with its left side on the yolk. A final caudal flexion causes the embryo to take its typical C-shaped configuration.

Extraembryonic membranes form from tissue outside the embryo to provide oxygen, nutrients, and waste storage. In birds, an outer chorion and amnion fuse to form a membrane with a large blood supply which provides for the exchange of oxygen and carbon dioxide between the embryo and the atmosphere. The allantois is a membranous sac to contain waste secretions.

In mammals, the outer chorion becomes extensively vascularized on one side and interconnects with the uterus to form the placenta. Nutrient and waste exchange between mother and baby take place in the placenta. The amnion forms a fluid-filled sac that lies closely around the embryo and cushions it. The allantois is not needed for waste storage and is not well developed.

Methods of Study

Human beings have always been intrigued with the question of how they come into existence. Aristotle questioned whether the embryo unfolds from a preformed condition and then enlarges to adult proportions or progressively differentiates from simple to complex form. Not until the eighteenth century were actual observations made of a developing embryo. The chick egg was the first to be studied, because of its large size. Early studies were descriptive as each stage of the embryo was observed and carefully described. It was found that development does proceed from simple form to forms increasingly complex.

In the late nineteenth century, great interest developed in evolutionary theory, and comparative embryology became the focal point of studies. Clues were sought for possible evolutionary relationships between organisms. The theory emerged that embryonic stages reflect the evolutionary past of an organism.

The twentieth century has seen the explosion of experimental embryology and multiplication of knowledge. Cleavage of the large fertilized egg was first observed in the eighteenth century, but not until the late twentieth century have the mechanics begun to be understood. With improved microscope techniques, a ring of microfilaments can be seen just below the egg cell surface. These protein filaments have contractile qualities, and it was thought perhaps they lined up around the equator to contract and squeeze the cell in two. To test this hypothesis, a drug which causes microfilament subunits to break down was added to the cell culture. It was found that cell division was inhibited, suggesting that microfilaments are involved in the division process. Removal of astral rays also hindered cleavage. Each new discovery answers some questions and raises more.

Embryologists have questioned how blastomeres all formed from the same cell could differentiate into many kinds of cells and tissues. Some of the earliest experiments in embryology involved separating the first two daughter cells to demonstrate that each could form two complete individuals. How and when cells differentiate continues to be a challenge to researchers. The substance in cells which predisposes them to differentiate between one another is still not understood.

It has been discovered that each part of the embryo surface is already divided into prospective organ areas by the blastula stage. Fate maps have been constructed by marking certain areas on the blastula with vital stains and observing the structures into which they develop.

Since the early days of experimental embryology, researchers have performed all kinds of operations on embryos, marking areas and observing their movement, transplanting cells from one area to another, exchanging cell nuclei and removing portions. These experiments have led to many discoveries and better understanding of the complicated developmental process.

Studies of cell migration in the embryo have led to ideas for procedures to inhibit tumor cell migration. Knowledge of normal cell development is helping to find ways to prevent abnormal cell development.

Context

The zygote, formed by fusion of sperm and egg, undergoes rapid cleavage divisions until the abnormally large egg cell has become a blastula, a mass of smaller cells. The cells undergo extensive rearrangement in the process of gastrulation, bringing them into position for organ differentiation. An increase in ectodermal cells begins the neurulation process, which gives rise to the central nervous system. In humans, the entire process occurs within the first month of embryonic development.

When one considers the multitude of complex events that must take place in the development of a new individual from a single cell, it might seem impossible that the entire developmental process could occur without a slip and a normal baby develop. Yet, more than 97 percent of all newborns have developed without malformation of any kind.

Abnormal development to some degree occurs in at least 2 percent of human births and is caused by a variety of circumstances. Malformation ranges in severity from an extra digit or nipple to a missing brain. Some babies are born with open neural tubes, abdominal viscera outside the body, a single eye, a hole in the heart, blindness, or deafness.

Malformation usually begins during early development. Deformities may arise from inherited mistakes in the genetic code or from the harmful influence of external factors such as radiation, medication of the mother, poor nutrition, or infection. Embryonic structures are in a sensitive state during the early stages and are likely to be damaged by drugs, chemicals, and alcohol. Mothers who take these substances into their bodies are exposing their developing children to substances definitely known to damage embryonic tissue.

Thalidomide, a sedative widely prescribed to pregnant women in the 1960's, resulted in limb abnormalities in 10 percent of children born to women who used it. Some agents cause severe defects in one species but not in another. Thalidomide was one of these. Deformities were produced in humans and rabbits but not in rats. Single animal studies do not always guarantee that a drug can be safely used by humans.

Diet deficiencies at the time of impregnation and during early pregnancy may cause abnormal embryonic development. Vitamin E has been found to be necessary for blastula implantation and development. There is some evidence that supplementing the diet with folic acid results in fewer incidents of neural tube defects. Each year in the United States, four thousand babies are born with incomplete neural tube closure, causing a spectrum of effects ranging from paralysis to death. Nonclosure at the anterior end of the neural groove results in anencephaly, which prevents development of the brain. Nonclosure at the posterior end causes spina bifida, which is characterized by incomplete body development and paralysis of lower extremities. Other studies have shown that as many as 40 percent of the women studied who bore malformed babies had poor diets during pregnancy.

A number of maternal infections can cause abnormalities in the embryo. The earlier in development that the embryo is infected, the more interference occurs. If the mother contracts rubella during her first month of pregnancy, abnormalities may result such as deafness and eye, heart, and brain damage. Smallpox, chicken pox, and toxoplasmosis have been documented to cause congenital diseases. Mothers with acquired immune deficiency syndrome (AIDS) will infect their unborn babies with the virus.

Bibliography

Arey, Leslie Brainerd. *Developmental Anatomy.* 7th ed. Philadelphia: W. B. Saunders, 1974. An intermediate-level college text designed for use in lecture and laboratory and one that has been widely used. History of embryology, experi-

mental methods, and unsolved problems are discussed. A comparison of embryonic developmental sequence in the different vertebrate classes is made. Germ
layer derivatives are explained, with special emphasis on human development.
The text is illustrated with line drawings.

Horder, T. J., J. A. Witkowski, and C. C. Wylie, eds. *A History of Embryology.*
Cambridge, England: Cambridge University Press, 1986. A sourcebook that covers the history of embryology from 1818, when the first human abnormalities were
described, until the production of radioisotopes at Oak Ridge in 1943. Contributions of scientists from around the world are described, and interesting sidelights
are given. The text provides a thorough summary of discoveries in embryology
from the early descriptive period through the advent of radioisotopes so useful in
marking and tracing development. The text includes an extensive bibliography on
all aspects of embryology.

Johnson, Leland G., and Rebecca L. Johnson. *Essentials of Biology.* Dubuque, Iowa:
Wm. C. Brown, 1986. An introductory-level college text designed to cover the
entire spectrum of biology topics in a one-semester course. The text is well
illustrated and includes study aids such as outlines, major concepts, key terms,
essays, summaries, questions, suggested readings, and a glossary. Chapter 19,
"Reproduction and Development," gives a concise summary of embryonic development in each vertebrate group and has an informative essay on animal cloning.

Mathews, Willis W. *Atlas of Descriptive Embryology.* 4th ed. New York: Macmillan, 1986. A paperback manual intended for laboratory work in an intermediate college course. The manual includes a complete series of large photomicrographs of developmental stages. A different form of development is noted
in eggs with differing amounts of yolk. A complete series of cross sections is
shown for sea-urchin, amphioxus, frog, chick, and pig embryos. Cross sections
include an illustration of a whole mount showing the exact location of each
section, helping to integrate the three-dimensional aspect of the embryo. The
complete series is helpful for laboratory identification of microscopic embryology sections. A thorough glossary is included.

Oppenheimer, Steven B., and George Lefevre, Jr. *Introduction to Embryonic Development.* 2d ed. Boston: Allyn & Bacon, 1984. An intermediate-level college text
which gives extensive coverage to the embryological stages in primitive chordate
and vertebrate classes. Molecular and cellular aspects of development are emphasized, and the discussion of molecular genetics is informative. The text reflects
the rapid advancement of the field of embryology, describing many experiments
that have led to understanding the mechanics of developmental processes. Chapters 6-8 give extensive coverage to the topics of cleavage, gastrulation, and
neurulation. The text is well illustrated and includes a glossary and references to
research in the journal literature.

Starr, Cecie, and Ralph Taggart. *Biology: The Unity and Diversity of Life.* 5th ed.
Belmont, Calif.: Wadsworth, 1989. An introductory-level college text that uses the
principles of evolution and energy flow as a conceptual framework for each

chapter. Clear writing style and color illustrations on every page make this an attractive and informative text. Chapter 34, "Principles of Reproduction and Development," gives a concise overview of the early embryological stages and describes experiments that have led to the understanding of mechanisms of development.

Katherine H. Houp

Cross-References

Determination and Differentiation, 606; Development: An Evolutionary Perspective, 615; Fertilization, 969; The Forebrain, 1032; Gametogenesis, 1061; The Hindbrain and Midbrain, 1291; Histology, 1307; Mammalian Hormones, 1368; Nuclear Transplantation in Developmental Analysis, 1980; Pregnancy and Prenatal Development, 2185.

CLINES, HYBRID ZONES, AND INTROGRESSION

Types of life science: Evolutionary biology and genetics
Other fields of study: Botany, ecology, systematics (taxonomy), and zoology

A cline is a genetic variation in the characteristics of populations of the same species that results from a variation in the geographical area that it occupies. Hybrid zones are areas where there are populations of a species composed of individuals with characteristics of one or more species that have interbred. Introgression is speciation that occurs when the genes of one species are incorporated into the gene pool of another as the result of successful hybridization.

Principal terms
    CLINE: a gradual, continuous variation from one population of a species to the next that is related to differences in geography
    DEME: a local unit of the population of any one species
    GENE: the unit of molecular information, a portion of a DNA molecule that codes for some product, such as a protein, that governs inherited traits
    GENE FLOW: the movement of genes from one part of a population to another part, or from one population to another, via gametes
    GENE POOL: the sum total of all the genes of all the individuals in a population
    HYBRID: the offspring of a mating between genetically differing individuals
    INTROGRESSION: the assimilation of the genes of one species into the gene pool of another by successful hybridization
    POPULATION: the members of a species that live in the same geographical area
    SPECIES: a group of similar organisms whose members can reproduce with one another to produce fertile offspring

Summary of the Phenomenon

Gene flow among populations tends to increase the similarity of characters among all the demes (local populations) of a species. Natural selection has the opposite effect: It tends to make every deme uniquely specialized for its specific habitat. Clines are one possible result of these two opposing forces; a cline is a phenomenon in which a genetic variation occurs that is caused by a difference in geographical habitat. Each species is continuously adjusting its gene pool to ensure that the species survives in the face of an environment that is continuously changing.

Comparing the characteristics of the demes of a single species usually will reveal that they are not identical. The greater the distance between the demes, the greater the differences between them will be. The maple trees in New York, for example, differ from the maple trees in Minnesota more than they differ from those in

Connecticut. The grass frogs in Wisconsin differ from the grass frogs in Texas more than they differ from those in Michigan. On the average, the song sparrows of Alaska are heavier and have darker coloration than those in California. Plants with wide distribution in mountainous regions tend to be shorter when they occur in alpine meadows than those that grow at sea level. These phenomena, in which a single character shows a gradient of change across a geographical area, are called clines.

Many birds and mammals exhibit north-south clines in average body size and weight, being larger and heavier in the colder climate farther north and smaller and lighter in warmer climates to the south. In the same way, many mammalian species show north-south clines in the sizes of body extremities such as tails and ears, these parts being smaller in northern demes and larger in southern demes. Increase in average body size with increasing cold is such a common observation that it has been codified as Bergmann's rule. The tendency toward shorter and smaller extremities in colder climates and longer and larger ones in warmer climates is known as Allen's rule. The trend toward lighter colors in southern climates and darker shades in northern climates has been designated Gloger's rule. The zebra, for example, shows a cline in the amount of striping on the legs. The northernmost races are fully leg-striped, and the striping diminishes toward the southern latitudes of Africa; this appears to be an example of Gloger's rule. In another example of a cline, human blood groups are controlled by three alleles (genes). There is a well-defined cline for the frequency of the B allele, which is highest in central Asia and progressively diminishes westward across Europe and eastward across Asia. A third example, which does not fit any of the biogeographical rules mentioned, is the number of eggs laid per reproductive effort (the clutch size) by the European robin: This number is larger in northern Europe than it is for the same species in northern Africa. Other birds, such as the crossbill and raven, which have wide distribution in the Holarctic realm, show a clutch-size cline that reveals a larger clutch size in lower latitudes. The manifestation of such clines in clutch size is a consequence of the interplay of two different reproductive strategies that may give a species a competitive advantage in a given environment. The stability of the environment is what elicits the appropriate strategy.

In unstable environments, such as those in the temperate zone, where there may occur sudden variations in weather and extremes between seasons, a species needs to reproduce rapidly and build its numbers quickly to take advantage of the favorable warm seasons to ensure survival of the species during the harsh, unfavorable conditions of winter. This strategy is known as r strategy (r stands for the rate of increase). In the tropics, the climate is more equable throughout the year. The environment, however, can only support a limited number of individuals throughout the year. This number is called the carrying capacity. When carrying capacity is reached, competition for resources increases, and the reproductive effort is reduced to maintain the population at the carrying capacity. This is called K strategy, with K standing for carrying capacity.

In birds, clutch size tends to be inversely proportional to the climatic stability of the habitat: In temperate climates, more energy is directed to increase the reproductive rate. In the tropics, the carrying capacity is more important, resulting in a reduced reproductive rate. In the apparent contradiction of the crossbills and ravens, it may be the harshness of the habitat at higher latitudes that limits the resources available for successfully fledging a larger number of young.

The cline exhibited by the common grass frog is one of the best known of all the examples of this phenomenon. It has the greatest range, occupies the widest array of habitats, and possesses the greatest amount of morphological variability of any frog species. This variability and adaptation are not haphazard. The species includes a number of temperature-adapted demes, varying from north to south. These adaptations involve the departmental processes from egg to larva. The northernmost demes have larger eggs that develop faster at lower temperatures than those of the southernmost demes. These physiological differences are so marked that matings between individuals from the extreme ends of the cline result in abnormal larvae or offspring that are inviable (cannot survive) even at a temperature that is average for the cline region. Leopard frogs from Vermont can interbreed readily with ones from New Jersey. Those in New Jersey can hybridize readily with those in the Carolinas, and those in turn with those in Georgia. Yet, hybrids of Vermont demes and Florida demes are usually abnormal and inviable. Thus, it appears that the Vermont gene pool has been selected for a rate of development that corresponds to a lower environmental temperature. The gene pool of the Florida race has a rate of development that is slower at a higher average temperature. The mixture of the genetic makeup of the northern and southern races is so discordant that it fails to regulate characteristic rates of development at any sublethal temperature, so the resulting embryo dies before it becomes a tadpole.

There are two primary reasons why characters within a species may show clinal variation. First, if gene flow occurs between nearby demes of a population, the gene pools of demes that are close to one another will share more alleles than the gene pools of populations that are far apart. Second, environmental factors, such as annual climate, vary along gradients that can be defined longitudinally, latitudinally, or altitudinally. Because these environmental components act as selective pressures, the phenotypic characters that are best adapted to such pressures will also vary in a gradient.

Hybridization is the process whereby individuals of different species produce offspring. A hybrid zone is an area occupied by interbreeding species. Partial species can and do develop on the way to becoming new species as products of hybridization. Natural hybridization and gene flow can take place between biological species no matter how sterile most of the hybrid offspring may be. As long as the mechanisms that prevent free exchange of genes between populations can be penetrated, there is the potential for a new species to develop. Because the parental species has a tendency to be replaced by the hybrid types if natural selection favors them, hybridization can be a threat to the integrity of the parental species as a distinct entity.

Hybridization between different species leads to various and unpredictable results. Any time that hybridization occurs, the isolation mechanisms of populations are overcome, forming bridging populations. Such connecting demes of hybrid origin fall into one of two general categories: hybrid swarms or introgressive demes. The formation of these types of demes reverses the process of speciation and changes the formerly distinct species into a complex mixture of highly variable individuals that are the products of the segregation and independent assortment of traits. This is the primary advantage of sexual reproduction: to produce variation in the population that is acted upon by natural selection over time. It cannot be overemphasized that hybrid swarms and introgressive demes are highly variable.

The environmental conditions that contour plant and animal communities have endured for a very long time. In long-lived communities, every available niche has been filled by well-adapted species. When populations with new adaptive characteristics occur, there is no niche for them to occupy, so they usually die out. In contrast, when such communities are disturbed, the parity among their component species is upset, which gives new variants an opportunity to become established.

Hybrid swarms can be readily observed in nature by the careful investigator. Hybrid swarms resulting from the breeding between two species of columbines occur in the Sierra Nevada of California. Hybrid swarms of juniper occur over a wide area of Kansas and Nebraska. A hybrid swarm resulting from a cross between three species of wild indigo has been reported from the Gulf Coast of Texas. A very well-known example of a hybrid swarm of wild iris that was observed in the Mississippi River delta has provided a number of horticultural varieties for gardens. The notable observation in this instance was that the hybrid swarm only formed in an area that was a cattle wallow—that is, it was a disturbed habitat. In the disturbed area, the hybrid individuals backcrossed with the parental types to form a third population, which resulted from the migration of the genes of one population into the other. Such a population is designated an introgressive population. The progeny of such populations resembles the parent species, but the variations are in the direction of one parental species or the other. If introgression is extensive enough, it may eradicate the morphological and ecological distinctions of the parental types. The parental types become rarer and rarer, until they are no longer the representatives of the species.

There appear to be three reasons that first-generation hybrids occurring naturally are more likely to form offspring by backcrossing to one of the parental species than by mating with each other. Primarily, the hybrids are always rarer than the parents. Second, the parental individuals are so much more fertile than the hybrids that many more parental gametes are available than hybrid ones. Finally, backcross progeny, since they contain primarily parentally derived genes, are more likely to be well adapted to the habitat in which they originated than are the purely hybrid individuals.

Thus, the most likely result of hybridization is backcrossing to one of the parental species. Genotypes containing the most parental genes usually have the selective advantage, and the fact that they contain a few chromosomal segments from another species gives them unique characteristics that may also be advantageous. This sequence of events—hybridization, backcrossing, and stabilization of backcross types—is known as introgression. Hybrid swarms are interesting phenomena, but they are unlikely to be of evolutionary significance except through introgression.

Methods of Study

Clines have been discovered through both observation and testing. An altitudinal plant cline, for example, was discovered when researchers noted plant species that appeared to be shorter at higher altitudes. Two plants that show altitudinal clines are the columbine and mountain cinquefoil plants. This variation was shown to be genetic when the researchers collected cuttings from plants found at several altitudes and planted them all in a test garden at approximately sea level. When grown under uniform conditions, the plants derived from cuttings taken from various altitudes still grew to heights that correlated with the altitudes at which the parent cuttings had been gathered. The researchers concluded that there were genetic differences among the clines, although the different cuttings were all from the same biological species.

In order to detect introgression in the field, keen powers of observation are needed. When an observer sees evidence of hybridization, such as in the irises of the Mississippi River delta, the next step is to conduct experimental repetition of the suspected cross. Whenever possible it is critical to study the offspring of artificial backcrosses of the hybrids with the parental species. This type of investigation will show whether such crosses can indeed take place and will give insight into what the putative hybrids will look like.

For the examination of hybrid swarms or populations in which hybridization is suspected, methods of analysis are needed that record as precisely as possible the extent to which one variation is linked to another or even several others. The human mind is quite inefficient in judging variation in more than one character at a time. A careful observer may examine three different populations of a flowering plant, for example, and record within them variations in flower color, hairiness of the leaves or stems, and leaf shape. This same observer, however, cannot look at three populations that vary simultaneously in flower color, furriness of leaves and stems, and leaf shape. A technique is needed for recording, at the same time, variation in several different traits; one such technique is the pictorialized scatter diagram, which employs dots on a two-axis graph to record three to four variable characteristics in a figurative way. The two axes of the graph account for two variables; on a pictorialized scatter diagram, six to eight variables can be visualized at the same time. By plotting the nonaxis variables across the diagram, the scientist can produce an accurate depiction of a multiple-characteristic cline, which in turn will reveal patterns and trends in hybridization and introgression.

Context

A well-documented example of introgression has been recorded for a domesticated species, maize. In Mexico, a weedy grass called teosinte is often found in or near fields of cultivated corn. The two species hybridize readily, and the hybrids are capable of producing viable seeds. The midden heaps (refuse heaps) of paleo-Indians occupying what is now Mexico have revealed, in a chronological sequence, corn with progressively larger and larger cobs that resemble the modern varieties of corn grown today in this region. These cobs also show an increasing number of characteristics derived from teosinte. Plants resembling these ancient varieties of corn have been produced artificially by hybridizing the most primitive varieties of modern corn with teosinte and selecting the plants that produce cobs most like the ancestral varieties. By this means it has been shown that some of the most valuable genes in modern varieties of corn can be attributed to the introgression of teosinte genes into the genotypes of maize.

Many weeds, such as the grasses, contain species that, on the basis of cytogenetic evidence, are of recent origin. A species of grass known as goat grass has been shown to have originated from hybrids between types of barley and wheat that were cultivated early in human history in the Middle East. It is also hypothesized that modern cultivated varieties of wheat are products of the hybridization of wild grasses, which resulted in hybrids that thrived in habitats that were disturbed by the activities of accompanying human populations. Subsequent generations of these hybrids were selected, and their genetic makeup was stabilized by domestication.

Examples of introgression in animals are not common. Those that have been demonstrated are usually associated with the domestication of livestock. In the Himalayan region of Asia, there exists a relative of cattle, the yak, which is also domesticated. Many of the herds of cattle found along the western edge of the Himalayas, in central Asia, contain characteristics that clearly are derived from the gene pool of the yak. Many of these characteristics are manifested as adaptations to the harsh climatic conditions in this region.

In western Canada there has been a modest introgression of the genes of the American bison into the gene pool of strains of range cattle. The bisonlike characters incorporated into beef cattle created a new breed called the beefalo, which exhibits such characteristics as greater body musculature, lower fat content of the flesh, and great efficiency in the utilization of range forage. A beefalo steer is ready for market in only eight months, while the same live weight is not obtained in the standard beef breed until eighteen months.

These examples serve to illustrate the concept that, as an evolutionary force, introgression is rather insignificant in natural biomes. It is almost always in the wake of human activity or the activities of their domesticated plants and animals that the process of introgression can and does result in new combinations of gene pools from different species.

Bibliography

Anderson, Edgar. *Introgressive Hybridization.* New York: Hafner Press, 1968. This book is a classic in the field of introgressive hybridization. It was first published in 1949, and this citation is a facsimile of the 1949 edition. This is the first time the technique of pictorialized scatter diagrams was fully described; the method remains in wide use today.

Chaeta, M. L. "A General Theory of Clutch Size." *Evolution* 20 (1965): 174-184. This is an excellent review of the concept of clutch size and its function in selection of adaptations that optimize population pressures in avian species.

Clausen, J., D. D. Keck, and W. M. Hiesey. *Experimental Studies on the Nature of Species: 3. Environment Responses of Climatic Races of* Achillea. Carnegie Institution of Washington Publication Number 581. Washington, D.C.: Carnegie Institution of Washington, 1948. This is a landmark of research into the mechanisms of the development of geographical races of plants belonging to the same genus and species. Its concepts are summarized in nearly every modern biology textbook.

Dobzhansky, Theodosius G. *Genetics and the Origin of Species.* 3d rev. ed. New York: Columbia University Press, 1951. This classic text is occasionally difficult reading, but it is one of the most important books on evolutionary genetics.

Grant, Verne. *Plant Speciation.* New York: Columbia University Press, 1971. This standard text contains a broad spectrum of information on speciation phenomena in higher plants.

Moore, J. A. "Geographic Variation of Adaptive Characters in *Rana pipiens* Schreber." *Evolution* 3 (1949): 1-24. This landmark publication contains one of the earliest definitive descriptions of the genetic mechanism that underlies the formation of clines in animals. It concerns the variations found in the leopard frog.

Simpson, G. G. *The Major Features of Evolution.* New York: Columbia University Press, 1953. This standard text contains a wealth of information on speciation in animals.

Stebbins, G. L. *The Process of Organic Evolution.* Englewood Cliffs, N.J.: Prentice-Hall, 1966. This is an introductory textbook on evolution that is strong on the concepts of speciation in plants.

_____. "The Role of Hybridization in Speciation." *Proceedings of the American Philosophical Society* 103 (1959): 231-251. This journal publication was one of the first to synthesize the state of the art in the mechanism of speciation through hybridization. Plants are the only examples given.

Thoday, J. M. "Components of Fitness." *Symposia of the Society for Experimental Biology* 7 (1953): 96-113. A classic review article that concisely enumerates the aspects of fitness.

Edward N. Nelson

Cross-References

Adaptive Radiation, 29; DNA Hybridization Analysis of Relatedness, 686; Evolution: A Historical Perspective, 903; Extinction, 953; Gene Flow, 1097; Isolating Mechanisms in Evolution, 1493; Natural Selection, 1870; Nonrandom Mating, Genetic Drift, and Mutation, 1965; Speciation and the Species Concept, 2521.

CLONING TO PRODUCE RECOMBINANT DNA

Types of life science: Genetics and molecular biology
Other fields of study: Biochemistry, bioethics, cell biology (cytology), and microbiology

Cloning is the method whereby individual DNA molecules can be accurately copied to produce numerous identical molecules, or clones. This technology has revolutionized virtually every aspect of biology and medicine.

Principal terms
AUTORADIOGRAPHY: the process whereby the radioactivity of isotopes is detected by photographic film applied to the isotope-labeled probe
GENOME: the sum of the entire genetic information of an organism
GENOMIC LIBRARY: a collection of recombinant DNA molecules obtained from total genomic DNA
HYBRIDIZATION: the process of bonding a sequence of nucleic acid bases to complementary bases
PLASMIDS: circular molecules of DNA present in the cytoplasm of bacteria that can replicate independently of the bacterial chromosome
PROBE: an agent that will accurately identify a specific nucleic acid or sequence of nucleic acids
RECOMBINANT DNA: DNA from one source that has been joined to DNA from another source
RESTRICTION ENZYMES: enzymes that recognize specific DNA sequences and cut the DNA within or near the recognition site
VECTOR: a cell used as a vehicle to carry or transfer the piece of DNA of interest

Summary of the Methodology

Genetic information is contained in a long, chainlike, two-stranded molecule known as deoxyribonucleic acid (DNA), which is made up of four molecules called bases. The total human genome, as represented in the genetic content of every single human cell, consists of approximately 2 to 3 billion of these four bases, arranged in forty-six separate long strings called chromosomes, each tens or hundreds of millions of bases long. Prior to the advent of techniques for cloning DNA, this molecule was the most difficult cellular compound to analyze. Enormously long and chemically monotonous, DNA could be analyzed only indirectly. DNA cloning to produce recombinant DNA molecules has made this macromolecule relatively easy to analyze and has provided powerful and novel approaches to understanding the structure and regulation of genes. It is now possible to cut specific regions of DNA and obtain them in essentially unlimited quantities.

DNA cloning to produce recombinant DNA molecules involves a mixture of techniques. First, specific cleavage of DNA by enzymes called restriction endonucleases is used to generate DNA fragments; then, a specific DNA fragment is integrated into a rapidly replicating genetic element such as a plasmid or a virus that acts as a vector, so that the DNA fragment of interest can be amplified in cells infected by the vector. Finally, powerful identification procedures, such as DNA hybridization, are required to isolate the required clone.

The most important tools for cloning DNA are restriction enzymes called restriction endonucleases. These enzymes, usually isolated from bacteria, will cut the DNA according to its specificity, either within or to either side of the gene of interest. It will also cut the total DNA in the sample at similar sites, generating perhaps a million different DNA samples. The DNA fragment of interest will have a discrete size, because it is delimited at either end by precise recognition sequences specified by the restriction endonuclease used. One then separates the fragments according to size by electrophoresis. Large series of such enzymes are available, and they recognize more than a hundred different target sites. DNA cut by these enzymes has short, single-stranded DNA ends which are cohesive and are called "sticky ends." These two ends can be joined back together because of complementarity, which is the ability of the single-stranded overhangs to form base pairs. DNA from any source that contains a specific enzyme recognition site can be cut and joined to another DNA molecule from another source that has been cut with the same restriction enzyme. Restriction enzymes are used to generate linear DNA and linearized vector DNA that are joined to form the recombinant DNA molecules.

When total genomic DNA is used to produce a collection of recombinant molecules, this is called a genomic library. In general, each somatic cell (all the cells in the body other than reproductive cells) from a person contains the same complement of DNA; genomic libraries are therefore usually made from a readily available source, such as the DNA from a blood cell. More than 90 percent of the DNA within a gene is not directly involved in protein biosynthesis and is called intronic. Regions of the gene that are directly involved in protein biosynthesis are called exonic. Within the cell nucleus, the ribonucleic acid (RNA) copy of the DNA is made by a process called transcription. This is followed by the removal of the intronic DNA sequence so that the messenger RNA (mRNA) consists only of the exonic sequence. To make this information accessible, DNA copies of the mRNA can be made and cloned. Libraries of these DNA copies of mRNA are called complementary DNA libraries. The source of mRNA used to produce a complementary DNA library is important, because not all genes are expressed in all tissues or cells or expressed all the time within the same cell. Therefore, complementary DNA libraries are usually made for a specific tissue or cell type, chosen because the protein coded for the desired mRNA is known to be present.

Linear DNA molecules from a suitable source are mixed with vector DNA and joined together, or ligated, with a specific enzyme called DNA ligase. This procedure generates a library of recombinant DNA molecules. The vector contains

DNA sequences that enable it to be copied after entering a suitable host cell. The most common host cell is a laboratory strain of bacteria called *Escherichia coli*, although other bacterial and yeast cells can be used. The host cell provides the machinery necessary for generating copies of the recombinant DNA molecules. Vectors are usually either plasmids or bacteriophages (viruses that infect bacterial cells). Host cells, each containing a single representative from the library of recombinants, are grown on agar plates. Plasmid vectors containing a gene that confers resistance to an antibiotic are used, so that bacterial host cells are grown as colonies on a medium containing the antibiotic, thus allowing for selective growth of the cells containing the plasmid vector. Bacteriophage infection produces a clearing, called a plaque, in a bed of bacterial host cells as the virus reproduces, destroys the host cell, and infects surrounding cells.

Each bacterial cell colony or bacteriophage plaque contains thousands of copies of a single recombinant DNA molecule, but only a few of these contain the sequence of interest; therefore, powerful identification procedures are required to isolate the desired clone. The most commonly used method is called DNA-DNA hybridization. The DNA from the bacterial colonies or the bacteriophage plaques containing the recombinant DNA molecules is transferred to a membrane, usually nitrocellulose paper, to form a replica. The DNA is then treated so that the double strands fall apart, a process called denaturation; then, a radioactively tagged piece of single-stranded DNA, specifically designed to identify the clone of interest, is hybridized to the DNA on the membrane. The base pairs of the probe will match only the base pairs of the relevant clone, so its location can be detected by autoradiography. Alignment of the replica with the original bacterial colony plate allows the colony or the plaque containing the region of interest to be identified. The clone can then be isolated, purified, and grown to provide unlimited quantities of DNA.

An alternative approach is to use rat DNA sequences as probes. The nucleotide sequences between rat and human genes are in some cases sufficiently identical to permit base pairing between DNAs. Hence, rat genes can be used as probes for isolating human genes. Another method of selection of a specific sequence of cloned recombinant DNA is called complementation. This requires the expression of the complementary DNA sequence to give a functional protein product. The host cell chosen is usually defective in the particular function of interest; that is, it contains a mutation in the gene encoding the function. Thus, growth of the host cell relies on a functional copy of the gene being introduced, in the form of a recombinant DNA molecule, to compensate for the defective gene and hence restore its function. By these and a variety of other biochemical, immunological, and genetic methods, most DNA sequences can be cloned and isolated.

Applications of the Method

The major applications of cloning to produce recombinant DNA are in the fields of molecular biology and genetics; in addition, the industrial applications of this technology have revolutionized medicine and biology in general.

This technology has been used to improve dramatically scientific knowledge regarding the structure of genes. Cloning techniques clearly show that in many cases the entire gene does not take part in producing the final product, the protein. Instead, cloning methods have shown that genes contain intervening sequences, or introns, which interrupt the continuity of genetic information and are not essential in protein synthesis. The areas of the gene crucial in directing protein synthesis are called exons. Therefore, a gene coding for a protein may be much larger than is required for the task of linking amino acids in the right order to make proteins. For example, this methodology has shown that in the mouse, the gene that codes for the enzyme dihydrofolate reductase contains five introns. The entire gene is 32,000 base pairs in length, whereas the length of the exonic portion of gene is only 568 base pairs. Similar methodology has added to geneticists' knowledge of abnormalities in gene structure, or mutations, that cause human diseases such as thalassemia, a blood disorder, or hemophilia, an inherited bleeding disorder.

Recombinant DNA technology has been used to elucidate the mechanisms by which immunoglobulin (or antibody) genes function to generate a dramatically diverse variety of antibodies. For example, humans can generate a million different antibodies. Cloning and sequencing of antibody genes has shown that antibody genes are generated by DNA recombination between two or three different types of antibody genes and that there are a variety of combinations possible to generate the diversity that is required.

Once a gene has been isolated, it can be altered in the laboratory using several of the techniques used in cloning DNA. This can be done with the use of restriction enzymes, endonucleases, or ligases. As an example, the technology can be used to probe the structural basis for function in enzymes. Suppose the proposed mechanism for the activity of an enzyme invokes a crucial role for a particular amino acid, for example, serine; it is possible to change the portion of the gene coding for serine to one coding for any other amino acid in order to produce a mutant enzyme, a process known as site-directed mutagenesis.

One of the major medical applications of gene cloning is in the diagnosis of genetic diseases. Gene cloning has the potential to diagnose mutations in gene structure directly. The knowledge gained from applying this technology to understanding normal gene structure enables the detection of mutations that result in disease. The inherited blood disorders sickle-cell anemia and thalassemia are both serious and potentially life-threatening disorders involving the beta globin gene. They result in defective beta globin protein, an important component of the oxygen-carrying, life-sustaining hemoglobin molecule in human blood. These diseases have been most extensively studied at the molecular level. This technology also has direct application in the prenatal diagnosis of these disorders, and fetal DNA samples obtained in early pregnancy can be analyzed for gene mutations using restriction endonucleases that cut regions of the normal beta globin gene, for example, at precise sites. In sickle-cell disease, restriction endonucleases will generate globin gene fragments of abnormal size because of the mutation in the globin gene, and this phenomenon can be easily detected.

This technology has been used to identify the precise location of genes on the chromosomes. Genetic analysis has indicated that several cancers, such as leukemia (cancer of the blood cells), have specific chromosomal abnormalities. Cloning techniques have revealed genes that appear to regulate orderly cell division that, when altered, is associated with the development of cancer. These genes are called oncogenes. Knowledge gained from the application of this technology will have a direct impact on the possibility of curing genetic disease by gene transfer or gene therapy.

Cloning to produce recombinant DNA and to make possible the ability to manipulate, change, and transfer genes has been harnessed for commercial ends. By using this technology, existing products (primarily protein products) can be made more efficiently, more cheaply, and more safely. One example is the manufacture of the hormone insulin. Insulin regulates blood sugar levels in humans; lack of this hormone results in the disease diabetes mellitus. Patients with this disease require exogenous insulin in the form of injections. Using recombinant DNA technology, the insulin gene was cloned and has been expressed in a vector such that the insulin made by this system is absolutely identical to human insulin made in the body normally. Other products, such as the antiviral agent interferon, an enzyme called plasminogen activator that destroys blood clots, and the blood-clotting factor called factor VIII, which patients with the bleeding disorder hemophilia lack, have also been produced in commercial amounts using gene cloning and recombinant DNA.

Outside the pharmaceutical industry, this technology has been used to alter bacteria and other microbes genetically to carry out processes of importance to the chemical, petroleum, and mining industries. Gene cloning technology also has direct applications in plant breeding and agriculture.

Context

Prior to the gene cloning and recombinant DNA era, the work of assembling nucleotides was slow and tedious. Only very indirect analysis of DNA, an enormous molecule, was possible. With current knowledge of gene cloning, DNA can be analyzed directly, can be manipulated, and can be obtained in virtually unlimited quantities. The sequence of the nucleotides can be determined at a rate of several hundred nucleotides a day. Molecular cloning requires only minute quantities (micrograms) of DNA, and once a desired clone is obtained, a continuous supply of the DNA fragment is ensured.

One of the major medical applications of cloning to produce recombinant DNA is in the diagnosis of genetic diseases in fetuses, so that abortion can be offered to prevent the birth of incurably sick children. Knowledge gained about normal gene structure by cloning has immensely added to understanding of genetic mutations that cause genetic diseases. Sickle-cell disease, muscular dystrophy, and cystic fibrosis are three examples of several hundreds of known genetic diseases that result from mutations in single genes. Typically, they afflict babies and young children, causing physically and mentally crippling symptoms that are often lethal, often killing their victims before they reach puberty. Although most genetic diseases are rare, together they represent an enormous public health burden, especially in economically underdeveloped areas of the world. More than half a million children are afflicted by such diseases each year. The impact of recombinant DNA technology on the diagnosis and treatment of these disorders is enormous. While gene therapy for genetic disorders may, in reality, be a remote prospect, much of the knowledge that exists regarding the feasibility of transferring genes has been gained through gene cloning and recombinant DNA.

For both the diagnosis and the treatment of genetic diseases, knowledge of the exact position of the gene on the chromosome is highly desirable. Cloning technology has provided high-resolution genetic maps of each chromosome. Using this technology, hundreds of genes have been accurately mapped to human chromosomes.

Knowledge obtained by cloning techniques regarding the molecular nature of cancer-related genes, or oncogenes, has dramatically improved understanding regarding the biology of cancer. This technology has also identified pieces of DNA normally present in human cells that appear to suppress the disorderly growth of cells. These pieces of DNA, called anti-oncogenes, have been known to be missing in cancers of the eye called retinoblastoma. Laboratory studies using recombinant DNA technology have reinserted the anti-oncogene, resulting in suppression of cancer growth. Thus, the potential for such technology in cancer therapy is great.

Commercial applications of this technology have resulted in many different proteins being produced on a scale and to a purity not before possible. Therefore, large quantities of these proteins can be made more cheaply and, because of their purity, without the side effects of similar proteins derived from animal sources. Cloning to produce recombinant DNA molecules has been characterized by an unprecedented level of activity and excitement. DNA cloning has touched, or has the potential for touching, virtually every aspect of medicine and biology and has appropriately been hailed as a revolution in biology.

Bibliography

Abelson, John. "A Revolution in Biology." *Science* 209 (September 19, 1980): 1319-1321. This scholarly review highlights the applications of recombinant DNA technology, with particular reference to gene structure and industrial applications of the technology. A list of thirteen references is provided.

Alberts, Bruce, Dennis Bray, Julian Lewis, Martin Raff, Keith Roberts, and James Watson. *Molecular Biology of the Cell*. New York: Garland, 1983. Contains a chapter on recombinant DNA technology. A thorough but simple review of cloning and recombinant DNA technology that provides ten simple line diagrams illustrating the various methods involved. Four general references are given, in addition to thirty-six cited references.

Hayes, Peter, Roland Wolf, and John Hayes. "Blotting Techniques for the Study of

DNA, RNA, and Proteins." *British Medical Journal* 299 (October 14, 1989): 965-968. This superb review outlines the general principles of blotting methods that are crucial in cloning and recombinant DNA technology. Three excellent figures illustrate the text, and a glossary of terms is provided. A list of references accompanies the article.

Kingston, Helen. "Techniques of DNA Analysis." *British Medical Journal* 299 (July, 1989): 37-39. A concise review of the various techniques used in cloning and recombinant DNA, this article is supplemented by nine photographs that illustrate procedures and equipment used in this technology. Three simple figures illustrate the restriction enzymes and their use.

Miles, John, and Roland Wolf. "Principles of DNA Cloning." *British Medical Journal* 299 (October 21, 1989): 1019-1922. An excellent review of the subject of DNA cloning. The authors review state-of-the-art knowledge, with four figures to illustrate the text and a list of fourteen pertinent references.

Watson, James, John Tooze, and David Kurtz. *Recombinant DNA: A Short Course*. New York: Scientific American Books, 1983. This 260-page paperback is rich in described information on every aspect of gene cloning and recombinant DNA. This book carries with it Watson's style of simplifying complex aspects of molecular biology. Generously illustrated, with an extensive index and a pictorial narrative of the history of recombinant DNA.

Anand Karnad
Sergio Salazar
Nikhil Patel

Cross-References

COEVOLUTION

Type of life science: Evolutionary biology
Other field of study: Ecology

Numerous stable and surprisingly complex relationships between various apparently unrelated organisms, such as plants and animals, have evolved over long periods of time. All these relationships, whether beneficial or harmful to one or more of the participants, represent adaptive interactions that can be used to understand ecological patterns and processes.

Principal terms

ANTAGONISM: any type of interactive, interdependent relationship between two or more organisms that is destructive to one of the participants

COEVOLUTION: the interactive evolution of two or more species that results in a mutualistic or antagonistic relationship

COMMENSALISM: a type of coevolved relationship between different species that live intimately with one another without injury to any participant

PARASITISM: a type of coevolved relationship between different species in which one species exploits the other to its physical detriment

PHYTOPHAGOUS: animals, also referred to as herbivorous, that feed on plants

RECIPROCAL RELATIONSHIP: any type of coevolved, highly interdependent relationship between two or more species

SELECTIVE PRESSURE: evolutionary factors that favor or disfavor the genetic inheritance of various characteristics of a species

SYMBIOSIS: a type of coevolved relationship between two species in which both participants benefit; a type of mutualism

Summary of the Phenomenon

Coevolution is an extremely important and widespread phenomenon in the world of living things; it is a biological factor that is global in influence. When two or more different species experience a relationship in which any of the participating species' evolution directly affects the evolution of the other members, coevolution is taking place. This interactive type of evolution is characterized by the fact that the participant life-forms are acting as a strong selective pressure upon one another over a period of time.

The assumption of the interdependence of all organisms is today such a commonplace and fundamental concept that it is surprising that the phenomenon of coevolution has not always enjoyed a more prominent position in evolutionary thinking. Many scientists seem to have considered sets of coevolved organisms as relatively unimportant phenomena, almost on the level of biological "curiosities." The consensus appears to have been that while numerous examples of coevolution existed in both plant and animal kingdoms, on the whole it was of relatively minor importance in comparison with other evolutionary phenomena, such as competition. This opinion has begun to change as researchers increasingly recognize the intrinsic and ubiquitous role that coevolution has played, and continues to play, in the evolution of life at all levels throughout earth history.

Organisms do not evolve in a biological vacuum. All organisms exist in, and have evolved within, the framework of one of a great number of delicately balanced and self-tuning biological systems or living communities termed ecosystems. Indeed, the entire planet can be regarded as one huge, incredibly complex ecosystem in which all the lesser ecosystems fit together and work together harmoniously. This planetary ecosystem has been called "Gaia" by some biologists, in reference to the ancient Greek earth goddess. In some respects, Gaia can be conceived of as actually one giant, worldwide organism. All the living communities in this huge ecosystem are products of coevolution. This phenomenon has been in effect over the vast expanses of geologic time and continues today. The only period in history when coevolution was probably not operating was at the dawn of life, billions of years ago, when the very first species of organisms appeared and had not yet established interactive communities. The importance of coevolution as a factor affecting life cannot be overstated.

Some biologists use the term coevolution in a more restricted sense to describe coevolved relationships that have developed between plants and animals, particularly between plants and animals that are herbivores or pollinators. The coevolution between plants and animals is one of the aspects of the field that has traditionally received the most attention, so this aspect of coevolution provides a useful departure point in describing the phenomenon.

The coevolution of plants and animals, whether animals are considered strictly in their plant-eating role or also as pollinators, is abundantly represented in every terrestrial ecosystem throughout the world where flora has established itself. Moreover, the overall history of some of the multitude of present and past plant and animal relationships is displayed (although fragmentally) in the fossil record found in the earth's crust. The most elemental relationship between plants and animals is that of plants as food source. This relationship has an extremely long history, beginning with the evolution of microscopic, unicellular plants that were the earth's first autotrophs (organisms that can produce their own food from basic ingredients derived from the environment). In conjunction with the appearance of autotrophs, microscopic, unicellular heterotrophs (organisms such as animals, which must derive food from organic sources such as autotrophs) evolved to exploit the simple plants. This ancient and basic relationship has resulted in uncounted numbers of plant and animal species evolving and coevolving over billions of years of earth history.

As both plants and animals became multicellular and more complex, more elaborate defense mechanisms evolved among plants, as did more elaborate feeding apparatuses and behavior among animals. This biological "arms race" grew ever more intense as groups of plants and animals eventually adapted to the more rigorous demands of a terrestrial existence, leaving the marine environment behind. New ecosystems developed that culminated in the world's first swamps, jungles, and forests. The plant-animal arms race engendered increasingly more sophisticated strategies of botanical defense and animal offense, and this coevolved interrelationship has continued unabated. This coevolutionary "warfare" between plants and animals has expressed itself partly through the evolution of botanical structures and chemicals that attempt either to discourage or to prevent the attentions of plant eaters. These include the development of spines, barbs, thorns, bristles, and hooks on plant leaf, stem, and trunk surfaces. Cacti, holly, and rose bushes illustrate this form of plant strategy.

Another type of deterrence evolved in the form of chemical compounds that can cause a wide spectrum of negative animal response. These compounds range in effect from producing a sensation of mild distaste, such as bitterness, to more extreme effects, such as actual poisoning of herbivore metabolisms. Plants that contain organic compounds such as tannin are examples of the chemical defensive strategy. Tannins produce several negative results in animals, including partially inactivating digestive juices and creating cumulative toxic effects that have been correlated with cancer. Plants containing tannin include trees, such as members of the oak group, and shrubs, such as those that produce the teas used as human beverages. Other plants have developed more lethal poisons that act more rapidly. Plants have also developed other strategies, such as possession of a high silica content (as found in grasses), that act to wear down the teeth of plant eaters. Animals have counteradapted to these plant defensive innovations by evolving a higher degree of resistance to plant toxins or by developing more efficient and tougher teeth with features such as harder enamel surfaces, or the capacity of grinding with batteries of teeth.

Not all coevolution is characterized by having an adversarial nature; mutually beneficial relationships are also very common. Sometime during the latter part of the Mesozoic era, angiosperms, the flowering plants, evolved and replaced most of the previously dominant land plants, such as the gymnosperms and the ferns. New species of herbivores evolved to exploit these new food sources. At some point, probably during the Cretaceous period of the late Mesozoic, animals became unintentional aids in the angiosperm pollination process. As this coevolution proceeded, the first animal pollinators became more and more indispensable as partners to the plants. Eventually, highly coevolved plants and animals developed relationships of extreme interdependence exemplified by the honeybees and their coevolved flowers. This angiosperm-insect relationship is thought to have arisen in the Mesozoic era by way of beetle predation, possibly on early, magnolialike angiosperms. The fossil record gives some support to this theory. Whatever the exact route along which plant-animal pollination partnerships coevolved, the end result was a number of plant and animal species that gained mutual benefit from the new type of relationship. Such relationships are in general termed mutualisms.

Eventually some of these plant-animal mutualisms became so intertwined that one or both participants reached a point at which they could not exist without the aid of the other. These obligatory mutualisms ultimately involved other types of animal partners besides insects. Vertebrate partners such as birds, reptiles, and mammals also became involved in mutualisms with plants. Contemporary ecosystems, such as the United States' southwestern desert, include mutualisms between aerial mammals, such as bats, and plants, such as the agave and the saguaro cactus. The bats involved are nectar drinkers and pollen eaters. They have evolved specialized feeding structures such as erectile tongues similar to those found among moths and other insects with similar life-styles. In turn, the plants involved with the pollinating bats have involved either reciprocal morphologies or behavior patterns to accommodate their warm-blooded visitors. For example, angiosperms coevolutionarily involved with bats have developed such specializations as bat-attractive scents, flower structures that minimize the chance of injury to bats, and petal openings timed to the nocturnal activity of bats.

Coevolved relationships are not restricted to beneficial or nonbeneficial relationships between plants and animals. They also include an immense number of relationships between animals and other animals, and even between plants and other plants. Among these various types of coevolved situations can be found subcategories, such as symbioses, commensalisms, and parasitisms. The first two involve relationships beneficial to varying degrees that feature interactions of increasing physical intimacy between or among two or more species. Parasitism involves an intimate relationship produced through coevolution in which one participant, the host, experiences serious harm or even death through exploitation by the parasite. Predation is probably the most obvious form of coevolution among higher animals such as vertebrates. Modern carnivores such as the canines and felines and their prey are a dramatic example of coevolution at work. Animal hunters over time responded to the improved defenses of their prey by evolving better senses, such as stereoscopic, three-dimensional vision, hearing with expanded range of frequency response, and more effective body structures, such as multifunctional teeth. Such teeth are termed heterodont and represent a great improvement over the simple dental array of the more primitive vertebrates, such as fish and amphibians.

Beginning with the more advanced reptiles appearing in the late stages of the Paleozoic era, teeth began to differentiate into specialized components—incisors, canines, premolars, and molars—that enhanced food acquisition and improved mastication. This, in turn, improved digestion and allowed quicker energy acquisition from food. This evolutionary advantage has reached a zenith of adaptive success among the mammals. Mammalian predators evolved fangs and efficient claws, sometimes retractible, to minimize injury and wear. Along with improved hunting senses and better dentition came increased speed from the evolution of improvements in pelvic and limb arrangements. In response to this process, vertebrate herbivores also became generally swifter or better defended, more alert, attained higher metabolic rates, and were thus better able to elude or defend against predation. Advanced predators placed an intense selective pressure on their prey herbivores, spurring ever more efficient and acutely tuned responses among the herbivore populations. Herbivores evolved either as swift forms, such as deer, or became efficiently defended, walking fortresses, such as porcupines or armadillos. Because of the pervasive effect of coevolution, the overall relationship between predator and prey has been a reciprocal one in which all participants affect one another in an interactive manner.

Methods of Study

Field research and laboratory research are pursued concurrently in the effort to unravel the intricacies of the subject of coevolution. Field research involves actual observation in nature of animals and plants, their behavior, and, especially, their interaction with other species. Special attention is given to useful clues that can be employed to establish evolutionary relationships, either presently existing or previously in effect. For example, cooperative behavior between or among several different species of animal or plant is often indicative of an established, coevolutionary relationship. If this behavior is consistent over time and can also be traced or inferred through the agency of the fossil record, more useful data are acquired concerning a possible, evolved, reciprocal relationship. Of particular importance is the confirmation of specialized physical structures that are unique to the members of the observed relationship. Examples are the specialized feeding apparatuses of pollinating animals and the specialized, accommodating flower structures of their angiosperm partners. Such physical structures are strong evidence for the handiwork of the coevolutionary process. Direct human observation is preferable in ascertaining coevolutionary behavior; however, this is not always possible because of the rapidity of the animals involved, their habitat, their extremely small size, their preference for nocturnal activity, or their determined avoidance of humans. Consequently, electronic and mechanical aids are sometimes indispensable. These include remote-controlled still and video cameras, microscopic or telephoto lenses, infrared or ultraviolet lighting units, sonar or radar sensors, trip wires and other mechanical triggering devices, and sound recording equipment with high-gain or long-range microphones.

Laboratory research in the field of coevolution involves investigations heavily reliant on modern, sophisticated laboratory equipment and techniques. High-powered conventional, optical microscopes are employed to determine tissue and cellular structures. Scanning electron microscopes (SEMs) are employed for study of extremely small unicellular animals or plants such as planktonic organisms or extremely small organic structures. In addition to these tools of laboratory specimen observation, there are the analytical equipment and techniques used to determine the genetic codes and blood protein complexes of animals and plants to establish the degree of relatedness or divergence between various species.

Context

Coevolutionary studies are increasingly important in the biological sciences. One of the aims is to determine the degree of interdependence between various species, whether the relationship is between animals and plants, animals and other animals, or plants and other plants. A key factor to be determined in all these coevolved relationships is that of the nature and degee of balance attained. Although most of the biological world is forever in a state of flux, some categorical, coevolved relationships have been of long duration and can be reasonably assessed as having been in existence for tens of millions of years, such as that of flowering plants and vertebrate and invertebrate pollinators, or even hundreds of millions of years, such as the oceanic, planktonic food chain.

The degree to which these large-scale, coevolved relationships, involving entire planetary ecologies, continue to enjoy their former degree of health and well-being is of the utmost importance to human society. The present depth of understanding of the biological sciences clearly indicates the interrelatedness of all nature. Many angles of study agree that the global life system is experiencing great stress from human intervention: industrialization, urbanization, and overpopulation. It becomes increasingly urgent to know with the utmost precision all facets of the way the global life system operates, and has operated with general stability, over geological expanses of time. Every detail that contributes to this knowledge—every coevolved relationship, no matter how seemingly insignificant—adds to the total effect. This information can be used as an important resource to help maintain the stability of the entire system for ourselves and future generations.

Bibliography

Bakker, Robert T. *The Dinosaur Heresies*. New York: William Morrow, 1986. An interesting book by one of the most fascinating and controversial writers on the subject of evolution. Although the emphasis of the book is on dinosaur evolution, the author's specialty, a number of good discussions of the coevolved interrelationships between predators and their prey make the book worthwhile to students of coevolution. The subtopic of animal-to-animal coevolved relationships and the concomitant evolutionary adaptations they engender is covered in chapter 11, "Mesozoic Arms Race," and chapter 12, "Defense Without Armor." Chapter 9, "When Dinosaurs Invented Flowers," discusses coevolved morphologies and strategies among angiosperm plants and extinct reptiles. A wonderful thought-provoking book for all reading audiences. Numerous detailed and beautiful line drawings.

Callahan, Philip S. *The Evoluton of Insects*. New York: Holiday House, 1972. A good, basic, introductory book on the subject of the evolutionary history of insects through geologic time. Discussed are the most common types of insect fossils and how they illustrate evolutionary concepts in general. The development of evolutionary theory in Western thought is also discussed, beginning with little-known writers of the Middle Ages and continuing to the twentieth century.

Chapter 11—"Why Study Evolution?"—is of particular interest. Suitable for all general readers.

Chaloner, William G., Peter R. Crane, and Else Marie Friis, eds. *The Origins of Angiosperms and Their Biological Consequences*. New York: Cambridge University Press, 1987. Chapter 7, "The Evolution of Insect Pollinators in Angiosperms," and chapter 8, "Interactions of Angiosperms and Herbivorous Tetrapods Through Time," will be of most interest to readers interested in coevolution. The book is a series of essays by professional researchers on the subject of flowering plant evolution with an emphasis on the deduced history of the angiosperms and their coevolved animal partners as recorded in the geologic record. Suitable for the college level.

Gilbert, Lawrence E., and Peter H. Raven, eds. *Coevolution of Animals and Plants*. Austin: University of Texas Press, 1975. A collection of scientific papers on the subject of evolved plant and animal relationships. The majority of the papers involve either analyses of plant and animal biochemical relationships and mechanisms or ecological processes and patterns. Although written by, and intended for, professional workers within the field, the papers are worthwhile reading for students of botany, entomology, zoology, ecology, and evolution at the advanced high school or college level.

Gottlieb, Joan Eiger. *Plants: Adaptation Through Evolution*. New York: Reinhold, 1968. A short but information-packed book on the evolution of plants in general, beginning with the simplest forms and proceeding to the higher flowering plants. Chapters on many subtopics of botany, such as plant tissues and morphology, lead the reader logically through the complicated subject of plant science. Sections useful to students of coevolution appear later on in the book in the form of discussions on angiosperm evolution and diversity and the role of animal pollinators. Intended as a short, introductory botany text.

Gould, Stephen Jay. *The Panda's Thumb*. New York: W. W. Norton, 1980. Each chapter of this book is a brilliant reflection on diverse aspects of organic evolution in essay form; the book is suitable for anyone interested in evolution. Chapter 27, "Nature's Odd Couples," focuses on a conspicuous example of a possible coevolution—an inferred mutualistic relationship between the extinct dodo bird and a large tree (*Calvaria major*) that is found on the island of Mauritius. Gould presents the evidence objectively, both for and against the dodo's possible role in facilitating the tree's germination. The chapter is a good example of the kind of investigations and speculations in which evolutionary biologists engage.

Grant, Susan. *Beauty and the Beast: The Coevolution of Plants and Animals*. New York: Charles Scribner's Sons, 1984. This is one of the best books devoted solely to the subject of coevolution written for a general audience. The book is easy and fun to read, and full of information that rests solidly on the most recent scientific research and thinking. Each of the ten chapters is devoted to a major subtopic within the phenomenon of coevolution, such as specific animal and plant symbioses or antagonisms. It is written in a lively style full of infectious enthusiasm.

Hughes, Norman F. *Paleobiology of Angiosperm Origins*. New York: Cambridge University Press, 1976. Readers interested in the subject of coevolution will find chapter 6, "Cretaceous Land Fauna," most germane to the topic. This chapter sketches out much of what is known about the earliest coevolved relationships between animals and the flowering plants (angiosperms) during the late Mesozoic period. The rest of the book is devoted to an exposition of various evidence supporting differing lines of thinking about the evolution of flowering plants from gymnosperms. A very detailed and rather scholarly work appropriate for readers who have some familiarity with botany, entomology, and evolutionary theory.

Lawton, J. H., Richard Southwood, and D. R. Strong. *Insects on Plants*. Cambridge, Mass.: Harvard University Press, 1984. Chapter 7, "Coevolution," is worthwhile reading for students of the subject. It gives detailed examples from the scientific literature of coevolved relationships between various insects and plants. An authoritative and dependable source of hard scientific information on the topic, the book tends to the abstract side of theorizing and biological modeling. Readers with a solid foundation in biology or scientific analysis will find this book of greatest use.

Powell, Jerry A. *Biological Interrelationships of Moths and Yucca Schottii*. Berkeley: University of California Press, 1984. This short book is one of the most detailed sources available explaining the pollination relationship between two species of desert moth and their coevolved partner, a particular genus of the yucca plant of the southwestern United States. Extremely detailed scientific documentation is used to describe the known aspects of the interrelationship between the moths and the plant. Appropriate for serious botany, entomology, and evolutionary biology students at the advanced high school or college level or as a general reference.

Frederick M. Surowiec

Cross-References

Adaptations and Their Mechanisms, 22; The Biosphere, Biomes, and Habitats, 210; Competition, 541; Ecological Interactions Between Plants and Animals, 722; Ecological Niches, 729; Ecological Principles, 736; Evolution: A Historical Perspective, 903; Convergent and Divergent Evolution, 910; Natural Selection, 1870; Predation, 2178; Speciation and the Species Concept, 2521; Symbiosis, Commensalism, and Parasitism, 2572.

COMMISSURES AND SPLIT-BRAIN PATIENTS

Type of life science: Neurobiology
Other fields of study: Animal anatomy, animal physiology, histology, and zoology

The two halves of the human brain are connected by a huge band of nerve fibers known as the "great cerebral commissure." When it is severed surgically, interesting facts about the different functions of the right and left cerebral hemispheres are revealed.

Principal terms

APHASIA: the loss of one or more modes of language; the loss of the ability to speak, read, write, or understand spoken words, resulting from brain damage

CEREBRUM: the largest structure of the human brain, consisting of a highly convoluted cortex divided into five lobes; it covers and surrounds most of the rest of the brain

CORPUS CALLOSUM: the huge band of nerve fibers connecting the right and left halves of the cerebrum; it is also known as the great cerebral commissure

EPILEPSY: a disorder of the brain in which an uncontrolled spread of activity passes through large areas of the cortex, usually resulting in convulsions and loss of consciousness

NEURON: a brain cell, consisting of a cell body and one or more long extensions (nerve fibers) that carry nerve impulses; the functional unit of mental activity

Summary of the Phenomenon

The human brain, like many organs in a bilaterally symmetrical animal, consists of two mirror-image halves. Superficially, these resemble each other as much as the two kidneys do. Unlike the kidneys, however, which function independently of each other, the two halves of the brain are very closely integrated—bound together functionally and anatomically by large bands of fibers crossing from left to right. One such bundle of fibers is the optic chiasma, which consists of half of the fibers of each optic nerve crossing over to the opposite side of the brain. Another is the pons—a bridge of nerve fibers encircling the upper end of the spinal cord that connects the right and left halves of the cerebellum. A third (and, by far, the largest of these structures) is the corpus callosum, consisting of some 200 million fibers connecting the two halves of the cerebrum.

The human cerebrum is responsible for most of the higher functions of the brain, including memory, language, consciousness, voluntary movement, and awareness of sensory stimuli. The right cerebral hemisphere controls the movements of the left side of the body and receives sensory messages from the left side. The left hemisphere communicates with the right side of the body. The other functions of the brain, which do not require bilateral representation, tend to be localized in one or the other of the two halves of the cerebrum. Language is thus controlled by an area about the size of a silver dollar located between the ear and the temple and typically on the left side of the brain. When injury from a stroke or a penetrating wound destroys nerve cells in this region, the patient usually suffers from "aphasia"—an inability to speak or to understand words. Aphasias are often quite specific, depending on the exact area of the brain that is destroyed. There can be a loss of speech with no impairment of writing ability, or a loss of grammatical structure without any obvious difficulty with vocabulary.

Because the majority of people are right-handed, and since language is so important, the half of the brain that controls both language and the right hand is often called the "dominant" hemisphere. This is, perhaps, a misnomer. The right hemisphere does control many important functions, and it is indeed "dominant" with respect to such abilities as the recognition of faces, musical appreciation, artistic creativity, and other traits.

Normally, the two halves of the cerebrum are in instantaneous communication with each other, and it is very difficult to discern any localization of function to one side of the brain or the other. Although some information as to the specific brain regions involved in a specialized activity can be gained by measuring the electrical brain waves or by more sophisticated techniques for detecting subtle differences in brain metabolism, most of our knowledge comes from clinical studies of brain-damaged patients. Accidental injuries, strokes, and brain tumors have provided an opportunity to observe the neurological or mental handicap resulting from damage to each area of the brain. It has been known for more than a hundred years that many intellectual functions were served by only one side of the cerebrum. In recent years, a new kind of evidence has become available. A group of patients has been treated for epilepsy by the cutting of the great cerebral commissure, separating the right and left halves of the cerebrum by the splitting of the corpus callosum. This operation has shown that many mental abilities are localized to one side of the brain or the other.

The most obvious unilateral specialization is that of language. Speaking requires synchronized control of both sides of the vocal apparatus, so it is not surprising that one brain region controls the muscles of both sides. Writing, on the other hand, can be performed by either hand, though it is usually done much better by the "dominant" one. In split-brain patients, the left hand can communicate what the "silent" right hemisphere is thinking, even when the right hand is simultaneously writing something else. Many left-handed people who normally write with their left hands nevertheless have their language center in the usual place in the left half of their brain. In these individuals, the right hemisphere is dominant for writing, and the left is dominant for speaking.

The control of certain kinds of mathematical and logical reasoning also appears to be located predominantly in the left hemisphere, while geometrical ability and pattern perception appear to be more developed on the right side. Pattern recognition and the ability to create mental images are functions of the right hemisphere, although mental imagery is a complex phenomenon involving several different strategies requiring both hemispheres.

The cerebral commissure is composed entirely of nerve fibers. There are no synapses, and hence no actual information processing in this structure. The fibers are more like telephone wires than switchboards. The effect of severing the fibers is a lack of communication between the two sides of the brain rather than a direct loss of information processing. In one series of patients, only the frontal two-thirds of the corpus callosum was severed. In some of these cases, epileptic seizures were controlled by this operation, and many of the undesirable symptoms of disconnection were avoided. Much right-left coordination, language accessibility (by the right hemisphere), and integrity of the visual field remained. A small portion of fibers can probably maintain a major part of the communication between right and left sides of the brain. Once the gap between right and left is bridged, the information may be shared with all parts of the respective half brain. The functions of both the forward area (where the corpus was severed) and the hind area (where the cross fibers were left intact) seemed to be accessible to both sides. It may be significant that women have many more fibers in the posterior region of the corpus callosum than men do.

The degree of specialization of various regions of the cerebrum on the left and right sides should not be overemphasized. Brain neurons retain an enormous amount of flexibility: All neurons share basic properties that enable them to serve many different functions. Although individual neurons never regenerate if they are injured, other neurons show an amazing capacity to take over the functions of an injured region. Recovery from neurological lesions is thus the rule rather than the exception. Split-brain patients typically show a gradual improvement in the language abilities in the nonlanguage hemisphere, and people who suffer aphasia following an injury to the brain often show complete recovery, which may be the result of the development of language capability in the brain regions on the uninjured side. A normal brain is not divided into two personalities or two sets of skills. The rapid and complete communication between the two sides through an unsevered corpus callosum results in a completely integrated mental function. The personality and the mental abilities of a normal person are the sum of the functions of both hemispheres.

Methods of Study

Patients with severe epilepsy that resists drug treatment can be saved by surgically severing the entire band of fibers connecting the right and left cerebral hemispheres—the corpus callosum. When they recover from the operation, they seem surprisingly normal unless the damage to the brain responsible for the epilepsy, or damage caused by the epileptic seizures, has been severe. One could talk to a patient who has had this operation and never suspect that there was anything wrong. Extensive testing reveals that the language-dominant hemisphere no longer "knows" what the other hemisphere is experiencing. When visual stimuli are presented so that each hemisphere receives a different image—a key to the left side and a pencil to the right, for example—the patient will say that he sees a key only, since that is what the language-dominant hemisphere sees: The hemisphere that controls language is the only one "talking." If the patient points to what he sees with the left hand (which is controlled by the right hemisphere), he will point to a pencil. The other hemisphere may express surprise or embarrassment at this and try to explain the "mistake." Each hemisphere is now independent. Although communication is more difficult with the nonlanguage hemisphere, each seems to possess normal intelligence and the capacity for similar functions. There are, however, important differences, and the study of these patients has provided one of the best sources of information about the special qualities of the right and left brains.

In normal humans, there is no such separation of right and left functions. Each half is in complete and instantaneous communication with the other—one personality with all the abilities of both hemispheres combined, in a single, integrated, self. Only in the split-brain patients can a separate personality be said to exist for the right brain and the left; each may have a different set of talents and skills. The left side is better at mathematics, language, logic, and reasoning. The right side is better at music, art, geometry, design, and "holistic thinking"—intuition. Each side has some of the skills of the other, but neither side is exclusively specialized. Several years after the operation, the right side of some patients begins to show considerable development of language skills. Patients can write words with either hand and can read with either hemisphere. Only the vocal apparatus remains completely controlled by the left hemisphere.

As of the late 1980's, only a few dozen patients had been studied, but there was much more information about the specialized functions of the right and left hemispheres. Since the greatest specialization occurs for the "highest" (and most human) functions, animal experiments, even with apes, do not reveal much. The accidental opportunity to experiment with the victims of severe epilepsy provides valuable insights into the normal brain functions that would most likely be unavailable by any other means.

Context

The study of human brain functions has been hampered by the impossibility of doing laboratory experiments on humans. Knowledge of what parts of the brain control the various functions has come largely from clinical observations of accident victims and others who have suffered specific brain injuries. Split-brain patients have provided a rich source of information about how the right and left cerebral hemispheres differ. Both halves are intact, and the patients are often able to cooperate fully with the investigators. The results of such studies have been coordinated with anatomical studies, nuclear magnetic resonance scans, electroencephalography, and other techniques to reveal many details about the specific functions of particular parts of the brain that were previously unknown.

Such studies are important for a variety of reasons. In medicine, the knowledge of where a particular function is localized in the body is of obvious help in both the diagnosis and the treatment of pathologies. Neurologists need to know what symptoms to look for in cases of suspected brain tumors or other brain injuries. Neurosurgeons can find where they have to operate by knowledge of the area of the brain responsible for a particular disorder. Psychologists can be helped in counseling and re-teaching brain-damaged patients if the precise functions of the injured area are understood.

Beyond the practical value of the knowledge gained by study of split-brain patients, enhancement of our theoretical understanding of the different functions of the right and left halves of the brain promises great future benefits. For example, the better understanding and localization of specific brain regions has already provided new insights into the perennial question about the biological basis of mental differences between men and women. Different rates of brain development in male and female embryos result in small, but apparently significant, differences in certain areas of the cerebrum. Males apparently have a slightly greater degree of specialization in the left hemisphere, possibly resulting in marginally better mathematical skills. Females retain a greater number of nerve fibers in the corpus callosum, resulting in somewhat better interplay between right and left brain areas. This has been proposed as a possible basis for the apparent advantage women have over men for "seeing the whole," and certain other types of intuitive judgments. The long, sad history of "scientific" theories proposed to justify the social and economic domination of women by men has generated a wariness and distrust of any claims for a biological basis of intellectual and behavioral differences between the sexes. If such differences do exist (and recent studies provide strong evidence that they do), the social and educational policies needed to nurture the good qualities in people and to fight unfair and unequal treatment can eventually be overcome by attaining a better understanding of the nature and extent of the physiological differences in men's and women's brains.

Bibliography

Eccles, John C. *The Understanding of the Brain*. New York: McGraw-Hill, 1977. Chapter 6, "Brain, Speech, and Consciousness," provides a good description of cerebral functions and describes early work on split-brain patients. Although much has been done since this book was written, Eccles remains one of the clearest and most creative writers about brain functions.

Gazzaniga, M. S. "Right Hemisphere Language Following Brain Bisection: A Twenty-Year Perspective." *American Psychologist* 38 (1983): 525-537. Although technical, this is a readable article, written by a fine researcher who explores language ability in the "nonlanguage" (right) hemisphere. This book is about the extent to which language ability is learned upon separation of the two hemispheres.

Geschwind, Norman, and Albert M. Galaburda. *Cerebral Lateralization*. Cambridge, Mass.: MIT Press, 1987. Although technical, this is the best available review of the subject. Geschwind discusses extensively his theories about the intricate relationships among brain laterality, learning disorders, hormones, and the immune system.

Sperry, R. W., F. O. Schmitt, and F. G. Worden. "Lateral Specialization in the Surgically Separated Membranes." In *The Neurosciences: Third Study Program*, edited by Francis O. Schmitt and Frederic G. Worden. Cambridge, Mass.: MIT Press, 1974. This is a good article about the early work in the field of microsurgery. The tone and style are intended for the general reader. Perhaps it is a special bonus to find that such a good physician can write well. The article contains a good bibliography about works produced before 1974.

Springer, Sally P., and Georg Deutsch. *Left Brain, Right Brain*. New York: W. H. Freeman, 1989. This book presents most of what is known about the difference in left and right cerebral functions. It contains many illustrations and an excellent bibliography.

Curtis Smith

Cross-References

Electrical Activity of the Brain, 292; Central and Peripheral Nervous System Functions, 404; Emotions, 765; The Forebrain, 1032; The Hindbrain and Midbrain, 1291; Memory, 1683.

COMMUNICATION

Type of life science: Ethology
Other fields of study: Evolutionary biology, invertebrate biology, systematics (taxonomy), and zoology

In animal communication, information is exchanged through signals. Such signals are vital for survival, finding mates, and rearing young.

Principal terms

DISCRETE SIGNALS: signals that are always given in the same way and indicate only the presence or absence of a particular condition or state

DISPLAY: a term used to indicate social signals, particularly visual signals

PHEROMONE: a chemical substance used in communication within a species

PRIMER PHEROMONE: a chemical substance that affects behavior by altering physiology and is therefore not rapid in its effects

RELEASER: a standard signal that elicits a standard response

TROPHALLAXIS: food exchange between organisms, particularly in social insects

Summary of the Phenomenon

A simple definition of animal communication is the transmission of information between animals by means of signals. Developing a more precise definition is difficult because of the broad array of behaviors that are considered messages or signals and the variety of contexts in which these behaviors may occur. Animal signals can be chemical, visual, auditory, tactile, or electrical. The primary means of communication used within a species will depend upon its sensory capacities and its ecology.

Of the modes of communication available, chemical signals, or pheromones, are assumed to have been the earliest signals used by animals. Transmission of chemical signals is not affected by darkness or by obstacles. One special advantage is that the sender of a chemical message can leave the message behind when it moves. The persistence of the signal may also be a disadvantage when it interferes with transmission of newer information. Another disadvantage is that the transmission is relatively slow.

The speed at which a chemical message affects the recipient varies. Some messages have an immediate effect on the behavior of recipients. Alarm and sex-attractant pheromones of many insects, aggregation pheromones in cockroaches, or trail substances in ants are examples. Other chemical messages, primers, affect recipients more slowly, through changes in their physiology. Examples of primers include pheromones that control social structure in hive insects such as termites.

Reproductive members of the colony secrete a substance that inhibits the development of reproductive capacity in other hive members. The chemicals important for controlling the hive are spread through grooming and food sharing (trophallaxis). Chemical communication is important not only among social and semisocial insects but also among animals, both vertebrate and invertebrate. Particularly common is the use of a pheromone to indicate that an animal is sexually receptive.

Visual communication holds forth the advantage of immediate transmission. A visual signal or display is also able to encode a large amount of information, including the location of the sender. Postures and movements of parts of an animal's body are typical elements of visual communication. Color and timing are additional means of providing information. Some visual signals are discrete; that is, the signal shows no significant variation from performance to performance. Other displays are graded so that the information content of the signal can be varied. An example of a graded display is found in many of the threat or aggressive postures of birds. Threat postures of the chaffinch vary between low-intensity and high-intensity postures. The elevation of the crest varies in ways that indicate the bird's relative readiness for combat. The song spreads of red-winged blackbirds and cowbirds show variation in intensity. In red-winged blackbirds, the red epaulets, or shoulder patches, are exposed to heighten the effect of the display. Discrete and graded signals may be used together to increase the information provided by the signal. In zebras, ears back indicates a threat and ears up indicates greeting. The intensity of either message is shown by the degree to which the mouth is held open. A widely open mouth indicates a heightened greeting or threat.

Visual displays depend upon the presence of light or the production of light. The ability to produce light, bioluminescence, is found most frequently in aquatic organisms, but its use in communication is probably best documented in fireflies, beetles belonging to the family Lampyridae. Firefly males advertise their presence by producing flashes of light in a species-specific pattern. Females respond with simple flashes, precisely timed, to indicate that they belong to the appropriate species. This communication system is used to advantage by females in a few predatory species of the genus *Photuris*. After females of predatory species have mated with males of their own species, they attract males of other species by mimicking the responses of the appropriate females. The males that are tricked are promptly eaten. The luminescence of fireflies does not attract a wide variety of nocturnal predators, because their bodies contain a chemical that makes them unpalatable.

Visual displays are limited in the distance over which they can be used and are easily blocked by obstacles. Visual communication is important in primates, birds, and some insects, but can be dispensed with by many species that do not have the necessary sensory capacities.

The limitation of visual communication is frequently offset by the coupling of visual displays with other modes of communication. Visual displays can be coupled with auditory communication, for example. There are many advantages to using sound: It can be used in the dark, and it can go around obstacles and provide directional information. Because pitch, volume, and temporal patterns of sound can be varied, extremely complex messages can be communicated. The auditory communication of many bird species has been studied intensively. Bird vocalizations are usually classified into two groups, calls and songs. Calls are usually brief sounds, whereas songs are longer, more complex, and often more suited to transmission over distances.

The call repertoire of a species serves a broad array of functions. Many young birds use both a visual signal, gaping, and calling in their food begging. Individuals that call more may receive more food. Begging calls and postures may also be used by females in some species to solicit food from mates. One call type that has been intensively studied is the alarm call. Alarm calls of many species are similar, and response is frequently interspecific (that is, interpretable by more than one species). Alarm calls are likely to be difficult to locate, a definite advantage to the individual giving the call. Calls used to gather individuals for mobbing predators are also similar in different species. Unlike alarm calls, mobbing calls provide good directional information, so that recruitment to the mobbing effort can be rapid.

Call repertoires serve birds in a great variety of contexts important for survival of the individual. Song, on the other hand, most often serves a reproductive function, that of helping a male hold a territory and attract a mate. Songs are species-specific, like the distinctive markings of a species. In some cases, songs are more distinctive than physical appearance. The chiffchaff and willow warbler were not recognized as separate species until an English naturalist named Gilbert White discovered, by examining their distinctive songs, that they are separate. The North American wood and hermit thrushes can also be distinguished more readily by song than by appearance. Bird song can communicate not only the species of the individual singing but also information about motivational state. Most singing is done by males during the breeding season. In many species, only the male sings. In some species, females sing as well. Their songs may be similar to the songs of the males of their species or they may be distinctive. If the songs are similar to those of the males, the female may sing songs infrequently and with less volume. In some instances, the female song serves to notify her mate of her location. An interesting phenomenon found in some species is duetting, in which the male and female develop a duet. Mates may sing in alternate and perfectly timed phrases, as is done by the African boubou shrike, *Laniarius aethiopicus*. An individual shrike can recall its mate by singing the entire song alone.

Individuals in some bird species have a single song, and individuals of other species have repertoires of songs. Average repertoire size of the individual is characteristic of a species. Whether songs in repertoires are shared with neighbors or unique to the individual is also characteristic of a species. Sharing songs with neighbors permits song matching in countersinging. Cardinals and tufted titmice are species that frequently match songs in countersinging. Possible uses for matching are facilitating the recognition of intruders and indicating which neighbor has the attention of a singer. Some species of birds have dialects. The species-specific songs of one geographic region can be differentiated from the song of another geographic region. The development of dialects may be useful in maintaining local adaptations within a species, provided that females select mates of the same dialect as their fathers.

Although auditory signals of birds have received a disproportionate share of attention in the study of animal communication, auditory communication is used by a broad spectrum of animals. Crickets have species-specific songs to attract females and courtship songs to encourage an approaching female. The ears of most insects can hear only one pitch, so the temporal pattern of sound pulses is the feature by which a species can be identified. Vervet monkeys use three different alarm calls, depending upon the kind of threat present; they respond to the calls appropriately by looking up, looking down, or climbing a tree, depending upon the kind of call given.

Tactile communication differs significantly from other forms of communication in that it cannot occur over a distance. This form of communication is important in many insects, equipped as they are with antennae rich in receptors. Shortly after a termite molts, for example, it strokes the end of the abdomen of another individual with its antennae and mouthparts. The individual receiving this signal responds by extruding a fluid from its hindgut. Tactile signals are frequently used in eliciting trophallaxis (food sharing) in social insects. Tactile signals are also important in the copulatory activity of a number of vertebrates.

Additional channels of communication available in animals are electrical and surface vibration. Many modes of communication are used in combination with other modes. The channels used will depend in part on the sensory equipment of the species, its ecology, and the particular context. Most messages will be important either for the survival of the individual or the group or for the individual's ability to transmit its genes to the next generation.

Methods of Study

Early study in animal communication depended primarily on careful observation of animals. This technique has been supplemented by a number of tools. The motion-picture or videotape camera permits the observer to analyze visual displays more completely. The tape recorder is a particularly versatile tool; acoustical communication can be recorded and the result used in playback experiments, in which the ethologist plays the recording in the field in order to test hypotheses about communication. Playbacks have helped scientists determine that some species of birds can discriminate between songs of neighbors and songs of strangers. Taped songs have been cut and spliced in various sequences to find out which features of a song's structure are important in species recognition.

The development of song in some species has been studied by means of isolation experiments. Birds that have been hatched and reared in the laboratory have been isolated from their species-specific song to determine whether the song needs to be learned. Some isolates are exposed to tutors (either tape recordings or living birds) at various intervals to examine the possibility of critical periods for song learning.

Sound spectrographs make it possible to produce pictures of calls and songs. Spectrographs represent song frequency on one axis and time on the other. These graphs have revealed the intricate structures of many auditory communication signals.

Information about sensory reception and about neural control of signals is an important research area. Some information in this area has come from ingenious but simple experiments. Bees have been trained to respond to color clues in association with a sugar source to determine which colors they are able to discriminate. Important knowledge in sensory research comes from determining the specific stimuli that will elicit a response in specific neurons. By using microelectrodes placed in or near the neuron, scientists can detect the presence of a response. Another technique used to determine the function of a presumed sense organ is to block or removeeither the organ or the neural connections to the organ. One of the earliest experiments of this type was done in 1793 by Lazzaro Spallanzani. He found that flying bats could not avoid obstacles when their ears were tightly plugged but that the bats were able to avoid obstacles when they were blinded. In 1938, the use of an ultrasonic recorder made it possible for Donald Griffin to discover the bat's use of ultrasonic sound.

Synthetic pheromones can be produced that have the same effects on behavior as natural pheromones. Scientists can also determine at what dilution a pheromone will still evoke response. Hence, the sophisticated tools of chemistry have important applications in ethology.

Context

Animal communication provides a fascinating frontier for humans to explore. Some of the knowledge acquired has had practical applications as well. Pheromones have been used to bait traps for insect pests. In some cases, this technique is used directly as a control measure; in other instances, the traps are used to estimate population size, and other control measures are used when pest populations are high. A key advantage of pheromone use is its specificity.

Recognizing the communication signals of pets and domestic animals is often useful in their care. Knowledge of releasers, standard signals that receive standard responses from animals, is important for survival in some contexts. Knowing which signals are perceived by animals as threats allows humans to avoid triggering an attack. This knowledge also allows control of animals in less destructive ways. Recordings of alarm signals of birds are used to disperse flocks that are creating problems.

Knowledge of a species' communication repertoire is critical in the training of animals for useful work or for entertainment. Also, knowledge of their sensory capacities makes it possible for appropriate signals to be selected—particularly important as it applies to human nonverbal communication. Knowing which signals of our nonverbal communication repertoire are characteristic of the whole species is both useful and interesting.

Bibliography

De Waal, Frans. *Chimpanzee Politics: Power and Sex Among Apes*. New York: Harper & Row, 1982. This paperback is a well-illustrated account of a group of chimpanzees using their communication skills with adroitness in the politics of their social group. Enjoyable reading for high school, college, and general audiences. Bibliography and index.

Goodall, Jane. *In the Shadow of Man*. Boston: Houghton Mifflin, 1971. This work is considered a classic. It provides a well-illustrated account of the beginnings of her long-term study of chimpanzees in their natural habitat, in which Goodall relates her experiences in doing the research. Chimpanzee communication is described in the context of its use in the social group. An index assists the reader in locating discussion of specific types of communication. Both informative and enjoyable.

Gould, James L. *Ethology*. New York: W. W. Norton, 1982. A very readable textbook. Part 2 emphasizes sensory perception; part 7, the social behavior of selected species. These descriptions place animal communication in the context of the species' social behavior and ecology. Chapters end with summaries and lists of additional readings. There is no glossary, but terms are adequately defined in the text and can be traced through the index.

Grier, James W. *Biology of Animal Behavior*. St. Louis: Times Mirror/Mosby, 1984. Chapter 9, "Communication: Modes, Mechanisms, and Ecological Considerations," and chapter 14, "Different Sensory Worlds," provide useful information for anyone interested in animal communication. The book is well illustrated, and the content is clearly presented, with end-of-chapter summaries and lists of additional readings. There is no glossary, but terms are well defined in the text and can be located by means of a good index.

Peters, Roger. *Mammalian Communication: A Behavioral Analysis of Meaning*. Monterey, Calif.: Brooks/Cole, 1980. A readable book covering a variety of mammalian species. Communication is treated in the context of the biology and ecology of the species. This paperback book has excellent drawings (although the quality of a few of the photographs could be improved). There is no glossary, but there is a useful reference list at the end of the text. Written at the college level but suitable for the high school student as well.

Wilson, Edward O. *Insect Societies*. Cambridge, Mass.: Harvard University Press, 1971. A thorough and well-written account of the behavior of social insects. Chapters 12, 13, and 14 describe the communication of alarm and assembly; recruitment; and recognition, food exchange, and grooming. A bibliography, glossary, and index assist the reader. Clear and understandable to the interested nonscientist.

Donna Janet Schroeder

Cross-References

Hormones and Behavior, 1377; Insect Societies, 1430; Instincts, 1438; Mammalian Social Systems, 1655; Neural Receptors, 1904; Pheromones, 2051; Reproductive Behavior and Mating, 2333; Rhythms and Behavior, 2398; Territoriality and Aggression, 2617.

COMMUNITY STRUCTURE AND STABILITY

Type of life science: Ecology
Other fields of study: Botany, microbiology, and zoology

Each ecological community has a characteristic structure and function that determines its ability to withstand and recover from disturbance. Since so many of the disturbances experienced by communities are caused by human activities, ecologists seek to understand why some communities are susceptible and why some disturbances cause irreversible damage.

Principal terms
COMMUNITY: the set of populations in a given place and time that interact with one another through the processes of competition, predation, parasitism, and mutualism
DOMINANT SPECIES: a species in a community that acts to control the abundance of its competitors because of its large size, extended life span, or ability to acquire and hold resources
ECOSYSTEM: a community together with its physical environment
FOOD CHAIN: a pathway through which energy travels in a community
FOOD WEB: the interconnections among all food chains in a community; a community may contain several loosely connected food webs in more or less separate compartments
FREQUENCY-DEPENDENT PREDATION: predation on whichever species is most common in a community; a frequency-dependent predator will switch prey if necessary
GLOBAL EXTINCTION: the loss of all members of a species; that is, extinction whereby all populations of a species disappear or are eliminated
KEYSTONE SPECIES: a species that determines the structure of a community, usually by predation on the dominant competitor in the community
LOCAL EXTINCTION: the loss of one or more populations of a species, but with at least one population of the species remaining
RESILIENCE STABILITY: stability exhibited by a community that changes its structure when disturbed but returns to its original structure when the disturbance ends
RESISTANCE STABILITY: stability exhibited by a community that absorbs the effects of a disturbance until it can no longer do so; then, it typically shifts permanently to an alternate structure
TROPHIC LEVEL: a single link in a food chain; all species that obtain energy in the same way are said to be at the same trophic level

Summary of the Phenomenon

An ecological community is the assemblage of species found in a given time and place. The populations that form a community interact through the processes of competition, predation, parasitism, and mutualism. The structure and function of communities are determined by the nature and strength of the population interactions within it, but these interactions are affected by the environment in which a community exists. An ecological community together with its physical environment is called an ecosystem. No ecological system can be studied apart from its physical environment; the structure and function of every community are determined in part by its interactions with its environment.

The species constituting a community occupy different functional roles. The most common way to characterize a community functionally is by describing the flow of energy through it. Correspondingly, communities usually contain three groups of species: those that obtain energy through photosynthesis (called "producers"), those that obtain energy by consuming other organisms ("consumers"), and those that decompose dead organisms ("decomposers"). The pathway through which energy travels from producer through one or more consumers and finally to decomposer is called a food chain. Each link in a food chain is called a trophic level. Interconnected food chains in a community constitute a food web. Food webs have no analogy in populations.

Very few communities are so simple that they can be readily described by a food web. Most communities are compartmentalized: A given set of producers tends to be consumed by a limited number of consumers, which in turn are preyed upon by only a few predators, and so on. Alternatively, consumers may obtain energy by specializing on one part of their prey (for example, some birds may eat only seeds of plants) but utilize a wide range of prey species. Compartmentalization is an important feature of community structure; it influences the formation, organization, and persistence of a community.

Some species, called dominant species, can exert powerful control over the abundance of other species, because of the dominant species' large size, extended life span, or ability to monopolize energy or other resources. Communities are named according to their dominant species: for example, oak-hickory forest, redwood forest, sagebrush desert, and tallgrass prairie. Some species, called keystone species, have a disproportionately large effect on community structure by preventing dominant species from monopolizing the community. Keystone species usually exert their effects through predation, while dominant species are good competitors (that is, better at obtaining and holding resources than other species).

The species that make up a community are seldom distributed uniformly across the landscape; rather, some degree of patchiness is characteristic of virtually all species. There has been conflicting evidence as to the nature of this patchiness. As one moves across an environmental gradient (for example, from wet to dry conditions or from low to high elevations), there is a corresponding change in species observed and in the type of community present. Some studies have suggested that changes in species composition usually occur along relatively sharp boundaries and that these boundaries mark the boundaries between adjacent communities. Other studies have indicated that species tend to respond individually to environmental gradients and that community boundaries are not sharply defined; rather, most communities broadly intergrade into one another.

These conflicting results have fueled a continuing debate as to the underlying nature of the community. Some communities seem to behave in a coordinated manner; for example, if a prairie is consumed by fire, it regenerates in a predictable sequence, ultimately returning to the same structure and composition it had before the fire. This coordinated response is to be expected if the species in a community have evolved together with one another. In this case, the community behaves analogously to an organism, maintaining its structure and function in the face of environmental disturbances and fluctuations (as long as the disturbances and fluctuations are not too extreme). The existence of relatively sharp boundaries between adjacent communities supports this explanation of the nature of the community.

In other communities, it appears that the response to environmental fluctuation or disturbance is determined by the evolved adaptations of the species available. There is no coordinated community response, but rather a coincidental assembly of community structure over time. Some sets of species interact together so strongly that they enter a community together, but there is no evidence of an evolved community tendency to resist or accommodate environmental change. Data support this explanation of the community as an entity formed primarily of species that happen to share similar environmental requirements.

Disagreement as to the underlying nature of communities usually reflects disagreement as to the relative importance of the underlying mechanisms that determine community structure. Interspecific competition has long been invoked as the primary agent structuring communities. Competition is certainly important in some communities, but there is insufficient evidence to indicate how widespread and important it is in determining community structure. Much of the difficulty occurs because ecologists must infer the existence of past competition from present patterns in communities. It appears that competition has been important in many vertebrate communities and in communities dominated by sessile organisms, such as plants; it does not appear to have been important in structuring communities of plant-eating insects. Furthermore, the effects of competition typically affect individuals that use identical resources, so that only a small percentage of species in a community may be experiencing significant competition at any time.

The effects of predation on community structure depend on the nature of the predation. Keystone species usually exert their influence by selectively preying on species that are competitively dominant. Predators that do not specialize on one or a few species may also have a major effect on community structure, if they attack prey in proportion to their abundance; this frequency-dependent predation prevents any prey species from achieving dominance. If a predator is too efficient, it can drive its prey to extinction, which may cause a selective predator to become extinct as well. Predation appears to be most important in determining community structure in environments that are predictable or unchanging.

A variable or unpredictable environment influences the structure of a community. No environment is completely uniform; seasonal or longer-term environmental fluctuations affect community structure by limiting opportunities for colonization, by causing direct mortality, and by hindering or exacerbating the effects of competition and predation. Furthermore, all communities experience at least occasional disturbance: unpredictable, seemingly random environmental changes that may be quite severe. It is useful in this regard to distinguish between disasters and catastrophes. A disaster is an event that occurs so frequently in the life of a population that adaptation is possible; for example, fire occurs so often in tallgrass prairies that most of the plant species have become fire-adapted—they have become efficient at acquiring nutrients left in the ash and at sprouting or germinating quickly following a fire. In comparison, a catastrophe is so intense, widespread, or infrequent that a population cannot adapt to it; the eruption of Mount St. Helens in 1980, for example, was so violent and so unpredictable that the species affected could not evolve adequate responses to it.

Natural disturbances occur at a variety of scales. Small-scale disturbances may simply create small openings in a community. In forests, for example, wind, lightning, and fungi cause single mature trees to die and fall, creating gaps that are typically colonized by species requiring such openings. Large disturbances are qualitatively different from small disturbances, in that large portions of a community may be destroyed, including some of the ability to recover from the disturbance. For example, following a large, intense forest fire, some tree species may not return for decades or centuries, since their seeds were consumed by the fire and arriving colonizers must travel a long distance.

Early ecologists almost always saw disturbances as destructive and disruptive for communities. Under this assumption, most mathematical models portrayed communities as generally being in some stable state, at equilibrium; if a disturbance occurred, the community inevitably returned to the same (or some alternative) equilibrium. It later became clear, however, that natural disturbance is a part of almost all natural communities. Ecologists now recognize that few communities exhibit a stable equilibrium; instead, communities are dynamic, always responding to the last disturbance, always adjusting to the most recent environmental fluctuation.

The evidence suggests that three conclusions can be drawn with regard to the long-term dynamics of communities. First, it can no longer be assumed that communities remain at equilibrium until changed by outside forces. Disturbances are so common, they occur at so many different scales and frequencies, and they so readily affect the processes of competition and predation that the community must be viewed as an entity that is constantly changing as its constituent species readjust to disturbance and to one another.

Second, communities exhibit several types of stability in the face of disturbance.

A community may absorb disturbance without markedly changing, until it reaches a threshold and suddenly and rapidly shifts to a new state, called resistance stability. Alternatively, a community may change easily when disturbed but quickly return to its former state; this characteristic is called resilience stability. Resilience stability may occur over a wide range of conditions and scales of disturbance; such a system is said to be dynamically robust. On the other hand, a community that exhibits resilience only within a narrow range of conditions is said to be dynamically fragile.

Finally, there is no simple way to predict the stability of a community. At the end of the 1970's, it appeared that complex communities were generally more stable than simple communities. It appeared that stability was conferred by more intricate food webs, by more structural complexity, and by higher species diversity. On the basis of numerous field studies and theoretical models, ecologists now conclude that no such relationship exists. Both very complex communities, such as tropical rain forests, and very simple communities, such as Arctic tundra, may be very fragile when disturbed.

Methods of Study

Most communities consist of thousands of species, and their complexity makes them very difficult to study. Most community ecologists specialize in taxonomically restricted subsets of communities (such as plant communities, bird communities, insect communities, or moss communities) or in functionally restricted subsets of communities (such as soil communities, tree-hole communities, pond communities, or detrivore communities).

The type of community under investigation and the questions of interest determine the appropriate methods of study. The central questions in most community studies are how many species are present and what is the abundance of each. The answers to these questions can be estimated using mark-recapture methods or any other enumeration method.

Often the aim is to compare communities (or to compare the same community at different times). A specialized parameter called similarity is used to compare and classify communities; more than two dozen measures of similarity are available. Measures of similarity are typically subjected to cluster analysis, a set of techniques that groups communities on the basis of their similarity.

Many multivariate techniques are used, especially by plant ecologists, to search for patterns in community data. Direct gradient analysis is the simplest of these techniques; it is used to study the distribution of species along an environmental gradient. Ordination includes several methods for collapsing community data for many species in many communities along several environmental gradients onto a single graph that summarizes their relationships and patterns.

Context

Every time a Douglas-fir forest is clearcut, or a tropical rain forest is burned to make room for cattle, or a prairie pothole wetland is drained and filled for agriculture, humans are disturbing a natural community. As human activities continue to damage and destroy communities, research into the nature of communities becomes increasingly important. Although our knowledge remains rudimentary, some patterns of community responses to disturbance have been identified.

At the most basic level, destruction of a community eliminates the species comprising the community. If the community is restricted in its extent, and if its constituent species are found nowhere else, those species become extinct. If the community covers a large area or is found in several areas, local extinction of species may occur without causing global extinction.

Destruction of a community can cause unexpected changes in environmental conditions that were modified by the intact community. For example, tallgrass prairies persisted for thousands of years, recycling nutrients and increasing the organic content of the soil. The soil was remarkably fertile, supporting a large and diverse community of soil organisms. Conversion to agriculture, however, has resulted in a rapid loss of nutrients and organic matter, decimation of the soil community, and often loss of the soil itself. The persistence of agriculture is made possible only by the input of energy in the form of fertilizers and machinery. Furthermore, a prairie community cannot readily establish itself on an abandoned cornfield, because of the loss of nutrients, organisms, and soil and the destruction of its seed source.

Even partial destruction of an extensive community can eliminate species. For example, the checkerboard pattern of clearcutting in Douglas-fir forests of the Pacific Northwest threatens the survival of the northern spotted owl, the marbled murrelet, Vaux's swift, and the red tree vole, even though fragments of the community remain. Many fragments are simply too small to support these species. A Douglas-fir forest is regenerated following cutting, but this young, even-aged stand is so different from an old, mixed-age forest that it functions as a different type of community.

Altering the population of one species can affect others in a community. The black-footed ferret was once found widely throughout central North America as a predator of prairie dogs. As prairie dogs were poisoned, drowned, and shot throughout their range, the number of black-footed ferrets also declined. As of 1989, fewer than one hundred black-footed ferrets were in a captive breeding program in Wyoming in a final attempt to preserve the species.

Introducing a new species into a community can severely alter the interactions in the community. The introduction of the European rabbit into Australia led to a population explosion of rabbits, excessive predation on vegetation, and resulting declines in many native marsupials. Similarly, cultivation and overgrazing by cattle in the western United States have allowed cheatgrass, which is native to Asia, to increase to the point where it has displaced native annual grasses from most of the region.

Finally, it appears that many communities exhibit stability thresholds; if a community is disturbed beyond its threshold, its structure is permanently changed. For example, acid deposition in lakes is initially buffered by natural processes. As acid deposition exceeds the buffering capacity of a lake, it causes insoluble aluminum in the lake bottom to become soluble, and this soluble aluminum kills aquatic organisms directly or by making them more susceptible to disease.

The lesson is clear: It is far easier to disrupt or destroy natural systems (even accidentally) than it is to restore or reconstruct them. Understanding their structure and function is an important step toward preventing their destruction.

Bibliography

Begon, Michael, John L. Harper, and Colin R. Townsend. *Ecology: Individuals, Populations, and Communities*. Sunderland, Mass.: Sinauer Associates, 1986. These authors have produced the most comprehensive college-level text currently available; it is particularly good at integrating the results of plant ecologists with those of animal ecologists. Part 4 of the book provides a thorough, well-documented discussion of the structure and function of communities; historical and current hypotheses as to the nature of the community; the influence of competition, predation, and disturbance on community structure; and community stability. The text contains an excellent bibliography of research in community ecology.

Bormann, Frank H., and Gene E. Likens. "Catastrophic Disturbance and the Steady State in Northern Hardwood Forests." *American Scientist* 67 (1979): 660-669. This article is based on nearly twenty years of work on the Hubbard Brook Forest in New Hampshire. It summarizes clearly and authoritatively the dominant understanding of disturbance and stability in natural communities. The article can be used as a good starting point for further investigation in this area.

Krebs, Charles J. *Ecological Methodology*. New York: Harper & Row, 1989. This book provides an excellent presentation of the most widely used methods in ecology. It is a college-level text, most suitable for those who have had some previous instruction in ecology, as well as a good facility with algebra.

_____. *Ecology: The Experimental Analysis of Distribution and Abundance*. 3d ed. New York: Harper & Row, 1985. One of the most widely used college-level texts, this book is written with excellent clarity and scope. Chapter 25 provides concise, complete coverage of community organization.

Pickett, S. T. A., and P. S. White, eds. *The Ecology of Natural Disturbance and Patch Dynamics*. Orlando, Fla.: Academic Press, 1985. Provocative and wide-ranging, this book is a gold mine of information and examples illustrating current hypotheses about the many kinds of natural disturbance and the ways in which communities respond. The entire book is readily accessible to the general reader. Chapters 1 and 21, written by the editors, provide an excellent overview of the topic. The bibliography is very complete through 1984.

Pielou, E. C. *The Interpretation of Ecological Data: A Primer on Classification and Ordination*. New York: John Wiley & Sons, 1984. The definitive book for those interested in cluster analysis and ordination, and in the classification of communities. Although it is an introductory textbook, the reader with a knowledge of matrix algebra and previous instruction would benefit most.

Sousa, W. P. "The Role of Disturbance in Natural Communities." *Annual Review of Ecology and Systematics* 15 (1984): 353-391. A good review by an authority on disturbance in intertidal communities, this article provides a good complement to the article by Bormann and Likens.

Alan D. Copsey

Cross-References

Biomass Related to Energy, 203; Coevolution, 512; Competition, 541; Demographics, 597; Ecological Niches, 729; Ecological Principles, 736; Mark, Release, and Recapture Methods for Population Analysis, 1668; Population Fluctuations, 2154; Predation, 2178; Sessile Community Sampling, 2473; Succession, 2566; Symbiosis, Commensalism, and Parasitism, 2572; Tropical Rain Forests, 2661.

COMPETITION

Type of life science: Ecology
Other fields of study: Botany, evolutionary biology, microbiology, and zoology

Competition is the conflict between different organisms for control of food, natural resources, territories, mates, and other aspects of survival. Competition can occur between individuals of the same species or between individuals of different species. In either case, it is natural selection for the fittest organisms and species; therefore, it is a major driving force in evolution.

Principal terms

ALLELE: a slightly altered version of a gene (DNA), caused by a mutation, that can be expressed as a new physical trait in organisms

EVOLUTION: gradual changes in organisms over time, caused by mutation and selected by the environment, resulting in better adapted organisms and new species

HABITAT: the type of environment in which a particular organism prefers to live, based upon various physical and chemical conditions

MUTATION: a genetic change in the nucleotide base sequence (DNA) that is caused by radiation or chemicals, and produces new traits (alleles) that may help or harm the organism

NATURAL SELECTION: the ability of an organism or species to survive, compete, and reproduce in its habitat; success is dictated by the alleles (traits) that it possesses

NICHE: an organism's role in its habitat environment, such as food producer, decomposer, parasite, plant eater (herbivore), meat-eater (carnivore)

PREDATION: a situation in which one animal species hunts and eats another species (examples: lynx versus hare; cheetah versus gazelle)

SPECIES: for eukaryotes, a group of organisms that can interbreed (mate) and produce viable, fertile offspring

TERRITORIALITY: a phenomenon in animal behavior whereby individual organisms occupy and defend an area from other individuals of the same or different species

THREAT DISPLAY: a territorial behavior exhibited by animals during defense of a territory, such as charging, showing bright colors, and exaggerating body size

Summary of the Phenomenon

Competition is the struggle between individuals of different species (interspecific competition) or between individuals of the same species (intraspecific competition) for food, territories, and mates in order to survive. It is a major driving force in evolution, the process by which living organisms change over time, with better-adapted species surviving and less well-adapted species dying. Evolution begins with mutation, changes in the nucleotide sequence of a gene or genes, resulting in the production of slightly altered genes called alleles which encode slightly different proteins. These altered proteins are the expressed traits of an organism and may give the organism an advantage over its competitors. The organism outcompetes its rivals in the environment, and hence the environment favors the better-adapted, fitter organism, a process called "natural selection." A mutation may help an organism in one environment but may hurt the same organism in a different environment (for example, an albino squirrel may flourish in snowy regions but may not do as well in warm regions). Mutations can be caused by chemicals called mutagens or by ionizing radiation such as ultraviolet light, X rays, and gamma radiation.

Ecology can best be defined as the experimental analysis of the distribution and abundance of organisms. Natural selection influences the distribution and abundance of organisms from place to place. The possible selecting factors include physical factors (temperature and light, for example), chemical factors such as water and salt, and species interactions. Any of these factors can influence the survivability of organisms in any particular environment. According to ecologist Charles Krebs, species interactions include four principal types: "mutualism," which is the living together of two species that benefit each other (for example, humans and their pets); "commensalism," which is the living together of two species that results in a distinct benefit (or number of benefits) to one species while the other remains unhurt (commensalism is shown in the relationship of birds and trees); "predation," which is the hunting, killing, and eating of one species by another (examples: cats and mice; humans and deer); and "competition," which is defined as an active struggle for survival among all the species in a given environment.

This struggle involves the acquisition of various resources: food, territory, and mates. Food is an obvious target of competition. All organisms must have energy in order to conduct the cellular chemical reactions (such as respiration) that keep them alive. Photoautotrophic organisms (plants, phytoplankton, photobacteria) obtain this energy by converting sunlight, carbon dioxide, and water into sugar, a process called photosynthesis. Photoautotrophs, also called producers, compete for light and water. For example, oak and hickory trees grow taller than most pines, thereby shading out smaller species and eventually dominating a forest. All other organisms—animals, zooplankton, and fungi—are heterotrophs; they must consume other organisms to obtain energy. Heterotrophs include herbivores, carnivores, omnivores, and saprotrophs. Herbivores (plant eaters such as rabbits and cattle) obtain the sugar manufactured by plants. Carnivores (meat eaters such as cats and dogs) eat other heterotrophs in order to get the sugar that these heterotrophs received from other organisms. Omnivores, such as humans, eat plants and animals for the same reason. Saprotrophs (such as fungi and bacteria) decompose dead organisms for the same reason. Life on earth functions by intricately complex food chains in which organisms consume other organisms in order to obtain energy. Each human being is composed of molecules that were once part of other living organisms, even other humans. Ultimately, the earth's energy comes from the sun.

Territoriality is equally important for two reasons: An organism needs a place to live, and this place must contain adequate food and water reserves. A strong, well-adapted organism will fight and drive away weaker individuals of the same or different species in order to maintain exclusive rights to an area containing a large food and water supply. Less well-adapted species will be relegated to areas where food and water are scarce. The stronger species will have more food and will tend to produce more offspring, since they will easily attract mates. Being stronger or more adapted does not necessarily mean being physically stronger. A physically strong organism can be overwhelmed easily by numerous weak individuals. In general, adaptability is defined by an organism's ability to prosper in a hostile environment and leave many viable offspring.

Within a species, males attempt to attract females to their territory, or vice versa, by courtship dances and displays, often including bright colors such as red and blue and exaggerated body size. Mating displays are very similar to the threat displays used to drive away competitors, although there is no hostility involved. Generally, females are attracted to dominant males having the best, not necessarily the largest, territories.

Competition for food and territory is interspecific and intraspecific. Competition for mates is intraspecific. In an environment, the place where an organism lives (such as a eucalyptus tree or in rotting logs) is referred to as its habitat. Simultaneously, each species has its own unique niche, or occupation, in the environment (such as decomposer or carnivore). More than one species can occupy a habitat if they have different ecological niches. When two or more different species occupy the same habitat and niche, competition arises. One species will outcompete and dominate, while the losing competitors may become reduced in numbers and may be driven away from the habitat.

In vertebrate organisms, intraspecific competition occurs between males as a group and between females as a group. Rarely is there male-versus-female competition, except in species having high social bonding—primates, for example. Competition begins when individuals are young. During play fighting, individuals nip or peck at each other while exhibiting threat displays. Dominant individuals exert their authority, while weaker individuals submit. The net result is a very ordered ranking of individuals from top to bottom, called a dominance hierarchy or pecking order. The top individual can threaten and force into submission any individual below it. The number two individual can threaten anyone except number one, and so on. The lowest-ranked individual can threaten no one and must submit to everyone. The lowest individual will have the least food, worst territory, and fewest (if any) mates. The number one individual will have the most food, best territory, and most mates. The pecking order changes over time because of continued group competition that is shown by challenges, aging, and accidents.

Pecking orders are evident in hens. A very dominant individual will peck other hens many times but will rarely be pecked. A less dominant individual will peck less but be pecked more. A correct ranking can be obtained easily by counting the pecking rate for each hen.

In The Netherlands, male black grouse contend with one another in an area called a "lek," which may be occupied by as many as twenty males. The males establish their territories by pecking, wing-beating, and threat displays. The most dominant males occupy small territories (several hundred meters) at the center of the lek, where the food supply is greatest. Less dominant males occupy larger territories with less food reserves to the exterior of the lek. Established territories are maintained at measurable distances by crowing and flutter-jumping, with the home territory owner nearly always winning. Females, which nest in an adjoining meadow, are attracted to dominant males in the heavily contested small central territories.

A baboon troop can range in size from ten to two hundred members, but usually averages about forty. Larger, dominant males and their many female mates move centrally within the troop. Less dominant males, with fewer females, lie toward the outside of the troop. Weak individuals at the troop periphery are more susceptible to predator attacks. Dominant males exert their authority by threat displays, such as the baring of the teeth or charging; weaker males submit by presenting their hind-quarters. Conflicts are usually peacefully resolved.

Female lions maintain an organized pride with a single ruling male. Young males are expelled and wander alone in the wilderness. Upon reaching adulthood, males attempt to take over a pride in order to gain access to females. If a male is successful in capturing a pride and expelling his rival, he will often kill the cubs of the pride, simultaneously eliminating his rival's descendants and stimulating the females to enter estrus for mating.

Interspecific competition occurs between different species over food and water reserves and territories. Two or more species occupying the same niche and habitat will struggle for the available resources until either one species dominates and the others are excluded from the habitat or the different species evolve into separate niches by targeting different food reserves, thus enabling all to survive in the same habitat. Numerous interspecific studies have been conducted, including crossbills, warblers, blackbirds, and insects, to mention a few.

Crossbills are small birds that live in Europe and Asia. Three crossbill species inhabit similar habitats and nearly similar niches. Each species has evolved a slightly modified beak, however, for retrieving and eating seeds from three different cone-bearing (coniferous) trees. The white-winged crossbill has a slender beak for feeding from small larch cones, the common crossbill has a thicker beak for feeding from larger spruce cones, and the parrot crossbill appropriately has a very thick beak for feeding from pine cones. The evolution of different niches has enabled these three competitors to survive.

Another example of this phenomenon is shown by five species of warblers that inhabit the coniferous forests of the American northeast. The myrtle warbler eats insects from all parts of trees up to 7 meters high. The bay-breasted warbler eats insects from tree trunks 6 to 12 meters above the ground. The black-throated green, blackburnian, and cape may warblers all feed near the treetops, from elaborate studies by R. H. MacArthur. The coexistence of five different species is probably the result of the warblers occupying different parts of the trees, with some warblers developing different feeding habits so that all survive.

G. H. Orians and G. Collier studied competitive exclusion between redwing and tricolored blackbirds. Introduction of tricolored blackbirds into redwing territories results in heavy redwing aggression, although the tricolored blackbirds nearly always prevail.

Two species of African ants, *Anoplolepis longipes* and *Oecophylla longinoda*, fight aggressively for territorial space. M. J. Way found that *Anoplolepis* prevails in sandy environments, whereas *Oecophylla* dominates in areas having thick vegetation.

Interspecific competition therefore results in the evolution of new traits and niches and the exclusion of certain species. Mathematical models of competition are based upon the work of A. J. Lotka and V. Volterra. The Lotka-Volterra equations attempt to measure competition between species for food and territory based upon the population size of each species, the density of each species within the defined area, the rate of population increase of each species, and time.

Methods of Study

Studies of competition between individuals of the same or different species generally follow one basic method: observation. Interactions between organisms are observed and carefully measured to determine if the situation is competition, predation, parasitism, or mutualism. More detailed analyses of environmental chemical and physical conditions are used to determine the existence of additional influences. Observations of competition between organisms involve direct visual contact in the wild, mark-recapture experiments, transplant experiments, measurements of population sizes in given areas, and competition experiments in artificial environments.

Direct visual contact involves the scientist entering the field, finding a neutral, nonthreatening position, and watching and recording the actions of the subject organisms. The observer must be familiar with the habits of the subject organism and must be keen to detect subtle cues such as facial gestures, vocalizations, colors, and patterns of movement from individual to individual. Useful instruments include binoculars, telescopes, cameras, and sound recorders. The observer must be capable of tracking individuals over long distances so that territorial boundaries and all relevant actions are recorded. The observer may have to endure long periods of time in the field under uncomfortable conditions.

Mark-recapture experiments involve the capture of many organisms, tagging them, releasing them into an area, and then recapturing them (both tagged and untagged) at a later time. Repeated collections (recaptures) over time can give the experimenter an estimate of how well the species is faring in a particular environment. This technique is used in conjunction with other experiments, including transplants and population size measurements.

In transplant experiments, individuals of a given species are marked and released into a specific environmental situation, such as a new habitat or another species' territory. The objective of the experiment is to see how well the introduced species fares in the new situation, as well as the responses of the various species which normally inhabit the area. The tricolored blackbird takeover of redwing blackbird territories is a prime example. Another example is the red wolf, a species that was extinct in the wild until several dozen captive wolves were released at the Alligator River Wildlife Refuge in eastern North Carolina. Their survival is uncertain. Accidental transplants have had disastrous results for certain species; for example, the chestnut blight fungus, a parasite, has virtually exterminated the American chestnut tree, while the African honeybee poses a threat to the honey industry in Latin America and the southern United States because it is aggressive and produces poorly.

Measurements of population sizes rely upon the point-quarter technique, in which numerous rectangular areas of equal size are marked in the field. The number of organisms of each species in the habitat is counted for a given area; an averaging of all areas is then made to obtain a relatively accurate measure of each population's size. In combination with mark-recapture experiments, population measurements can provide information for birthrates, death rates, immigration, and emigration over time for a given habitat.

Laboratory experiments involve confrontations between different species or individuals of the same species within an artificial environment. For example, male mouse (*Mus musculus*) territoriality can be studied by introducing an intruder into another male's home territory. Generally, the winner of the confrontation is the individual that nips its opponent more times. Usually, home court advantage prevails; the intruder is driven away. Similar studies have been performed with other mammalian, reptile, fish, insect, and bird species.

Context

Interactions between different species are subtle and intricate. Seeing how organisms associate enables scientists to understand evolution and to model various environments, eliminate pests, and improve agriculture. Competition is a major driving force in evolution. The stronger species outcompete weaker species for the available ecological niches. Mutations in organisms create new traits and, therefore, new organisms (more species), which are selected by the environment for adaptability.

All environments consist of a complex array of species, each dependent on the others for survival. The area in which they live is their habitat. Each species' contribution to the habitat is that species' niche. More than one species in a given habitat causes competition. Two species will struggle for available territory and food resources until either one species drives the other away or they adapt to each other and evolve different feeding habits and living arrangements. Competition can be interspecific (between individuals of different species) or intraspecific (between individuals of the same species). The environment benefits because the most adapted species survive, whereas weaker species are excluded.

Competition can also be used as a means of pest control. Insect-killing chemicals such as pesticides can pose a threat to human, animal, and plant life. The introduction of competitor species into the environment can sometimes be more effective than the use of chemicals because it can create a fight for available resources, which often results in the undesirable species being reduced in number.

The same principle is useful in agriculture. Certain plant species (such as sunflowers and peach trees) release chemicals into the soil that inhibit the growth of other plants. Plant competition can be used to fight the growth of weeds. Plant competition is useful in understanding which plants are compatible. The result is better crop yields.

Competition is useful in medical microbiological research. Certain fungal species produce and secrete molecules called antibiotics, which kill bacteria. Antibiotics give these fungi an edge in their competition against bacteria. Laboratory production of these antibiotics (such as ampicillin) can treat bacterial diseases such as strep throat and cystitis in humans.

Competition is evident in the intraspecific associations between humans. Humans compete for food, territories, and mates in much the same way that other animals do, although, in addition to sharing the attributes of other animals, they use the tools of technology. Humans exhibit the same competitive behaviors, including territoriality, mating, threat displays, aggression, and fighting, that other species of animals do. Humans will resort to almost any means to gain the competitive edge over an opponent. The viciousness of some human competition greatly exceeds that of any other species.

Bibliography

Andrewartha, H. G. *Introduction to the Study of Animal Populations*. Chicago: University of Chicago Press, 1967. From one of the great animal ecologists, this classic textbook is a tremendous source of information for practical animal behavior research. The book concisely covers all aspects of ecology, including competition. Part 2, "Practical Course," is a valuable guide for conducting precise experiments.

Hartl, Daniel L. *Principles of Population Genetics*. Sunderland, Mass.: Sinauer Associates, 1980. Hartl's work, aimed at graduate-level biologists, is a detailed mathematical approach to species interactions and evolution. The book approaches the study of populations from a genetic and statistical viewpoint and provides numerous examples and references.

Krebs, Charles J. *Ecology: The Experimental Analysis of Distribution and Abundance*. 2d ed. New York: Harper & Row, 1978. This advanced textbook is a wonderfully comprehensive survey of ecology. Numerous experiments are cited, with a thorough but understandable discussion of mathematical modeling in ecology. Many references are cited in this truly fine work.

Lorenz, Konrad. *On Aggression*. New York: Harcourt, Brace & World, 1963. This book by the 1973 Nobel laureate in Physiology or Medicine is a readable survey of animal interactions, especially that of competition and its aggressive nature. Lorenz discusses major theories with great clarity and wit and provides examples of applications to human and animal behavior.

Manning, Aubrey. *An Introduction to Animal Behavior*. 3d ed. Reading, Mass.: Addison-Wesley, 1979. Manning's survey of animal behavior is concise while retaining comprehensive coverage of the subject. Major theories and classic experiments are discussed. An extensive reference list is provided for further study.

Marler, Peter, and William J. Hamilton. *Mechanisms of Animal Behavior*. New York: John Wiley & Sons, 1966. Marler and Hamilton's work is a major survey of animal behavior research, including many important experiments and major theories describing species interactions. It is well organized, is excellently illustrated, and has an extensive reference list.

Raven, Peter H., and George B. Johnson. *Biology*. 2d ed. St. Louis: Times-Mirror/ Mosby, 1989. Raven and Johnson's *Biology* is a beautifully illustrated, clearly written, well-diagrammed introductory biology textbook for undergraduate biology majors. Chapter 23, "Population Dynamics," is a clear presentation of species interactions, such as competition, that contains numerous examples.

Wallace, Robert A., Jack L. King, and Gerald P. Sanders. *Biosphere: The Realm of Life*. 2d ed. Glenview, Ill.: Scott, Foresman, 1988. An excellent introductory biology textbook for biology majors and nonmajors alike. Excellent diagrams, photographs, and writing make this work widely comprehensible. Chapter 47, "Populations and How They Change," is a good summary of species interactions.

Wilson, Edward O. *Sociobiology: The New Synthesis*. Cambridge, Mass.: The Belknap Press of Harvard University Press, 1975. Wilson's work is a major contribution to animal behavior research in terms of its unique approach and enlightening theories concerning species interactions. It is well written, illustrated, and referenced.

David Wason Hollar, Jr.

Cross-References

Adaptations and Their Mechanisms, 22; The Biosphere, Biomes, and Habitats, 210; Coevolution, 512; Community Structure and Stability, 533; Demographics, 597; Ecological Niches, 729; Ecological Principles, 736; Ethology, 858; Mammalian Social Systems, 1655; Mark, Release, and Recapture Methods for Population Analysis, 1668; Predation, 2178; Reproductive Behavior and Mating, 2333; Sessile Community Sampling, 2473; Territoriality and Aggression, 2617.

THE COMPLEMENT SYSTEM

Types of life science: Animal physiology and immunology
Other fields of study: Biochemistry and zoology

The complement system is a system of proteins present in the blood and body fluids that, when activated, sets off a series of reactions which play a major role in the defense mechanism against invading organisms.

Principal terms

ANTIBODY: a protein produced in response to a specific antigen and which, along with a complement, can neutralize the antigen

ANTIGEN: proteins, bacteria, or foreign matter that can stimulate the immune system

GRAM-NEGATIVE BACTERIA: a bacteria that stains pink with a stain (dye) called Gram stain; those that stain blue are called gram positive

IMMUNOFLUORESCENT DYES: dyes that can stain antigen-antibody complexes and glow when visualized under special microscopes

INFLAMMATION: the process by which the body responds to injury and tries to limit the damage or destroy the invading organisms

PHAGOCYTOSIS: the most important function of white blood cells, which literally "eat" foreign material

PLASMA: the fluid portion of the blood, which contains proteins and no cells

PROTEOLYSIS: the breakdown of protein molecules

SERUM: plasma without certain proteins, such as factors that cause clotting to occur

Summary of the Phenomenon

The complement system is a system of independent plasma proteins that represents one of the earliest defense mechanisms of the body. It is an integral part of the immune system, which is designed specifically to protect the body against disease. The immune system may be divided into two types, the humoral and the cellular. In the humoral type, antibodies, which are molecules of proteins called globulins, are formed in the blood in response to foreign material. These globulins circulate in the blood and react with invaders such as microorganisms to destroy them. In the cellular type, white blood cells, such as lymphocytes, are able to recognize and destroy cells that are altered by bacteria, viruses, cancer, and similar invaders. In reality, each type helps the other to ingest and destroy foreign matter. The process of ingestion is called phagocytosis. The complement system mainly enhances and aids humoral immunity.

The proteins of the complement system are synthesized by widely differing cells, such as lymphocytes, fibroblasts, and macrophages, the last of which are simply altered white blood cells with the ability to fight infectious agents. There are at least twenty plasma proteins that make up the complement system. They are designated by arabic numerals preceded by a "C," which stands for complement, such as C_1, C_2, C_3, and so on. Other proteins of the complement system are factor B, factor D, and properdin. In addition, there also are a few proteins called regulatory proteins, which, as their name implies, regulate or control the system.

The proteins of the complement are normally present in an inactive state. For the complement to be effective, it needs to be activated. Activated complement can then kill cells or bacteria that have interaction with antibodies. It is also one of the mechanisms by which an inflammatory response is produced. Once the proteins of the complement system are activated, they are designated by an overbar (such as $\overline{C_1}$). The phenomenon by which the complement system becomes effective is called fixation. In this process the proteins of the complement system are activated and used up or consumed in a series of reactions which result in the mediation of its effects. The whole process for the sake of simplicity may be divided into two phases, which are really continuous. They are an initial activation phase followed by a terminal phase.

During the activation phase, sequential biochemical events occur that cleave portions of the protein molecule at precise points. This process of cleavage is called proteolysis and activates the whole system. Continuation of the process is then maintained in the following manner: The activated components of the complement system interact with each other, so that the products of one reaction form the stimulus for the next reaction, and so on. Therefore, a small initial stimulus results in an increasing amount of activity and leads to the completion of the activation phase and initiation of the terminal phase.

The activation phase may proceed by two pathways. These are called the classical pathway and the alternate pathway, respectively. The classical pathway is typically initiated by a combination of antigen and antibody, such as the combination of an invading bacteria, which represents an antigen to whose surface is attached an antibody. Also, the classical pathway uses mainly the proteins labeled C_1, C_2, C_3, and so on. The alternative pathway, however, can be initiated in the absence of an antibody. A variety of factors activate this pathway, one of them being bacterial endotoxins, which are toxic substances produced within certain types of bacteria. Both of these pathways converge through their sequence to the terminal phase.

In the terminal phase, five of the activated proteins of the complement system assemble and form what is known as the membrane attack complex. This membrane attack complex now attaches to cell walls and causes holes to form in them, resulting in their lysis, or destruction. Some of these include bacteria, viruses, and certain red blood cells.

When the activation process is taking place, some of the protein molecules are broken up into smaller fragments. These fragments are designated by adding the letter "a" or "b," such as C_3a and C_3b. Some of these fragments are released into the circulation. They have specialized functions and serve as substances mediating inflammation or as substances that help to attract and/or mobilize white blood cells to areas where they are needed.

The complement system acts mainly against certain foreign particles in the body, or cells in the body that have been modified in some way. How the complement system is able to differentiate between host (the body's) proteins, and foreign particle proteins is a function that seems to be regulated by host proteins. Here the regulatory proteins also play a part.

Methods of Study

The complement system was initially described when it was found that certain heat-sensitive factors in the human serum were necessary to kill bacteria and break down red blood cells, which are called erythrocytes. This has been demonstrated very effectively by a test using sheep red cells. In this test, the complement system is evaluated by its ability to destroy sheep erythrocytes (red blood cells) and release hemoglobin contained in them. For the complement system to be activated by the classical pathway, antigen antibody complexes must be present, called the Forssman antigen. These cells are exposed to serum of the rabbit, which does not have this antigen; antibodies are formed in the rabbit serum and bind to the sheep red blood cells. When complement proteins are added to this mixture, they are activated and destroy the red blood cells and release the hemoglobin contained in them. This process demonstrates complement activity and can be measured in the laboratory.

The alternate pathway was discovered later, when it was found that the cell wall of certain bacteria, called gram-negative bacteria, could activate the C_3 component of the complement system. It was also found that cobra venom produced a similar effect. These theories are still valid today, and electron microscope studies have now shown that the membrane attack complex attaches to cell walls and causes holes in them. This results in material from the cell escaping to the outside and outside material entering the cell, thus killing the cell.

Current studies are directed at finding evidence for the role of the complement in human disease. This is done by studying individuals who lack specific components of complement and also appear to be susceptible to certain diseases. Other methods study animal models of human disease, and still others directly measure complement levels in specific human diseases. The last of the three involves many assay systems that have been developed over a period of time. Assays that measure complement factors in the serum of patients with diseases are based on the principle that when there is complement activation as part of the disease process, levels of certain components of complement are reduced. This results from the fact that, once complement is activated, the cleaved particles are rapidly removed from the circulation, and levels fall. Since C_3 and C_4 components are present in higher amounts in the circulation, they are most commonly measured.

Assays also exist that measure the functional activity of complement, and those that can demonstrate the presence of complement components in damaged tissues. The former are not very accurate because they measure transient levels, as synthesis and breakdown of components of the complement system are very rapid. The latter involves examination of a piece of tissue. For example, antigen antibody complexes that have activated complement and are therefore bound to the complement proteins can be trapped by filtering membranes such as those present in the kidney. Staining of this tissue with immunofluorescent dyes (such as fluorescein) reveals the complement deposits, which light up under special microscopes. In the same way, tissues of the body that have been damaged by the deposition of antigen antibody complex bound to complement can be examined. This is an excellent way of demonstrating that complement has been activated and also helps immensely in the understanding of certain disease processes.

There are many more assays, and most of these study either specific features of the complement activation process or measure reactivity. Most of these experiments are used to study the relationship of the complement to certain diseases, but they have definitely proven that the complement system is active in the immune mechanism of the body and that it is a potent mediator of inflammation.

Context

The complement system is an essential part of the body's defense mechanism against many forms of foreign invasion. The body's ability to resist this invasion is called immunity, and this may be mediated by antibodies or by white blood cells. Complement is an essential part of the former and aids and enhances this system. It causes lysis of bacteria and other cells. It neutralizes viruses by attacking their molecular structure. It is capable of doing this even in the absence of antibody, but antibody enhances the effect.

The complement system by its many effects on white blood cells enhances their potency. By activation of some of its proteins, such as C_3 and C_5, and by releasing their fragments in the blood, it helps in the movement of certain white blood cells, such as macrophages, to injured areas, where they usually destroy the invading organism. By similar methods and by causing the release of certain biological catalysts called enzymes, it helps in localizing the damage. By binding to antigen antibody complexes, it influences the white blood cells to increase the rate and extent of phagocytosis, which enables the body to destroy a foreign invader much more quickly and efficiently than would otherwise be possible.

It is evident that complement is needed to help protect the human body from many common bacteria and viruses to which it is exposed every day. This need is demonstrated by the fact that people born with a lack of certain components of complement are susceptible to extremely severe recurrent infections. The absence of factor C_2 is associated with certain diseases called collagen vascular diseases and serves as another example of the importance of complement.

The complement system has also been implicated in mediating tissue injury and disease. Lack of regulatory factors for some proteins of the complement system, such as C_1, results in a condition which may cause severe swelling of the upper respiratory tract and death caused by suffocation. In certain diseases such as rheumatoid arthritis, which occur in middle-aged people and involve the joints, injury is caused by antigen antibody complexes that have reacted with complement proteins and have deposited in the membranes lining the joint. This causes the severe pain and joint deformities that develop.

The importance of the complement system in defense against disease has been well recognized. Further understanding of the system should therefore provide better means to alter and possibly treat disease processes.

Bibliography

Bowry, T. R. *Immunology Simplified*. 2d ed. London: Oxford University Press, 1984. Provides information in a short, intelligible, and simplified form. Not a book for great details. Describes the two pathways of the complement system; mentions the regulatory proteins and the main functions of the complement.

Goldstein, Ira M. *Complement in Infectious Diseases: Current Concepts*. Kalamazoo, Mich.: The Upjohn Company, 1980. A detailed description of the complement system, the pathways, the mechanisms of action, the products of activation, and their effects. Discusses the role of the complement system in defense against disease. Briefly discusses the components of complement and their individual properties. Mentions the role of certain components in human disease in terms of deficiency and autoimmune disease. Also has a list of 109 references for the interested reader.

Guyton, Arthur C. *Textbook of Medical Physiology*. 6th ed. Philadelphia: W. B. Saunders, 1981. A textbook designed for medical students but written in very simple and clear language, easily understandable. Presents the topic concisely without delving into great detail. Good illustrations.

Mueller-Eberhard, H. J., and P. A. Miescher. *Complement*. New York: Springer-Verlag, 1985. A more advanced book that discusses the complement system in great detail. It contains many figures and tables. All aspects are thoroughly described, down to the level of molecular reactions. Excellent chapter on methods of study of the complement. The structure of each component of the complement is described in detail, as are its individual receptors. Describes experimental models relatively well.

Oppenheim, Joost J., D. L. Rosenstreich, and M. Potter, eds. *Cellular Functions in Immunity and Inflammation*. New York: Elsevier North-Holland, 1981. Contains a chapter on the complement system which describes history, dates, and methods of detection of complement. Discusses in moderate detail the activation process and the role of the system in inflammation. Describes different aspects of how complement aids in inflammation. Also discusses the consequences of lack of control and involvement in diseases mediated by the complement. A good book for the college student.

Ali Jaffar
Abraham Verghese

Cross-References

Allergies, 58; Antibodies, 112; Antigen-Presenting Cells, 119; Autoimmunity, 141; Blood Clotting, 255; Blood Components, 262; Cellular Immunity, 382; The Immune Response, 1384; Leukocytes and Erythrocytes, 1556; T-Lymphocyte Differentiation, 2601.

COMPLEMENTATION AND ALLELISM:
THE CIS-TRANS TEST

Type of life science: Genetics
Other fields of study: Biochemistry and molecular biology

The cis-trans test is the classic method of determining whether two mutations are in the same or different genes. Mutations in different genes are said to "complement" one another; this kind of information gives scientists important clues to gene function.

Principal terms

ALLELE: one of many possible alternate forms of a gene; one form is usually designated as normal (typical or wild-type), and all other variant alleles are mutant

CIS: a configuration in which two mutants are both present on the same chromosome; the opposite of trans

CISTRON: a portion of a DNA molecule that contains the instructions for making a single polypeptide chain; sometimes used as a synonym for "gene"

HETEROZYGOTE: an organism that has two different alleles of a gene; most higher organisms will have two copies of any given gene

HOMOLOGUE: one of two chromosomes of a pair in diploid organisms; for example, humans have twenty-three pairs of chromosomes, each pair consisting of two similar or homologous chromosomes

HOMOZYGOTE: an organism that has two copies of the same allele; the alleles may both be wild-type or both be mutant

PHENOTYPE: the physical expression of a gene or group of genes

RECOMBINATION: the process by which material between two homologous chromosomes is exchanged; sometimes called crossing over

TRANS: a configuration in which two mutants are present in an organism but are on separate homologues; the opposite of cis

Summary of the Methodology

The cis-trans test is the classic method of determining whether two mutations are in the same or different genes. While this is of great importance to a scientist studying a particular organism, the test originally was developed in an attempt to provide a better definition of the concept of the gene.

Genes are located on cellular structures called chromosomes. For many years, scientists thought that genes were lined up along the chromosomes like beads on a string. Each bead represented a different gene controlling a separate function, such as hair color in people or seed shape in plants. If "normal" or "wild-type" alleles were represented by black beads, a red or white or green bead would represent a changed, or "mutant," allele. This analogy was popular for many years, and genes, like beads, were thought to be indivisible. The work of scientists in the 1940's and 1950's challenged this theory and led to its eventual demise. The cis-trans test was a key part of this work.

The basis of the cis-trans test is the functional role of the gene. It is now known that each gene is made up of a particular sequence of nucleotides, defining the nucleotide sequence of a strand of ribonucleic acid (RNA). This RNA may, in turn, be used to define the sequence of amino acids in a protein. A mutant allele is a stretch of deoxyribonucleic acid (DNA) in which the nucleotide sequence has been altered, resulting in an altered RNA. The result may be an altered protein, or, sometimes, no protein at all.

In most of the higher organisms, including humans, chromosomes occur in pairs. That means every gene (except those on the sex chromosomes) is normally found in two copies. If one copy is mutated and the other gene makes a normal product that compensates, the mutation is said to be recessive. If both copies of the gene are mutated and no normal product is made, then the phenotype of the organism (that is, the expression of the gene) will be mutant.

In the cis-trans test, genetic crosses are arranged so that one yields an organism in which two recessive mutant alleles to be tested are on opposite homologues. In other words, one chromosome of a pair will have one mutant allele, and the other chromosome will have the other mutant allele. The alleles are then said to be in a trans configuration. If the two alleles are mutations of the same gene, the phenotype of the organism will be a mutant one; if the alleles belong to separate genes, the organism will have a normal, or wild-type, phenotype. When alleles produce a normal phenotype, they are said to complement each other. If the mutant alleles are arranged in the cis configuration, so that both are on the same chromosome, the resulting phenotype will be normal, whether the alleles are in the same or different genes.

Eye color mutations in *Drosophila melanogaster* (the fruit fly) are one example of the application of the cis-trans test. The mutations raspberry (*ras*) and prune (*pn*), when homozygous, can change the normal, brick-red eye color of the fly to a deep, brown or reddish purple. The question is whether these mutations represent different alleles of the same gene or are alleles of two different genes that happen to be close together. After a few matings, it is possible to obtain the following genotypes (in each case, the + symbol represents the normal, or wild-type allele):

Fly 1: ras pn / + +   *Fly 2: ras + / + pn*
Phenotype: wild type   *Phenotype:* wild type
(cis configuration)   (trans configuration)

Fly 1 has two mutant alleles on the same chromosome, and fly 2 has the same two alleles separated, so that they are on separate homologues. The phenotype of the second fly, the one with the trans configuration, is the key. In this fly, the wild-type alleles in each case complement or compensate for the mutant form of the gene on the opposite chromosome. When such complementation occurs, the mutations must be in separate genes.

Two more eye color mutations in *Drosophila* show how the cis-trans test can identify alleles of the same gene. The white (*w*) mutation in *Drosophila*, first found in the laboratory of Thomas Hunt Morgan in 1910, results in flies with pure white eyes. Another mutation, originally called spotted (*sp*) and recovered in 1944, results in flies with mottled, yellowish-brown eyes. If a cis-trans test is done with these two mutants, the following results are seen:

> *Fly 1: w sp / + +*   *Fly 2: w + / + sp*
> *Phenotype:* wild type   *Phenotype:* brown eye
> (cis configuration)   (trans configuration)

When two mutants are alleles and are placed in trans configuration, both chromosomes then carry a mutant or defective copy of the same gene. This means the trans fly will have a mutant phenotype, unlike the wild-type phenotype seen in the first example. In this case, spotted is actually an allele of the white gene, although that was not obvious at first from its phenotype.

Before the structure of DNA was understood, the gene was also defined as the basic unit of recombination; recombination within a gene was not thought to occur. In the analogy of genes as beads on a string, recombination was thought to involve the breakage and reunion of the string at positions between beads, never within them. It is now known that, in the process of recombination, pieces of chromosomes break off and rejoin in new combinations, although the rules that this process follows are not fully understood.

Recombination is essential to the cis-trans test. Only through recombination can cis configurations be obtained. The frequency of the occurrence of recombination is related to the closeness of two points on a chromosome. If recombination is desired between two regions that are very close, the chance that crossing over will occur is very low. Recombination can even be used to map mutations within a gene (a process called fine structure analysis), but it is a very long process, because the distance separating mutations within a gene will be very small.

Using the cis-trans test and recombination together led to the discovery of a small group of mutations called pseudoalleles. When two pseudoalleles are examined using the cis-trans test, an organism in trans configuration will have a mutant phenotype, leading to the conclusion that the alleles belong to the same gene. When recombination is used to try to map these mutations, however, it turns out that they are in separate structural genes. Pseudoalleles, then, are found in separate structural genes that interact in some functions. Several examples of interaction between pseudoalleles can be found in *Drosophila*. In one such example, the two genes postbithorax (*pbx*) and bithorax (*bx*) are both involved in determining the normal formation of the fly's balancing organs (also called halteres), a pair of winglike structures that help the fly in its flight. These genes are adjacent on the chromosome but are structurally distinct. The fact that the gene products must interact is revealed by the results of the cis-trans test; when mutants for these genes are placed in trans configuration, the phenotype of the fly is mutant.

Applications of the Method

The cis-trans test was developed by Seymour Benzer and his coworkers in the 1950's. They worked with a particular virus, called T4, which attacks only bacteria, and they studied one T4 viral gene, called *rII*. Mutants of *rII* could be easily identified by the size of the plaques they made. (A plaque is a clear circle in a spread of bacteria which results when viruses attack and destroy the bacteria in that area.)

Complementation (cis-trans) tests between mutants in different viruses can be performed by using a procedure called a spot test. Viruses carrying one mutation are added to bacterial cells, then spread out on a plate containing nutrients and a solidifying agent (usually agar). Later, a drop of fluid containing viruses with a different mutation is spotted onto the solid surface. In the area of the drop, some bacterial cells will be attacked by viruses of both types. If the mutations complement each other, a normal plaque will result in that area. After looking at hundreds of different mutations, all of which had the same phenotype (large plaques), scientists at Benzer's laboratory determined that the *rII* gene was actually made up of two functional groups (which they called cistrons) and that every mutant could be assigned to one or the other of these groups.

Cis-trans testing has also played a critical role in bacterial genetics and the study of the function and regulation of bacterial genes. While eukaryotic genes are found on paired chromosomes, bacteria normally have only a single chromosome and, therefore, only one copy of each gene. Using plasmids, scientists can create cells with two copies of one or more genes. These partially diploid cells are called merozygotes.

The techniques of genetic engineering rely heavily on plasmids. Plasmids are small, circular pieces of DNA that are easily transferred between bacterial cells. Using restriction endonucleases, enzymes that cut DNA, genes can be removed from one chromosome and placed in a plasmid, using another enzyme, called ligase, as a molecular glue. In bacterial cells, such artificially created plasmids are essential to complementation testing.

Cis-trans and recombination tests can determine the relative location of mutations, but learning the DNA sequence of a gene requires molecular techniques. In one method developed by A. Maxam and Walter Gilbert, identical strands of DNA are "labeled" by attaching radioactive phosphorus to one end, then exposed to different chemicals that destroy one or two specific bases. When a base is destroyed, the strand tends to break at that point. The resulting fragments can then be separated by gel electrophoresis, and this information is used to determine the original base sequence. In gel electrophoresis, samples are placed in a depression in a gelatinlike slab swimming in a buffered liquid. An electrical current is then applied to the liquid, and negatively charged molecules, such as DNA fragments, move toward the positive pole. Smaller fragments move faster than larger ones, so this technique can be used to separate molecules on the basis of size.

Context

Understanding complementation of alleles, as determined by the cis-trans test, is essential to the understanding of genes. Genes control nearly every aspect of human development; changes in genes may result in benefits for an organism, but more often, changes result in undesired effects, as seen in human genetic diseases such as cystic fibrosis, Huntington's disease, and sickle-cell anemia.

One important application of complementation may come in the treatment of genetic diseases. Gene therapy involves the use of genetic-engineering techniques to alter a patient's own cells to correct a genetic mutation. In some cases, this means the addition of a normal gene to compensate for (complement) a person's own defective genes. In other instances, it may be possible to add a whole new gene that will produce a drug or other chemical needed by the body.

Agricultural geneticists also use complementation studies in their efforts to develop strains of plants that can resist pests, droughts, or extreme heat. Molecular technology can help introduce the desired genes into an important crop plant, but only classical genetic techniques can allow those desired genes to be identified in the first place.

Information from complementation tests helped develop the operon model of gene regulation in bacteria. In this work, scientists found that some portions of DNA act as control regions, determining whether the structural parts of the gene will be translated. These control regions are cis-acting; that is, they regulate only genes that are on the same chromosome. Such cis-acting control regions have been found in higher organisms, including humans. Without knowledge of how genes are regulated (turned on and off), processes such as development and aging will never be understood.

Before the 1940's, genes were believed to be the units of function, recombination, and mutation in cells. Through work involving cis-trans tests, scientists have found that most mutations affect only a single nucleotide pair and that recombination can take place between two nucleotide pairs within a gene. Although the gene is the unit of function in cells, the existence of pseudoalleles has shown that more than one gene may interact in a single function.

Traditional methods of genetic analysis using the cis-trans test and controlled crosses cannot be used in humans for obvious ethical reasons. Therefore, past discoveries of human genes relied heavily on the study of rare genetic diseases and birth defects. Genes that control important metabolic reactions were difficult to locate, because an embryo with such a defect could die long before birth. The techniques of molecular genetics may help with this problem. One day, scientists hope to know the nucleotide sequence of every human gene; this is the ultimate goal of the Human Genome Project. Through the coordinated efforts of scientists around the world, every human gene will be located and sequenced. Once this is done, the search will still not be over. Knowledge about the genotype of an organism does not ensure understanding of how the genotype causes a certain phenotype to appear. New techniques of employing complementation testing and recombination, perhaps using cultured cells, will play an important role in the process of understanding the interaction between genetic information and the actual structure of any organism, including humans.

Bibliography

Benzer, Seymour. "The Fine Structure of the Gene." *Scientific American* 206 (January, 1962): 70-84. The classic review article on the investigation of the *rII* gene of the T4 virus, written by the scientist who headed the investigations. Designed for readers with some familiarity with viruses and bacteria.

Rothwell, Norman. *Understanding Genetics*. 4th ed. New York: Oxford University Press, 1988. An intermediate-level text with excellent diagrams, this book is a fine introduction to Benzer's viral work. Chapter 16, "Viruses and Their Genetic Systems," discusses viral life cycles and classifications, RNA viruses, and the role of viruses in cancer.

Russell, P. J. *Genetics*. 2d ed. Glenview, Ill.: Scott, Foresman, 1990. A well-written intermediate-level college text with many touches of humor. Complementation analysis is discussed in chapter 14, "Genetic Fine Structure and Gene Function." In addition to an extensive index, the author includes a thorough bibliography and a glossary.

Suzuki, D., A. Griffiths, J. Miller, and R. Lewontin. *An Introduction to Genetic Analysis*. 4th ed. New York: W. H. Freeman, 1989. This intermediate-level college text reviews the important concepts in genetics and presents the experimental work that led to the development of important theories. Chapter 12, "The Nature of the Gene," gives an in-depth analysis of Benzer's viral work. Chapter 15, "The Manipulation of DNA," also explains many of the important techniques of molecular genetics.

Weaver, R. F., and P. W. Hedrick. *Genetics*. Dubuque, Iowa: Wm. C. Brown, 1989. Written for college audiences, the discussion is nevertheless readable by advanced high school students. Unlike many texts, it includes full-color photographs and diagrams. Chapter 13 discusses the cis-trans test using bacterial genes as an example. Benzer's work with *rII* is covered briefly in the same chapter. Recombination and potential mechanisms of how it works on the molecular level are clearly explained in chapter 7.

Lisa A. Lambert

Cross-References

CONCEPTION

Type of life science: Reproduction
Other fields of study: Animal anatomy, animal physiology, anthropology, and developmental biology (embryology)

Conception is the fertilization of a female's egg to produce a living organism. It is the means by which life is perpetuated and by which species keep from going extinct.

Principal terms

ACROSOME: the structure at the forward tip of sperm that is the first to fuse with the egg membrane and enter the egg cell
MEIOSIS: a type of cell division that occurs during the production of sex cells (sperm and egg) in which the species chromosome number is cut in half
PLASMA MEMBRANE: a membrane that surrounds the cytoplasm of cells and regulates the passage of molecules into and out of the cell
ZONA PELLUCIDA: the gelatinous layer that surrounds an ovulated egg
ZYGOTE: a fertilized egg cell that results from the fusion of sperm and egg

Summary of the Phenomenon

Conception, better known in scientific communities as fertilization of eggs by sperm, is the means by which sexual reproduction takes place in nearly all multicellular organisms and is fundamental to the maintenance of life. In both mammals and nonmammals, the pathway that leads to fusion of an egg with a single sperm consists of many compulsory steps that occur in order. These steps include species-specific cellular recognition, intracellular and intercellular membrane fusions, and enzyme-catalyzed modifications of cellular investments.

Mature sperm have three major regions: a head, a midpiece, and a tail, which correspond roughly to genetic, metabolic, and locomotor regions, respectively. The head of the sperm consists almost entirely of the spermatid nucleus, which contains deoxyribonucleic acid (DNA). Surrounding the plasma membrane, which encloses the nucleus, is a helmetlike area called the acrosome. This area contains hydrolytic enzymes that will enable the sperm to penetrate and enter the egg. The sperm midpiece consists of mitochondria spiraled tightly around the contractile filaments of the tail. The mitochondria provide the metabolic energy needed for the whiplike movements of the tail that propel the sperm at a speed of 1 to 4 millimeters per minute. In mammals, sperm are ejaculated into the vagina or the uterus and swim to the female's Fallopian tubes (oviduct), where fertilization can occur. The seminal fluid contains prostaglandins, which cause mild uterine contractions that help the sperm reach the Fallopian tubes. In mammals, before a sperm can fertilize the egg, the sperm must reside for a time in the female genital tract (less than an hour in mice and up to six hours in humans). During this time, proteins that coat the outer surface of the head region are removed so that the acrosome membrane becomes fragile and the acrosomal enzymes can be easily released.

At ovulation, a mammalian egg is surrounded by a thick, transparent membrane called the zona pellucida. The thickness of this "egg envelope" varies in different species of animals. Between the plasma membrane of the egg and the zona pellucida there is a gap called the perivitelline space. Within the egg's cytoplasm are cortical granules. In an unfertilized mouse egg there are approximately four thousand of these granules, a modest number compared with the fifteen thousand or so found in sea urchin eggs. These granules play a role in inactivating the sperm receptors and will form a fertilization envelope if the egg is fertilized.

The pathway leading to fertilization consists of several steps. Sperm first attach to the ovulated egg at the surface of the zona pellucida. This is a relatively loose association and is species-specific. Sperm of one species rarely will attach to the egg of another species (although some exceptions can occur; as when a horse and donkey produce a mule). In vitro, as many as fifteen hundred sperm have been seen to bind to a single mouse egg. The zona pellucida is made up of sperm receptors, molecules named ZP3. Each zona pellucida contains approximately a billion copies of ZP3. The sperm attach to these molecules of ZP3 much as a key goes into a lock. The ZP3 molecules vary in structure from species to species, and this variation is what causes the attachment to be species-specific.

The attached sperm now compete in the acrosomal reaction in preparation for penetration of the zona pellucida. The acrosomal reaction is the release of acrosomal enzymes. Hundreds of acrosomes must rupture to penetrate the zona pellucida. Once a path is cleared, a single sperm can then make contact with the egg's plasma membrane. A sperm that approaches the egg after hundreds of sperm have undergone acrosomal reactions to expose the membrane is in the best position to be the fertilizing sperm.

As soon as one sperm makes contact with the egg's plasma membrane, sodium channels in the membrane open and ionic sodium moves out from the perivitelline space into the egg's cytoplasm. This rapid change in ionic charge prevents other sperm from fusing with the plasma membrane. This mechanism ensures that only the DNA from one sperm will enter the egg, thereby providing the correct chromosomal complement for the offspring.

The presence of ionic sodium in the cytoplasm brings about the next step, the cortical reaction. The cortical granules spill out their contents, and these molecules move into the perivitelline space. These molecules inactivate the ZP3 sperm receptors and help to form a fertilization envelope that will surround the fertilized egg. This envelope will provide a protective layer around the embryo. The altered ZP3 molecules detach all sperm still in contact with the plasma membrane, and a permanent block to the entry of any other sperm is established.

Once a sperm has successfully entered the egg, changes occur in the egg's nucleus. Meiosis, which was stopped in the ovary, is completed. The sperm and egg nuclei swell and approach each other. When they touch, their membranes rupture, releasing their chromosomes. Combination of the maternal and paternal chromosomes constitutes the act of fertilization and produces the zygote. As soon as the chromosomes come together, they replicate and two new cells are formed. This early division of the zygote is called cleavage. During this time, the dividing cells are contained by the zona pellucida. Although cleavage increases the number of cells, it does not result in an increase in the size of the developing organism.

In humans, the first cleavage is completed after about thirty-six hours, and each succeeding division takes slightly less time. By the second day after conception, the second cleavage is completed. By the end of the third day, there are sixteen cells. A few days after fertilization, the successive cleavages have produced a solid mass of cells called the morula, which is still surrounded by the zona pellucida.

As the number of cells in the morula increases, it moves from the original site of fertilization down through the Fallopian tube into the uterus. By this time the dense cluster of cells has altered to form a hollow ball of cells referred to as a blastocyst. The blastocyst is differentiated into an outer covering of cells called the trophoblast and an inner cell mass. In mammals the trophoblast ultimately forms the placenta, and the inner cell mass develops into the embryo.

Methods of Study

It was not until the early nineteenth century that the first penetration of a mammalian egg by a sperm was observed. Prior to that time, the role played by each sex in the process of reproduction was greatly misunderstood. Among the ancient Greeks, it was believed that semen and menstrual blood combined to form the embryo and fetal membranes. Aristotle suggested that the semen contributed in a nonmaterial sense, giving only form to the developing embryo, which he regarded as arising entirely from the female. Opposed to this view, was the Epicurean, Lucretius, who believed that the embryo was formed of the material elements of both parents. The naturalists of the Middle Ages and of the Renaissance based their concepts in part on Aristotle and in part on the ideas of Epicureans, as handed down by Galen and his Arabian followers.

By the seventeenth century, the English physician William Harvey realized that all creatures come from an egg—a remarkable insight, since he had not seen the minute eggs of mammals. Knowledge of eggs was advanced further by Marcello Malpighi, a professor at the University of Bologna, who described the development of the chicken embryo in detail in 1673. Unfortunately, he claimed to see the form of an embryo in an unfertilized egg and so launched the erroneous theory of preformation. Mammalian sperm were discovered by Antoni van Leeuwenhoek six years later, and it was then claimed that the sperm, rather than the egg, contained the homunculus, or a preformed organism. Thus, two schools of thought arose, the permatists, who held that the testes of Adam must have contained all humankind, and the ovists, who held the same belief for the ovaries of Eve.

This state of affairs was not corrected until the eighteenth century, when Kaspar

Wolff observed that the leaves of plants developed from undifferentiated tissue at the growing point and argued that this could not be a process of unfolding, since the leaves were not preformed. Wolff made similar observations in the developing chick, showing that the abdominal organs developed from apparently homogeneous tissue.

At this time only the large eggs of fish, amphibians, reptiles, and birds were known, and it was naturally thought that the mammalian ovum must be comparable in size. Thus, when Regnier de Graaf, in 1672, described the growth of ovarian follicles, these were at first thought to be mammalian eggs. This error was corrected some 150 years later by Karl Ernst von Baer, who, on examining human ovaries, discerned in each follicle a yellowish-white point. In 1843, Martin Barry observed sperm with a rabbit egg. The male nucleus and its union with the egg were recorded by Pierre Joseph van Beneden in 1875 and by Oscar Hertwig in 1876. Soon afterward, the significance of chromosomes was realized and van Beneden showed that the chromosomes of the first cleavage are derived equally from the sperm and egg.

Further morphological details of fertilization were recorded in the rat (1910), in the guinea pig (1913), in the ferret (1930), and in the mouse (1941). With the development of phase-contrast microscopes, living eggs could be observed. By the 1930's, several scientists had tried to initiate oocyte maturation in culture solutions. Gregory Pincus, one of the major contributors to the development of the contraceptive pill, showed how the rabbit egg would mature in vitro. The procedure was remarkably simple: A fully grown primary oocyte was removed from its ovarian follicle and placed in a simple culture media, where it promptly matured in preparation for fertilization.

Fertilization of mammalian eggs in vitro is a topic of only the late twentieth century. Before that time, it was considered impossible in most mammals because of the time the sperm cells had to reside in the uterus before they were able to fertilize the egg. Using freshly ovulated oocytes from hamsters and "ripened" sperm, scientists finally achieved fertilization in a culture medium. The sperm cells were ripened by placing them in a chamber that was inserted overnight into the uterus of a female hamster. The era of in vitro fertilization had begun. The practice was tried on many laboratory animals. Through surgery, developed oocytes could be removed, fertilized in the petri dish, and then surgically implanted into the uterus to develop. The idea was quickly accepted in agriculture, and today these techniques are commonly used in breeding cattle.

In vitro fertilization enabled scientists to discover and outline the details of sperm penetration and fertilization. Many of the details of the ZP3 molecules were worked out by Paul M. Wassarman and his associates while he was at Harvard. For a decade they worked on finding the answers to major questions concerning sperm receptor sites, the initiation of the acrosome reaction, and the biochemical changes that occur to make the zona pellucida impermeable to sperm after fertilization.

Context

The work on in vitro fertilization in animals set the stage for experiments in humans. The American Medical Association estimates that 15 percent of all couples in the United States are unable to have any children—in many cases, because fertilization never takes place. In vitro fertilization in humans could help some of these couples.

On July 12, 1978, Louise Joy Brown was born near Manchester, England. Her birth was the first recorded case of in vitro fertilization in humans. The procedure now is well documented; today more than one hundred human babies have been conceived in this way. The infertile woman is given a follicle-stimulating hormone soon after menstruation so that several eggs will be produced. Just before the time of ovulation, a small incision is made near the ovary and, using a laparascope with a suction needle, the newly formed eggs are aspirated. They are then placed in a medium that simulates the fluids in the female reproductive tract. Concentrated sperm from the male is placed into the same solution in the hope that fertilization will occur. Zygotes are then placed in a second solution and observed for cleavage. When a zygote reaches the eight-cell or sixteen-cell stage, it is introduced into the uterus for implantation and subsequent growth.

It is also possible to freeze unused embryos to permit parents a successive pregnancy several years later or allow a second attempt at implantation if the first attempt is unsuccessful. The first instance in the United States of two successful pregnancies from a single in vitro fertilization procedure occurred on November 19, 1988, when a woman gave birth to two daughters two years after the birth of her son.

Gamete intrafallopian transfer (GIFT), a type of in vitro fertilization that tries to mimic the normal process of conception, was devised as a means to overcome the low success rate (15 to 20 percent) of the previously described method. The eggs are removed in the same manner but, instead of growing in a medium, eggs and sperm are immediately placed in the Fallopian tubes after they have been brought together. GIFT has the advantage of being a one-step procedure for the woman and of being less expensive.

Another type of in vitro fertilization currently in use is embryo transfer. With this procedure, the husband's seminal fluid is used to inseminate a donor female artificially. Following fertilization, the morula or blastocyst is transferred from the donor to the infertile wife, who carries it to term. Embryo transfer is indicated for females who are infertile because of surgically untreatable blocked Fallopian tubes or who are afraid of passing on their own genes because they are carriers of serious genetic disorders.

Work is currently being done on a contraceptive vaccine. A vaccine has been developed using genetic-engineering techniques that produces long-term contraception in female mice. The vaccine works by binding with the sperm receptor sites on the zona pellucida, thus inhibiting the attachment of sperm. In the experimental mice it has been effective for up to thirty-six weeks. Researchers are hoping that a similar vaccine can be developed for humans.

Bibliography

DeWitt, William. *Human Biology: Form, Function, and Adaptation.* Glenview, Ill.: Scott, Foresman, 1989. A college textbook written for the nonscience major. Chapter 18 deals with human reproduction in simple terms and contains four pages of color plates describing the events from fertilization to birth. Easy to read.

Hole, John W., Jr. *Human Anatomy and Physiology.* 2d ed. Dubuque, Iowa: Wm. C. Brown, 1981. A college text designed for students pursuing careers in allied health fields who have minimal backgrounds in the biological sciences. Chapter 22 deals with human growth and development and has several pages of color plates depicting embryos and fetuses. Good glossary and textual summary.

Mader, Sylvia. *Human Biology.* Dubuque, Iowa: Wm. C. Brown, 1988. A college textbook designed for the nonscience major that contains a number of chapters dealing with human reproduction. Well illustrated. Color diagrams describe fertilization in a clear, concise manner. Suitable for high school students.

Moore, Keith L. *Before We Are Born.* 3d ed. Philadelphia: W. B. Saunders, 1989. A simplified embryology textbook that deals with human conception and birth defects. Excellent charts describe daily events from fertilization until birth, and a thorough discussion deals with birth defects.

Wassarman, Paul M. "Fertilization in Mammals." *Scientific American* 259 (December, 1988): 78-84. A major reference for the latest work involving sperm receptor sites. Somewhat technical but has excellent illustrations and photographs.

Roberta B. Williams

Cross-References

Birth, 226; Fertilization, 969; Gametogenesis, 1061; Genetic Screening and Counseling, 1170; Lactation, 1528; Pregnancy and Prenatal Development, 2185; Prenatal Diagnostic Techniques, 2194; The Female Reproductive System, 2346; The Male Reproductive System, 2354.

CONDITIONING

Type of life science: Ethology
Other fields of study: Anthropology, neurobiology, and zoology

Classical conditioning and operant conditioning are two forms of learning in which a stimulus comes to be paired with a response. Both are considered forms of conditioned or associative learning; they differ in the manner in which the unconditioned response first appears.

Principal terms

ASSOCIATIVE LEARNING: a form of learning in which a particular stimulus becomes regularly associated with a particular response; also called conditioned learning

CLASSICAL (PAVLOVIAN) CONDITIONING: conditioned learning in which the unconditioned response is induced as an automatic reflex whenever the conditioned stimulus is present, regardless of the animal's behavior

CONDITIONED LEARNING: a form of learning in which a particular stimulus becomes regularly associated with a particular response; also called associative learning

CONDITIONED RESPONSE: a response paired with a stimulus as the result of conditioned learning

CONDITIONED STIMULUS: a stimulus which becomes paired with a particular response as the result of conditioned learning

OPERANT CONDITIONING: conditioned learning in which the unconditioned response first occurs spontaneously, without being paired to any unconditioned stimulus, and reinforcement depends on the animal's behavior

REINFORCEMENT: anything that makes a certain behavior more likely to occur again

RESPONSE: the reaction of a living organism to a stimulus of any kind

UNCONDITIONED RESPONSE: an automatic response to an unconditioned stimulus

UNCONDITIONED STIMULUS: a stimulus that automatically evokes an unconditioned response

Summary of the Phenomenon

Classical conditioning and operant conditioning are two forms of learning in which a particular stimulus becomes regularly associated with a particular response. Learning of this type is called either conditioned or associative learning.

The discovery of conditioning took place in the laboratory of the Russian physiologist Ivan P. Pavlov (1849-1936), who found that dogs salivated in response to food (a true reflex); in some cases, however, they began salivating even before the food was given to them. Pavlov thought that the dogs were responding to some stimulus other than food, perhaps the opening of the kitchen door and the appearance (and sound) of the assistant carrying the food dish. He called this response a "conditioned reflex" to distinguish it from the original (unconditioned) reflex of salivating in response to food. Pavlov investigated many stimuli and found that dogs could be trained to respond to almost any kind of stimulus as long as it was presented in the right way. Some of the terminology he introduced is still in use: The stimulus to which the dog learned to respond was called the conditioned stimulus, and the response (salivation) was called the conditioned response. Before the learning took place, the dog salivated automatically in response to food or vinegar, an inborn reaction that is now known to be controlled by the autonomic nervous system. In this case, the food is called an unconditioned stimulus and the response (salivation) an unconditioned response. Unconditioned responses usually take place automatically and involuntarily. In several cases, they can even be demonstrated in animals whose cerebral hemispheres have been cut from the rest of the brain, proving that conscious thought is not needed for the response. The conditioned stimulus is usually a neutral stimulus, one that neither evokes nor prevents the unconditioned response (salivation) in unconditioned animals. Pavlov's basic discovery can be summarized as follows: If an unconditioned stimulus (such as food) closely follows a conditioned stimulus (such as a bell) on repeated occasions, and if the unconditioned stimulus evokes a response, then the conditioned stimulus will eventually come to evoke that same response. The learned association between the new (conditioned) stimulus and the conditioned response depends on the reinforcement of the association by experimentally inducing the response each time that the conditioned stimulus appears, regardless of the animal's behavior. This type of conditioning is called classical or Pavlovian conditioning.

Pavlov also tried to make his dogs forget what they had learned. To do that, he trained dogs to respond to the sound of a bell. Then he presented the bell without giving any food. At first, the dogs salivated because of the conditioned response, but after a while they stopped responding. This type of "unlearning" is called extinction. Pavlov found, however, that the response could be relearned in many fewer trials than were necessary for the response to be learned the first time.

Pavlov also investigated second- and third-order conditioning. For example, a dog could be trained to salivate in response to a bell. If a light were turned on just before the bell was rung, the dog would learn to salivate in response to the light. Salivating in response to food was an unconditioned response; salivating in response to the bell was a conditioned response; salivating in response to the light was a second-order conditioned response. Once the first conditioned response had been learned, the original, unconditioned stimulus (food) did not need to be presented in order to establish a second-order response. Pavlov thought that very complex behavioral patterns could be learned as the result of higher-order conditioning.

A later investigator in Pavlov's tradition, V. M. Bekhterev, studied the conditioning of avoidance, or fear. If a light or other stimulus were given and an electric shock applied soon afterward, the dogs learned to show an avoidance or fear response whenever the light was turned on. This type of learning took place in very few trials. It also lasted a very long time without extinction.

The other major type of conditioning is instrumental, or operant, conditioning. Operant conditioning involves learning in which the pleasant or unpleasant consequences of behavior leads to increases or decreases in the probability that the behavior will occur again. For example, a rat might be put in a cage equipped with a bar that it can push. If a light is turned on, the pressing of the bar causes a pellet of food to appear in a food dispenser. The light, or conditioned stimulus, is now called a discriminating stimulus. The bar-pressing is called an operant form of behavior, and the food pellet is called the reinforcement. Operant conditioning begins very slowly, as the rat explores its surroundings and makes dozens or hundreds of voluntary movements of all kinds. By chance at first, the rat may happen to press the bar when the light is on. Since it is rewarded with a food pellet, it tries to repeat this behavior. After many trials, the rat learns to press the bar only when the light is on. Experiments in operant conditioning have often focused on bar-pressing in rats and pecking behavior in pigeons and other birds.

In all cases of operant conditioning, the animal's response is voluntary and occurs the first time spontaneously, or "by chance," in the sense that there is no particular stimulus that brings it about. Reinforcement occurs only when the operant response takes place in the presence of the discriminating stimulus. Reinforcement by a pleasant stimulus (such as food) is called positive reinforcement; removal of a painful stimulus (such as turning off an electric shock) is called negative reinforcement. Both types of reinforcement make the operant behavior more likely to occur again. Punishment by an unpleasant stimulus (such as an electric shock or a loud noise) will make the operant behavior less likely to occur in the future.

Early investigators of operant conditioning included John B. Watson and Edward L. Thorndike. Watson, like Pavlov, believed in the automatic pairing of a stimulus with its response. Thorndike and his followers believed that unconditioned responses could be voluntary and that reinforcement could be made to depend on this voluntary behavior. Thorndike expressed this relationship in his "law of effect": The frequency of any voluntary behavior, he said, could be modified by modifying its outcome. It remained for Burrhus Frederic Skinner to distinguish clearly between operant and Pavlovian conditioning: In Pavlovian conditioning, the reinforcing (unconditioned) stimulus is given in all cases, regardless of the animal's behavior, but in operant conditioning, the reinforcing stimulus is given only if the animal makes the correct response. Skinner also improved and perfected the apparatus used for operant conditioning experiments; this apparatus is now usually called a "Skinner box."

Skinner discovered that operant conditioning can lead to the formation of what he called "superstitious" behavior. In an experiment in which pigeons were reinforced for pecking at a disk, some pigeons made slight turning movements or other unrelated movements just before they pecked. Any reward given to these birds reinforced both the pecking and the irrelevant movement that preceded it. Eventually, some pigeons learned an irrelevant movement along with the pecking behavior: They turned and then pecked, even though it was only the pecking that was reinforced. Another way to teach superstitious behavior to pigeons is to provide reinforcement frequently but randomly. When reinforcement (usually a grain of food) is given, it reinforces whatever the pigeon was doing just before. The pigeon tries to repeat the behavior and soon receives another reinforcement. Using this procedure, Skinner found that one pigeon had learned to stand on one leg; a second had learned to turn to one side.

Investigators who study operant conditioning have discovered a tendency that they call stimulus generalization. If an animal is taught to respond to a red light, it also tries responding to a green or yellow light; an animal that responds to a sound might try to respond to other, similar sounds. Only after many trials does the animal learn to make the proper discrimination, responding only to the appropriate stimuli. In this way, operant conditioning can be used to test the animal's sensory abilities: An animal can distinguish two stimuli if it can be trained, through operant conditioning, to respond differently to each.

Modern experiments on operant conditioning have shown that reinforcement works best if given immediately; delayed reinforcement makes the learning experience more difficult. Delay is possible, however, if a secondary reinforcer is given immediately. A secondary reinforcer is a naturally neutral stimulus whose positive value is learned through previous association with a primary (naturally positive) stimulus. For example, chimpanzees were trained to use colored poker chips in a vending machine that dispensed grapes and other pieces of food. Once they had learned that poker chips could be used in this way, they could be rewarded for good behavior if they received poker chips immediately, even though the poker chips could be exchanged for food only on infrequent occasions. The food dispensed by the vending machine was a primary reinforcer; the poker chips were a secondary reinforcer. Humans learn to use money as a secondary reinforcer in much the same way.

Like all learning, classical conditioning and operant conditioning take place against a background of inherited abilities and limitations. All animals have genetically inherited predispositions to pay attention to certain kinds of stimuli and to respond within a certain inherited range of behavioral abilities. The limits of sensory discrimination (for example, being able to distinguish two notes differing only slightly in pitch) are also inherited. Last, animals can learn complex sequences of behavior only up to some limit of complexity, which varies from species to species and is probably innately controlled. Humans have the highest limits of all, meaning that they can learn the most complex sequences of behavior.

Methods of Study

Classical, or Pavlovian, conditioning was studied initially by surgically connecting the duct of one of the salivary glands of the experimental animal to an external tube. The animal was then placed in a restraining harness, and stimuli were presented to it. Tubes inserted into the mouth could be used to supply vinegar or to spray meat powder. The strength of any response was measured by the amount of saliva produced. In general, an apparatus for the study of classical conditioning in nonhuman animals must include some kind of restraining device appropriate to the species, plus the instrumentation necessary to measure whatever conditioned response is being tested.

Operant conditioning in nonhuman animals is generally studied using some version of a Skinner box of a size appropriate to the species. The apparatus must include mechanisms to display stimuli, to allow (and often to record) operant responses, and to provide reinforcements, punishments, or both. These mechanisms may be operated by the experimenter, but nowadays they are more often operated electronically under the control of a computer, which also makes a record of all responses. These devices, and the programs that control them, have become more complex and sophisticated with each passing decade.

Studies on human beings using either classical or operant conditioning generally take place in artificial settings such as classrooms or mental hospitals. In a large percentage of cases, the aim of these studies is to help correct a behavioral problem in one individual at a time. The goal of studying conditioning scientifically in numerous similar individuals is often of secondary importance to the clinical psychologists treating the patient. Therefore, hundreds of studies have been done on one or a few patients at a time. While much can be learned from examining and comparing the results of these studies, there is always the possible objection that the conditions used in one hospital were not exactly the same as the conditions used in another, thus perhaps accounting for some of the variation in results. For this reason, it is important for researchers who publish these studies to describe the conditions as fully as possible, so that later researchers, replicating their experiments, can keep conditions as similar as possible.

Context

There are several practical applications of classical conditioning in which positive or negative attitudes toward certain things are formed. Advertising and political propaganda both use classical conditioning to help form positive associations with certain things (such as a sponsor's product) and negative associations with others (such as an enemy in time of war). Some people learn phobias (intense, debilitating fears) by classical conditioning under unusual circumstances. For example, young children who survive a devastating earthquake often develop intense fear of anything that reminds them of the conditions that preceded the quake.

The practical applications of operant conditioning are more numerous and more diverse. Parents and teachers usually reinforce good behavior and punish misbehavior, but they sometimes make mistakes, and the child consequently learns the wrong thing. Operant conditioning under controlled conditions can be used to reverse this situation. Operant conditioning is also used by teachers when they reward correct answers with a smile or a compliment. Programmed instruction is based on the premise that most children are rewarded sufficiently simply by arriving at correct answers and discovering that they are right.

The major clinical applications of operant conditioning are in behavior modification or behavior therapy. Without worrying very much about the patient's remote past or subconscious, behavior therapists focus on the present situation, especially on the conditions that reinforce and sustain the inappropriate behavior. In one case, for example, a mental patient was making a large number of delusional statements, such as "I'm the queen. The queen wants a smoke. How's King George?" Often, these statements provoked conversations with the hospital attendants about how the patient could not possibly be the queen. The patient was thus being rewarded with attention. When psychologist Teodoro Ayllón persuaded the attendants to pay more attention to these delusional statements but to ignore normal ones, the frequency of delusional statements increased. Then he reversed the procedure and told the attendants to ignore all delusional statements but to respond with attention to any normal communication. Over a short time, the patient made far fewer delusional statements and was eventually cured of the tendency. Not all patients respond as well as this one did, but the results when patients do respond are very encouraging. In less extreme cases, behavior modification techniques using operant conditioning help people break bad habits such as smoking or overeating.

One special application of operant conditioning is called biofeedback. In this technique, electrodes or other sensing devices are used to monitor physiological conditions such as blood pressure or brain waves and make them visible to the patient. The patient can then be rewarded for keeping blood pressure low under stress, for example. Some individuals with high blood pressure respond favorably (at least temporarily) to this technique, but the expense and specialized equipment involved prevent its widespread use.

Bibliography

Kalish, H. I. *From Behavioral Science to Behavior Modification*. New York: McGraw-Hill, 1981. The book begins by presenting a well-organized review of both classical and operant conditioning, including many examples drawn from the voluminous literature on this subject. The book then proceeds to present and discuss the many practical applications of both types of conditioning. Classroom applications are covered, but greater emphasis is placed on clinical uses. Biofeedback and behavior modification are described and discussed.

Kimble, G. A. *Hilgard and Marquis' Conditioning and Learning*. 2d ed. New York: Appleton-Century-Crofts, 1961. A comprehensive treatment of the subject, now considered a classic. The book contains a good glossary and an extensive survey of the research literature. It is written at the college level and is illustrated with simple graphs only.

King, Donald L. *Conditioning: An Image Approach*. New York: Gardner Press, 1979. An easy-to-read summary of both classical and operant conditioning and their implications for the theory of learning and language acquisition. The illustrations are few, but they are well chosen and fully explained.

Klein, S. B., and R. R. Mowrer, eds. *Contemporary Learning Theories: Instrumental Conditioning Theory and the Impact of Biological Constraints on Learning.* Hillsdale, N.J.: Lawrence Erlbaum, 1989.

_____. *Contemporary Learning Theories: Pavlovian Conditioning and the Status of Traditional Learning Theory.* Hillsdale, N.J.: Lawrence Erlbaum, 1989. Each chapter in this two-volume set is a review article written by a different author summarizing the current status of behavioral psychologists' knowledge of conditioning and learning. Together, the two volumes contain a gold mine of information for those who are serious about reviewing research on these topics. The first volume covers operant conditioning and the inborn limits to learning; the second volume covers Pavlovian conditioning. Each chapter has an extensive bibliography.

Lahey, Benjamin B. *Psychology: An Introduction.* 2d ed. Dubuque, Iowa: Wm. C. Brown, 1986. A good and well-illustrated introductory text in psychology. Chapter 5 deals with conditioning and other forms of learning.

Mackintosh, N. J. *Conditioning and Associative Learning.* New York: Oxford University Press, 1983. A very good summary of all previous research, beginning with Pavlov, on all forms of conditioning and associative learning. The explanations are understandable, clear, and to the point. A few graphs and a lengthy bibliography round out the treatment.

Reynolds, G. S. *A Primer of Operant Conditioning.* Glenview, Ill.: Scott, Foresman, 1968. A short but clear summary of previous research studies on operant conditioning, based largely on the work of B. F. Skinner and his followers. The book suffers from the lack of a bibliography.

Schwartz, Barry. *Psychology of Learning and Behavior.* New York: W. W. Norton, 1978. A thorough and comprehensive treatment of both Pavlovian and operant conditioning. The explanations are clear and thorough, and there is a lengthy bibliography.

Williams, J. L. *Operant Learning: Procedures for Changing Behavior.* Monterey, Calif.: Brooks/Cole, 1973. This short book begins with a brief introduction to the principles of operant conditioning and the major research findings on various forms of operant learning. Concludes with a summary of the applications of operant learning to behavior therapy and to programmed instruction. Good bibliography.

Eli C. Minkoff

Cross-References

Ethology, 858; Habituation and Sensitization, 1254; Instincts, 1438; Memory, 1683; Nerve Circuits, 1890; Reflexes, 2301; The Sympathetic and Parasympathetic Nervous Systems, 2580.

THE CYTOPLASM

Type of life science: Cell biology (cytology)
Other field of study: Biochemistry

The nature of the cytoplasm is crucial to an understanding of cell behavior. In turn, an understanding of cell behavior is necessary for understanding biology, in that cells are the units of biological structure and function.

Principal terms

ARTIFACT: an alteration of a cell that is caused by preparations for its examination

BULK WATER: the water available to act as a solvent

CENTRIFUGATION: the separation of cell components according to their densities by spinning them at high rates of speed

CYTOPLASMIC MATRIX: that portion of the cytoplasm found among the organelles, cytoskeletal elements, and inclusions

CYTOSOL: the part of the cell that remains after organelles and inclusions have been removed by centrifugation

FIXATION: the treatment of cells with fixatives to minimize distortion of their structures (artifacts) in preparation for examination

WATER OF HYDRATION: water that is adsorbed to ions and molecules and is therefore not available to act as a solvent

Summary of the Phenomenon

The cytoplasm of eukaryotic cells is the entire portion of the cell between the plasma membrane and the nuclear membrane. It may be subdivided into four domains on the basis of its following components: organelles, the cytoskeleton, inclusions, and the cytoplasmic matrix. Organelles are subcellular components that are specialized for specific functions. Single-membrane organelles include the Golgi apparatus, vacuoles, lysosomes, and the endoplasmic reticulum (ER). Double-membrane organelles include the nucleus, mitochondria, and chloroplasts.

Elongated elements of the cytoplasm make up the cytoskeleton; they include microtubules, made of the protein tubulin; microfilaments, made of the protein actin; and intermediate filaments, composed of a variety of different proteins, depending on the cell type. Inclusions are considered to be nonliving components of the cytoplasm—for example, the liquid cell sap found in the cell sap vacuoles of many plant cells, starch granules found in plastids, and glycogen granules and pigment grains found free in the cytoplasm. The background material of the cytoplasm, in which the organelles, cytoskeleton, and inclusions are found, is widely referred to as the cytoplasmic matrix. Formerly, it was referred to as the cytosol.

A powerful technique used in cell biology is centrifugation, in which the various components of the cell are separated from one another by exposing homogenized cells to centrifugal forces. After the various components of the cell were removed, what remained was considered to be the "background" of the cytoplasm and was referred to as the cytosol. This term was then also applied to the intact cell. Examination of intact eukaryotic cells with the high-voltage (1-million-volt) electron microscope, however, has revealed that the cytoplasmic matrix is not the structureless background it was thought to be. A model that is accepted by many, but not all, cell biologists is that a gossamer latticework appears to pervade this region of the cytoplasm. Termed the microtrabecular lattice (MTL), it is considered to be composed of two phases: a protein phase making up the trabeculae (strands) and an aqueous phase composing the interstices between the trabeculae.

Although important activities also occur in the nucleus or in association with the plasma membrane, many of the activities carried on by the cell occur in the cytoplasm. The organelles, for example, conduct specialized functions: cell respiration by the mitochondria, photosynthesis by the chloroplasts, and direction of macromolecular "traffic" by the Golgi apparatus. Many aspects of cell shape and movement are orchestrated by elements of the cytoskeleton, such as cell polarization by intermediate filaments, chromosome movement by microtubules, and cytokinesis by microfilaments.

In addition to these specialized activities, however, a number of generally important cell activities take place in the cytoplasmic matrix. Although the beginning of gene expression, transcription, occurs in the nucleus, the overt aspect of gene expression, protein synthesis or translation, occurs in the cytoplasm on ribosomes. It has been known for many years that ribosomes may or may not be attached to the endoplasmic reticulum, depending on whether the protein being synthesized is destined for secretion from the cell or for internal use, respectively. Those ribosomes not on membranes of the endoplasmic reticulum were thought to be free in the cytosol (cytoplasmic matrix). Evidence indicates, however, that these "free" ribosomes may be attached to some formed elements of the cytoplasm (perhaps the trabeculae of the proposed microtrabecular lattice) during protein synthesis, much as the "attached" ribosomes are to the ER when they synthesize protein.

Another generally important cell activity is anaerobic metabolism, whereby cells are able to extract metabolic energy from organic molecules in the absence of free molecular oxygen. Observations have suggested that the responsible enzymes are not free in the cytoplasmic matrix, but are attached to formed elements of it.

Polar molecules (such as epinephrine, growth factors, and the apoprotein of low-density lipoprotein particles) that interact with cells will generally do so by attaching to receptors on the plasma membrane; however, the effects of these polar molecules are propagated through the cytoplasm, frequently in the form of a second messenger, such as cyclic adenosine monophosphate (cAMP) or calcium ions. Nonpolar molecules (such as estrogens, testosterone, and the synthetic hormone RU 486), however, generally pass through the plasma membrane and attach to receptors found in the cytoplasm. Subsequently, the hormone-receptor complex passes through the nuclear membrane to exert its effects on the genome of the cell.

Some substances, such as water, pass through the cytoplasm by simple diffusion, whereas others are moved through the cytoplasm in bulk. The latter movement involves the processes of pinocytosis and phagocytosis, known collectively as endocytosis (if the material is incoming) or exocytosis (if the material is outgoing). Exocytosis, or secretion, has been demonstrated to depend on intracellular calcium ions, which are released from intracellular stores into the cytoplasmic matrix. The movement of pinosomes, phagosomes, and secretion vacuoles through the cytoplasm and between the organelles indicates that the microtrabecular lattice, if it exists, must be a dynamic rather than a static structure.

In a brief, thought-provoking review, A. B. Fulton asked the question, "How crowded is the cytoplasm?" and brought some interesting observations to light. Although protein crystals can form with less than 10 percent protein by weight, actively growing cells contain between 17 percent and 26 percent protein by weight. Therefore, the volume occupied by protein in researchers' models of cytoplasm should more closely approximate crystals than dilute solutions, in which proteins are 0.1 percent or less. The presence of two significant phases of water, water of hydration and bulk water, must also be considered in any model of cytoplasm, considering that water of hydration is the water that proteins can use and that it is water of hydration that is required for enzyme activity. Experiments with dehydration of *Artemia* (brine shrimp), as well as with mammalian cells, exclude the possibility that the cell is exquisitely sensitive to reductions in the size of the bulk water phase. Furthermore, experiments have shown that the actual enzyme activity in the cytoplasm is a function not only of which enzyme is there but also of the concentration of all the other proteins. Fulton answers her own question, because the foregoing considerations (and others) suggest that the cell is a very crowded place. It appears that the cytoplasm is compact and is only a few times more open than a crystal, even though some proteins exist free in solution.

In summary, the nature of the cytoplasmic matrix is not clearly understood. It was controversial at the beginning of the twentieth century, and it remains controversial. It does appear, however, to have viscoelastic properties and be a thixotropic gel; that is, it is capable of becoming fluidlike. Any persistent model of the cytoplasmic matrix will have to explain the relationship of its water and protein; how it orchestrates the interaction of organelles, inclusions, and cytoskeleton, resulting in coordinated cell behavior; and its role in signal transduction between the cell nucleus and the cell environment.

Methods of Study

K. R. Porter, in writing a short history of the cytomatrix, has divided its study into three periods. The early period (1820-1910) was a mostly descriptive period, during which light microscopes improved and chemical fixatives, microtomes, and staining procedures were introduced. Biologists became aware of cells, how they divide, and how they assemble into tissues; additionally, cell pathology was pioneered. Biologists were divided as to whether the cytoplasm had a fibrillar, alveolar, or granular nature. Some believed that these natures were artifacts (unnatural alterations) of cell treatment, which stimulated the study of living cells. During the middle period (1910-1940), living cells were studied by the applications of microsurgery, centrifugation, hydrostatic pressure, iron particles and magnetic fields, and polarization and ultramicroscopy. In the recent period (beginning around World War II), the techniques of phase-contrast microscopy, cell fractionation, and electron microscopy were applied to cells, and the distinct discipline of cell biology emerged.

After World War II, the electron microscope (EM) began to be applied to biological specimens. Unlike optical microscopes, which use visible light as their source of illumination, the EM uses a beam of electrons for its "illumination." The penetrating power of such a beam of electrons depends on the amount of voltage applied to the instrument. For ordinary EMs, using about 60,000 volts, the penetrating power of the beam is minimal and the specimens being examined must be sectioned (sliced) very thin. For some components of the cell (membranes and ribosomes, for example), this is not particularly a problem; however, for other cellular structures, such as chromosomes, it is a severe limitation. This limitation has hampered efforts to understand the organization of the cytoplasm.

Fibrous structures oriented in three dimensions do not readily reveal their organization when sectioned into thin two-dimensional slices. The elements of the cytoskeleton, microtubules (MTs), microfilaments (MFs), and intermediate filaments (IFs) are fibrous structures, and the understanding of their distribution in the cytoplasm only began in the early 1970's.

The development of the high-voltage electron microscope has aided in attempts to understand the organization of the cytoplasm and its matrix. The high-voltage EM uses 1 million volts to generate a beam of great penetrating power. So powerful is this beam that it is not necessary to section cells: It is possible to view whole cells and thus gain insight into the organization of the cells in three dimensions. It was the application of this instrument that seemed to reveal the presence of a microtrabecular lattice (MTL) making up the cytoplasmic matrix.

The quick-freeze deep-etch technique is the other procedure that has had a major impact on attempts to understand the nature of cytoplasmic organization. The quick-freeze part of this technique involves rapidly cooling the cell down to almost absolute zero temperature; such rapid freezing avoids the formation of ice crystals and distortion of cell structure. Then, in a procedure reminiscent of making freeze-dried coffee, a vacuum is used to remove water from the frozen cell. The cells are deep-etched by prolonged freeze drying, which exposes structures in the interior of the cells. Before the preparation is examined with the EM, it is coated with a thin layer of platinum.

In preparation for this technique, cells may be treated with detergents, which remove the membranous and soluble parts of the cell (plasma membrane, nuclear membrane, cytosol, and the like), leaving the insoluble elements of the cell. Alternatively, they may not be treated with detergents. If cells are not pretreated with detergents, an extensive filamentous network, the MTL, is found dispersed throughout the cytoplasm. When pretreated with a nonionic detergent, however, elements of the cytoskeleton (MTs, MFs, and IFs) are not extensively cross-linked by strands.

As a consequence of such results, the reality of the MTL is questioned; some investigators believe that the lattice is real, but solubilized by detergents; others believe that the lattice is an artifact resulting from the preparative procedures for electron microscopy.

Context

The cytoplasm of cells has been under examination since 1810 (to use Porter's date), but biologists still do not completely understand its nature. Yet, understanding of it has progressed markedly during the twentieth century, even though there are still questions, in some cases, about what are and what are not artifacts. Since World War II, two powerful techniques, electron microscopy and centrifugation, have revealed much of value about the cell. They allowed biologists to put much of what was learned about cellular biochemistry during the first half of this century into a cellular context. Scientists now know of the existence of all the common cellular organelles, and their function(s) are worked out in most cases.

Beginning in the early 1970's, cell biologists began to gather information about the cytoskeleton at a rapid rate. The structures and chemical compositions of the microtubules, microfilaments, and intermediate filaments were revealed. Although it is still not understood how these filaments carry out their roles in many instances (exactly how microtubules are involved in chromosome movement during mitosis, for example), biologists are now asking questions about the regulation of the activities of these structures rather than asking whether they exist or what goes into their makeup. This is a good measure of the progress that is being made.

Perhaps the most enigmatic part of the cytoplasm is its matrix, the portion among the organelles and cytoskeletal elements. Research involving microinjection of fluorescent antibodies into cells and the monitoring of their distribution rates and locations in living cells will add to scientific understanding.

During human development, cells undergo extensive movement. Germ cells arise elsewhere and migrate into the developing gonads; neural crest cells arise in the region of the developing central nervous system and then migrate extensively throughout the developing embryo. It is unlikely that biologists will understand cell movement until they understand how the cytoskeleton's coordination is regulated; it is difficult to imagine that the cytoplasmic matrix does not play a role in this regulation. Cancer would be less of a health problem if the malignant cells would remain stationary, but they do not; rather, they metastasize to distant regions of the body, sometimes making the chore of the oncologist impossibly difficult.

Just as the assignment of biochemistry to structure (for example, the Krebs cycle to the matrix of the mitochondrion, and digestion to lysosomes) was intellectually satisfying, so too will it be if the cytoplasmic matrix is found to organize additional biochemistry, such as glycolysis and protein synthesis.

Whether receptors for growth factors, antigens, or hormones are found on the cell surface or in the cytoplasm, it is apparent that received information must pass through the cytoplasm if that information is to be used. The transmission of hereditary information from one generation to the next is better understood than the transmission of functional information from one region of a cell to another.

Bibliography

Alberts, Bruce, Dennis Bray, Julian Lewis, Martin Raff, Keith Roberts, and James D. Watson. *Molecular Biology of the Cell*. 2d ed. New York: Garland, 1989. A widely used college textbook in cell biology. Well written and including extensive references, this is a good introduction to the field. Some of the techniques used to study the cytoplasmic matrix are presented, including deep-etching, high-voltage electron microscopy, and fluorescence recovery after photobleaching. The authors state that the degree of organization in the cytosol is a matter of debate.

Avers, C. J. *Molecular Cell Biology*. Reading, Mass.: Addison-Wesley, 1986. A college textbook of cell biology that examines the techniques used to study the nature of the cytoplasm and the resulting observations. The author states that whether or not the major protein fibers are interconnected by microtrabeculae, some system of cross-linking does indeed characterize the cytoskeletal fibers and provides a physical basis for interactions in vivo.

Cold Spring Harbor Laboratory. *Cold Spring Harbor Symposia on Quantitative Biology*. Vol. 46, *Organization of the Cytoplasm*. Cold Spring Harbor, N.Y.: Cold Spring Harbor Laboratory, 1982. This two-volume symposium report contains many articles by the leaders in studies of organization of the cytoplasm, as understood at the beginning of the 1980's. Nonspecialists will find value in perusing the foreword and summary of these volumes as well as the introductions and discussions of the articles. The articles are organized into twelve sections, which facilitates locating information of interest. Additionally, there are many stereo-pair illustrations presented, which allow the reader to see components of the cytoplasm in three dimensions.

Darnell, James, Harvey Lodish, and David Baltimore. *Molecular Cell Biology*. New York: Scientific American Books, 1986. A widely used college textbook in cell biology; very well written. Compares the different views of the cytoplasm resulting from high-voltage electron microscopy (microtrabeculae) and the quick-freeze deep-etch technique (a cytoplasm composed almost exclusively of microfilaments, microtubules, and intermediate filaments). The authors state that the exact composition, structure, and arrangement of the fibers (cytoskeletal network) remain a source of controversy.

Fulton, A. B. "How Crowded Is the Cytoplasm?" *Cell* 30 (September, 1982): 345-347. This short review article considers the nature of the cytoplasm from a biophysical point of view: the physical state of cell water and cell protein. (Cell water exists in two phases; protein in the cytoplasm of the cell is at a much higher concentration than that in the dilute protein solutions of the laboratory.) A short, well-written article that presents topics whose consideration is a prerequisite for studying the nature of the cytoplasm.

Kleinsmith, L. J., and V. M. Kish. *Principles of Cell Biology.* New York: Harper & Row, 1988. A college textbook of cell biology. The authors point out the early 1970's work of Porter's group with high-voltage electron microscopy that resulted in the suggestion of the microtrabecular network and the more recent work of Ris suggesting that the MTL is a distortion generated by fixation conditions. Contains an interesting discussion of the suggestion that protein-synthesizing "free" ribosomes are actually attached to the cytoskeleton.

Luby-Phelps, Katherine, D. Lansing Taylor, and Frederick Lanni. "Probing the Structure of Cytoplasm." *The Journal of Cell Biology* 102 (June, 1986): 2015-2022. This article may be read at two different levels. By reading it and scanning the more difficult parts, one can gain an insight into modern techniques for studying the cytoplasmic matrix, such as microinjection, fluorescence recovery after photobleaching, and video-image analysis. At a deeper level, understanding it more fully will require a fair background in physics, physical chemistry, and colloid chemistry. The authors state that this study represents the first demonstration in living cells that the cytoplasm contains barriers restricting the free diffusion of macromolecules in a size-dependent manner.

Porter, K. R. "The Cytomatrix: A Short History of Its Study." *The Journal of Cell Biology* 99, part 2 (July, 1984): 3s-12s. This article is written by one of the major contributors to understanding of the cell and the nature of the cytoplasm. The title summarizes the content of this interesting article. This issue of *The Journal of Cell Biology*, in fact, is devoted to the topic, "The Cytoplasmic Matrix and the Integration of Cellular Function" and is an excellent reference source for graduate-level studies of the cytoplasmic matrix.

Frank J. Dye

Cross-References

THE CYTOSKELETON

Type of life science: Cell biology (cytology)
Other fields of study: Biochemistry and neurobiology

The cytoskeleton is a supportive network inside cells that holds cellular structures in position and reinforces cellular membranes. An intact cytoskeleton is vital to cellular functions and characteristics as varied as shape, position in the body, growth, and division.

Principal terms

ACTIN: the protein subunit from which microfilaments are assembled

AMINO ACID: one of twenty different structural units assembled into unbranched chains to form proteins

CELL CENTER: a location near the nucleus in animal cells from which cytoskeletal elements, particularly microtubules and intermediate filaments, radiate

CYTOSKELETON: a supportive structure inside cells consisting primarily of microtubules, microfilaments, and intermediate filaments

INTERMEDIATE FILAMENT: a cytoskeletal element about 10 nanometers in diameter, consisting of solid fibers assembled from one or more of a variety of related proteins

MICROFILAMENT: a cytoskeletal element about 5 to 7 nanometers, consisting of solid fibers assembled from actin subunits

MICROTUBULE: a tubular cytoskeletal element about 25 nanometers in diameter, assembled from tubulin subunits

NUCLEAR MATRIX: a cytoskeletal network of unknown structural elements that is believed to support the interior of the cell nucleus

PROTEIN: a cellular macromolecule assembled from one or more linear, unbranched chains of amino acids

TUBULIN: the protein subunit from which microtubules are assembled

Summary of the Phenomenon

For many years, cells were regarded simply as internally unstructured "bags of enzymes." One of the revelations of contemporary cell biology was the finding that, rather than being a simple solution, the interior of cells is supported by a complex network of fibers known as the cytoskeleton. The fibers of the cytoskeleton are crosslinked by molecular connectors into systems that support cellular membranes and hold internal structures such as the nucleus in place.

Cytoskeletal systems extend internally from the membrane covering the cell surface to the surface of the membrane system surrounding the nucleus. There are indications that a cytoskeletal support system reinforces the interior of the nucleus as well. The fibers of the cytoskeleton also anchor cells to external structures through linkages that extend through the surface membrane. The cytoskeletal systems of most animal cells are so extensive that they make up a major fraction of the total cellular protein—as much as one-third in some cells. The cytoskeletal material, rather than being fixed and unchanging, varies in makeup and structure as cells develop, move, grow, and divide.

The cytoskeleton, depending on the cell type, is assembled from one or more of three major structural fibers. One of these structural elements is the microtubule, a fine, unbranched hollow tube with walls built up from subunits consisting of the protein tubulin. Microtubules are about 25 nanometers in diameter, have walls about 4 to 5 nanometers thick, and range in length from a few to many micrometers. These structural elements, which may be arranged singly or in networks or parallel bundles, probably provide tensile strength and rigidity to cellular regions containing them. The use of a tubular form as a structural element is not limited to cells; human engineers also use the same type of element as a support because a tube combines lightness with strength and elasticity. Furniture, building scaffolds, and supportive assemblies in aircraft, for example, are commonly constructed from metal tubes.

A second major structural element of cytoskeletons is the microfilament, a linear, unbranched fiber built up from the protein actin. Microfilaments are solid fibers that are much smaller than microtubules—about 5 to 7 nanometers in diameter, not much thicker than a microtubule wall. Microfilaments also occur singly in networks, and in parallel bundles in the cytoskeleton. The consistency of the cytoplasm, which can vary from highly liquid to solid and gel-like, is regulated by the degree to which microfilaments are crosslinked into networks. Microfilaments are also arranged in parallel bundles that give tensile strength and elasticity to cell regions and extensions. Many cell types, such as those lining the intestinal cavity, contain numerous fingerlike extensions that are reinforced internally by internal parallel bundles of microfilaments.

Both microtubules and microfilaments also form the basis for almost all cellular movements. In these motile systems, microtubules and microfilaments are acted upon by motile proteins that are able to convert chemical energy into the mechanical energy of movement. The motile proteins cause the microtubules or microfilaments to slide forcefully, or move cell structures and molecules over the surfaces of the two elements. The forces generated are responsible for movements such as muscle contraction, the beating of the heart, and the whiplike movements of sperm tails.

Microtubules and microfilaments occur as structural supports of the cytoskeleton of all plant, animal, fungal, and protozoan cells. The third structural element, the intermediate filament, is limited primarily to animal cells. This type of fiber, called "intermediate" because its dimensions fall between those of microtubules and microfilaments, is about 10 nanometers in diameter. Unlike microtubules and microfilaments, which are each highly uniform in structure and made from a single type of protein, intermediate filaments occur in six different types, each made up of a different protein or group of proteins. Although the proteins making up the various intermediate filaments are different, they are related in both their three-dimensional structures and amino acid sequences.

The most complex intermediate filaments are those making up a group called the keratin filaments. This group of intermediate filaments forms cytoskeletal structures in cells of the skin and cells of the layers covering internal organs and lining ducts and body cavities. Hair, wool, and the horns of animals such as cows and steers are also formed primarily from keratin intermediate filaments, left in place after the cells forming these structures die. The second type of intermediate filament, the vimentin filament, occurs in a wide variety of animal cell types, including those of the blood, bone, cartilage, and other connective tissues. The third type of intermediate filament, the desmin filament, forms part of cytoskeletons in muscle cells of all types. The fourth type of intermediate filament, the neurofilament, occurs as a supporting structure in nerve cells. Neurofilaments are most numerous in the long, microscopic extensions of nerve cells that communicate from the brain and spinal cord to all regions of the body. The fifth type of intermediate filament group, the glial filament, occurs in glial cells, a cell type that makes up supportive tissues surrounding the nerve cells of the brain and spinal cord. The final group of intermediate filament, the lamins, forms a network supporting the inner surface of the membrane system covering the cell nucleus.

Each of the intermediate filament types is built up from long chains of proteins of individual types. Keratin filaments are built from proteins called cytokeratins. As many as thirty different cytokeratins assemble in different mixed combinations to form a wide variety of keratin filaments. The cytokeratins that remain in animal hair, wool, and horns are so-called hard proteins that are stabilized by numerous chemical links between sulfur atoms. The links make these cytokeratins, and the hair and horn structures formed from them, highly resistant to physical and chemical destruction. The chemicals and heat treatments used to make "permanent waves" in human hair are designed first to break the sulfur links to make the hair pliable and then to reform the links to "set" the hair in curls.

Vimentin and desmin intermediate filaments are each built up from a single protein, named for its filament type as vimentin or desmin. A small group of three different neurofilament proteins makes up neurofilaments. Glial filaments are assembled from a single protein type known as glial fibrillary acidic protein. The final intermediate filament group, the lamins, contain three different proteins, also called lamins.

Intermediate filaments occur in networks and bundles in the cytoplasm. They appear to be much more flexible than either microtubules or microfilaments, so it is considered likely that they form elastic ties holding cell structures in place, much like cellular rubber bands. It must be mentioned, however, that the actual roles of these elements in the cytoskeleton remain unknown.

Both microtubules and microfilaments can be readily converted between assembled and disassembled forms. In the conversion, the protein subunits of microtubules and microfilaments are exchanged rapidly between the fully assembled element and large pools of disassembled subunits in solution in the cytoplasm. Cells can control the balance between assembly and disassembly with high precision. As a result, the protein subunits can be recycled, and cytoskeletal structures containing microtubules and microfilaments can be set up or taken apart as the cell changes its function. As cells enter division, for example, microtubules and microfilaments forming cytoskeletal structures typical of growing cells are rapidly disassembled, and then reassembled into structures that take part in cell division. The assembly-disassembly reactions of microtubules and microfilaments proceed so readily that it is relatively easy to carry them out in the test tube. Microtubules and microfilaments, in fact, were among the first cell structures to be taken apart and put back together experimentally.

In contrast to microtubules and microfilaments, most of the intermediate filament types are highly stable both inside and outside the cell. In order to disassemble cytoskeletal structures containing most intermediate filaments, cells evidently must break the proteins of these elements into individual amino acids by enzymatic digestion, thereby destroying the proteins. Therefore, for these intermediate filaments there is probably no balance between the assembled fibers and a cytoplasmic pool of unassembled protein subunits, as there is for microtubules and microfilaments. Only the lamins appear to assemble and disassemble readily inside cells. These intermediate filament proteins, which reinforce the membrane system surrounding the nucleus, are disassembled into subunits as cells enter division, and then reassembled as division becomes complete.

The cytoskeleton of animal cells has four major subdivisions associated with major cellular regions. One of the most complex is associated with the surface membrane of the cell. This system, which is constructed primarily from microfilaments, supports the inner surface of the surface membrane and supports elements embedded in the membrane, such as receptors of various kinds. The system also supports extensions of the cell surface and junctions formed between cells. The second subdivision, located just underneath the surface membrane, consists primarily of a network of microfilaments and, to a limited extent, of intermediate filaments. This system gives the cytoplasm under the surface membrane a semirigid consistency and forms what is known as the cortex of the cell.

The third major subdivision extends from the cortex to the surface of the nucleus and includes most of the volume of the cell interior. In most animal cells, this subdivision, which is formed primarily from microtubules and intermediate filaments, is organized in a pattern in which the cytoskeletal elements radiate from a center near the nucleus to the cortex. The center of radiation is known appropriately as the cell center. The microtubules and intermediate filaments of this subdivision hold the nucleus and many of the cytoplasmic organelles in place. The fourth subdivision is the system of lamin intermediate filaments that reinforces the inner surface of the membrane system surrounding the nucleus. There is also considerable evidence suggesting that the interior of the nucleus is supported by its own fibrous network.

This system, called the nuclear matrix, is believed to hold the hereditary molecules in place and organize the enzymes duplicating and copying their information.

The three cytoskeletal elements, microtubules, microfilaments, and intermediate filaments, are held together in cytoskeletal structures by a variety of proteins that act as interlinkers. The linkages are so extensive that none of the individual cytoskeletal elements is likely to be completely independent as a supportive element in the cytoplasm. The cytoskeleton is thus a complex network that ties by interlinking proteins into a totally integrated supportive system.

Methods of Study

All three of the major cytoskeletal elements—microtubules, microfilaments, and intermediate filaments—are directly visible in the electron microscope. The tubular form of microtubules, which is almost unique among cellular structures, makes them unmistakable. Although less distinct, intermediate filaments also take forms and dimensions that allow them to be identified with a fair degree of certainty. Microfilaments would be barely recognizable except for a technique known as myosin decoration, which specifically identifies them. In this technique, a segment of myosin, the protein molecule involved in microfilament-based motility, is reacted with cells. The myosin segments attach along microfilaments in a pattern that appears under the electron microscope as a series of arrowheads. The pattern, which is readily seen, is produced only with microfilaments and makes these structures fully identifiable.

The true extent of the cytoskeleton was not established, however, until techniques were developed to make microtubules, microfilaments, and intermediate filaments visible in the light microscope. This was made possible through a technique known as immunofluorescence. In this technique, the protein subunits of a cytoskeletal element are injected into an animal such as a rabbit. In response, the animal develops antibodies that can specifically recognize and bind to the protein subunit. The antibodies are extracted, purified, and attached chemically to a dye molecule that glows (or fluoresces) under ultraviolet light. The dye-labeled antibodies are then reacted with cells, where they react specifically with the cytoskeletal element containing the protein subunit used to develop the antibodies. When viewed under a light microscope illuminated with ultraviolet light, the cytoskeletal element glows brightly against a dark background and is made highly visible. By this means, the three-dimensional arrangement of cytoskeletal microtubules, microfilaments, and intermediate filaments could be traced throughout the cytoplasm. Investigators were surprised when this approach revealed that the cytoplasms of many animal cells, as well as those of plants, fungi, and protozoans, are packed with an extensive cytoskeletal network. The same technique has been adapted for electron microscopy. In this variation of the method, atoms of a metal such as iron or gold are attached to the antibody instead of a fluorescent dye. The metal atoms, which can be directly seen under the electron microscope, mark the cytoskeletal structures to which the antibodies attach.

Another approach used with much success for microtubules and microfilaments is the application of "poisons" that cause these elements to disassemble. Colchicine, a substance made as a defensive molecule by certain groups of plants, causes microtubules to disassemble when added to cells. Another substance, cytochalasin, a defensive molecule made by some fungi, has the same effect on microfilaments. The role of microtubules or microfilaments in a cytoskeletal structure can often be identified by noting the effects of either poison on the structure.

The protein subunits of the three cytoskeletal elements have also been analyzed by a battery of chemical and molecular techniques that have revealed vital statistics such as molecular weight, three-dimensional shape, and amino acid sequence. These techniques have also revealed the chemical and physical conditions required for self-assembly of each of the elements in the test tube. Much has been learned from these studies about the mechanisms probably used inside cells to assemble and disassemble the cytoskeleton at specific locations and times. Investigations using all these approaches—microscopic, physiological, chemical, and physical—continue today in research into the cytoskeleton, which remains one of the most actively investigated areas of cell biology.

Context

Disturbances in the cytoskeleton are responsible for or associated with a number of human diseases. Several common forms of hereditary anemia are caused by deficiencies in the cytoskeleton supporting the surface membrane of red blood cells. The cells are so fragile, as a result, that they are easily broken during passage through narrow vessels or turbulent regions such as the valves and chambers of the heart.

Even more significant and potentially deadly are the changes in the cytoskeleton associated with cancer. As cells develop into malignant forms, microfilaments and intermediate filaments of the cytoskeleton partially disassemble and become disorganized. Linkages between microfilaments and intermediate filaments and the surface membrane are weakened, including those associated with cell junctions. Partly as a result of these changes, cancer cells lose close contact with their neighbors. Breakage of contacts with other cells removes two inhibitions that depend on tight associations with neighboring cells: the inhibitions of movement and of cell division. As a result, the cancer cells divide more rapidly and, when not dividing, move constantly among and over neighboring cells. They also break loose from their tissues and are carried by the circulatory system to other locations in the body. In the new locations, the cancer cells grow and divide to form secondary tumors. This detachment and movement, called metastasis, is one of the primary distinguishing characteristics of cancer cells. In some types of cancer, cytoskeletal changes occur well in advance of the full development of cancer. In some hereditary cancers involving tumors of the lower intestine, children show characteristic cytoskeletal rearrangements some years before onset of the disease.

Because many types of body cells have distinct types of intermediate filaments, the tissue from which cancer cells originated can often be determined simply by noting the types of intermediate filaments inside them. For example, the presence of desmin-based intermediate filaments is an indicator that the tumor is a sarcoma originating from muscle tissue. This information can be highly useful as a factor determining the type of cancer treatment to be used. The identification is carried out routinely by means of fluorescent antibodies that react specifically with each intermediate filament type.

Bibliography

Alberts, Bruce, Dennis Bray, Julian Lewis, Martin Raff, Keith Roberts, and James D. Watson. *Molecular Biology of the Cell*. 2d ed. New York: Garland, 1989. Chapter 11, "The Cytoskeleton," includes many structural and molecular details about the organization of the cytoskeleton and outlines both the supportive and the motile roles of microtubules and microfilament. The book is clearly written at the college level and contains many informative diagrams and photographs. An extensive bibliography of technical scientific articles is included at the end of the cytoskeleton chapter.

Allen, Robert D. "The Microtubule as an Intracellular Engine." *Scientific American* 256 (February, 1987): 42-49. This article introduces and traces the history of investigations, many of them made by the author, into the roles of microtubules as elements on which cytoplasmic structures and molecules are moved from place to place in the cell. Particular attention is given to the movements of cytoplasmic structures through the long extensions of nerve cells. Many highly illustrative photographs, made in both the light and electron microscopes, and color diagrams are included.

Darnell, James, Harvey Lodish, and David Baltimore. *Molecular Cell Biology*. New York: Scientific American Books, 1986. An excellent textbook written at the college level. Chapter 18, "The Cytoskeleton and Cellular Movements: Microtubules," and chapter 19, "The Cytoskeleton and Cellular Movements: Actin," cover the roles of microtubules, microfilaments, and intermediate filaments in the cytoskeleton. Many diagrams and photographs are included. An extensive bibliography of technical articles and books at an advanced level is included at the end of each chapter.

Dustin, Pierre. "Microtubules." *Scientific American* 243 (August, 1980): 66-76. This article, written for a more general reading audience, outlines the structure and function of microtubules in both cytoskeletal and motile systems. Several highly informative diagrams in color extend and amplify the discussion presented in the text.

Karp, Gerald. *Cell Biology*. 2d ed. New York: McGraw-Hill, 1979. Chapter 15, "The Cytoskeleton," covers the structural roles of microfilaments, microtubules, and intermediate filaments in the cytoskeleton. The chapter, written at the college level, includes many excellent photographs of cytoskeletal structures in both the light and electron microscopes.

Porter, K. R., and J. B. Tucker. "The Ground Substance of the Cell." *Scientific American* 244 (March, 1981): 56-67. This article, written for a general audience, traces the history and development of investigations into the cytoskeleton and outlines the authors' hypotheses about the extent of cytoskeletal structures in the cell. The hypothetical structure proposed by the authors, called the "microtrabecular lattice," stimulated much interest and controversy among cell biologists.

Schliwa, M. *The Cytoskeleton*. New York: Springer-Verlag, 1986. Although written as an introduction at a more technical level, this book contains many sections describing the components of the cytoskeleton, cytoskeletal structures, and the history of developments in this field that can be understood by the general reader. The book has one of the best collections of photographs of cytoskeletal structures assembled in one source.

Stephen L. Wolfe

Cross-References

Cilia, Flagella, Basal Bodies, and Centrioles, 470; The Cytoplasm, 575; Electron Microscopy, 744; Fluorescent Antibody Staining of Cytoskeletal Elements, 1025; Amoeboid and Gliding Motion, 1790; Flagellar and Ciliary Motion, 1797; Muscular Contraction: The Molecular Basis, 1849; Plasma Membranes, 2134; Proteins, 2272.

DEFORESTATION AND THE GLOBAL ENVIRONMENT

Type of life science: Ecology
Other fields of study: Botany and systematics

Deforestation—or the mass removal of whole forests or very large forested or woodland areas from the earth—is a process driven by population increase, economic pressures, and political forces. Such large areas of forest are being destroyed that the environment of the earth is being adversely affected, and, in the process, countless species are being rendered extinct.

Principal terms

BIODIVERSITY: the diversity of life; the number of species that can be found in a given habitat or area

BIOMASS: the mass of living materials

ECOSYSTEM: the living community of organisms and their environment considered as a functioning unit

GREENHOUSE EFFECT: an environmental consequence of gases, such as carbon dioxide and nitrous oxide, which trap energy from the sun in the atmosphere, causing the earth's temperature to rise

HARVESTING and MINING NATURAL RESOURCES: harvesting refers to removing natural resources—such as crops or trees—from the environment and replacing them with new plants; mining refers to the removal of natural resources and not replacing them

PHOTOSYNTHESIS: the chemical process in which carbon dioxide is removed from the atmosphere by plants, which, by the energy from sunlight, produce plant materials

SLASH-AND-BURN AGRICULTURE: the process in which forest or woodland is cut down en masse, the forest products burned in place, and the land converted directly into agricultural use

Summary of the Phenomenon

Every minute of every day, an area of forest the size of ten city blocks vanishes from the earth. That is equal to the destruction of an area the size of the state of Pennsylvania in one year. Much of this deforestation occurs in tropical regions. Many of these forests are in countries that are, for the most part, poor and not as developed as the industrial nations. The forests are cut down for use as fuel or to give quickly growing populations land for farming.

Deforestation also often serves the political interests of the nations involved because it allows whole segments of the population to obtain land of their own, thereby taking some of the pressure off the governments to improve the economic viability of the nation and allowing the country to avoid land reform. It also serves political needs by allowing politically powerful interests access to unlimited mining of valuable forest hardwoods, thereby leaving whole tracts of grazing lands available for wealthy cattle interests.

One of the biggest threats facing forests all over the globe is the destruction of forests for firewood. Two thirds of the earth's population relies on wood for fuel. In many underdeveloped nations, the continual foraging for woods to be used as fuel in activities ranging from cooking to heating has completely stripped bare millions of hectares of forest. In equatorial Africa, where forest growth is slow and population densities are high, the forests have been decimated because the populations must have the wood to survive in already desperate conditions.

Deforestation also occurs in the United States and other nations. Yet, forest management programs characteristically replace the parts of forests that are cut down. This replacement is the difference between mining a natural resource and harvesting it. A forest that is not replaced and allowed to grow back to maturity has been mined. A forest that is planted back has been harvested. Either process, however, is one of deforestation. Such deforestation typically occurs as whole regions are being colonized—such as happened in Europe and the United States. Indeed, only a third of the world's original forests and woodlands remain. While the process usually occurs in developing countries, they have historically been replaced. France saw nearly 90 percent of its forests removed in the seventeenth and eighteenth centuries, but it has since replaced a significant portion of them.

Yet, even such harvesting measures rarely reestablish the original biodiversity of the area that has been harvested. No replanting technique in current use replaces all the species of plant and animal life removed from the original harvest. Also, in an area set aside for harvesting, typically only the fast-growing species are replanted so that the area may be reharvested in the shortest time possible, for economic reasons.

In areas where the forest is removed for farming and settlement, the trees that are cut down are usually burned in place—only a small percentage of those cut down are actually used for export lumber. The process of burning releases large amounts of carbon dioxide into the air. The forests, as living plants, took carbon dioxide from the air and, through photosynthesis, stored it internally over many years of growth. The process of burning releases this carbon dioxide into the air all at once. In a satellite picture of Brazil (taken in 1988), more than six thousand such fires were seen burning at once. This daily burning, worldwide, accounts for nearly 10 percent of all the man-made carbon dioxide released into the air of the planet, second behind the burning of fossil fuels, which releases 80 percent. It is a large enough amount to be of concern.

The greenhouse effect is a process in which carbon dioxide (and a few other gases released by burning fossil fuels and forests) traps solar energy in the atmosphere in much the same way that a closed automobile traps sunlight. There is a large body of evidence that suggests such extraordinary releases of carbon dioxide have already caused significant global warming, which could easily result in catastrophic planetary consequences. Carbon dioxide is the cause of about half the greenhouse effect, with other gases, such as nitrous oxide and chlorofluorocarbons, responsible for the rest.

One common myth about the world's tropical rain forests is that they supply the earth with very large quantities of oxygen. Actually, accounting for the very large amount of decomposition that occurs in these forests, the amount of oxygen produced by the plant canopy is estimated to equal roughly the amount consumed by the same area of forest.

Yet, on the other side of the equation of photosynthesis, the huge biomass of the tropical rain forest (some 400 metric tons of life per hectare of tropical rain forest) locks up carbon in the form of plant mass. A single tree removes about 5.5 kilograms of carbon from the atmosphere each year: That is about 6 metric tons per hectare of trees. They get this carbon from carbon dioxide in the atmosphere. When so many of the organisms that lock up that carbon are eliminated from the planet altogether, the ability of the earth to respond to increases in carbon dioxide increases is lessened and the greenhouse effect is accelerated.

The forest is a delicate ecosystem in many respects. The rain forests that exist in a belt that extends roughly between 20 degrees latitude north and 20 degrees south of the equator are being destroyed at unprecedented rates. An astonishing abundance of life has developed in this area and evolved with inextricable ties to the forest. In these rain forests, composing only 7 percent of the earth's surface, more than half the world's species live. Some of these species exist within only a few square kilometers. If those few square kilometers are destroyed, the species are rendered extinct. Since scientists have catalogued only a small percentage of these organisms, it is probable that many are rendered extinct each day as deforestation continues.

The loss of these organisms, both plant and animal, is incalculable to the planet and to humankind. Once an organism has disappeared, it can never reappear. It is estimated that every hectare of rain forest may contain 42,000 species. Each rain-forest tree may support more than four hundred unique species of insect, and the rain forest itself probably supports in excess of 20 million unique species, most dependent on the trees. The whole community of life within the rain forest and on the entire planet is linked together in very complex and poorly understood ways.

Once a species has been eliminated, the population of life on the planet must shift, even if only in small ways, to account for the loss of that organism. Even though 98 percent of all species that have ever lived are now extinct, such shifts have occurred slowly over billions of years. Mass extinctions almost always accompany planetary cataclysm; there have been no mass extinctions since the evolution of humans. It appears that the cataclysm now in progress is caused by humans.

One of the principal reasons for the destruction of the rain forest is to use the cleared areas for agriculture, a practice called slash-and-burn agriculture. The soils of the rain forest, however, are extremely nutrient-poor. Most of what nutrients are available have been locked up by the organisms that densely pack the forest. Nearly 75 percent of the nutrients are thus locked out of the soil, either in the trees themselves or in the plants of the floor; about 17 percent can be found in the decomposing plant material on the forest floor, leaving only 8 percent of the forest's nutrients available in the soil. Thus, the struggling farmer who has been given forest land for agriculture finds that his crops start out poor and, after only a few growing seasons, use what nutrients there are available—after which, his crops will fail altogether. Then, the individual will have to move elsewhere, clear more forest, and start again. Thus, such land allocations to the poor amount to little more than a political maneuver by the governments afraid of land reform. In Brazil, nearly half the fertile farmland is distributed to wealthy landowners, who make up less than 1 percent of the population.

The earth's forests, though far removed from most of the earth's population, still provide a wealth of products for civilization, and there are still vast unexplored regions, most of whose secrets await discovery. Such tropical products as non-synthetic rubber, medicines, foodstuffs, and fuels come exclusively from the forests. Indeed, of the three thousand plant species that are known to contain anticancer properties, 70 percent are from tropical rain forests. It is estimated that considerably less than 1 percent of forest plants have been examined for beneficial products.

One insidious by-product of deforestation is erosion. Because tropical rain forests are usually located in areas of the world with high rainfall, removal of the forests causes extreme erosion and silting of major waterways. The resultant loss of topsoil causes already nutrient-poor soils to be lost, rendering the land totally unfit for agriculture. The silted waterways fill with the soil materials and result in cata-strophic flooding. On the Brahmaputra River in India, erosion resulting from de-forestation caused the peak flood level to rise an average of 1 meter every three decades since 1913.

Methods of Study

In the United States and other developed nations, estimations of deforestation and replanting are relatively easy to generate accurately. In these countries, the management of forests is controlled by law, and the reporting of statistics is man-dated. Also, the forested areas are carefully monitored by both aerial photography and direct survey, and they are even monitored by environmental groups.

In countries with tropical rain forests, this sort of regulation is usually not the case. In fact, the gathering of statistics, when existent at all, is subject to inaccura-cies in reporting both by the parties gathering the information and by the govern-ments that release the information. The regions are also very remote, of enormous size, and not subject even to frequent aerial photography.

For example, Brazil had issued an estimate of its own deforestation activities. When it established the Brazilian Institute of Space Research and looked by satellite remote-imaging techniques at the actual deforestation that was occurring, it was dis-covered that the actual rate was occurring at a much higher level than had been es-timated. Before the satellite data, they had estimated some 11 million hectares were being destroyed annually worldwide. The satellite images revealed 8 million hectares were destroyed in the Brazilian Amazon basin alone in a single year.

Scientists have been gathering carbon dioxide levels over the earth for more than a century. They are able to calculate the amount of buildup of carbon dioxide in the atmosphere by direct measurements. The estimates of how much carbon dioxide is loaded into the atmosphere from fossil fuels or burning trees are made by rather straightforward calculations of basic chemical reactions.

Information about tropical agriculture has been gathered for many decades. From basic soil analyses and analyses of the nutrient loads of living species in the forests, it is relatively simple to estimate the nutrient quality of a given area. It is even common knowledge among the poor that the tropical lands are of poor quality. Yet, the fertility issue aside, they "slash and burn" because they have little alternative.

The measurement of the biodiversity of the tropical rain forest is not a simple or straightforward matter at all. Indeed, it has been one of the most challenging tasks that life scientists have ever faced. In the face of a natural catastrophe in progress, biologists, zoologists, entomologists, microbiologists, and ecologists have descended on the rain forests to gather information on the disappearance of millions of species never before recorded. Surveys are taken, often square meter by square meter, but with so many species packed so tightly into such a small space, it is very difficult to make accurate measurements or to catalog all that is found.

The rain forest is a multilayered world, consisting of the upper tree canopy, the trunks and the floor of the forest, itself a multiple layer of growth, and below them, dead, decaying plant materials, laced with insects and profuse microbial populations.

Investigators climb to the top of the tree canopy by various methods and gather organisms by directly capturing them or by netting them. On the floor of the forest, where the greatest density of life exists, scientists gather information directly, bringing some of the samples back for cataloging and recording in the relative comfort of the laboratory.

Context

In the forests of the earth resides the greatest abundance and the greatest diversity of life. These habitats are being destroyed with startling swiftness. In the rush to remake the planet, pivotal, irreplaceable losses are being incurred, both to the habitats being destroyed and to the human condition itself.

The increase in the levels of global carbon dioxide, a significant amount of which is caused both by deforestation and by destruction of the mechanism (photosynthesis) that takes carbon dioxide out of the atmosphere, seems to be already causing alarming changes in the earth's natural balance of weather. Whole, previously fertile regions, such as America's central breadbasket region, could be rendered a desert by the end of the twenty-first century. Sea levels may rise, engulfing whole cities and forcing the mass evacuation of millions of people.

The loss through forced mass extinction of one fifth of the world's species is a distinct possibility. Such a massive loss of biodiversity on the planet would be beyond the range of human understanding and experience. The loss of potential medicines and useful products cannot be estimated. Never before in human history has so much life been destroyed in such a short span of time. Although deforestation has historically preceded any dramatic human advance, never before has so much forest been lost.

The reasons for this deforestation are political and economic; they are linked to the realities of dramatic human population increases in the nations with the greatest density of forests. The solutions are difficult; they must be based on reason and understanding of the life cycle of the forests and its interlinkages with the planet as a whole. This predisposition is not a powerful force in the international political arena, but it is the only weapon available if humankind is to slow or stop the process that threatens all life on the earth.

Bibliography

Boughey, Arthur S. *Man and the Environment*. New York: Macmillan, 1971. This text details the linkages between humankind and the environment through an evolutionary approach, illustrating how humans are connected both biologically and physically with the world around them. It is a unique approach and one important to the understanding of how humans' very survival can depend on understanding that interrelationship. Thoroughly indexed, with diagrams and illustrations.

Carson, Rachel. *Silent Spring*. Boston: Houghton Mifflin, 1962. This book is widely acknowledged as the work that inspired environmental consciousness around the world. It details the use of pesticides and how the chemicals have wound their way through the food chain, ultimately killing whole populations of birds, hence, the "silent spring." It is a classic, elegantly written book that should be (and usually is) required reading for every student of the environment. It is the book against which all other books on the environment are compared.

Caufield, Catherine. *In the Rainforest*. New York: Alfred A. Knopf, 1985. This book tells the story of the decline of the rain forest throughout the world by methods of deforestation and links it with both detailed descriptions of the ecology and the political drives to destroy it. It is written in segments as the author's personal accounting of the rain forests at first hand. It is not illustrated but is thoroughly indexed and referenced and is readable by anyone.

Stanley, Steven M. *Extinction*. New York: W. H. Freeman, 1987. This book describes the natural processes of extinction since the dawn of geologic history. It defines the processes that account for extinction of a living species. It is an important work in understanding the processes of mass extinctions that are human-induced and ongoing now as the process relates to the natural periods of mass extinctions in the billions of years of the earth's history. It is heavily illustrated and indexed.

Toffler, Alvin. *The Third Wave*. New York: William Morrow, 1980. Toffler, widely known as a futurist, describes the oncoming social advances and changes by demonstrating the interrelationships between changing social orders and motivators. One of those motivators, according to Toffler, will be environmental concerns. For a very wide and panoramic view of the probable influence of environmental issues on tomorrow's world, this book lends an interesting viewpoint of what people face not only environmentally but also how they may respond to the issues as a society. Not illustrated but well indexed and referenced.

Weiner, Jonathan. *Planet Earth*. New York: Bantam Books, 1986. This companion book to the Public Broadcasting Service's television series by the same name is a detailed accounting of the earth and its geological and biological history. It accounts for humankind's influence and effect on the biosphere, detailing the damage humanity may be causing to its environmental life-support system. Beautifully illustrated and indexed in detail.

Wilson, Edward O. *The American Forests*. November/December, 1988. Special issue on deforestation. The journal published this entire issue on deforestation, discussing principally the tropical deforestation problem. It is a very comprehensive look at the problem and discusses the issue from most angles—political, population dynamics, and scientific. The only caution the reader should have is that it specifically omits any detailed discussion of American deforestation problems and decreasing of biodiversity. Illustrated with figures and many sidebars. Fine for the general reader.

_____. "Threats to Biodiversity." *Scientific American* 261 (September, 1989): 108-116. This article was written specifically to catalog the "dire consequences" of human-induced mass extinctions caused by deforestation in tropical rain forests. It discusses the process of deforestation and what is happening to the biodiversity in the ecological systems. It is illustrated and is readable by those with some background in ecology and zoology.

Dennis Chamberland

Cross-References

Bioethics: Ecological Decisions, 171; The Biosphere, Biomes, and Habitats, 210; Community Structure and Stability, 533; Demographics, 597; Ecological Niches, 729; Ecological Principles, 736; The Greenhouse Effect, 1225; Insect Societies, 1430; Life's Effect on Earth, 1589; Photosynthesis: A Historical Overview, 2066; The Population Explosion, 2147.

DEMOGRAPHICS

Type of life science: Ecology
Other fields of study: Botany and zoology

Demography is the study of the numbers of organisms born in a population within a certain time period, the rate at which they survive to various ages, and the number of offspring that they produce. Many different patterns of birth, survival, and reproduction are found among organisms in nature.

Principal terms

COHORT: a group of organisms of the same species, and usually of the same population, that are born at about the same time

FECUNDITY: the number of offspring produced by an individual

LIFE TABLE: a chart that summarizes the survivorship and reproduction of a cohort throughout its life span

MORTALITY RATE: the number of organisms in a population that die during a given time interval

NATALITY RATE: the number of individuals that are born into a population during a given time interval

POPULATION: a group of individuals of the same species that live in the same location at the same time

SURVIVORSHIP: the pattern of survival exhibited by a cohort throughout its life span

Summary of the Phenomenon

No plant or animal lives forever. Instead, each individual has a generalized life history that begins with fertilization and then goes through embryonic development, a juvenile stage, a period in which it produces offspring, and finally death. There are many variations on this general theme. Still, the life of each organism has two constants: a beginning and an end. Many biologists are fascinated by the births and deaths of individuals in a population and seek to understand the processes that govern the production of new individuals and the deaths of those already present. The branch of biology that deals with such phenomena is called demography.

The word "demography" is derived from Greek; *demos* means "population." For many centuries, demography was applied almost exclusively to humans as a way of keeping written records of new births, marriages, deaths, and other socially relevant information. During the first half of the twentieth century, biologists gradually began to census populations of naturally occurring organisms to understand their ecology more fully. Biologists initially focused on vertebrate animals, particularly game animals and fish. Beginning in the 1960's and 1970's, invertebrate animals, plants, and microbes also became subjects of demographic studies. Studies clearly show that different species of organisms vary greatly in their demographic properties. Often, there is a clear relationship between those demographic properties and the habitat in which these organisms live.

When conducting demographic studies, a demographer must gather certain types of basic information about the population. The first is the number of new organisms that appear in a given amount of time. There are two ways that an organism can enter a population: by being born into it or by immigrating from elsewhere. Demographers generally ignore immigration and concentrate instead on newborns. The number of new individuals born into a population during a specific time interval is termed the natality rate. The natality rate is often based on the number of individuals already in the population. For example, if ten newborns enter a population of a thousand individuals during a given time period, the natality rate is 0.010. A specific time interval must be expressed (days, months, years) for the natality rate to have any meaning.

A second demographic parameter is the mortality rate, which is simply the rate at which individuals are lost from the population by death. Losses that result from emigration to a different population are ignored by most demographers. Like the natality rate, the mortality rate is based on the number of individuals in the population, and it reflects losses during a certain time period. If calculated properly, the natality and mortality rates are directly comparable, and one can subtract the latter from the former to provide an index of the change in population size over time. The population increases whenever natality exceeds mortality and decreases when the reverse is true. The absolute value of the difference denotes the rate of population growth or decline.

When studying mortality, demographers determine the age at which organisms die. Theoretically, each species has a natural life span that no individuals can surpass, even under the most ideal conditions. For humans, the natural life span appears to be about 110 years. Normally, however, few organisms reach their natural life span, because conditions are far from ideal in nature. Juveniles, young adults, and old adults can all die. When trying to understand the dynamics of a population, it makes a large difference whether the individuals are dying mainly as adults or mainly as juveniles.

Looking at it another way, demographers want to know the pattern of survival for a given population. This can best be determined by identifying a cohort, which is defined as a group of individuals that are born at about the same time. That cohort is then followed over time, and the number of survivors is counted at set time intervals. The census stops after the last member of the cohort dies. The pattern of survival exhibited by the whole cohort is called its survivorship. Ecologists have examined the survivorship patterns of a wide array of species, including vertebrate animals, invertebrates, plants, fungi, algae, and even microscopic organisms. They have also investigated organisms from a variety of habitats, including oceans, deserts, rain forests, mountain peaks, meadows, and ponds. Survivorship patterns vary tremendously.

Some species have a survivorship pattern in which the young and middle-aged individuals have a high rate of survival, but old individuals die in large numbers. Perhaps the best example of such a survivorship pattern can be found in humans who live in industrialized countries. Several species of organisms that live in nature, such as mountain sheep and rotifers (tiny aquatic invertebrates), also exhibit this survivorship pattern. At the other extreme, many species exhibit a survivorship pattern in which mortality is heaviest among the young. Those few individuals that are fortunate enough to survive the period of heavy mortality then enjoy a high probability of surviving until the end of their natural life span. Examples of species that have this pattern include marine invertebrates such as sponges and clams, most species of fish, parasitic worms, and most long-lived plants. An intermediate pattern is also observed, in which the probability of dying stays relatively constant as the cohort gets older. American robins, gray squirrels, and hydras all display this pattern.

These survivorship patterns are usually depicted on a graph that has the age of individuals in the cohort on the x axis and the number of survivors on the y axis. Each of the three survivorship patterns gives a different curve when the number of survivors is plotted as a function of age. In the first pattern (high survival among juveniles), the curve is horizontal at first but then swings downward at the right of the graph. In the second pattern (low survival among juveniles), the curve drops at the left of the graph but then levels out to form a horizontal line. That curve resembles a backward letter "J." The third survivorship pattern (constant mortality throughout the life of the cohort) gives a straight line that runs from the upper-left corner of the graph to the lower right (this is best seen when the y axis is expressed as the logarithm of the number of survivors).

In the first half of the twentieth century, demographers Raymond Pearl and Edward S. Deevey labeled each survivorship pattern: Type I is high survival among juveniles, type II is constant mortality through the life of the cohort, and type III is low survival among juveniles. That terminology became well entrenched in the biological literature by the 1950's. Few species exhibit a pure type I, II, or III pattern, however; instead, survivorship varies so that the pattern may be one type at one part of the cohort's existence and another type later on. Perhaps the most common survivorship pattern, especially among vertebrates and higher plants, is composed of a type III pattern for juveniles and young adults followed by a type I pattern for older adults. This pattern can be explained biologically. Most species tend to suffer heavy juvenile mortality because of predation, starvation, cannibalism, or the inability to cope with a stressful environment. Juveniles that survive this hazardous period then become strong adults that enjoy relatively low mortality. As time passes, the adults reach old age and ultimately fall victim to disease, predation, and organ-system failure, thus causing a second downward plunge in the survivorship curve.

Demographers are not interested only in measuring the survivorship of cohorts. They also want to understand the patterns of reproduction, especially among females. Different species show widely varying patterns of reproduction. For example, some species, such as annual plants, octopi, and certain salmon, reproduce only once in their life and then die soon afterwards. Others, such as humans, most birds, and trees reproduce several or many times in their life. Species that reproduce only once accumulate energy throughout their life and essentially put all of it into producing young. Reproduction essentially exhausts them to death. Conversely, those that reproduce several times devote only a small amount of their energy into each reproductive event.

Species also vary in their fecundity, which is the number of offspring that an individual makes when it reproduces. Humans and other large mammals have low fecundity, because they produce only one or two progeny at a time. Birds, reptiles, small mammals, and palm trees have higher fecundity because they typically produce a "clutch" or "litter" of several offspring. Fish, frogs, parasitic worms, weedy plants, and most trees have very high fecundity, producing hundreds or thousands of offspring.

A species' pattern of reproduction is often related to its survivorship. For example, a species with low fecundity or one that reproduces only once tends to have type I or type II survivorship. Conversely, a species that produces huge numbers of offspring generally shows type III survivorship. Many biologists are fascinated by this interrelationship between survivorship and reproduction. Beginning in the 1950's, some demographers proposed mathematically based explanations as to how the interrelationship might have evolved as well as the ecological conditions in which various life histories would be expected. For example, some demographers predicted that species with low fecundity and type I survival should be found in undisturbed, densely populated areas (such as a tropical rain forest). In contrast, species with high fecundity and type III survival should prevail in places that are either uncrowded or highly disturbed (such as an abandoned farm field). Ecologists have conducted field studies of both plants and animals to determine whether the patterns that actually occur in nature fit the theoretical predictions. In some cases the predictions were upheld, but in others they were found to be wrong and had to be modified.

Another feature of a population is its age structure, which is simply the number of individuals of each age. Some populations have an age structure characterized by many juveniles and only a few adults. Two situations could account for such a pattern. First, the population could be rapidly expanding, with the adults successfully reproducing many progeny that are enjoying high survival. Second, the population could be producing many offspring that have type III survival. In this second case, the size of the population can remain constant or even decline. Other populations have a different age structure, in which the number of juveniles only slightly exceeds the number of adults. Those populations tend to remain relatively constant over time. Still other populations have an age structure in which there are relatively few juveniles and many adults. Those populations are probably declining or are about to decline because the adults are not successfully reproducing.

Since most animals are unisexual, an important demographic characteristic of a population is its sex ratio, defined as the ratio of males to females. While the ratio for birds and mammals tends to be 1:1 at conception (the fertilization of an egg), it tends to be weighted toward males at birth, because female embryos are slightly less viable. After birth, the sex ratio for mammals tends to favor females, because young males suffer higher mortality. The post-hatching ratio in birds tends to remain skewed toward males, because females devote considerable energy to producing young and suffer higher mortality. As a result, male birds must compete with one another for the opportunity to mate with the scarcer females.

Methods of Study

To understand the demography of a particular species, one must collect information about its survivorship and reproduction. The best survivorship data are obtained when a demographer follows a group of newly born organisms (this being a cohort) over time, periodically counting the survivors until the last one dies. Although that sounds relatively straightforward, many factors complicate the collection of survivorship data; demographers must be willing to adjust their methods to fit the particular species and environmental conditions.

First, a demographer must decide how many newborns should be included in the cohort. Survivorship is usually based on one thousand newborns, but few studies follow that exact number. Instead, demographers follow a certain number of newborns and multiply or divide their data so that the cohort is expressed as one thousand newborns. For example, one may choose to follow five hundred newborns; the number of survivors is then multiplied by two. Demographers generally consider cohorts composed of fewer than one hundred newborns to be too small. Second, methods of determining survivorship are much more different for highly motile organisms, such as mammals and birds, than for more sedentary ones, such as plants or bivalves (oysters and clams). To determine survivorship of a sedentary species, demographers often find some newborns during an initial visit to a site and then periodically revisit that site to count the number of survivors. Plant demographers often use maps to help locate individuals from previous census periods. Highly motile animals are much more difficult to census because they do not stay in one place waiting to be counted. Vertebrates and large invertebrates can be tagged, and individuals can be followed by subsquently recapturing them. Some biologists use small radio transmitters to follow highly active species. The demography of small invertebrates such as insects is best determined when there is only one generation per year and members of the population are all of the same age-class. For such species, demographers merely count the number present at periodic intervals.

Third, the frequency of the census periods varies from species to species. Short-lived species, such as insects and annual plants, must be censused every week or two. Longer-lived species (humans and trees) need be counted only once a year. Fourth, the definition of a "newborn" may be troublesome, especially for species with complex life cycles. For humans, demographic studies begin with the birth of an infant. Some would argue, however, that the fetus should be included in the analysis because the starting point is really conception. That reasoning can logically be applied to other mammals. Studies of plant demography have typically used the newly germinated seedling as a starting point, but some now include seed survival as well. Many sedentary marine invertebrates (sponges, starfish, and barnacles) have highly motile larval stages, and these should be included in the analysis for survivorship to be completely understood. Parasitic roundworms and flatworms that have numerous juvenile stages, each found inside a different host, are particularly challenging to the demographer.

The survivorship of long-lived species, such as large mammals and perennial plants, is really impossible to determine by the methods given above. Because of their sheer longevity, one could not expect a scientist to be willing to wait decades or centuries until the last member of a cohort dies. Demographers attempt to overcome this problem by using the age distribution of organisms that are alive at one time to infer cohort survivorship. This is often termed a "horizontal" or "time-specific" approach, as opposed to the "vertical" or "age-specific" approach that requires repeated observations of a single cohort. For example, one might construct a time-specific survivorship curve for a population of fish by live-trapping a sufficiently large sample, counting the rings on the scales on each individual (which for many species is correlated with the age in years), and then determining the number of one-year-olds, two-year-olds, and so on. Typically, demographers who use age distributions to infer age-specific survivorship automatically assume that natality and mortality remain constant from year to year. That is often not the case, however, because environmental conditions often change over time. Thus, demographers must be cautious when using age distribution data to infer survivorship.

Methods for determining fecundity are relatively straightforward. Typically, fertile individuals are collected, their ages are determined, and the number of progeny (eggs, live young, or seeds) are counted. Species that reproduce continually (parasitic worms and tropical plants) or those that reproduce several times a year (small mammals and many insects) must be observed over a period of time.

Demographers usually want to determine whether the production of new offspring (natality) balances the losses attributable to mortality. To accomplish this, they construct a life table, which is a chart with several columns and rows. Each row represents a different age of the cohort, from birth to death. The columns show the survival and fecundity of the cohort. By recalculating the survivorship and fecundity information, demographers can compute several interesting aspects of the cohort, including the life expectancy of individuals at different ages, the cohort's reproductive value (which is the number of progeny that an individual can expect to produce in the future), the length of a generation for that species, and the growth rate for the population.

Context

Demographic methods were originally developed to understand important aspects of human populations, and demography remains an important field with many practical applications. Insurance companies rely very heavily on survivorship data to help determine the premiums that they must charge their customers. On an international level, human demographers seek to understand population trends in various countries, particularly underdeveloped countries that are experiencing rapid population growth. Information gathered by demographers has helped planners and legislators develop social policies intended to stabilize explosive population growth. Sociologists also rely heavily on demographic data to compare birthrates and death-rates in various cultures, especially as they relate to economic wealth and available medical facilities.

Demographers and historians have learned that developing cultures often undergo a "demographic transition" at some point in the modernization process. Pre-industrialized societies exhibit both high natality rates and high mortality rates, resulting in a stable or slowly growing population. As development proceeds, improved medical care reduces the mortality rate, while the birthrate remains high. The effect is that the population increases rapidly. Ultimately, people learn to use birth control, which reduces the natality, and the population enters a second period of slow growth, thus marking the end of the transition. The United States and countries of Western Europe went through the transition during the nineteenth and the early twentieth centuries. The less developed tropical countries of Africa, South America, and Central America were midway through the transition near the end of the twentieth century.

Demographic techniques have been applied to nonhuman species, particularly by wildlife managers, foresters, and ecologists. Wildlife managers seek to understand how a population is surviving and reproducing within a certain area, and therefore to determine whether it is increasing or decreasing over time. With that information, a wildlife biologist can then estimate the effect of hunting or other management practice on the population. By extension, fisheries biologists can also make use of demographic techniques to determine the growth rate of the species of interest. If the population is determined to be increasing, it can be harvested without fear of depleting the population. Alternatively, one can conduct demographic analyses to see whether certain species are being overfished.

Foresters often use "yield tables," which are modified versions of life tables that denote the likely numbers and sizes of individual trees in a given area having a particular age. For example, one yield table for Douglas fir in the western United States predicts that a hectare of twenty-year-old trees will contain about fourteen hundred individuals, while a hectare of eighty-year-old trees will contain 250 individuals, and a hectare of 160-year-old trees will contain 125 individuals. Yet, while the numbers decline because of competition or removal, the total volume of wood in the hectare increases. Thus, these yield tables are used primarily to help foresters determine how much lumber is in an area. Both the information in yield tables and the demographic studies of trees under natural conditions clearly show that, in order to sustain a forest for many centuries, each tree that is removed must be replaced by several saplings to compensate for the expected mortality.

An often unappreciated benefit of survivorship analyses is that they can help ecologists pinpoint factors that limit population growth in an area. For example, a study was conducted in the 1970's to determine why a limestone quarry in New York State was still rather barren fifty years after mining had ceased. The germination, survival, and reproduction of the plants that managed to grow on the site were intensively studied over a period of six years. The study found that, although many seedlings emerged, many were killed during rain-free periods that lasted at least five days. Thus, periodic drought was probably the most important factor limiting vegetation development in the quarry, and through irrigation the site would quite probably support a lush cover of plants.

The ability to pinpoint factors that limit population growth may be especially important in efforts to prevent rare animals and plants from becoming extinct. Once the factor is identified, the population can be appropriately managed. Increasing amounts of public and private money are allocated each year to biologists who conduct demographic studies on rare species.

Bibliography

Begon, Michael, John L. Harper, and Colin R. Townsend. *Ecology: Individuals, Populations, and Communities*. 2d ed. Boston: Blackwell Scientific Publications, 1990. Although not the most concise text on the market, the first edition published in 1986 was adopted by many college-level professors for their introductory ecology courses. Chapter 4 includes information on demography centered on the question "what is an individual?" The discussion of life tables includes many perspectives not found in other texts.

Brewer, Richard. *The Science of Ecology*. Philadelphia: Saunders College Publishing, 1988. This clearly written textbook is aimed at upper-level undergraduates and was written by an author who has experience researching both plants and animals. Chapter 4 contains a succinct, well-presented discussion of life tables and survivorship curves. Some of the evolutionary applications of demography is treated in chapter 5.

Elseth, Gerald D., and Kandy D. Baumgardner. *Population Biology*. New York: Van Nostrand, 1981. Intended for graduate students and advanced undergraduates, this book is recommended for anyone who desires a rigorous mathematical treatment of population biology. Demography is presented in chapter 8, which includes detailed discussions about age structure, the calculation of population growth rates from demographic data, the evolution of demographic traits, and sex ratios.

Emmel, Thomas C. *An Introduction to Ecology and Population Biology*. New York: W. W. Norton, 1973. Although slightly dated, this brief book provides a highly readable summary of the major concepts of population, community, and ecosystem ecology. Chapter 5 includes a brief, nontechnical review of the demographic attributes of populations, focusing on natality, mortality, and survivorship.

Hutchinson, G. Evelyn. *An Introduction to Population Ecology*. New Haven, Conn.:

Yale University Press, 1978. Presents an engaging account of the study of populations by a very well-respected ecologist. Chapter 2, "Interesting Ways of Thinking About Death," provides the reader with a perspective on survivorship analysis that includes examples from humans, vertebrates, invertebrates, and plants. Chapter 3 discusses the interrelationships between fecundity and other demographic properties.

Smith, Robert Leo. *Elements of Ecology.* 2d ed. New York: Harper & Row, 1986. This textbook does an excellent job of covering the breadth of topics found in modern ecology. The treatment of the topics is unusually complete and provides a close linkage between theoretical principles and numerous examples from specific ecological situations. Chapter 10 is devoted to population age structure, while chapter 11 focuses on natality, mortality, and survivorship.

Wilson, Edward O., and William Bossert. *A Primer of Population Biology.* Sunderland, Mass.: Sinauer Associates, 1977. This classic handbook has been used extensively by students wishing to master the basics of population biology. Demography is discussed in chapter 3 in a way that emphasizes the estimation of population growth rates from survivorship and reproduction data, as well as the determination of age distributions.

Kenneth M. Klemow

Cross-References

Bioethics: Ecological Decisions, 171; Competition, 541; Ecological Principles, 736; Mark, Release, and Recapture Methods for Population Analysis, 1668; The Population Explosion, 2147; Population Fluctuations, 2154; Exponential and Logistic Population Growth, 2161; Reproductive Behavior and Mating, 2333; Reproductive Strategies, 2339; Sessile Community Sampling, 2473.

DETERMINATION AND DIFFERENTIATION

Type of life science: Developmental biology (embryology)
Other fields of study: Animal anatomy, animal physiology, cell biology (cytology), and molecular biology

Determination is the process whereby the fate of embryonic cells becomes fixed, and differentiation is the process whereby cells acquire their ultimate specialized structure and function. These processes lead to the wide diversity of cell types found in multicellular organisms.

Principal terms

COMMITMENT: the "decision" by an embryonic cell to develop in a certain way, which may be reversed if the cell is removed from its normal surroundings

EMBRYONIC INDUCTION: the point at which one embryonic tissue signals another embryonic tissue to develop in a certain way

GENOME: all the genes of one organism or species

MORPHOGENESIS: the development of form, including the overall form of the organism and the form of each organ and tissue

MOSAIC DEVELOPMENT: the process whereby early embryonic cells are determined by the cytoplasm they receive from the egg; also called determinate development

REGULATIVE DEVELOPMENT: the process whereby early embryonic cells are determined by their interactions with other cells; also called indeterminate development

RESTRICTION: reduction of the developmental potency of a cell

TOTIPOTENT: the ability of a cell to develop into any kind of cell in the body

Summary of the Phenomenon

From the time a fertilized ovum begins to divide (cleavage) until it forms a complete organism, it passes through successive stages in which groups of cells become increasingly specialized. This process of cell specialization involves two key steps: determination, in which cells become committed to a certain developmental pathway, and differentiation, in which cells acquire their ultimate structure and function. The term "differentiation" may also be used in a broader sense to describe the entire process of cell specialization. A third process, called morphogenesis, is needed in order to mold the embryonic cells structurally into the various tissues and organ systems of the mature organism. For example, in eye development the specialized photoreceptor cells of the retina are a product of determination and differentiation, but their organization into the overall structure of the eye is a product of morphogenesis.

In animal development, the fertilized ovum (zygote) has the potential to develop into any type of cell in the body; it is said to be totipotent. As it undergoes cell division beyond the first few cleavages, the resulting cells (blastomeres) lose their totipotency. This point is reached at different stages in different species. In the sea urchin, for example, isolated cells of the two- or four-cell embryo are capable of developing into complete new adults; in other species, such as the tooth shell clam (*Dentalium*), these early cleavage cells, when isolated, do not have the potential to develop into a complete organism. In all animals, the cells of later embryos lose their ability to form complete new organisms. This loss of developmental potency of cells is called restriction and is dictated to some extent both by the type of cytoplasm with which the cell is endowed and the influence of surrounding cells. As development progresses, restricted cells become "committed" to develop into a specific tissue. Under normal conditions, these cells will always develop into this designated tissue; if, however, the cells are moved experimentally to some other part of the embryo or to another embryo, they will develop in a different way. That is why commitment is said to be reversible but determination is not.

Determination occurs when a group of cells becomes irreversibly assigned to develop into a specific tissue. Determination is the final step in restriction; beyond this point, the cells have no other developmental options. Determined cells may or may not look different from other embryonic cells, but they have changed internally so that they are committed to a particular developmental pathway. Determined cells are said to be self-perpetuating, because they can pass on heritable information about their identity and do not require stimulation by surrounding cells to develop in a certain way.

Once the fate of a cell is determined, then differentiation (also called cell differentiation or cytodifferentiation) can take place. During differentiation, the cell undergoes structural and functional changes which result in a highly specialized, mature, differentiated cell. For example, the red blood cell becomes specialized by losing its nucleus and other organelles in order to fill itself completely with the oxygen-carrying molecule hemoglobin. It also maximizes its surface area by becoming flattened and doughnut shaped. Primitive muscle cells, called myoblasts, become specialized by fusing together to form elongated multinuclear cells called myotubes. These cells further specialize by forming contractile organelles called myofibrils, composed primarily of the proteins actin and myosin.

At one time it was believed that the genetic determinants (genes) were divided up and parceled out as determination and differentiation progressed, such that each cell type received certain genes. This hypothesis was disproved in several ways, one of them being nuclear transplantation experiments, in which adult cell nuclei were transplanted into fertilized eggs whose nuclei had been removed or inactivated. A small percentage of these eggs were able to develop into normal adults, thus proving that the adult nuclei implanted in them retained all the genes necessary to form a complete organism. These and other experiments have led to the conclusion that both determination and differentiation occur because certain genes are expressed at certain times during the life history of the cell. There remains, however, the question of how genes are turned on and off to control development.

All developmental processes are believed to be controlled by genes as part of an intricate developmental program. The genes of individual cells are activated or de-activated via various signaling mechanisms in order to provide the correct cellular responses at the appropriate times. This process begins very early in development and even occurs in the egg before fertilization. Messenger ribonucleic acid (RNA) and proteins are produced by the egg and distributed unequally in the cytoplasm of different parts of the egg. When cleavage occurs, blastomeres in one part of the em-bryo receive cytoplasm that differs from the cytoplasm received by blastomeres in another part of the embryo; thus, some cells are endowed with one kind of messen-ger RNA and protein and other cells with another kind. In some species, cleavage is even unequal, in order to ensure that certain cells receive the desired cytoplasm. For example, in the nematode *Caenorhabditis elegans*, unequal cleavage results in the establishment of five different tissue types by the sixteen-cell stage. As the messen-ger RNA is expressed in the form of new proteins, it gives unique qualities to the cells. Some of these new proteins and the proteins made earlier in the egg may be signal molecules, which stimulate new and unique gene expression in the nucleus.

Another mechanism for turning genes on and off is called embryonic induction, which occurs when one embryonic tissue influences the development of another by releasing chemical factors called inductors. The inductors are signal molecules that instruct cells of another tissue how to develop by directly or indirectly activating certain genes. Induction is especially noticeable after the formation of distinct tissues, such as the three germ layers, ectoderm, endoderm, and mesoderm. In ver-tebrates, the mesoderm induces the formation of the neural tube and various other parts of the nervous system.

Another set of mechanisms, similar to embryonic induction, that controls differ-entiation involves the microenvironment in which the embryonic cells exist. These mechanisms include such parameters as the position of a cell in relation to other cells in the embryo; the interactions of cells with the extracellular milieu, including ions, pH, oxygen, and extracellular matrix proteins such as collagen; direct cell-to-cell contact; and the presence of specific growth and differentiation factors. The cells in one part of the developing embryo will experience a completely different set of microenvironmental influences from that of cells in another part of the embryo and consequently will be prompted to express their genes in different ways. Once the genes have been expressed, there must be a means for the daughter cells to re-tain the unique gene expression of the parent cell. That is most likely accomplished by proteins passed on to the daughter cells that continue to activate or deactivate the appropriate genes.

Although the genome is not modified extensively during embryonic development, there is evidence that certain changes occur in order to enhance differentiation. One of these mechanisms is called genetic recombination and involves breaking and rejoining deoxyribonucleic acid (DNA) at defined sites. For example, in maize, segments of DNA called transposons move around the genome and presumably take control of specific genes at certain times during development. Another example of genome modification occurs in the nematode *Ascaris*, in which parts of the chromosomes are discarded (in a process called chromosome diminution) during cleavage. The discarded chromatin is believed to be composed of extra copies of DNA sequences that are not ordinarily transcribed. The genome is also modified through the making of extra copies of essential genes (gene amplification). For example, some genes in the follicle cells surrounding the maturing oocyte of *Drosophila* are amplified about thirty times in order to code for the large amount of protein needed to make the egg chorion. As cells differentiate, the types of messenger RNA and protein they produce become increasingly selective, so that eventually each cell type has a unique pattern of gene expression. There will always, however, be common genes expressed in every cell that are needed for basic housekeeping processes, such as respiration and transport.

Selective gene transcription is carefully controlled by various mechanisms involving the blocking and unblocking of DNA. Two classes of nuclear proteins are believed to be involved in switching genes on and off: histones and nonhistones. Histones associate with DNA molecules in such a way that they block the DNA from being transcribed. The nonhistones are believed to remove or rearrange histones so that the DNA can be replicated or transcribed. Some nonhistone proteins are gene-regulatory proteins, which recognize a particular DNA sequence. The binding of these proteins with DNA can either facilitate or inhibit transcription. An additional control found only in vertebrates is methylation, by which methyl groups are added to the DNA base cytosine. In general, the inactive genes of vertebrates are more highly methylated than active genes; thus, methylation may serve to strengthen decisions involving gene expression that are made during differentiation.

Once the appropriate messenger RNA has been produced, it still must be translated into protein and the protein must be assembled and made functional. For example, hemoglobin protein (globin) translation is controlled by the presence of heme, the iron-containing portion of the hemoglobin molecule. In the absence of heme, the factor that initiates globin translation is inactivated; thus, even though the appropriate messenger RNA and other necessary ingredients are present, without heme no hemoglobin protein will be produced. Even after proteins are translated, they are subject to further regulatory mechanisms, such as assembly into functional units, activation or inactivation by various enzymes and other factors, and transport to their cellular destination.

Methods of Study

The study of embryology was transformed from a purely descriptive science into an experimental science by investigators who developed microsurgical techniques in the 1890's. They discovered that the separated blastomeres of some early embryos, such as the sea urchin, could develop into complete normal larva (regulative or indeterminate development) and that the blastomeres of others, such as the tunicate, could form only parts of embryos (mosaic or determinate development). This led to an appreciation of the importance of nuclear-cytoplasmic interactions and the fact that egg cytoplasm distribution plays an important role in determining how certain blastomeres develop. Further microsurgical separation studies on embryos in later stages (thirty-two-cell to sixty-four-cell stages) demonstrated that the microenvironment of some embryos approximates a double gradient consisting of animal pole factors in one half and vegetal pole factors in the other half. These two chemical gradients influence the cell nuclei in their respective zones and cause the cells to become progressively determined in certain ways. Thus, simply by manipulating embryonic cells, scientists were able to demonstrate the concepts of restriction and determination.

Another microsurgical technique developed in the first half of the twentieth century involves transplanting tissue from one embryo to another. When tissue that normally forms the brain is transplanted to an area of another embryo that normally forms skin, the transplanted tissue develops independently and begins to form into brain. Thus, the tissue has become irreversibly committed or determined to form a particular adult tissue. If the same transplant is done at an earlier stage, the transplanted tissue conforms to its surroundings and forms epidermis. These results indicate that tissues are capable of changing their normal fate if they are influenced by another tissue before determination. In some instances, the transplanted tissue induces the surrounding tissue to change its normal fate. Such is the case when tissue from the dorsal lip of the blastopore of an amphibian gastrula is transplanted to the lateral lip area of another gastrula. The transplanted tissue induces the formation of a second complete embryonic axis, resulting in laterally conjoined twins.

Another elementary method that has yielded a large amount of information about determination is cell marking and tracing. At first, investigators took advantage of different natural pigments that are present in certain animal embryos by following the fate of each blastomere. They discovered that each colored cytoplasm gives rise to a specific embryonic fate. For example, the yellow crescent cytoplasm of the tunicate (*Styela partita*) embryo gives rise to adult muscle cells. In other studies, cells were marked with vital dyes, carbon particles, enzymes, radioactive labels, and distinctive cells transplanted from another embryo. By tracing these labeled cells, investigators were able to ascertain their ultimate fate and when and where cell determination takes place.

One question that needed to be answered by experimental embryologists was whether the nuclei of determined and differentiated cells are irreversibly modified. That all the genetic material is present in differentiated cells could be shown by microscopic observations of the chromosomes, especially the large polytene chromosomes of larval flies, such as *Drosophila*. The only way to show whether these chromosomes are functional, however, was to transplant the nucleus of a differentiated cell into an enucleated egg and see if it could direct the development of a complete organism. The technique of nuclear transplantation (sometimes called cloning), developed in the 1950's, did indeed prove that nuclei from differentiated cells are totipotent. Success was not universal with all tissue types, however, and only a small percentage of the transplants actually succeeded, which indicates that restriction of potency does involve changes in the nucleus but not permanent modification of the genome itself.

The study of differentiation can be approached by several methods. The simplest is to observe tissues microscopically as they differentiate. That is done most often by fixing embryos at various stages of development and observing thinly sliced sections of them with a light or electron microscope. Another method is to explant cells, tissue, or organs from embryos and observe them in culture (in vitro). By doing so, scientists can manipulate the environment of the cultured cells in order to find out precisely what conditions are necessary for differentiation to occur. In vitro culture also makes possible such techniques as synchronizing cell growth in order to study the relationship between cell division and cell differentiation, and cell fusion in order to see how the contents of one cell affect the behavior of another.

Various biochemical and molecular techniques are used to study the roles of many biological molecules in differentiation. Of particular interest are separation methods that allow scientists to isolate and identify proteins and other factors involved in the differentiation process. These molecules can be isolated by first homogenizing the cells and then separating the desired molecules by centrifugation (based on density), electrophoresis (based on electrical charge), or chromatography (based on molecular size). Once the molecules are isolated, their properties can be studied, including the biological activity. At times it is important to know if a particular sequence of DNA or RNA is present in an embryonic cell. That can be determined by a technique called hybridization, whereby single-stranded DNA is allowed to match up and adhere to a complementary strand of DNA or RNA. Usually one of the strands is radioactively labeled so that the sequence in question can be detected and measured. The usefulness of this technique has become greatly enhanced by the development of recombinant DNA technology, which allows for the construction of specific molecular probes (DNA sequences) that can be radiolabeled and used to detect cellular DNA and RNA by hybridization. One step beyond this is the technique of DNA transformation, whereby isolated genes are modified and then reintroduced into cells to determine the new properties of the altered gene when it is expressed.

Context

Determination and differentiation are the foundations of cell diversification. There are approximately two hundred distinctly different cell types in mammals. Without cell specialization, organisms would not be able to move, breathe, think, or perform any of the many other functions necessary to sustain life. Understanding how cells are determined and how they differentiate not only will contribute to the overall understanding of development but also will result in important applications in the fields of medicine and agriculture.

The realization that development is controlled by genes and that the genes are under the influence of various factors in their surroundings led to the discovery that developmental defects such as spina bifida and Down syndrome are caused by disruptions to the same processes that control differentiation and morphogenesis. Understanding the genetic and environmental causes of developmental defects will help physicians to develop new diagnostic and prevention strategies and eventually will lead to new therapeutic methods for treating and overriding these defects.

Development is not a process that ends at the time of birth; it continues throughout life and has special significance during such periods as growth, puberty, menopause, and aging. Cell differentiation continues in many tissues throughout life in response to various control mechanisms. An understanding of these control mechanisms has helped physicians to treat growth- and development-related problems. Age-related osteoporosis, for example, can be treated with calcium and hormone supplements accompanied by exercise and abstinence from alcohol and tobacco. Several neural disorders, including Parkinson's disease and Alzheimer's disease, result when certain cells die or stop producing neurotransmitter substances. New treatments involve implanting cells that produce the missing neurotransmitter in these patients; in the future, however, treatment may include gene therapy of the deficient cells in which the proper genes are inserted and/or activated.

The study of regeneration of lost limbs in amphibians and other animals has determined that regeneration involves dedifferentiation of cells in the wound area followed by regrowth and redifferentiation to restore the lost part. Investigators have found that regeneration is enhanced by temporarily delaying the healing process, by the presence of nerves, and by movement of electrical current away from the damaged area. Further understanding of the control processes involved in dedifferentiation and redifferentiation may lead to procedures for restoring lost limbs and other organs in humans and other mammals.

Cancer occurs when cells continue to undergo cell division instead of differentiation; thus, understanding the control of cell differentiation has been very important in the study of cancer. Cells become cancerous when certain genes controlling cell division become activated as the result of mutations or infection by cancer-causing viruses. A family of genes called oncogenes has been implicated as the cause of cancer. These same genes are also active during embryonic development and cell division but are inactivated as cells differentiate. A better understanding of the mechanisms that keep cancer-causing genes under control in differentiated cells will lead to better prevention and treatment methods in the future.

Some of the methods used in the study of differentiation, especially recombinant DNA technology, are being used by agricultural scientists to develop new plant varieties in order to increase food-crop production with less reliance on fertilizers and pesticides. Also, as scientists discover growth-control mechanisms in plant pests such as insects, they will be able to create safer pesticides.

Bibliography

Alberts, Bruce, Dennis Bray, Julian Lewis, Martin Raff, Keith Roberts, and James D. Watson. *Molecular Biology of the Cell.* 2d ed. New York: Garland, 1989.

A readable, complete, and coherent text intended for use in colleges and medical schools. Chapter 10, "Control of Gene Expression," and chapter 16, "Cellular Mechanisms of Development," provide the details of many processes involved in determination and differentiation. Emphasis is on molecular biology, but the overall processes are well described and illustrated with many diagrams and photographs. Contains an extensive list of references.

Carlson, Bruce M. *Patten's Foundations of Embryology.* 5th ed. New York: McGraw-Hill, 1988. A widely available introductory college embryology text. Chapter 1, "Embryology: Its Scope, History, and Special Fields," has excellent introductory sections on determination and differentiation as well as a complete description of methods used in the study of embryonic development. Chapter 9, "Cellular Differentiation and Development of Muscular and Skeletal Tissues," presents a more detailed discussion of cell differentiation, followed by an excellent account of muscle and skeletal cell differentiation. The book is well referenced and provides many excellent diagrams and photographs.

Gilbert, Scott F. *Developmental Biology.* Sunderland, Mass.: Sinauer Associates, 1985. A college textbook written clearly and concisely and providing an excellent historical perspective, especially with regard to the investigation of determination and differentiation. Part 2, "Mechanisms of Cellular Differentiation," includes several chapters dealing with nuclear and cytoplasmic interactions during determination and differentiation. The author cites key original articles on most of the important discoveries in the field of developmental biology and provides many informative diagrams and photographs.

Ruddon, Raymond W. *Cancer Biology.* New York: Oxford University Press, 1987. A widely available book designed as a primary or supplementary text for college and medical school cancer courses. Chapter 3, "Regulation of Cellular Differentiation," provides an interesting and readable account of differentiation. The narrative is interspersed with a few helpful diagrams, and the author cites more than two hundred references related to differentiation. An interesting presentation on the relationship between differentiation and cancer (chapter 4) is also included.

Walbot, Virginia, and Nigel Holder. *Developmental Biology.* New York: Random House, 1987. A contemporary, well-illustrated, college-level developmental biology text that includes substantial coverage of both plant and animal developmental biology. Basic molecular and cell biology are reviewed in chapters 1-5. Chapter 7, "The Differentiation of Cells in Animals and Plants," provides a good background on the structural aspects of differentiation, and chapter 9, "The Control of Cell Differentiation," presents blood and muscle cell differentiation as models to illustrate control processes.

Rodney C. Mowbray

Cross-References

Cell Lineage Analysis in *Caenorhabditis elegans* Development, 361; Chromatin

Structure for Active Genes, 445; Cleavage, Gastrulation, and Neurulation, 490; Eukaryotic Post-transcriptional Control, 880; Gene Amplification and Deletion, 1090; Homeotic Genes and Homeoboxes, 1314; Nuclear Transplantation in Developmental Analysis, 1980.

DEVELOPMENT: AN EVOLUTIONARY PERSPECTIVE

Types of life science: Developmental biology (embryology) and evolutionary biology
Other fields of study: Genetics, invertebrate biology, systematics (taxonomy), and
  zoology

The relationship between ontogeny (individual development) and phylogeny (the evolution of species and lineages) is an enduring theme in the life sciences. Changes in developmental timing produce parallels between ontogeny and phylogeny. The subject illuminates the biology of regulation, the evolution of ecological strategies, and the mechanisms for evolutionary change in form.

Principal terms

ACCELERATION: the appearance of an organ earlier in the development of
  a descendant than in the ancestor as a result of an acceleration of
  development in ontogeny

BIOGENETIC LAW: Ernst Haeckel's term for his generalization that the
  ontogeny of an organism recapitulates the adult stages of its
  ancestors (recapitulation)

HETEROCHRONY: changes in developmental timing that produce parallels
  between ontogeny and phylogeny; changes in the relative time of
  appearance and rate of development for organs already present in
  ancestors

NEOTENY: either the retention of immature characteristics in the adult
  form or the sexual maturation of larval stages; it results in new kinds
  of adult body plans

ONTOGENY: the successive stages during the development of an animal,
  primarily embryonic but also postnatal

PAEDOMORPHOSIS: the appearance of youthful characters of ancestors in
  later ontogenetic stages of descendants

PHYLOGENY: a series of stages in the evolutionary history of species and
  lineages

RECAPITULATION: the repetition of phylogeny in ontogeny or of the
  ancestral adult stages in the embryonic stages of descendants

RETARDATION: the appearance of an organ later in the development of a
  descendant than in the ancestor as a result of a slowing of
  development

Summary of the Phenomenon

The idea of a relationship between individual development, or ontogeny, and the evolutionary history of a race, or phylogeny, is an old one. The concept received much attention in the nineteenth century and is often associated with the names of Karl Ernst von Baer and Ernst Haeckel, two prominent German biologists. It was

Haeckel who coined the catchphrase and dominant paradigm: Ontogeny recapitulates (or repeats) phylogeny. Since Haeckel's time, however, the relations between ontogeny and phylogeny have been portrayed in a variety of ways, including the reverse notion that phylogeny is the succession of ontogenies. Research in the 1970's and 1980's on the parallels between ontogeny and phylogeny focused on the change of timing in developmental events as a mechanism for recapitulation and on the developmental-genetic basis of evolutionary change.

During the early nineteenth century, two different concepts of parallels between development and evolution arose. The German J. F. Meckel and the Frenchman E. R. Serres believed that a higher animal in its embryonic development recapitulates the adult structures of animals below it on a scale of being. Von Baer, on the other hand, argued that no higher animal repeats an earlier adult stage but rather the embryo proceeds from undifferentiated homogeneity to differentiated heterogeneity, from the general to the specific. Von Baer published his famous and influential four laws in 1828: The more general characters of a large group of animals appear earlier in their embryos than the more special characters; from the most general forms, the less general are developed; every embryo of a given animal, instead of passing through the other forms, becomes separated from them; the embryo of a higher form never resembles any other form, only its embryo.

By the late nineteenth century, the notion of recapitulation and von Baer's laws of embryonic similarity were recast in evolutionary terms. Haeckel, and others, established the biogenetic law: That is, ontogeny recapitulates the adult stages of phylogeny. It was, in a sense, an updated version of the Serres-Meckel law but differed in that the notion was valid not only for a chain of being but also for many divergent lines of descent; ancestors had evolved into complex forms and were now considered to be modified by descent. More specifically, Haeckel thought of ontogeny as a short and quick recapitulation of phylogeny caused by the physiological functions of heredity and adaptation. During its individual development, he wrote, the organic individual repeats the most important changes in form through which its forefathers passed during the slow and long course of their paleontological development. The adult stages of ancestors are repeated during the development of descendants but crowded back into earlier stages of ontogeny. Ontogeny is the abbreviated version of phylogeny. These repeated stages reflect the history of the race. Haeckel considered phylogeny to be the mechanical cause of ontogeny.

The classic example of recapitulation is the stage of development in an unhatched bird or unborn mammal when gill slits are present. Haeckel argued that gill slits in this stage represented gill slits of the adult stage of ancestral fish, which in birds and mammals were pressed back into early stages of development. This theory differed from von Baer's notion that the gill slit in the human embryo and in the adult fish represented the same stage in development. The gill slits, explained the recapitulationists, got from a large adult ancestor to a small embryo in two ways: first, terminal addition (in which stages are added to the end of an ancestral ontogeny); and second, condensation (in which development is speeded up as ancestral features are pushed back to earlier stages of the embryo). Haeckel also coined another term widely used currently in another sense: "heterochrony." He used the term to denote a displacement in time of the appearance of one organ in ontogeny before another, thus disrupting the recapitulation of phylogeny in ontogeny. Haeckel was not, however, interested primarily in mechanisms or in embryology for its own sake, but rather for the information it could provide for developing evolutionary histories.

With the rise of mechanistic experimental embryology and with the establishment of Mendelian genetics in the early twentieth century, the biogenetic law was largely repudiated by biologists. Descriptive embryology was out of fashion, and the existence of genes made the two correlate laws to recapitulation—terminal addition and condensation—untenable. One of the most influential modifications for later work on the subject was broached in a paper by Walter Garstang in 1922, in which he reformulated the theory of recapitulation and refurbished the concept of heterochrony. Garstang argued that phylogeny does not control ontogeny but rather makes a record of the former: That is, phylogeny is a result of ontogeny. He suggested that adaptive changes in a larval stage coupled with shifts in the timing of development (heterochrony) could result in radical shifts in adult morphology.

Stephen Jay Gould resurrected the long unpopular concept of recapitulation with his book *Ontogeny and Phylogeny* (1977). In addition to recounting the historical development of the idea of recapitulation, he made an original contribution to defining and explicating the mechanism (heterochrony) involved in producing parallels between ontogeny and phylogeny. He argued that heterochrony—"changes in the relative time of appearance and rate of development for characters already present in ancestors"—was of prime evolutionary importance. He reduced Gavin de Beer's complex eight-mode analysis of heterochrony to two simplified processes: acceleration and retardation. Acceleration occurs if a character appears earlier in the ontogeny of a descendant than it did in an ancestor because of a speeding up of development. Conversely, retardation occurs if a character appears later in the ontogeny of a descendant than it did in an ancestor because of a slowing down of development. To demonstrate these concepts, Gould introduced a "clock model" in order to bring some standardization and quantification to the heterochrony concept.

He considered the primary evolutionary value of ontogeny and phylogeny to be in the immediate ecological advantages for slow or rapid maturation rather than in the long-term changes of form. Neoteny (the opposite of recapitulation) is the most important determinant of human evolution. Humans have evolved by retaining the young characters of their ancestors and have therefore achieved behavioral flexibility and their characteristic form. For example, there is a striking resemblance between some types of juvenile apes and adult humans; this similarity for the ape soon fades in its ontogeny as the jaw begins to protrude and the brain shrinks. Gould also insightfully predicted that an understanding of ontogeny and phylogeny would lead to a rapprochement between molecular and evolutionary biology.

By the 1980's, Rudolf Raff and Thomas Kaufman found this rapprochement by synthesizing embryology with genetics and evolution. Their work focuses on the developmental-genetic mechanisms that generate evolutionary change in morphology. They believe that a genetic program governs ontogeny, that the great decisions in development are made by a small number of genes that function as switches between alternate states or pathways. When these genetic switch systems are modified, evolutionary changes in morphology occur mechanistically. They argue further that regulatory genes—genes that control development by turning structural genes on and off—control the timing of development, make decisions about the fates of cells, and integrate the expression of structural genes to produce differentiated tissue. All this plays a considerable role in evolution.

Methods of Study

Both embryology and evolution have traditionally been descriptive sciences using methods of observation and comparison. By the end of the nineteenth century, a dichotomy had arisen between the naturalistic (descriptive) and the experimentalist tradition. The naturalists' tradition viewed the organism as a whole, and morphological studies and observations of embryological development were central to their program. Experimentalists, on the other hand, focused on laboratory studies of isolated aspects of function. A mechanistic outlook was compatible with this experimental approach.

Modern embryology uses both descriptive and experimental methods. Descriptive embryology uses topographic, histological (tissue analysis), cytological (cell analysis), and electron microscope techniques supplemented by morphometric (the measurement of form) analysis. Embryos are visualized using either plastic models of developmental stages, schematic drawings, or computer simulations. Cell lineage drawings are also used with the comparative method for phylogenies.

Experimental embryology, on the other hand, uses more invasive methods of manipulating the organism. During this field of study's early period, scientists subjected embryos to various changes to their normal path of development; they were chopped into pieces, transplanted, exposed to chemicals, and spun in centrifuges. Later, fate maps came into usage in order to determine the future development of regions in the embryo. It was found that small patches of cells on the surface of the embryo could be stained, without damaging the cell, by applying small pieces of agar soaked in a vital dye. One could then follow the stained cells to their eventual position in the gastrula. Amphibian eggs are used as material because they are big, easy to procure, and can undergo radical experimental manipulation.

Evolutionary theory primarily uses paleontology (study of the fossil record) to study the evolutionary history of species, yet Gould has also used quantification (the clock model, for example), statistics, and ecology to understand the parallels between ontogeny and phylogeny. Most scientists interested in the relationships between ontogeny and phylogeny chiefly use comparative and theoretical methods. They, for example, compare structures in different animal groups or compare the adult structures of an animal with the young stage of another. If similarities exist, are the lineages similar? Are the stages in ontogenetic development similar to those of the development of the whole species?

Yet, the study of relationships between ontogeny and phylogeny is an interdisciplinary subject. Not only are methods from embryology and evolutionary theory of help, but also, increasingly, techniques are applied from molecular genetics. Haeckel's method was primarily a descriptive historical one, and he collected myriad descriptive studies of different animals. Although scientists in those days had relatively simple microscopes, they left meticulous and detailed accounts.

A fusion of embryology, evolution, and genetics involves combining different methods from each of the respective disciplines for the study of the relationship between ontogeny and phylogeny. The unifying approach has been causal-analytical, in the sense that biologists have been examining mechanisms that produce parallels between ontogeny and phylogeny as well as the developmental-genetic basis for evolutionary change. The methods are either technical or theoretical. The technical ones include the use of the electron microscope, histological, cytological, and experimental analyses; the theoretical methods include comparison, historical analysis, observations, statistics, and computer simulation.

Context

The relationship between ontogeny and phylogeny is one of the most important ideas in biology and a central theme in evolutionary biology. It illuminates the evolution of ecological strategies, large-scale evolutionary change, and the biology of regulation. This scientific idea has also had far-reaching influences in areas such as anthropology, political theory, literature, child development, education, and psychology.

In the late nineteenth century, embryological development was a major part of evolutionary theory; however, that was not the case for much of the twentieth century. Although there was some interest in embryology and evolution from the 1920's to 1950's by Garstang, J. S. Huxley, de Beer, and Richard Goldschmidt, during the first three decades of the twentieth century genetics and development were among the most important and active areas in biological thought, yet there were few attempts to integrate the two areas. It is this new synthesis of evolution, embryology, and genetics that has emerged as one of the most exciting frontiers in the life sciences.

Although knowledge to be gained from a synthesis of development and evolution seems not to have any immediate practical application, it can offer greater insights into mechanisms of evolution, and a knowledge of evolution will give similar insights into mechanisms of development. A study of these relations and interactions also enlarges humankind's understanding of the nature of the development of individuals and their relation to the larger historical panorama of the history of life.

Bibliography

Bonner, J. T. *Morphogenesis: An Essay on Development*. Princeton, N.J.: Princeton University Press, 1952. A delightful treatment of ideas and concepts of development. Good introduction on development for both high school and college students.

De Beer, Gavin. *Embryos and Ancestors.* Oxford, England: Clarendon Press, 1951. A short, clearly written argument repudiating the theory of recapitulation. The first part is accessible to both advanced high school and college students; the second part, on his theory of heterochrony, is more difficult and complex.

Gould, Stephen Jay. *Ontogeny and Phylogeny.* Cambridge, Mass.: Harvard University Press, 1977. A detailed history of the relationship between ontogeny and phylogeny from the Greeks to the present. The historical part is accessible to both high school and college students. The portion on Gould's theory is more suitable for advanced college students. Includes glossary of terms and comprehensive bibliography.

Haeckel, Ernst. *The Evolution of Man: A Popular Exposition of the Principal Points of Human Ontogeny and Phylogeny.* New York: D. Appleton, 1879. In addition to being a renowned nineteenth century biologist, Haeckel was a talented populizer. As the title indicates, the book is aimed at a general audience and is suitable for both high school and college students.

Raff, Rudolf A., and Thomas C. Kaufman. *Embryos, Genes, and Evolution: The Developmental-Genetic Basis of Evolutionary Change.* New York: Macmillan, 1983. A cogently argued and comprehensive textbook on the subject of ontogeny and phylogeny with the added modern element of molecular genetics. Includes an introductory historical chapter that differs from Gould's in its emphasis on morphology and its reference to Richard Goldschmidt's influential work on developmental genetics. Comprehensive bibliography with emphasis on recent, not historical, works.

Sussman, Maurice. *Animal Growth and Development.* Englewood Cliffs, N.J.: Prentice-Hall, 1960. Part of the Foundations of Modern Biology series. A concise and clear exposition of the basics of development from its central problems to the life cycle, the development of primitive and vertebrate embryos, cellular differentiation, and growth and form. A good introduction to development for all levels.

Kristie Macrakis

Cross-References

Aging in Humans, 42; Determination and Differentiation, 606; Evolution: A Historical Perspective, 903; Growth and Growth Control in Plants, 1232; Growth in Animal Development, 1240; Morphogenesis and Pattern Formation, 1783; Neoteny and Other Heterochronic Effects, 1885; Regeneration, 2310.

DIFFUSION IN CIRCULATION

Type of life science: Cell biology (cytology)
Other field of study: Biochemistry

Diffusion is the process that supplies necessary nutrients from the circulation to animal cells and removes waste products back into the circulation. Understanding the principles of diffusion allows one to appreciate how the cardiovascular system is responsible for sustaining the life of cells in the body.

Principal terms
ARTERIOLES: the vascular segments that control the volume of blood entering the tissues
BLOOD FLOW: the volume of blood passing through an organ in a given time
CAPILLARY: the segment of the vascular system across which diffusion takes place most easily
DIFFUSION: the movement of a substance from a higher to a lower concentration by random motion
ENDOTHELIAL CELLS: the very thin cells that form the walls of capillaries and that line the walls of the rest of the vascular system
GRADIENT: the difference of the concentration between two points divided by the distance between the points
INTERSTITIAL SPACE: the volume of fluid that occupies the spaces between cells (the interstices) in the body
PERMEABILITY: a measure of the ease with which a molecule diffuses across a barrier or through a medium
THERMAL ENERGY: the force that makes molecules undergo random motion as a result of the temperature
VELOCITY OF FLOW: the distance traveled by a particle in a given time as occurs in a volume flow
VOLUME FLOW: the flow of a solution expressed as a volume passing a point in a given time

Summary of the Phenomenon

Diffusion is the physical process by which molecules move from a higher to a lower concentration. Diffusion is a passive process and uses the thermal, or heat, energy causing the random motion of molecules in solution (thermal agitation). At the temperature of the body, this random motion is able to move molecules very rapidly over short distances. The distance between a capillary in the body and the cells nearest to it (about 20-50 micrometers) can be traversed in a few thousandths of a second to a few seconds depending on the size of the molecule that is diffusing. Smaller molecules move faster than larger molecules, but the wall of the capillary superimposes a barrier to diffusion in addition to the distance. Therefore, molecules that can cross the capillary wall easily will diffuse faster than molecules that cross less easily. Diffusion supplies cells with materials that they consume because the cells are lowering the concentration in their vicinity by the consumption. Diffusion removes materials that the cells are producing because the cells are increasing the concentration in their vicinity by the production.

Diffusion itself occurs whenever a substance is at a higher concentration in one part of a solution as compared to another. A classic example is a sugar cube gradually dissolving in water. Molecules begin to dissolve in the water and are at a relatively high concentration at the surface of the sugar cube. Random movement will occur, and the dissolved sugar molecules will diffuse in all directions. Any individual molecule is as likely to diffuse one way as another. Because there are more sugar molecules at the surface of the cube, there will be a greater probability that net movement will be away from the cube. Diffusion will continue until there is a very similar concentration of sugar throughout the solution. In theory, however, there will never be exactly the same concentration. The concentration will always be slightly greater near the volume that originally contained the sugar cube (now completely dissolved) as compared to the volume farther away. Hence, the diffusion will approach, but never reach, complete equilibrium where there are the same number of molecules moving toward the initially higher concentration as toward the initially lower.

The principle of diffusion is expressed by Fick's law, or equation, which states that the rate of diffusion of a substance (the amount that moves per unit of time) is proportional to the area available for diffusion, a diffusion coefficient, and the concentration gradient for the substance. The area available for diffusion is the total surface area of all the open capillaries. The diffusion coefficient is a measure of how rapidly a molecule moves by random motion through a solution. It is a constant that is specific for a given substance and the medium through which it is diffusing. For example, a small molecule diffusing through water would have a high diffusion coefficient, but a large molecule diffusing through a viscous solution would have a small diffusion coefficient. The concentration gradient is a measure of how fast the concentration decreases over distance. It is approximately equal to the concentration difference between two points divided by the distance between the points.

The sole purpose of the capillary diffusion is to supply cells with adequate amounts of nutrients or to remove waste products as fast as they are formed. Substances that diffuse easily require only a small concentration gradient to move in sufficient amounts, because their diffusion coefficient is large. Substances that diffuse less easily have a larger concentration gradient, which compensates for the lower diffusion coefficient in order to move substances to and from the cells as fast as they are needed or produced.

There are two diffusion barriers between the blood and the tissue cells: the capillary wall and the interstitial space between the cells and the capillary. In general, substances that pass through the capillary easily diffuse more slowly through the interstitial space between the cells, because it is thicker than the capillary wall, and vice versa. Gases, however, diffuse quickly through both. A substance that diffuses quickly will have a relatively small concentration gradient between the blood and the cells, but a slowly diffusing substance will have a relatively large concentration gradient.

Under certain pathological conditions that cause edema, an additional diffusion barrier is added between the capillaries and the tissue cells. Edema is the accumulation of fluid in the interstitial spaces between the cells. It occurs when an increase in capillary blood pressure causes fluid filtration out of the capillaries and into the tissues. Another cause of edema is a reduction in plasma proteins, which normally cause retention of fluid in the blood because the proteins create an osmotic pressure called colloid osmotic or oncotic pressure. Increased fluid in the tissues increases diffusion distances and reduces the supply of nutrients to cells.

The cardiovascular system maintains diffusion by circulating blood past the cells, thus replenishing materials used by the cells and washing away materials produced by the cells. There are two aspects of the vascular supply that affect the rate of diffusional exchange between the cells and the blood. The first is the blood flow itself and the second is the permeability and the surface area of the capillaries. The larger the blood flow, permeability, and surface area, the greater the rate of diffusion. For any given level of these factors, the rate of diffusion will also be greater for a larger concentration difference of a substance between the cells and the blood.

Substances that are used by cells include oxygen, hormones, and nutrients such as glucose, fats, amino acids, and vitamins. Some cells, however, have the function of producing these substances and thus will supply them to the blood because the substances will be at a higher concentration near the cells. For example, liver cells produce glucose, adipose tissue cells produce fatty acids, and endocrine glands produce hormones. Cells produce waste products such as carbon dioxide, lactic acid, degradation products of molecules, and urea; these are removed by diffusion into the blood.

The amount of a substance that diffuses from the circulation into a given weight of tissue depends on characteristics of the capillary bed in that tissue. The total amount of a substance that diffuses across the capillary walls in a unit of time depends on the total surface area of the capillaries that is effectively open and permeability (reflecting the diffusion coefficient) of the capillaries to that substance. The product of the total surface area times the permeability of a unit of the surface area equals the overall permeability of the capillary bed. The overall permeability multiplied by the concentration gradient between the blood and the tissue equals the total rate of diffusion. The efficiency of diffusion is greatest when a very thin layer of fluid is in contact with a very large surface area. An appreciation of the efficiency of exchange in capillaries can be gained from considering the small volume of blood (about 250 milliliters) that is in all the body capillaries at any one time in relation to the very large total surface area of the capillaries (about 1,000 square meters). This relationship is about equal to spreading a cup of coffee over a football field.

The permeability of capillaries to various substances depends on the physical-chemical characteristics of the substance. Capillaries are composed of cells called endothelial cells. These cells are very thin (about 1 micrometer), irregularly shaped, and joined at their lateral edges to adjacent cells by an intercellular cement substance. Their cell membrane, similar to the cell membranes of any other cell, has a lipidic, or fatty, nature. Thus, substances that are soluble in lipids will diffuse across the membrane very easily. Fat-soluble substances include gases such as oxygen and carbon dioxide and fatty acids or other forms of nutritional fats. Small neutral molecules, such as water, will also diffuse across cell membranes but not as fast as gases. Charged molecules, such as sodium ions, and larger uncharged molecules, such as glucose, diffuse very slowly across cell membranes because they are not soluble in the capillary membrane. These molecules, however, can diffuse between the cells through pores in the intercellular cement. The pore area is very small, less than 0.1 percent of the total capillary wall, but still allows an adequate surface area for the diffusion. The pores are narrow and charges on their walls can repel molecules of the same charge. Molecules ranging in size from that of water to glucose diffuse through pores at similar rates. For example, water diffuses only twice as fast as glucose through the pores. Larger molecules, such as proteins, diffuse across the capillaries extremely slowly, because they are not soluble in lipids and are too big to fit through the pores.

Typically, a molecule of a gas can exchange (move between the blood and the tissue and back again) about a thousand times during the time it is in a capillary. A single molecule of water can exchange about a hundred times, sodium about fifty times, and glucose about ten times as they pass through the tissue in the capillaries. Thus, a cell can have that many chances to take up a molecule that it needs or to lose a molecule that is a waste product. The higher the concentration of the molecule in the blood the more molecules that can exchange with the cells.

Capillaries in different organs have different permeabilities, depending on the function of the organ. The permeabilities can be roughly correlated to the modified structure of the capillary. Liver capillaries have relatively large gaps between the capillary endothelial cells. These gaps allow proteins to diffuse relatively easily. This ease of diffusion is an important adaptation because the liver makes most of the plasma proteins that enter the blood. In addition, many nutrients that the liver produces are bound to plasma proteins. Many endocrine glands that produce protein hormones also have capillaries that are permeable to proteins, so that the hormones can enter the blood. Capillaries in these organs have strucures called fenestrations (windows). Fenestrations are thin circular areas of the capillary wall that are sometimes formed of "spokes" extending across the fenestration. Fenestrations are also found in the kidney and intestine. These capillaries are highly permeable to small molecules but relatively impermeable to proteins. The function of capillaries in these organs includes allowing the easy passage of the large volume of water and nutrients involved in digestion-absorption and excretion. In contrast, capillaries in the brain are relatively impermeable even to small molecules. This impermeability is required to protect the fluid surrounding the brain cells from rapid changes in composition when the composition of the plasma changes. This so-called blood-brain barrier is formed partly of very tight capillaries and partly of certain cells (belonging to a group of cells called glial cells) of the brain itself. These brain cells surround the wall of the capillary with extensions of their cell membrane, which form an additional diffusion barrier.

There are two aspects of blood flow that influence the rate of diffusion between tissues and blood. The first is the volume flow and the second is the velocity of flow. Volume flow is the volume of blood passing through the capillaries in a given time, for example, milliliters per minute per 100 grams of tissue. Flow velocity is the distance a molecule travels in a given time, for example, millimeters per second. The two are related by the total cross-sectional area of the open capillaries. The larger the total cross-sectional area then the slower the velocity of flow for a given volume flow. A capillary is about 1 millimeter long and 5 micrometers in diameter. A molecule typically spends one to two seconds in a capillary. That may seem a relatively short time, but it is more than adequate to allow nearly complete exchange of small molecules between the blood and tissue cells except under conditions of extreme activity.

The volume flow through tissue is controlled primarily by arterioles, which feed blood into capillaries. Arterioles dilate, and thus reduce resistance to flow, when a tissue is active and constrict when a tissue is resting. Capillaries also dilate or constrict depending on tissue needs but do not greatly change volume flow. The dilation of individual capillaries in an active tissue is relatively small. More important, there is also an opening of a large number of previously closed capillaries, called recruitment. Capillary dilation increases the surface area for diffusional exchange and decreases the velocity of blood flow. The reduced velocity increases the time over which exchange can occur. In addition, increasing the number of open capillaries reduces the diffusion distance between the capillaries and the adjacent cells.

Methods of Study

The rate of diffusion across capillaries can be studied by injecting a substance into the arterial supply to a tissue and collecting the venous blood that leaves the tissue. Knowing the amount injected, the concentration in the blood, and the amount that leaves the blood into the tissue allows one to calculate diffusion. In practice, the molecule is frequently "labeled" with a radioactive isotope so that the unidirectional movement into the tissue can be distinguished from molecules that were already in the tissue diffusing into the blood. Also, measurements of the venous concentration change in the blood over time can be compared to mathematical models of postulated diffusion barriers in the tissue. If the results are similar, they are taken as support for the model. Pore sizes can be determined in a similar manner. Molecules of different sizes, shapes, and charges can be infused into the arterial blood. If a molecule is larger than the pores, it will not enter the tissue from the blood. Similarly, if a molecule has the same charge as the walls of the pore, it will diffuse into the tissue more slowly than a molecule of the same size but with an opposite charge.

Another method of study is called the osmotic transient technique. This method is used to determine pore sizes in the vascular bed of a tissue. A substance is injected into the arterial supply to a tissue or an organ, and the change in its weight or volume is measured. If the molecule is too large to pass through the capillary pores into the tissue, then it will exert an osmotic pressure. Fluid will be drawn out of the tissue into the blood, and the weight of the tissue will decrease as the fluid is removed by the blood. The weight will decrease until the substance is removed from the tissue, and then the tissue will regain the fluid from the new blood entering. Hence, the weight change is transient and the result of an osmotic pressure. Molecules that pass through capillary walls to a greater or lesser extent will have a greater or lesser osmotic transient.

A measure of the combined effect of the permeability (P) and surface area (S) of the open capillaries in an organ can be obtained by calculating the so-called PS product. Radioactive rubidium is injected into the arterial supply to an organ. Rubidium is relatively diffusible, and once it has crossed the capillary it is taken up by cells quickly. Therefore, its concentration in the interstitial space is assumed to be nearly zero. Measuring the amount of rubidium removed from the blood flow allows the PS product to be measured because the diffusion is essentially one-way and only limited by the structures across which the diffusion takes place.

Context

Diffusion is the process that supplies cells of the body with nutrients. Even if an organ gets a plentiful blood supply, unless sufficient capillaries are open the cells will be starved because of inadequate diffusion. Studying the rates of diffusion, in turn, can allow scientists to infer certain characteristics of the nature of capillaries and the control of tissue perfusion with blood.

Many present studies are concerned with the mechanisms that control the rate of diffusion through opening or closing capillaries. Control mechanisms include the autonomic nervous system, hormones, and local metabolites. These metabolites include compounds produced or consumed during cell activity, such as lactic acid, carbon dioxide, and adenosine (a breakdown product of adenosine triphosphate, frequently abbreviated ATP).

A number of disease states involve problems that result from inadequate diffusion from the blood to the tissue cells. A relatively common one is coronary, or heart, disease, in which reduced arteriolar diameters reduce blood flow through cardiac capillaries. Another problem is encountered in diabetes, which causes increased connective tissue around the capillaries. The connective tissue structure involved is called the basement membrane, or basal lamina. The normally very thin basal lamina surrounds the capillary and provides structural support. When its thickness increases, diffusion out of the capillary is reduced and leads to tissue death resulting in gangrene, damage to the retina of the eye, and other pathologies. Edema is also a pathologic condition that can reduce diffusion and consequently the supply of nutrients to cells. Edema is a problem that is encountered when there is a weakened heart that cannot pump all the blood it receives. This condition is called congestive heart failure and results in fluid accumulating in the blood vessels, thus increasing capillary pressure.

Another area of research interest is the differences between capillary responses and function in the adult and the fetus or newborn. The areas of investigation include determination of the stage at which adult characteristics of vascular regulatory mechanisms appear and the adaptation of the fetal circulation to uterine existence.

Bibliography

Ganong, William F. *Review of Medical Physiology.* 14th ed. East Norwalk, Conn.: Appleton and Lange, 1989. An advanced text but with well-illustrated and concise explanations of physiological phenomena. Chapters 1, 30, and 32 provide descriptions and mechanisms of diffusion and capillary circulation. The text is useful because the topics are presented in small sections and subsections. Well indexed for locating information.

Guyton, Arthur C. *Human Physiology and Mechanisms of Disease.* Philadelphia: W. B. Saunders, 1982. An intermediate-level animal physiology text by a world expert on the cardiovascular system. Includes several general and specific chapters on diffusion across capillaries and cardiovascular regulatory mechanisms. Well written and verbally oriented.

_____. *Textbook of Medical Physiology.* Philadelphia: W. B. Saunders, 1986. An advanced-level medically oriented physiology text by a world expert on the cardiovascular system. Chapter 9 provides clear descriptions of diffusion and the rates of diffusion of selected molecules across capillaries. Chapters 19 and 20 deal with vascular functions and regulatory mechanisms.

Keele, Cyril A., and Eric Neil. *Samson Wright's Applied Physiology.* London: Oxford University Press, 1978. An older text but one that provides detailed analysis of diffusion, theoretical models, and the experimental and analytical techniques. It is very well written and provides excellent insights into the phenomenon of diffusion. The presentation is mathematical but with sufficient information to allow an in-depth understanding with some extra effort. Chapters 4 and 5 provide more information on capillary diffusion than almost any other general text.

Rhoades, Rodney, and Richard Pflanzer. *Human Physiology.* Philadelphia: Saunders College Publishing, 1989. A current and well-written intermediate-level animal physiology text. Includes treatments of diffusion at a general and circulatory level. Excellent illustrations and clear, direct, and pertinent writing. Chapters 2, 4, and 19 treat diffusion and the circulation.

David Mailman

Cross-References

The Blood-Brain Barrier, 233; Blood Circuits, 248; Circulatory Systems of Invertebrates, 476; Circulatory Systems of Vertebrates, 483; Fluid Balance, 1017; Gas Exchange in Animals, 1069; The Lymphatic System's Function, 1619.

DIGESTION OF CARBOHYDRATES

Types of life science: Animal physiology and biochemistry
Other field of study: Respiration

Digestion of carbohydrates involves the ingestion of starch and sugars and the enzymatic breakdown of these molecules by the digestive tract into glucose. Glucose and other simple sugars are then absorbed directly from the small intestine into the blood for use as metabolic energy.

Principal terms

BRUSH BORDER: the outermost edge of the small intestine, with fingerlike projections that have microscopic cells with numerous extensions to facilitate enzyme production and absorption of nutrients into the bloodstream

CELLULOSE: a straight-chain polymer of glucose molecules, used by plants as a structural support

FIBER: thick-walled cells in plants that are indigestible by nonruminating animals

GLUCOSE: the most common sugar, made by plants and used by animals as their major energy source

RUMINANT: an animal that digests food through a three- or four-chambered stomach and is characterized, among other things, by chewing its cud

STARCH: a polymer of glucose molecules, used by plants as a means of storing energy

SUCROSE: table sugar obtained from sugar cane or sugar beets

Summary of the Phenomenon

Carbohydrates appear to be the most efficient energy source for the nutrition of both plants and animals. Carbohydrates include sugars, starches, and cellulose. Simple carbohydrates are represented by a variety of sugars, chemical compounds based on combinations of carbon, hydrogen, and oxygen atoms in a ratio of 1:2:1.

Glucose (the most important source of mammalian energy), fructose (sugar found in fruit), and galactose have the same number of carbon, oxygen, and hydrogen atoms, but those atoms are joined in a slightly different configuration in each. Glucose, fructose, and galactose are known as monosaccharides. When two of these six-carbon sugars join, a disaccharide is formed. Sucrose (table sugar) is a disaccharide made of glucose and frustose. Lactose (milk sugar) is also a disaccharide. It is composed of glucose and galactose. Monosaccharides, particularly glucose, are what the body needs for energy. The process of digestion splits disaccharides into their two components; little effort is then required for the digestive system to absorb and utilize the resulting monosaccharides.

Plants make glucose through the process of photosynthesis and tend to store excess glucose molecules in the form of the starch amylose, which is composed of chains containing one hundred or more glucose units. Starches are called polysaccharides or complex carbohydrates because they consist of many monosaccharide units. For a mammal to use amylose, its digestive system has to break it down into individual glucose units. These will eventually be burned up to produce energy for the body's cells.

Although animals are not able to store large amounts of carbohydrates, some is stored in both the liver and the muscles as glycogen. Glucose units are joined together to make a glycogen macromolecule; up to sixty thousand of these molecules may be stored at any one time. To be readily usable to an animal, carbohydrates stored in the liver or muscle must be water-soluble. The branched chemical structure of glycogen is much more water-soluble than the straighter chained structure of amylose.

The enzymes involved in the digestion of carbohydrates are similar among most nonruminating animals. Amylase works to break down starch and glycogen into maltose or glucose, and it is made by salivary glands and by the pancreas. Sucrase breaks sucrose into glucose and fructose. Maltase changes maltose into glucose, and lactase splits lactose into glucose and galactose.

Not all animals can digest all of the carbohydrates. Cellulose, the material that makes up plant cell walls, is, like starch, a complex carbohydrate. Unlike starch, however, it is indigestible to humans and carnivores. Herbivores and invertebrates can utilize cellulose because they have cellulose-digesting microorganisms in their guts.

The digestive system of cattle and other ruminants is highly effective in digesting carbohydrates. Cows have a four-chambered stomach. As they feed, they swallow masses of incompletely chewed grass, which enter the first chamber of the stomach. Here, billions of anaerobic microorganisms (cellulose-digesting bacteria and starch-digesting ciliates) reduce the grass to a pulp, which is then compressed into a mass called the cud. The cow regurgitates the cud and rechews it at leisure. After reswallowing, the cud enters another chamber of the stomach, where gastric enzymes complete the digestive process.

Protozoa in the gut of termites efficiently break down cellulose; the termites derive needed energy from the sugars liberated. Earthworms can also digest cellulose, although reports differ on whether earthworms secrete a cellulose-digesting enzyme (cellulase) or rely on microorganisms in their gut to break down this carbohydrate.

In humans, the digestion of carbohydrates begins in the mouth. Amylase is produced by the salivary glands and is secreted into the mouth in response to the ingestion of food. The amylase beings to break down starch, generally into the disaccharide maltose, before the bolus of food is swallowed. Salivary amylase works best at a pH range of 6.35 to 6.85. This range is maintained in the saliva by the buffering effects of bicarbonate and phosphate ions. Starch digestion continues in the stomach until amylase is inactivated by stomach acid and broken apart by the stomach's protein-digesting enzymes. Within ten minutes after starch enters the small intestine, it is acted upon by a second amylase. This enzyme is produced by the pancreas and is secreted into the duodenum (the first part of the small intestine). Residual starch is reduced to maltose and glucose molecules within about ten minutes after entering the duodenum. Maltase, which is made by the intestinal brush border, then finishes the job by splitting the disaccharide into two glucose molecules. Other enzymes embedded in the intestinal cell membranes act on sucrose and lactose to yield glucose, fructose, and galactose. These are all relatively small molecules that are readily transported from the intestine into the bloodstream.

In nonruminant animals, most of the absorption of simple sugars occurs in the upper small intestine. The rate at which simple sugars are released from the stomach is controlled by a negative feedback mechanism that involves receptors in the upper intestine and motility of the stomach. The intestine is responsive to sugar, so a load of monosaccharides in the gut will cause the water balance to shift. When too much sugar gets out of the stomach at once, dumping syndrome may occur: Water is drawn to the gut and osmotic diarrhea is the result. In general, the stomach empties at a rate that supplies a constant amount of calories to the intestine. Hence, a high-fat diet slows the emptying of the stomach. The presence of glucose in the stomach retards emptying to a greater extent than does that of fructose.

Glucose and galactose are absorbed across the gut wall by active transport, whereas fructose goes across by facilitated diffusion. Active transport means that the process requires energy, involves a specific carrier, and can occur against a concentration gradient. Facilitated diffusion, on the other hand, does not require energy and so it can proceed only from a high concentration to a lower concentration. There is a carrier involved, however, so the system can be saturated, because the carrier is not specific for fructose. Competitive inhibition by similar compounds can occur. As fructose is very efficiently trapped from the bloodstream by the liver, virtually no fructose circulates in the bloodstream.

In ruminant animals, there is a large microbial and protozoal community in the rumen fluid. The contents of the rumen are maintained anaerobically at 39 degrees Celsius, with a pH of 5 to 7. Maintenance of pH is aided by large volumes (80-100 liters per day for cows) of alkaline saliva. Any simple sugars in the diet are rapidly fermented by rumen organisms to lactate, volatile fatty acids, carbon dioxide, or methane, or are used by these microbes to make their own cellular components. Therefore, virtually no dietary simple sugar would be left for absorption by the animal.

Ruminants play a very important role in the food chain. For the most part, they do not compete for the same foodstuffs as nonruminant animals. Ruminants can get useful energy from grasses and woody materials and ultimately turn it into high-quality meat and milk for humans and other carnivores. Since nonruminating animals and humans can derive little benefit from grasses, the ruminant is a vital energy link between plants and nonruminant animals.

Methods of Study

Much of the research work dealing with carbohydrate digestion has been concerned with identifying the enymes involved and determining where they are produced and determining the nature of their chemical activity. It is now known that the digestive enzymes originate in the salivary glands, the pancreas, and the mucosal lining of the small intestine. The amylases have been isolated, crystallized, and thoroughly characterized. The multiplicity of enzymes from the intestinal mucosa, on the other hand, have relatively recently been subjected to intensive experimentation, and they are not well characterized.

To study the enzymes produced in the intestinal mucosa, scientists prepare homogenates from mammalian intestines. The homogenates are dissolved in various solutes and are analyzed by means of gel column chromatography. This method separates molecules by size (molecular weight), and each of the resulting band can then be analyzed for chemical activity. Seven intestinal enzymes that catalyze carbohydrate breakdown have been isolated and identified by this means.

The next question to be answered concerning the enzymes of intestinal origin was whether they are secreted into the lumen of the intestine, as amylase is, or whether they function in association with the mucosal lining. The electron microscope gave some insight into this question. Pictures of the brush border of the small intestine showed clusters of rodlike structures near the plasma membrane. Analysis of these structures confirmed that enzymatic production occurred in this area; it is now known that sucrase, maltase, lactase, and isomaltase are produced here and hydrolyze disaccharides as they come in contact with the brush border of the microvilli.

Some details of the specificity and nature of the active transport system for glucose and galactose have been determined. The exact nature of the glucose carrier is unclear. It is known, however, to be a protein complex connected to the sodium/potassium pump. Sodium ions are required for glucose uptake. Glucose or galactose cannot attach to the carrier until it is preloaded with sodium ions. Some cases of monosaccharide malabsorption have been shown to be attributable to a reduced number of carriers. Children suffering from this condition cannot absorb either glucose or galactose and have severe diarrhea. When fed a high-fructose diet, they have no problems.

Active transport is actually a combination of three processes. There is an unstirred layer of material immediately contiguous to the mucosal cells, on the lumen side, through which glucose must first diffuse. Then the actual transport occurs. Finally, there is extrusion of glucose from the cell to the serosal side and into the interstitial fluid.

The desire for sweets appears to be universal among the human population. Why this is so has intrigued researchers. It appears that a sweet taste is something with which mammals are born rather than something that they acquire. The ability to taste various substances is associated with specialized organs called taste buds. In lower animals, such as fish, taste buds are found not only in the mouth but, in some species, dispersed over the entire body as well. Only limited research has been carried out to define the range of compounds to which such receptors are sensitive. In the adult human, taste buds are found on the lips, pharynx, and epiglottis in addition to the tongue. These organs appear in the fetus about the time it starts swallowing, about three to four months into gestation.

The cells involved in taste sensations are highly innervated. Although the nerve fibers themselves can respond to a variety of taste sensations, the ability to discriminate sweet taste results from the presence of lectins. Lectins are carbohydrate-binding proteins that are capable of recognizing a variety of different carbohydrates. The binding of sugar with lectin is necessary for transmission to the brain of the nerve impulse that indicates that a sugar is being ingested.

Glucose, fructose, and sucrose are chemically distinguished in mammals; sucrose causes a greater neural discharge than any other natural sweetener. The environment of the compound also affects the sweetness. Compounds in the dry state are not as sweet as they are in dilute solution. Presumably, a solution allows greater access of the sugar to the lectin; a threshold exists beyond which low but increasing concentrations of sugar no longer evokes a response of increased sweetness; this suggests that the limited number of lectin molecules can be readily saturated. Sweetness also depends in part on pH and the presence of other compounds.

The sensation of a sweet taste is probably part of the body's "prepriming" mechanism for the initiation of the process of digestion, absorption, and utilization of dietary carbohydrates.

Context

Carbohydrates are essential to the human diet. They account for 80 percent of the diet in many underdeveloped countries. These populations obtain a balanced supply of simple and complex carbohydrates along with an adequate amount of fiber. Western diets have changed considerably in the twentieth century, and the majority of calories in these diets are obtained from fats and proteins. The percentage of fiber in the Western diet has dropped from 8 percent to 3 percent, and today Americans are encouraged to increase their dietary fiber consumption. Based on epidemiological data, there has been increasing concern that diets low in fiber contribute to the etiology of severity of such diseases as diabetes, hypercholesterolemia, diverticular disease, colon cancer, obesity, and hemorrhoids.

There are several hypotheses as to the mechanism by which fiber acts. The first has to do with the transit time of fecal material through the gut. Foods containing insoluble plant fibers move through the gut more quickly; if material passes more rapidly, pushing other dietary components along with it, then perhaps certain dietary components (for example, cholesterol) are not absorbed as efficiently if they get moved beyond the sites of their optimum absorption. In addition, if toxic products are formed as the result of microbial action, these products would not be in the gut as long. Thus, toxins might not interact with gut cells for sufficient time or promote colon cancer. The more soluble fibers absorb larger quantities of water and could form gel filtration columns in the gut. These gels could bind substances, such as cholesterol, and minimize their absorption into the bloodstream.

Lactose intolerance is a common, genetically influenced disorder seen in humans worldwide. Lactose is the primary carbohydrate in most mammalian milk (the notable exception is the sea lion). Most young mammals depend on milk as their predominant source of nutrients. Lactose is broken down into glucose and galactose by lactase. Levels of lactase are high in children and decrease with age. It is estimated that 70 percent of the world's adult population is lactose-intolerant. Non-Caucasians are more susceptible than are Caucasians. A study in 1975 reported that 50 percent of Peruvians are intolerant by the age of three and 50 percent of the U.S. black population is afflicted by age thirteen. Less than 20 percent of the U.S. white population becomes intolerant of lactose at any age. Early attempts to address protein deficiencies in underdeveloped countries included widespread distribution of dry milk solids. Adverse reactions to these products greatly reduced the effectiveness of this program. The degree of discomfort varies considerably with the individual. One person may have no trouble resulting from drinking an eight-ounce glass of milk, while another person suffers severe consequences. Symptoms may range from flatulence to mild gastrointestinal-tract discomfort to severe diarrhea. Efforts have been made to treat milk products in such a way as to make them "safe" for lactose-intolerant individuals. These have included treating milk with lactase isolated from microorganisms. Cheese products do not pose a significant problem, because the lactose is essentially removed with the whey during the cheese-making process. The fermentation of yogurt also lowers lactose content.

About 18 percent of total calories in Western diets comes from sucrose. In the past, a number of disease states had been linked with sucrose consumption. Dental caries, diabetes, and heart disease are chief among these. Sucrose was once suggested to cause hyperactivity in children and criminal behavior among adults. With the exception of dental caries, sucrose is not to blame for any of those physical or mental disorders. Elevated sucrose levels may contribute to obesity, and obesity is a strong risk factor for insulin-independent (late-onset) diabetes. There is no evidence, however, that excess dietary sucrose may also be considered a risk factor for onset of diabetes. Once a person becomes diabetic, it is generally recommended that intake of simple sugars be considerably restricted. This precaution helps to control large swings in blood glucose levels. Although studies have shown that elevated sucrose consumption results in increased serum triglyceride levels, no effect on serum cholesterol has been observed and no direct correlation between sucrose and heart disease has been reported.

Bibliography

Christian, Janet L., and Janet L. Greger. *Nutrition for Living*. Menlo Park, Calif.: Benjamin/Cummings, 1985. A nutrition book written for college students who have little or no background in science. Chapter 6 deals with carbohydrate digestion, lactose intolerance, and hormones involved with carbohydrate transport in the blood. Easy to read.

Marieb, Elaine N. *Human Anatomy and Physiology*. Menlo Park, Calif.: Benjamin/ Cummings, 1989. A very thorough discussion of digestion is presented in chapter 24. College-level text.

Mitchell, Lawrence G., John A. Mutchmor, and Warren D. Dolphin. *Zoology*. Menlo Park, Calif.: Benjamin/Cummings, 1988. Chapter 4 presents a thorough discussion of digestion of carbohydates in many animal species. Easy to read.

Roehrig, Karla L. *Carbohydrate Biochemistry and Metabolism*. Westport, Conn.: AVI, 1984. A thorough, well-written outline of digestion, metabolism, and metabolic disorders involved with carbohydrates. Some science knowledge is necessary to understand the book.

Wallace, Robert, Jack L. King, and Gerald P. Sanders. *Biosphere, the Realm of Life*. 2d ed. Glenview, Ill.: Scott, Foresman, 1988. Chapter 37 offers a discussion of digestion in invertebrates as well as vertebrates. Freshman-level college text with good illustrations.

Roberta B. Williams

Cross-References

Carbohydrates, 323; Digestion of Fats, 636; Digestion of Proteins, 644; Digestion Regulation, 650; Digestion Strategies, 656; Digestive Processes in Humans, 663; The Digestive Tract, 670.

DIGESTION OF FATS

Types of life science: Animal physiology and biochemistry
Other field of study: Respiration

Fats, when digested, provide animals with a rich source of energy in addition to other vital nutrients. A lack of fat in the diet or failure of fat digestion and absorption can lead to impaired health and functioning.

Principal terms

ABSORPTION: the movement of digested, soluble material from the gastrointestinal tract into the circulatory system

BILE SALTS: cholesterol-based compounds produced by the liver and secreted into the small intestine to aid in fat digestion by emulsifying fat

CHYLOMICRON: a particle composed of phospholipids and protein that packages absorbed dietary lipids for transport into the circulatory (lymph) system

DIGESTION: the breakdown of foodstuffs by mechanical, chemical, and enzymatic action in preparation for absorption

EMULSIFY: to disperse lipids (fat) into small droplets for digestion

LIPASE: a major fat-digesting enzyme produced by cells of the pancreas and secreted into the small intestine

LIPIDS: those components of plant and animal tissue not soluble in water but soluble in organic solvents such as ether or hexane

MICELLE: a particle composed of bile salts, phospholipids, and digested dietary fats and other lipids; it transports dietary lipids into cells lining the small intestine for absorption

POLYUNSATURATED FAT: triglycerides that contain fatty acids having two or more double bonds in the fatty acid chain

TRIGLYCERIDE: a major form of dietary lipid, composed of three fatty acids attached to glycerol; fats and oils are triglycerides

Summary of the Phenomenon

Dietary fat consists primarily of fats and oils, chemically known as triglycerides. They provide approximately 2.25 times as much energy per unit weight as do carbohydrates or proteins when oxidized. The chemical structure of triglycerides requires that they be digested in order to be absorbed and available for use. Lipids are those compounds found in foods—plant and animal tissue—that are not soluble in water but soluble in organic solvents, such as hexane or ether. Fats and oils are but one group of compounds classified as lipids. In addition to fats and oils, fat-soluble vitamins, fat-soluble pigments, cholesterol and its various derivatives, and phospholipids are all considered lipids.

Fats and oils are quantitatively the most significant group of lipids in the diet. Their chemical structure consists of a three-carbon molecule of glycerol to which three fatty acids are attached to form a triglyceride. Differences in carbon chain length of fatty acids and the presence and number of double bonds determine the physical properties of the triglyceride. The shorter the carbon chain length or the greater the number of double bonds in the fatty acid, the more likely it is to be a liquid, an oil, at room temperature. Fats that are solid at room temperature have a preponderance of either long-chain fatty acids or fatty acids with few, if any, double bonds.

Digestion of triglycerides (hereafter referred to as fats) is a complex process whereby compounds that are not water-soluble are made soluble and capable of being absorbed. In the digestion of fats, complex structures are broken down into small constituent molecules. These subunit molecules are used by tissues primarily for energy. The end products of fat digestion are also used in the body to construct various components of animal tissue such as cell membranes. Some of the end products provide the molecular structure to synthesize hormones and other growth factors such as vitamin D.

Several organs are involved in the process of fat digestion. The site of digestion is the upper two-thirds of the small intestine. Digestion commences upon entering the duodenum, the first segment of the small intestine. The liver synthesizes a secretion known as bile. Bile is composed of water, bile salts, bile pigments, cholesterol, and a phospholipid known as lecithin, in addition to other, minor constituents. Bile flows from the liver through the hepatic duct to the gall bladder in those species, including humans, that have one. It is stored in the gall bladder, where it becomes more concentrated by the removal of some of the water. The gall bladder is also said to acidify bile. Bile is released from the gall bladder into the duodenum under the control of several factors. These include the presence of food in the mouth as well as hormones associated with digestion.

The pancreas, situated in the first loop of the duodenum, performs several roles critical to digestion of fat. It synthesizes and secretes the fat-digesting enzyme lipase. The pancreas also secretes hormones that influence the rate of passage of ingested food through the tract. These hormones influence the composition of digestive secretions as well. Emulsification of fats in the duodenum is necessary before the digesting enzymes can gain access to them. During emulsification, lipids are dispersed into small droplets suspended in watery digestive juices. Bile salts from the liver and phospholipids from digestive secretions have special chemical properties to act as emulsifying agents. These compounds are not unlike detergent or soap, in that they are water-soluble and fat-soluble simultaneously. Mixing of these agents with fats results in formation of an emulsion inside the small intestine. The churning action of the small intestine aids the emulsification process. Once emulsified, fats are acted upon by enzymes. The pancreatic enzyme lipase is the enzyme responsible for breaking bonds between fatty acids and glycerol. Lipase functions only at the surface of lipid droplets, explaining the need for prior emulsification. In addition to lipase, another compound, colipase, forms a complex with bile salts and lipase, enhancing the emulsification action.

The end result of lipase activity is the release of two fatty acids from triglycerides, yielding a monoglyceride. The third fatty acid remains attached at the middle position of glycerol. A small portion of the monoglycerides may be modified by moving the fatty acid to the end position of glycerol. This allows lipase to detach the third fatty acid. There is some evidence for a gastric lipase produced by the stomach, but its role in fat digestion is insignificant. The text of fat digestion depends to some extent on the fatty acid composition of the fat. The presence of palmitic acid in fats and the position of glycerol to which it is attached may affect the end products of fat digestion. A small amount of dietary fat may remain undigested and intact.

Fatty acids that have been removed from glycerol become associated with either sodium or potassium ions to make soaps of the fatty acids. Fatty acid soaps and monoglycerides are subsequently prepared for absorption. Bile salts and other agents responsible for forming the emulsion become aggregated into small particles called micelles. Inside micelles are found fatty acid soaps and monoglycerides, in addition to other fat-soluble compounds, such as vitamins A, D, E, and K. Micelles associate with mucosal cells lining the small intestine, releasing their contents into the mucosal cells. Most of the fat absorption occurs in the upper two-thirds of the small intestine. Bile salts remain outside mucosal cells, passing to the lower portion of the small intestine, the ileum, where they are absorbed.

The fate of fatty acids in mucosal cells depends on the size of the molecule. Fatty acids with chain lengths of less than ten to twelve carbons may pass directly from mucosal cells into the portal bloodstream. From there they are transported, unattached, to the liver. Fatty acids with longer carbon chain lengths are reattached to either monoglycerides or a modified form of glycerol to form triglycerides. Triglycerides and other fat-soluble materials are packaged inside a transport particle known as a chylomicron. The chylomicron's exterior is composed of lipoprotein, cholesterol, and phospholipids, making it effectively water-soluble. Chylomicrons move out of mucosal cells of the small intestine into the body, entering the lymph system. They eventually enter the bloodstream, where they are distributed throughout the circulatory system. On a diet with a moderate fat level, 95 percent or more of ingested fat may be digested and absorbed. Blood plasma will appear milky shortly after consumption of a meal high in fat, a result of elevated levels of chylomicrons in the circulation. Within one or two hours, chylomicrons are taken up from the blood, especially by storage fat tissue.

Rate of movement of ingested food from the stomach into the small intestine is affected by the amount of fat consumed. Coordinated by several gastric, intestinal, and pancreatic hormones, emptying of the stomach is slowed when fat content of the diet is high. The result is a slower rate of passage through the intestinal tract, allowing a greater time for digestive action. In addition to slowing rate of passage, the composition of pancreatic secretions is altered by the action of the hormones favoring more complete digestion of fats. One of the hormones released in response to a high-fat diet causes contraction of the gall bladder. The more complete emptying of the gall bladdder resulting from contractions allows more bile salts and other emulsifying agents to be secreted into the duodenum.

Bile salts, which are so critical to fat digestion and absorption, are sodium or potassium salts of bile acids. Bile acids are derivatives of cholesterol. Attached to the bile salt is a molecule of either glycine or taurine, giving rise to sodium glycocholate and sodium taurocholate, respectively. Between 90 and 95 percent of bile salts are absorbed in the ileum and are recycled through the liver. From there they are secreted back into the duodenum for lipid emulsification and digestion. The entire pool of bile salts is estimated to recycle twice per meal and six to eight times per day.

The true digestibility of dietary fats is generally very high, around 95 percent. Undigested dietary fat is excreted in the stool. Long-chain saturated fatty acids in dietary fat tend to depress fat digestion. It is for this reason that fat in human milk is better digested and absorbed by humans than cow's milk. Cow's milk contains appreciable amounts of long-chain saturated fatty acids, such as palmitic and stearic acids. If calcium ions are present in the intestinal tract during fat digestion and absorption, formation of unabsorbable calcium fatty acid soaps may result. These are excreted in the stool and result in depression in calcium absorption. This lowered absorption of calcium is of more nutritional concern than the decrease in fat absorption.

Some of the fat in the stool is nondietary in origin. It consists of unabsorbed bile secretions, fats from mucosal cells sloughed from the intestinal lining, and lipids synthesized by intestinal microorganisms. It is referred to as metabolic fecal fat.

Defects in fat digestion and absorption or many factors resulting in increased fat excretion in the stool can lead to significant nutritional and medical problems. Deficiencies of important nutrients may result, causing conditions unrelated to the energy-supplying role of dietary fat.

Methods of Study

The processes of fat digestion and absorption can be evaluated using direct or indirect methods. Direct methods generally require invasive procedures, such as surgery. Tubes known as cannulas can be surgically inserted into accessible segments of the gastrointestinal tract of an experimental animal or a human patient. Samples of the gastrointestinal contents can then be taken at periodic intervals and evaluated for lipid quantity and types. Comparisons with the food consumed provide an assessment of the progress of fat digestion. Other direct methods involve use of isolated digestive juices and pieces of intestinal wall reacting with diet samples in vitro. Changes in lipid composition, determined over time, reflect changes associated with fat digestion.

Fat digestion can be measured indirectly through analysis of food and feces. By determining the amount of dietary fat consumed and the quantity of fat excreted in the feces or stool, the quantity digested is calculated as the difference between the two. Digestibility is usually expressed as a percentage of total nutrient consumption. Digestibility determined in this fashion is known as apparent digestibility. It does not take into account that a portion of fecal lipids is not dietary in origin. Estimation of the amount that metabolic fecal fat contributes to fecal lipids allows the mathematical calculation of true digestibility of fat. True digestibility is generally between 90 and 95 percent.

The study of lipid digestion and absorption is complicated by the heterogeneous chemical nature of lipids. Determination of the total quantity of lipids in food, tissue, or feces is integral to studying fat digestion. It is affected by the method used to isolate lipids. Identification of specific types of lipids present is also necessary to understand digestion. Digestion and absorption of fat are influenced by the presence and distribution of fatty acids in the molecule.

Analytical methods to determine the quantity of nutrients in food and feces were first developed during the 1860's in Europe, a procedure known as proximate analysis. Determination of total lipid content, known as ether extract in proximate analysis, involves extracting a sample with ether, an organic solvent. Most, but not all, lipids are soluble in ether. The ether extract method is simple but provides only an approximation of total lipid content. For this reason, the extract obtained using this method is often referred to as crude fat.

Improved analytical methods for determining lipid content have been, and continue to be, developed. These methods take into account the heterogeneity of lipids. Sequential extractions of samples are performed using different chemical reagents and different chemical conditions. More complete lipid extraction and collection are thus accomplished.

The relative fatty acid composition of triglycerides has been determined for many years using two comparatively simple procedures. One method evaluates reaction of double bonds in fatty acids with iodine to reveal the degree of unsaturation, a high iodine number indicating a great degree of unsaturation. The second method measures the saponification number of fats by analyzing the reaction of fatty acids in triglycerides with sodium hydroxide to estimate chain length. A high saponification number reflects the presence of large numbers of short-chain fatty acids.

Lipid separation into specific types is accomplished using equipment such as chromatographs and ultracentrifuges. Fatty acid composition can be determined using gas-liquid chromatography. Chromatography in conjunction with enzyme analyses and centrifugation has allowed the specific fatty acid composition of fats and presence and content of other lipid types in food and body tissue samples to be determined.

The techniques described have allowed the effect of fatty acids and where they are attached to glycerol to be evaluated relative to fat digestion. It has been discovered that some fatty acids are more commonly attached to glycerol at certain positions. Saturated fatty acids are most often attached to the end carbons of glycerol in vegetable fats but are more equally distributed among the three carbons of glycerol in animal fats. Further research has revealed that triglycerides that contain the saturated fatty acid palmitic acid tend to be lower in digestibility and less readily absorbed than those with unsaturated fatty acids attached to glycerol. It has been found, however, that if palmitic acid is attached at the middle position of glycerol, as in animal fats such as lard, its presence does not appear to depress fat digestibility.

The effect of fat digestion on tissue lipid in fat content has also been investigated. Fatty acid composition of body storage fat and milk fat is known to reflect dietary fatty acid composition in most species. Blood samples can be evaluated for various lipid types, providing valuable information. Changes in blood lipids measured at periodic intervals before and after a meal reveal the course of lipid digestion, absorption, and transport. Elevated levels of some lipid types in the blood, such as low density lipoproteins (LDLs), may indicate increased risk of coronary heart disease.

Context

Energy needs of individuals vary considerably, depending on factors such as level of activity, physiological state (growing, pregnant), and environmental temperature. Dietary fat provides a concentrated source of energy to meet these demands. Conditions causing a depression in appetite may result in poor energy or poor calorie intake, with subsequent loss of body weight. In those cases, increasing dietary fat content can counteract the low calorie intake without substantially increasing total food intake.

The typical American diet obtains between 30 and 40 percent of its calories from fat, compared to a level of 5 to 10 percent in the diets of most domestic animals. Consequently, a lack of energy is unlikely in the American diet. Digestion and absorption of fat is, however, critical to provide other vital nutrients. Because fat is insoluble in water, digestion and absorption of fat requires more complicated digestive activity than the digestion of proteins or carbohydrates.

Defects may occur at several points in the process. Insufficient pancreatic lipase activity results in depressed fat digestion. Inadequate production or secretion of bile salts for emulsification also results in decreased fat digestion and absorption. Some diseases may impair digestive secretion of the pancreas, preventing release of bicarbonate into the small intestine. Micelle formation is inhibited under those conditions. Diseases such as cystic fibrosis, tropical sprue, and celiac disease affect the lining of the small intestine seriously, depressing absorption of micellar contents. The result of any of these defects is depressed lipid absorption, with consequent excretion in the stool. The stool becomes thick, greasy, and clay colored, a condition known as steatorrhea.

Excreted in the stool along with undigested, unabsorbed dietary fat are the fat-soluble vitamins A, D, E, and K. Without the fat-soluble vitamins, a wide range of deficiency symptoms result. Some symptoms are very general and include depressed appetite, reduction in growth rate, and hair and skin changes. Other deficiency symptoms are specific to the particular vitamin's biochemical function. Correction of the digestion or absorption defect would allow these vitamins to be absorbed. Alternate, more soluble, readily absorbed forms of some of the fat-soluble vitamins are available. Dietary supplementation of these forms could alleviate the deficiencies as well.

Several specific long-chain polyunsaturated fatty acids are required in the diet. These essential fatty acids—linoleic, linolenic, and arachidonic acids—perform several vital roles. The most significant of these functions is to act as one of the major structural components of cell membranes, which surround cells and intracellular organelles. The content of essential fatty acids in most American diets is more than adequate. As with fat-soluble vitamins, however, impaired fat digestion or absorption could cause depressed uptake of essential fatty acids. Animals fed a diet devoid of either fat or essential fatty acids may demonstrate symptoms of deficiency, including poor growth and dermatitis. Feeding small amounts of essential fatty acids reverses the conditions.

While a diet high in fat may lead to serious medical problems, including excessive weight gain and cardiovascular disease, fat digestion and absorption are critical to provide energy and vital nutrients.

Bibliography

Ganong, W. F. *Review of Medical Physiology.* 8th ed. Los Altos, Calif.: Lange Medical Publications, 1977. Though intended for medical student use, provides a clear, concise, readable summary of mammalian and human physiology. Chapters 25 and 26 describe digestion and absorption of major nutrients and regulation of digestive activity. Brief discussions of medical implications are included. Numerous diagrams complement the discussion, and references are listed at the end of each section.

Hamilton, Eva May Nunnelly, and Sareen Annora Stepnick Gropper. *The Biochemistry of Human Nutrition.* St. Paul, Minn.: West, 1987. Written as a desk reference, this book is designed to explain concepts in biochemistry and nutrition for those being introduced to the topics for the first time. Topics are listed in alphabetical order and cross-referenced to other relevant topics. Each discussion is complete and self-contained. Suggested readings are listed after many entries.

Isselbacher, Kurt J. "Biochemical Aspects of Lipid Malabsorption." *Federation Proceedings* 26 (September/October, 1967): 1420-1425. This paper was originally presented at a symposium of the Federation of American Societies for Experimental Biology. It reviews briefly aspects of triglyceride digestion and lipid absorption, using diagrams and figures to illustrate concepts. Examples of clinical and experimental impaired lipid absorption are discussed, and technical references are included.

Kritchevsky, David. "Effect of Triglyceride Structure on Lipid Metabolism." *Nutrition Reviews* 46 (May, 1988): 177-180. A brief review article describing research done on the effect of fatty acid composition of triglycerides on digestion and absorption. Also discusses the effect of fatty acids on serum cholesterol. Data from trials are reported, with interpretation provided in conclusions. Lists references cited.

Lehninger, Albert L. *Principles of Biochemistry.* New York: Worth, 1982. A text written for undergraduate college students taking their first course in biochemistry, but takes the view that knowledge of biochemistry is useful for all well-informed persons. Addresses relevant societal, medical, agricultural, and environmental issues. Chapter 24 covers digestion of nutrients. Many illustrations, glossary; references are listed at the end of each chapter.

Lloyd, L. E., B. E. McDonald, and E. W. Crampton. *Fundamentals of Nutrition.* 2d ed. San Francisco: W. H. Freeman, 1978. Covers fundamental concepts of nutrition applying to both humans and livestock. Fat digestion is discussed in chapter 9. Interesting information on the application of concepts and biographical descriptions of investigators is boxed, stimulating further reading. A brief list of suggested readings appears at the end of each chapter.

The Nutrition Foundation. "Changes in Postprandial Plasma Lipids and Lipoproteins in Humans." *Nutrition Reviews* 47 (January, 1989): 13-15. Written for clinical nutritionists, this article reports a trial evaluating changes in plasma lipids over time after meals. Analytical methods used are described, and trial results are briefly discussed. Implications for clinical application of data are suggested.

_____. *Present Knowledge in Nutrition.* 4th ed. Washington, D.C.: Author, 1976. Supplemental reading for those interested in nutrition. Updated periodically, it provides an authoritative review of literature and an extensive list of references. Historical overviews of nutrition research enrich the reader's appreciation. Fat digestion and metabolism are described in chapter 4.

_____. "Rapid Hydrolysis and Absorption of Structured Medium-Chain Triglycerides." *Nutrition Reviews* 46 (June, 1988): 228-230. A brief article describing the role that medium-chain length fatty acids in triglycerides may play in increasing absorption of long-chain length essential fatty acids important in malabsorption syndromes. Data are reviewed, and references are cited at the end of the article.

Doreen H. D. Swakon

Cross-References

Digestion of Carbohydrates, 629; Digestion of Proteins, 644; Digestion Regulation, 650; Digestion Strategies, 656; Digestive Processes in Humans, 663; The Digestive Tract, 670; Lipids, 1598; Lipoproteins and Familial Hypercholesterolemia, 1606.

DIGESTION OF PROTEINS

Types of life science: Animal physiology and biochemistry
Other field of study: Respiration

Digestion is the mechanical and chemical process of breaking down ingested food into smaller molecules that can be absorbed into the bloodstream. In the case of proteins, these small molecules are amino acids.

Principal terms

AMINO ACID: a unit of protein that takes its name from the fact that it contains an amino group (nitrogen and two hydrogens) and an acid group (carbon, two oxygens, and a hydrogen)

ENZYME: a protein catalyst that speeds up a specific reaction or type of reaction

HORMONE: a chemical messenger that is made in one part of the body and does its job in another part of the body; hormones are transported by the blood

PEPTIDES: short chains of amino acids

PH: a measure of the hydrogen ion concentration; any pH below 7 is acid and any pH above 7 is basic

VILLI: fingerlike projections that line the small intestine and function in the absorption of small molecules into the blood

Summary of the Phenomenon

Protein is a substance necessary to the life of all cells and tissues in the body. The name "protein" is from the Greek word *proteios*, meaning "of prime importance." Today it is known that proteins are essential building blocks for many body parts. They are also central to the way in which the body works, since all the thousands of chemical processes upon which human life depends are controlled by chemical regulators called enzymes. All enzymes are proteins. Whether weed or wheat, flower or redwood tree, mouse, elephant, or human being, life as we know it would not be possible without proteins.

Proteins are composed chemically of nitrogen, carbon, oxygen, and hydrogen. A single protein molecule may contain thousands of these atoms. Although proteins may have large and complex structures, they are all constructed in a similar fashion: Every protein consists of a string of much smaller subunits called amino acids. Each protein, however, is designed for a specific purpose in a particular tissue of a specific kind of animal or plant. When an animal eats food protein, whether in cereals, vegetables, meat, or cheese, its body must break this protein down into amino acids and then reassemble the amino acids into unique sequences that can be used by that individual.

Protein formation requires twenty different types of amino acids. Of these, eight (the "essential amino acids") are required in the human diet, because the body is unable to produce them. These eight are leucine, isoleucine, lysine, methionine, phenylalanine, threonine, tryptophan, and valine. The twenty amino acids can be chained together like beads on a string to make thousands of different kinds of proteins. When two amino acids are chained together, a dipeptide is formed, and when ten to twenty amino acids are linked together, the resulting compound is often called a polypeptide. A very long polypeptide—usually seventy-five or more amino acids in length—is called a protein. Since proteins become so large, the chains wrap around themselves and show a distinct three-dimensional structure.

Proteins come from both plant and animal materials; some protein sources, such as meat, are complete in the sense that they provide all the different types of amino acids. Vegetables and grains do supply amino acids, but each of these sources alone is incomplete, because at least one of the essential amino acids is absent. It is possible to get all the amino acids when different foods are eaten in combination.

If the body takes in more protein than it needs for the growth and repair of its tissues and for its chemical activities, it can use some of the excess as a simple energy-producing fuel. The remainder is excreted: The body has no way of storing protein for future use. Protein must be ingested daily, as an adequate supply is needed to maintain health. Protein-rich foods, especially the meats, require more tenderizing through cooking and more thorough chewing than most other foods. One of early humankind's giant steps was acquiring control of fire, because this permitted the cooking of meats and thereby greatly expanded the choice of foods.

Once it is ingested, very little happens to protein until it reaches the stomach. In the stomach, protein fibers are broken, the structure is uncoiled, and the large molecules are broken down into peptides and amino acids. Gastric glands, found in the inner membrane of the stomach, produce gastric juices that contain mucus, pepsinogen, and hydrochloric acid. The latter two substances are involved in protein digestion. Pepsinogen is inactive when it is secreted, but when it comes into contact with the acidic gastric juices, it is changed chemically into pepsin. Pepsin is a protein-splitting enzyme capable of beginning the digestion of nearly all types of protein in human diets. This enzyme is most active in an acid environment; the hydrochloric acid in gastric juice seems to function mainly to provide such an environment. The hydrochloric acid may also aid in the denaturing (uncoiling) of the protein structure. Stomach contractions compress, knead, twist, and continually mix the food with the gastric secretions, aiding in the digestion of the proteins.

The chemical reaction that occurs when pepsin reacts with a protein is called hydrolysis. When the bonds holding the amino acids together are originally formed, a molecule of water is removed. When the bonds are broken, the water is replaced so that the amino acids can separate. Pepsin splits the large molecules to allow water to react, and it functions optimally at the pH range of 1.5-3.5. It preferentially cleaves the bonds involving the amino acids tyrosine and phenylalanine. Responsible for the hydrolysis of about 15 percent of ingested protein-producing polypeptides and a small amount of free amino acids, pepsin is inactivated when the partially digested mass is secreted into the duodenum (the upper part of the small intestine).

In infants, the gastric glands also produce large amounts of rennin. This enzyme works primarily on the milk protein casein, converting it to a curdy substance that resembles sour milk. Rennin is apparently not produced in adults.

Protein digestion is continued in the small intestine. Proteins digested in this area include not only dietary proteins (typically about 125 grams per day) but also 15 to 25 grams of enzyme protein secreted into the gastrointestinal tract by various glands and an equal amount of protein derived from sloughed and disintegrated cells. In normal individuals, virtually all this protein is digested and absorbed.

Protein fragments entering the small intestine from the stomach are cleaved into smaller peptides by the enzymes trypsin and chymotrypsin, which are secreted by the pancreas. Each of these acts to split the bonds between particular combinations of amino acids in proteins. As no single enzyme can split all possible combinations, the presence of several enzymes is necessary for the complete digestion of protein molecules. These additional enzymes are found at the brush border of intestinal microvilli. Carboxypeptide splits off one amino acid at a time from the end of the polypeptide chain that bears the carboxyl group (carbon, oxygen, and hydrogen). Aminopeptidase works to digest a protein, one amino acid at a time, by working from the amine (nitrogen and hydrogen) end. Both carboxypeptidase and aminopeptidase are independently capable of completely dismantling a protein, but the teamwork between these enzymes and between trypsin and chymotrypsin, which attack the more internal parts of the protein, speeds the process tremendously. A number of specific types of carrier molecules transport the different classes of amino acids that result from protein digestion through the intestinal villi. Short chains of two or three amino acids (dipeptides and tripeptides) are also actively absorbed, but they are digested to their amino acids before entering capillary blood.

It has been discovered that the secretion of gastric juices in the stomach is under hormonal control. When a person has eaten a meal particularly rich in protein, the hormone gastrin, produced by the lower part of the stomach, enters the bloodstream and is transported to the upper part of the stomach. There it causes the gastric glands to secrete more pepsinogen. The duodenal wall also produces hormones. Hydrochloric acid stimulates the release of secretin, and partially digested protein appears to stimulate the release of cholecystokinin (CCK). Secretin stimulates the pancreas to produce bicarbonate, which will neutralize hydrochloric acid (increase the pH), and CCK stimulates the pancreas to secrete digestive enzymes. Finally, gastric inhibitory peptide (GIP) is produced by the small intestine and inhibits gastric acid secretion, thereby stopping the digestion of proteins.

Methods of Study

It was chance that first gave a physician the opportunity to study gastric juices in the stomach and report on protein digestion. William Beaumont, a United States Army surgeon, was called in June, 1822, to see a French Canadian, Alexis St. Martin, who had been seriously wounded by a shot in the stomach. St. Martin eventually recovered, but he was left with a permanent hole, or fistula, from his stomach to the skin of his abdomen. Through this opening, the lining of the stomach could be seen, and the changes in secretions that occurred under various stimuli could be recorded. When St. Martin recovered from his wound, Beaumont started a series of crucial experiments. Beaumont tied pieces of food to a string, inserted them through the hole into St. Martin's stomach, and withdrew them periodically to observe whatever changes had taken place.

Beaumont's results were both interesting and exciting. After an hour in the stomach, pieces of bread and cabbage were half-digested, but slices of raw and cooked beef were unchanged. After two hours, the cabbage, bread, and cooked beef were gone from the string, but the raw beef was still unchanged. Not until another hour had elapsed did the raw beef begin to disappear. Beaumont worked with St. Martin for eight years, and in that time he was able to isolate the acid secretion of the stomach and to demonstrate that it was not produced continuously. He observed that acid was produced in synchrony with the presence or anticipation of food in the stomach. He identified the acid as hydrochloric acid and determined that it was produced separately from mucus in the stomach. Finally, he showed that in addition to the acid that the stomach made, another substance active in digestion was present. Two years after Beaumont's publication of his findings, Theodor Schwann showed this to be the enzyme pepsin.

Once it was realized how important proteins are in human diets (and that storage of protein is minimal), nutritionists began to analyze how much protein is required on a daily basis. To do this, they measured major losses that occur via the urine, in which the breakdown products of some internal proteins are excreted: Nitrogen is measured to determine how much protein has been discarded. Much smaller amounts of proteins are lost in the feces, sweat, skin, hair, and nails. It is not enough, however, only to measure the body's losses; intake of dietary protein is another important part of the equation. Some of the urinary nitrogen may come from excess protein that was in the diet. If a person has eaten more protein than his or her body needs for replacement of worn tissues, the unneeded amino acids either are metabolized for energy or are converted to fat and stored. In either case, the nitrogen from the surplus is excreted in the urine along with the unrecycled nitrogen from worn internal tissues.

Protein needs, then, are determined in metabolic studies that measure both intake and output of nitrogen. If output and intake are equal, the person is said to be "in balance." If output is greater than intake, the person is losing protein, or is in "negative balance"; this occurs with injury, surgery, illness, or starvation. If intake is greater than output, the body is creating new protein and is in "positive balance"; this occurs during growth, pregnancy, lactation, healing, and muscle building. From these studies, scientists have established the recommended daily allowance (RDA) for protein. For healthy adults, the RDA is 0.8 gram for each kilogram (or 2.2 pounds) of body weight. For growing children, the RDA is higher per unit of body weight: 1.0-1.8 grams per kilogram of body weight, depending on age. For infants it is highest of all: 2.0-2.2 grams per kilogram of body weight.

Another common guideline for protein intake is a suggested percentage of calories that should come from protein. For most adults, 10 to 12 percent of the total caloric intake is adequate, but the elderly might need 12 to 14 percent to be sure of maintaining a balance. Most people in Western countries easily meet this percentage recommendation; a food consumption survey of almost ten thousand Americans found that, on the average, they got 16 percent of their calories from protein.

Context

In the United States, it is usually quite easy to get enough protein, but there are places in the world where the common foods are very low or incomplete in protein, or where there is simply an inadequate quantity of food of any kind. In either of these circumstances, concern about adequate protein is legitimate. Cassava (a starchy root) and yams are foods that have only about a third of the protein provided by grains (when compared on a weight basis). A study done in Nigeria, where these foods are staples, found that only 5 to 8 percent of the calories in people's diets came from proteins. Protein deficiency manifested itself in low weight gains during pregnancy, low maternal milk production, high infant mortality (40 percent in the first five years), extremely low weights and heights in children, poor intelligence scores for children, and increased susceptibility to infections. When protein was supplemented, all these abnormalities were reversed.

It is common to find long-term protein deficiency associated with severe energy deficiency: This condition is called protein-energy malnutrition (PEM), a fairly widespread situation in the developing countries. Usually the problem is that people simply do not have enough to eat; PEM would be relieved if they had access to more of what their diet already contains. PEM affects young children more than adults, because their need for protein and other nutrients is greater per unit of body weight. PEM manifests itself in a variety of ways: Two severe conditions are marasmus and kwashiorkor, both of which lead to a decreased resistance to infection. Because infection raises the body's needs for both calories and protein, it creates an even wider gap between what the body needs and what the diet supplies. PEM and infection create a downward spiral in the health of many people in developing countries. Diseases such as measles, which would run a short course in well-nourished populations, become killers among poorly nourished people.

Excess protein levels, however, may have some drawbacks also, in that many commonly consumed high-protein foods are also high in fat. With a high intake of high-protein, high-fat foods, the total fat content of the diet will be high, making one a candidate for the problems associated with high fat intake. When very high levels of protein are consumed, the body dismantles the amino acid surplus. The separated amino groups are metabolized into urea, which is excreted in the urine. A sizable volume of water is needed to excrete urea in the urine: To metabolize 100 calories of protein, the body uses 350 grams of water, whereas 100 calories of carbohydrate or fat use only 50 grams. Therefore, if a person who consumes much protein does not also consume a large quantity of water, dehydration is a possibility.

Another complication arising from overconsumption of protein is osteoporosis, a condition in which bone mass gradually decreases as a result of gradual loss of calcium over time. The loss of calcium results from overdependence on low-calcium sources of protein (such as meat) as opposed to some high-calcium sources (such as dairy products).

Bibliography

Christian, Janet L., and Janet L. Greger. *Nutrition for the Living*. Menlo Park, Calif.: Benjamin/Cummings, 1984. A college text written for the nonscience major that deals with many concepts of nutrition. Chapter 8 is devoted to proteins and describes structure, function, digestion, absorption, and requirements. Many charts.

Hamilton, Eva May Nunnelley, Eleanor Noss Whitney, and Francis Sienkiewicz Sizer. *Nutrition: Concepts and Controversies*. 3d ed. St. Paul, Minn.: West, 1985. A college text that both presents hard facts and explores debated topics in an inviting and thought-provoking manner. Chapter 6 deals with proteins and amino acids. The book has many inserts that deal with controversial materials.

Hole, John W., Jr. *Human Anatomy and Physiology*. 2d ed. Dubuque, Iowa: Wm. C. Brown, 1981. A college text written for students pursuing careers in allied health fields who have minimal backgrounds in physical and biological sciences. Chapter 13 deals with the digestive system and gives a detailed account of the major enzymes involved in protein digestion. More technical than the previously cited texts.

Jackson, Gordon, and Philip Whitfield. *Digestion: Fueling the System*. New York: Torstar Books, 1984. This book is written for those who have an interest but little background in science. It has excellent pictures and illustrations, and it details the entire digestive system. There are no chapters strictly devoted to protein digestion, but historical perspectives are mentioned.

Marieb, Elaine N. *Human Anatomy and Physiology*. Menlo Park, Calif.: Benjamin/Cummings, 1989. Another college text written for the allied health student. Presents a clear explanation of the fate of ingested protein and gives much information on the hormones involved with the secretion of gastric juices. Good illustrations.

Sanford, Paul A. *Digestive System Physiology*. Baltimore: University Park Press, 1982. The most technical of the books mentioned in this bibliography; written for medical students. Detailed report of protein digestion and absorption. Much chemical information.

Roberta B. Williams

Cross-References

Digestion of Carbohydrates, 629; Digestion of Fats, 636; Digestion Regulation, 650; Digestion Strategies, 656; Digestive Processes in Humans, 663; The Digestive Tract, 670; Metabolic Pathways, 1691.

DIGESTION REGULATION

Types of life science: Animal physiology and biochemistry
Other fields of study: Neurobiology and respiration

In humans and other mammals, local and central (brain) mechanisms regulate digestion. The expectation and presence of food in the mouth can stimulate these mechanisms to ensure gut motility and release of hormones that stimulate the digestive enzymes and fluids that move food through the digestive system.

    Principal terms

DUODENUM: the first part of the intestine, which follows the stomach into the small intestine

ENZYMES: protein molecules that act as catalysts to break down (hydrolyze) large molecules into smaller molecules

ESOPHAGUS: the narrow tube between the pharynx and the stomach that acts as a conducting passage to move the bolus of food into the stomach by peristalsis

GALL BLADDER: the organ that stores bile, synthesized in the liver, to release it through a common bile duct into the duodenum

HORMONE: a protein or steroid molecule that is synthesized in a special gland, to be released in and transported by the blood to act at some specific site

INTESTINE: the large tube that runs between the stomach and the anus; it is composed of a small intestine (the duodenum, jejunum, and ileum) and a large intestine that opens to the exterior through the anus

PANCREAS: the major appendage and endocrine organ of the digestive system, which secretes digestive juices that enter the duodenum via a pancreatic and/or common bile duct

PYLORUS: the last, or posterior, part of the stomach, which communicates via a channel with the duodenum; cells of the pylorus release gastrin into the blood

SALIVA: the secretion of the salivary gland, the mucus, which contains mucin (a lubricant), water, salts, and the enzyme amylase (which digests starch)

STOMACH: the first chamber of the digestive system, where mechanical digestion is completed and the enzymatic breakdown of proteins starts

Summary of the Phenomenon

The passage of food through the digestive tract and the digestion, secretion of digestive juices, absorption of digested molecules, and evacuation of wastes are stages that work in a programmed sequence. Each of these stages is regulated by the nervous system, by hormones, by intrinsic factors, or by a combination of these. The regulatory mechanisms affect these stages according to the type of food, as well as other physiological factors.

In mammals, using humans as an example, salivary glands are stimulated by the touch, sound of food preparation, or any thought, sight, or taste of food. These glands are under nervous system control—they are stimulated by parasympathetic and inhibited by sympathetic nerves. Anger and fear, for example, make the mouth dry, and sensory receptors in the pharynx will respond to the drying of the mouth by inducing a sensation of thirst. The composition of food (its components), moreover, determines the balance of water, mucin, salts, and enzymes that form the saliva. As food is chewed, it is mixed with saliva, forming a bolus that is ready to enter the next phase of digestion.

The swallowing of the bolus starts as a voluntary movement, but it involves a chain of reflexes, including the movement of food by peristalsis, the closure of nasal and tracheal openings, and the cessation of breathing. Several cranial nerves are involved in these reflexes. Peristalsis (a wave of alternate contractions and relaxations of gut muscles from the oral to the anal end) moves the food in a posterior direction. The peristaltic wave in the esophagus starts at the upper end, when food enters the pharynx, and moves downward all the way to the esophageal sphincter, through which it opens into the stomach. Control of stages from this point on is involuntary.

The secretion of gastric juices and the muscular activity of the stomach are under both nervous and hormonal control. Gastric controls are of four kinds: First, sight, smell, taste, touch, and even thought of food stimulate the brain (the cerebral cortex) to send impulses to the medulla which, via the parasympathetic fibers of the vagus nerve, stimulate gastric activity in preparation for food. Second, the distension of the stomach by food causes a reflex contraction; this wave-causing alternate contraction and relaxation, along with opening and closing of the pylorus, causes good mixing of food and gastric juices and allows the liquefied food (chyme) to enter in bits into the duodenum. Third, the presence of food (especially proteins, peptones, and peptides) in the stomach exerts a stimulating chemical effect; the receptors in the stomach walls send impulses (over a reflex arc of vagal fibers) to the medulla and from there, as well as directly, to the gastric glands; also, cells near the pyloric end of the stomach produce a hormone called gastrin, released into the blood and transported to the anterior part of the stomach. This process stimulates the secretion of gastric juices, particularly hydrochloric acid and pepsinogen. Finally, as the liquefied gastric contents (chyme) leave the stomach and enter the duodenum, tissues of the duodenum produce the hormone enterogastrone, which is released into the blood and transported to the stomach to inhibit the activity of the stomach. The duodenal hormones secretin and pancreozymin can also inhibit gastric acid secretion. Thus, the expectation and actual presence of food in the stomach, both stimulate its digestive activity and "turn off" the stomach by a final mechanism as soon as digestive activity is completed and the stomach becomes empty. Emotions (anger, fear, anxiety, depression) can alter gastric motility via the sympathetic nervous system by inhibiting parasympathetic pathways.

In the duodenum, the food continues to be moved by peristalsis, controlled by the deep nerve plexus in its walls. Some antiperistalsis here provides good mixing and causes some regurgitation into the stomach. The duodenum also undergoes segmentation and pendular movements by which the food contents are thoroughly mixed. The presence of chyme stimulates secretion of hormones (enterokinin and duocrinin) from the intestinal glands. These hormones may also be involved in the foregoing movements to cause mixing of the chyme with digestive juices. Another intestinal hormone, villikinin, may stimulate the activities of villi (fingerlike extensions from the inner wall of the small intestine) by altering their length and lateral movements. The presence of fats in chyme stimulates the release of the hormone cholecystokinin, which causes the gall bladder to release its bile into the duodenum. The bile causes emulsification of fat, so that the fat becomes suspended as small droplets on which the enzyme lipase can act. The acidity in chyme causes the release of yet another hormone, secretin, into the blood, which transports it to the pancreas to cause the release of digestive enzymes into the duodenum to hydrolyze suspended fat and proteins at a less acidic pH. The presence of food in the mouth, stomach, and intestine as perceived by the brain can also stimulate, via the vagus nerve, the pancreatic cells to release their digestive juices.

The release of digestive juices is very precisely timed, and the mechanisms regulating this process are activated and deactivated as needed. This timing, as has been shown, is under neural, mechanical, and hormonal control, as well as a combination of these factors. The hormonal mechanism appears to be independent of the nervous system. For example, gastrin works through a feedback mechanism. The release of gastric juices, which include hydrochloric acid, lowers the stomach's pH. When the stomach's pH has been lowered to 2, gastric secretion slows greatly. Thus, the product of gastrin action shuts down the hormone release.

The digested molecules of food are absorbed in the small intestine. The undigested food enters the ileum and thereafter the colon, approximately four hours after the meal. From this point, the movement is very slow, aided by the next food intake, which finally leads to defecation out of the rectum and is further aided by voluntary abdominal muscles.

Most of the enzymes (pepsinogen, trypsinogen, chymotrypsinogen, lipases) are secreted as inactive zymogens or proenzymes and are activated by other digestive secretions. For example, hydrochloric acid converts pepsinogen into active pepsin; intestinal enterokinase converts trypsinogen into trypsin, which in turn converts chymotrypsinogen into active chymotrypsin. Pancreatic lipase also requires activation. If these hormones were secreted as active enzymes, they would digest membranes of the cells lining the digestive tract. In addition to the initial secretion of enzymes as inactive substances and the inhibition of gastric juices after food passage, the digestive process offers another safeguard: The presence of mucus, chitinous lining, and secretion of peritrophic membranes in other animals can protect the digestive epithelium from physical damage resulting from solid food and chemical damage resulting from acids and enzymes.

Methods of Study

Observation has revealed much about how animals digest their food. Dissection of animal bodies shows the organs of digestion at work: For example, a rat can be anesthetized and surgically opened to reveal liver, stomach, and small and large intestines at work.

The movement of food in the stomach and intestine (rate of motility) can be measured by dissecting the animal and observing visually or using a kymograph, a device consisting of a motor-driven cylindrical, rotating drum covered by paper on which a stylus records motion or pressure. The samples of digestive fluids in the presence of food can be withdrawn using a syringe or by removing that part for further analysis. The pH of a particular part of the digestive tract, plus the presence of certain enzymes and hormones, can be analyzed using various spectrophotometric and chromatographic procedures. Some of these hormones require the use of specific radioimmunoassays. The motility of the digestive system can be increased or decreased by stimulating or inhibiting the sympathetic and parasympathetic system, either neurally or by using specific chemicals, to determine their involvement in this process.

Researchers have taken a portion of a rat's intestine and placed it in a solution to flush out its internal contents, then have subjected it to conditions to make the muscle contract. After performing a number of other procedures, the researcher is able to note the number of contractions per minute and the relative intensity and rhythm of the contractions. These contractions can be measured under different conditions of acidity, alkalinity, heat, cold, or in the presences of other chemicals, such as the neurotransmitters epinephrine and acetylcholine, to determine their effect.

An even simpler means of studying the digestive tract, one that can be performed by anyone, is to observe the actions of one's own digestive system before, during, and after intake of food or water. In swallowing a mouthful of cold water, for example, one can feel the peristaltic action of the esophagus and stomach as the cold liquid travels downward. A partner can observe the movement of the tongue and larynx (more obvious in males because of the Adam's apple). The partner can place the diaphragm of a stethoscope over the abdominal wall, approximately 2.5 centimeters below the xiphoid process (the posterior segment of the sternum) and slightly to the left. After two swallows of water, there are two audible sounds: one when the water splashes against the closed end of the esophagus and the second when the peristaltic wave of the esophagus arrives at the end, to cause its opening to allow water to enter the stomach. The interval between the two sounds gives an estimate of the time it took the water to travel through the approximately 25-centimeter-long esophagus.

Context

The coordination of the chemical and muscular activities involved in the process of digestion requires complex neuronal, hormonal, and intrinsic mechanisms with input from precephalic (psychological), cephalic (central nervous system), and postcephalic sources. These mechanisms are well understood for mammals, especially dogs and humans. Since feeding in these and other vertebrate and nonvertebrate macrophages, or large animals, is noncontinuous (while it is continuous in microphages, or microscopic animals), the secretion of digestive fluids is also noncontinuous. Therefore, regulatory mechanisms—such as the hormonal inhibition of gastric acids after stomach activity has ended—are essential to ensure that secretion of the right type of digestive enzymes in the right amounts starts and stops as needed.

In humans (and, as Ivan Pavlov demonstrated, in dogs), one of the most interesting aspects of digestion regulation is its interaction with higher brain functions. Salivary gland secretions under nervous control are stimulated by sight, smell, touch, taste, sound, and even thought of food. These stimuli normally initiate the nervous reflex that results in salivary secretion. Some of these stimuli constitute psychological activation and involve learned behavior. Memories stored in the cerebral cortex that associate the stimuli with food are activated. The cortex sends motor impulses to centers in the brainstem, which then activates the salivary glands. As Pavlov showed, these conditioned reflexes can result from visual or auditory sensory stimulation. It has been suggested that many eating disorders among humans are a result of this brain-stimulus interaction. Inappropriate eating habits are formed in response to inappropriate stimuli: For example, a person learns that noon is "time" to eat, although he may not actually be hungry; a child learns that a sugary treat will make him "feel better" and thus associates poor food with pleasure or relief. Such associations may trigger digestive responses (salivation), further motivating the person to eat. The behavioral patterns that are formed as a result can lead to obesity or other dangerous disorders, such as bulimia. With this understanding of how the digestive system interacts with external stimuli to the brain, persons prone to such disorders can impose conscious choice to maintain healthy eating habits.

Bibliography

Davenport, Horace W. *Physiology of the Digestive Tract*. 5th ed. Chicago: Year Book Medical Publishers, 1982. An advanced but complete text on digestion and its regulation. A good reference for scientific terms that are used by professionals to discuss digestion and its regulation.

Grossman, M. I. "Neural and Hormonal Regulation of Gastrointestinal Function: An Overview." *Annual Review of Physiology* 41 (1979): 27. A review article including all the information that one needs to know about regulation of digestion. Contains the most complete information in one place. Excellent reference.

Guyton, Arthur C. *Textbook of Medical Physiology*. Philadelphia: W. B. Saunders, 1986. A text for premedical and medical students. Section 9, on the gastrointestinal system, deals exclusively with digestion and its regulation. The basic information on human digestion and its control is easy reading for beginning students.

Hoar, William S. *General and Comparative Physiology.* 3d ed. Englewood Cliffs, N.J.: Prentice-Hall, 1983. An advanced undergraduate-level text with coverage of the biochemistry and physiology of digestion.

Madge, D. S. *The Mammalian Alimentary System: A Fundamental Approach.* London: Edward Arnold, 1975. A good elementary text for study of the digestive system and its functioning and regulatory mechanisms. Provides structural and functional details.

Moog, Florence. "The Lining of the Small Intestine." *Scientific American* 245 (November, 1981): 154-176. A description of intestinal cells and their role in digestion and absorption. This is the best source for a beginner and contains almost all that one should know about digestion and absorption of food. Highly recommended.

Stroud, Robert M. "A Family of Protein Cutting Proteins." *Scientific American* 231 (July, 1974): 74-88. An article dealing with enzymes that break down protein molecules. Written for a general audience, this article is highly recommended.

M. A. Q. Khan

Cross-References

Digestion of Carbohydrates, 629; Digestion of Fats, 636; Digestion of Proteins, 644; Digestion Strategies, 656; Digestive Processes in Humans, 663; The Digestive Tract, 670; Ingestion, 1414; Ingestion Regulation, 1422; Macronutrients and Micronutrients, 1642.

DIGESTION STRATEGIES

Types of life science: Animal physiology and biochemistry
Other field of study: Respiration

The structure of different organisms' digestive systems and the presence of various digestive enzymes are correlated with the physical and chemical nature of the food they eat. Plant eaters (herbivores) and meat eaters (carnivores) have predominantly carbohydrate- and protein-digesting enzymes, respectively, while omnivores, which feed on both plants and meat, have all enzymes.

Principal terms

CARNIVORE: an animal, such as a tiger, cat, or dog, that feeds on animal meat

ENZYME: a protein that acts as a catalyst under appropriate physiological conditions to break down bonds of a large protein, fat, or carbohydrate

ESOPHAGUS: the part of the oral cavity (pharynx) that transfers morsels to the stomach; it is usually a long, muscular tube with no digestive function other than transport

HERBIVORE: an animal that feeds on plants and their parts; cows, horses, camels, rabbits, and snails are herbivores

HORMONE: a chemical released into the blood for transport to a specific site, where it will perform a specific function; many hormones stimulate chemical and mechanical aspects of digestion

INTESTINE: the part of the digestive system involved in completing the process of digestion and absorption of nutrients; usually divided into the small intestine and the large intestine, which opens to the exterior by way of the anus

MACROPHAGES: animals that feed on whole plants or animals or their parts; these can be carnivores, herbivores, or omnivores

MICROPHAGES: animals that feed on small microscopic particles suspended in water or deposited on bottom sediments

MOUTH: the anterior part of the digestive system, used for ingesting food; it leads into the oral cavity, which opens into the esophagus

MUCUS: a secretion of the salivary glands and other parts of the digestive system which lubricates passages

OMNIVORE: an animal that feeds on plants, animals, and other types of food

STOMACH: the part of the digestive system where mechanical breakdown of food is completed and chemical digestion begins

Summary of the Phenomenon

The bulk of animal food consists of proteins, carbohydrates, and fats. In addition, smaller molecules that make up these complex molecules—such as vitamins, nucleic acids, and minerals—are essential components of animal food. Animals obtain their food in the form of solutions, suspensions, dry particles, aggregates, and masses of particles, or whole animals and plants and their parts. It is the selection of food and the feeding behavior of animals that distinguish different animal populations and allow them to live together in the same habitat without competing for the same resources. The organs that break down the food mechanically into small particles and particles into molecules by the processes called "digestion" constitute what is called a digestive system. Usually the fore (anterior) part of the digestive system of animals is adapted for capturing and breaking down food (the bills and beaks of birds and the jaws of mammals are examples), and the remaining system can become specialized to store, chemically digest, and absorb the digested food and eliminate the unabsorbed food.

A typical functional sequence of digestion can be summarized as follows: First is the mouth, its appendages, and the oral cavity. These are involved in selecting (by taste, smell, touch), capturing, and initial breaking down of food. Secretions here can include lubricants (mucus coming from salivary glands as well as other fluids), anticoagulants (in blood suckers), paralyzing toxins (in carnivorous coelenterates, spiders, reptiles), proteases (in cephalopod mollusks), and carbohydrases (in plant eaters). In microphages, locomotory appendages, oral tentacles with cilia, can drive currents of water containing food toward the mouth. In macrophages, locomotory appendages can be modified to capture food and ingest it. Most small aquatic animals and some large ones strain small particulate material with the help of their body surface projections (cilia, setae, bristles, legs, mucus, or nets); these microphages are called filter-feeders. In vertebrates, movable jaws, and in invertebrates, hard structures or surfaces, can be used for crushing food. The mouth leads into an oral cavity whose posterior chamber is a muscular pharynx that opens into the esophagus.

Second, the muscular, tubular esophagus transfers the food, in bits, to the stomach. Sometimes, a distension in this part of the digestive system (the "crop" found in cockroaches and birds, for example) is used to store food.

Third, the stomach, a muscular vessel into which the esophagus leads, mechanically breaks down the food through contractions and wavelike motions, and begins the process of chemical digestion via enzymes. Sometimes the stomach is equipped with hard projections (such as the gizzards and gastric mills of birds, cockroaches, earthworms, or alligators). The lining of the stomach or of its diverticula (branches) secretes digestive enzymes and, in vertebrates, hormones and hydrochloric acid. The stomach opens into the next chamber, the intestine.

Fourth, the small intestine completes the digestive process. Its cells and the cells of its glands (the pancreas, liver, hepatic cecae) secrete digestive fluids containing enzymes and hormones that enable absorption of the resulting molecules and water into the cells of the intestine and from there into the blood. The inner lining of the intestine can be thrown into ridges and microridges, which greatly increase the surface area and thus the amount of absorption.

Fifth, the large intestine, or hindgut, reabsorbs water. The undigested food is evacuated in the form of feces through an opening to the exterior called the anus. This part of the digestive tract also stores colonies of microorganisms, especially in plant eaters, to digest cellulose, lignin, and other substances, and to provide some vitamins that the animal cannot synthesize.

In animals that feed on soluble or suspended particles, called "continuous feeders," digestion is a continuous process. In these animals, which include sponges, coelenterates, and flatworms, the digestive system is in the form of a tube open at one end only, and the chemical digestion of particles takes place inside each cell lining this tube. Annelids, arthropods, mollusks, and echinoderms have digestive systems that are open at both ends. These animals have developed various other systems, and the digestive system has become independent of the circulatory system. The opening of the digestive tube has allowed these animals to specialize their parts into various regions for capturing, grinding, masticating, mechanically breaking down, chemically digesting, absorbing, and eliminating their food. That, in turn, has allowed them to conduct extracellular digestion in the digestive cavity: to become "discontinuous feeders."

Hence, with the evolution of a digestive tube dedicated to digestion only, animals started secreting their cellular enzymes into this cavity in response to food. This, then, constituted extracellular digestion. Extracellular digestion is present in small animals that feed on particles (microphages) or larger animals that feed on bulk food (macrophages). The animals with intracellular digestion and those microphages with extracellular digestion feed continuously and nonselectively. The evolution of a complete digestive tract, opening at both ends, and extracellular digestion have allowed evolution of larger, more active, and more advanced animals. These macrophages feed discontinuously and select their food. The time that they have saved from feeding had been spent to perform other activities and evolve complex behavior patterns. Also, ingestion of a large mass of food has enabled them to obtain the bulk of their energy from this food, which provides a tremendous amount of dependable power to move and even fly.

The evolution of a complete digestive tube has resulted in the specialization of its parts for various digestive processes. The general pattern of functional sequence that was outlined above is evident: The digestive system is usually divided into foregut (mouth and its appendages), midgut (for chemical digestion and absorption), and hindgut (for absorption of water and elimination of undigested food). Within this general structure, however, are innumerable and complex variations in adaptation to the type of food and feeding mechanisms of different animals. Those animals that feed on solid food, for example, have appendages (such as jaws and teeth) to enable them to grind, crush, or masticate it. In addition, these may have parts of the stomach modified for storage (such as rumen in ruminants, the crops of birds) or for further grinding (the gizzards of various insects, birds, and alligators). Cows and goats, for example, have four-chambered stomachs, one of which stores colonies of bacteria. These ruminants swallow the food as a whole while grazing. Then, later, while resting, they bring the food and bacteria back to the mouth as cud to mix them together, subsequently swallowing the food. The bacteria then digest cellulose by fermentation. The microorganisms are then digested by the animal in the intestine. These animals also secrete copious amounts of saliva, which prevents abrasive damage by the solid food to the cells lining the foregut.

In fluid feeders, by contrast, the oral end is equipped with sucking apparatus containing piercing devices (as in moths, bees, flies, mosquitoes, and leeches). Some feeders on plant juices ingest large amounts of water with sugars. The last part of their foregut becomes connnected with the anterior part of the hindgut, forming a filtering apparatus (as in insect leaf hoppers). Only water passes from the foregut to the hindgut, while food enters the midgut, which now does not have to process large amounts of water.

The chemical breakdown of food particles takes place by means of enzyme catalysts, which are proteins that are released into the stomach and intestine (midgut) from their cells or from cells of appendages (hepatic cecae in insects, hepatopancreas in crustaceans and mollusks, and pancreas and liver in vertebrates) opening into the intestine. These enzymes are secreted in response to the entry of food in the gut. Moreover, the presence and release of specific enzymes depend on the chemical nature of the food. In plant-eating herbivores, which eat an abundance of carbohydrates (sugars), these secretions are rich in carbohydrates (carbohydrate-hydrolyzing enzymes), while in animal eaters (carnivores) protein-digesting enzymes, proteases, and fat-hydrolyzing enzymes, lipases, are predominant. In omnivores (which feed on both plants and animals), all three groups of enzymes are present. In food specialists, such as sheep blow flies (which feed on wool keratin), head lice (which feed on hair keratin), cloth moths (which feed on textile fibers), wax moths (which feed on wax), or carpet and leather beetles (which feed on keratin), the digestive fluid is rich in specific enzymes for handling one kind of food. In wood-eating termites, snails (*Helix*), and ruminant mammals, the cellulose is digested by colonies of microorganisms that are carried in parts of these animals' guts.

In addition, different enzymes are present in different stages of an animal's life cycle. For example, maggots feeding on flesh have proteinases, while adult flies feeding on sugars have sucrases. The intestinal enzyme lactase, which breaks down the milk sugar lactose, is always present in land mammals at or before birth. It usually decreases after weaning. In humans (except in certain Africans and Asians who do not consume milk and lack lactase), this decrease is much less than in other mammals. On the other hand, after weaning, the presence of sucrase and maltase increases as a result of the inclusion of sucrose and maltose in the diet. The enzyme rennin, which clots milk into curd to delay its passage, is present in human babies, whose sole diet consists of milk; human adults lack this enzyme. Among insects, certain leaf hoppers and moths which feed on soluble sugars (which do not require further breakdown) have no enzymes, while hoppers feeding on mesophyll cells and caterpillars actively chewing plant parts have carbohydrases and lipases. Among bees, nurses have more proteases than foragers; wax bees have no proteases; the carbohydrases are predominant in foragers, especially during midsummer, and lipase is found only in wax bees. The carnivorous turbellarians, coelenterates, cephalopod mollusks, crustaceans, scavenger insects, and starfish have more proteases and fewer carbohydrases.

In humans and other mammals, most of the enzymes (pepsinogen, trypsinogen, chymotrypsinogen, lipase) are secreted as zymogens (proenzymes) and are activated by other secretions. For example, hydrochloric acid converts pepsinogen into active pepsin in the stomach; enterokinase converts chymotrypsinogen into active chymotrypsin, which in turn activates trypsinogen to trypsin. Secretion of zymogens and their activation are precisely controlled and occur when food is present in the gut. For example, when chyme leaves the stomach, the duodenal hormone enterogastrone inhibits the release of hydrochloric acid from parietal cells so that no activation of pepsinogen occurs; otherwise, pepsin could destroy the proteins in the membranes of cells lining the gastric cavity. The digestive epithelia of animals are thereby protected from damage by physical (solid food) and chemical (enzymes, acids) sources. This digestive strategy became necessary as discontinuous feeding evolved, since the presence of food for digestion was intermittent.

Methods of Study

A variety of observations and experiments have been performed to study the different types of digestive systems. Simple examination of the anterior (mouth) end of different animals, for example, reveals the broad range of strategies used to collect and initially break down food.

Soluble food feeders, for example, can be examined under the microscope. Observation of a microscopic slide of the head of a human tapeworm shows that it is equipped with hooks and suckers by means of which it attaches itself to the digestive tract of a person. The soluble, predigested food in the intestine needs no further breakdown and is absorbed through the flat body surface of the worm, which lacks any digestive organs. Observed under the microscope, the anterior end of a liver fluke has hooks and suckers to suck fluid; a lamprey has a round mouth and rasping tongue with which to suck the blood of its host fish; a mosquito has a piercing device to break skin and suck blood; and the mouth parts of an adult moth include a long, coiled proboscis designed to suck nectar from flowers.

Intracellular digestion of food by a variety of microorganisms can be observed in progress under the microscope. Amoebae can be starved for one or two days and then transferred to drops of a culture on a shallow depression slide. The amoebae will exhibit phagocytosis (cell eating) with the help of their "feet" (pseudopodia), surrounding the food and ingesting it. A change in the color of the *Blepherisma* pigment (in the food vacuole of the amoeba) can be seen—from red (indicating acidic) to neutral or colorless (indicating alkaline pH). This indicates that earlier stages of digestion are acidic; later stages, alkaline.

Paramecium can also be observed feeding on starch solution with and without a drop of iodine (which turns starch blue and inhibits feeding). If this procedure is repeated using compressed yeast in a 3 percent solution of congo red, one can observe the direction of movement of the yeast (which has taken on the red color) as it travels in the direction of the beating of the paramecium's cilia and into the food vacuole, then as it circulates through the cytoplasm. The change in color from red to blue indicates digestion. Paramecia will also reject algae particles and ingest only yeast, indicating the presence of chemical sensory mechanisms.

Solid food eaters, which can be observed with the naked eye, reveal a variety of specially adapted parts: hard, strong mandibles for crushing leaves in the caterpillar; similar mandibles for handling solid food in the cockroach; the "Aristotle's lantern" of the sea urchin, used for grinding; the tentacles of the *Hydra*, which feeds on fine, suspended food particles; and the human jaw and teeth, with incisors, canines, and molars designed to break down a variety of food in a variety of ways.

The activity of various digestive enzymes can be determined by using appropriate substrates (the food molecules) and physiological conditions in a test tube. The source of the enzyme is the part of the digestive tract where it is produced and used. Tissue from this area is ground in a small blender/homogenizer using an appropriate buffer at about 4 degrees Celsius. The homogenate of the tissue is either used as is or fractionated using a high-speed, refrigerated centrifuge, which can fractionate cell membranes, various organelles, and cytoplasm. Then the subcell fraction, where the enzyme is located, can be used as the source of the enzyme. The enzyme is further purified by means of biochemical devices. The substrate is either natural or synthetic. The pH, temperature, and other conditions are controlled in the incubation mixture containing enzyme and substrate. Time-course aliquots (samples) are withdrawn, and the activity of the enzyme is measured by analyzing the hydrolysis product of the substrate using various spectrophotometric devices. The enzymes, from the same tissue or its subcell fraction, of animals feeding on plants, meat, or both are compared to determine how active various enzymes are in these animals. The presence of certain enzymes can be related to the chemical nature of the food.

Context

Food selection, feeding behavior, and the structure and function of the digestive apparatus of animals form an important mechanism of survival, by which animals in a population isolate themselves from other populations to avoid competition for the same source of food. The feeding behavior depends on the type of food available (soluble, suspended, aggregates, or large organisms), and the form of the feeding apparatus (shapes and sizes of bills of birds and jaws and teeth of mammals, for example) depends on the physical nature of the food. The anatomy of the digestive system is closely adapted to the physical nature of the food, while the chemical functioning (enzymes) of the digestive systems depends on its chemical nature.

The adaptations of the digestive systems have enabled the evolution of larger and more active animals, which feed less frequently on greater bulks of food as compared with less active small animals, which may have to feed more often and even continuously.

The broad variety of different digestive systems and their enzymes has enabled animals to make the best use of the food resources available in their environment. Those animals able to exploit their environment more fully than others (such as omnivores, including humans) have a wide array of digestive enzymes that can chemically break down a wide variety of foods. They are more successful at survival than those confined to a particular type of food (food specialists with a limited ability to digest only one type of food) and, hence, are likely to survive longer as a group.

Bibliography

Baldwin, R. L. "Digestion and Metabolism of Ruminants." *BioScience* 34, no. 4 (1989): 244-249. This article discusses the digestion and metabolism of ruminants in a simple, lucid manner.

Barrett, James M., Peter Abramoff, A. Krishna Kumaran, and William F. Millington. *Biology*. Englewood Cliffs, N.J.: Prentice-Hall, 1986. An introductory biology text. Chapter 29 covers most of the aspects of feeding and digestion in animals, with illustrations.

Moog, Florence. "The Lining of the Small Intestine." *Scientific American* 245 (November, 1981): 154-176. A simple and clear description of digestion and absorption of the digested food molecules in the human intestine.

Penry, Deborah, and Peter A. Jumars. "Modeling Animals Guts as Chemical Reactors." *American Naturalist* 129 (January, 1987): 69-96. This article discusses the evolutionary aspects of digestive tracts in animals.

Prosser, C. L., ed. *Comparative Animal Physiology*. 3d ed. Philadelphia: W. B. Saunders, 1973. An advanced undergraduate text. Chapter 4 covers the strategies of digestion and feeding in animals in a simple manner that can be grasped at the high school level.

Raven, P. R., and G. B. Johnson. *Biology*. St. Louis: Mosby, 1989. An introductory biology text. Chapter 49 deals with digestion and its strategies in animals, with illustrations.

M. A. Q. Khan

Cross-References

DIGESTIVE PROCESSES IN HUMANS

Type of life science: Animal physiology
Other fields of study: Biochemistry and respiration

Digestion is the process of breaking down in the gastrointestinal tract, by physical and chemical means, food substances into their constituent nutrient molecules, which are absorbed into the body fluids and utilized in metabolic processes. By studying the digestive process, scientists have learned how the body uses food and physicians have learned how to treat diseases of the alimentary tract.

Principal terms
AMINO ACID: one of twenty organic molecules that constitute the building blocks of peptides, polypeptides, and proteins
BOLUS: a portion of chewed food, lubricated with saliva and formed into a ball by the tongue
CARDIA: the opening at the upper end of the stomach, at its junction with the esophagus
CHYME: the pastelike mass of partly digested food passed from the stomach into the duodenum
DUODENUM: the first section of the small intestine, extending from the pylorus to the junction with the jejunum
FATTY ACIDS: organic molecules made up of chains of carbon atoms, with attached hydrogens, which combine with glycerol to form fats
GLUCOSE: a six-carbon sugar molecule that is the building block of starch, glycogen, and cellulose; it is used by most living cells as fuel
GLYCEROL: a three-carbon alcohol that binds to fatty acids to make up fats
METABOLISM: the total of all biochemical reactions occurring in the cells of an organism
MICROVILLI: projections of the cell membranes of the villi (folds) which greatly increase the surface area of the small intestine
MUCUS: a clear, viscous secretion consisting mainly of mucin
PEPSIN: a digestive enzyme of the stomach; it converts proteins into smaller molecules (peptones and proteoses)
POLYPEPTIDE: a compound made up of a number of linked amino acids
PYLORUS: the opening at the lower end of the stomach, at its junction with the duodenum

Summary of the Phenomenon

Digestion is the process whereby food introduced into the alimentary canal, or gastrointestinal (GI) tract, is broken down, first mechanically into small particles and then chemically into simple nutrient molecules. As a consequence, these simple nutrient molecules can pass through the intestinal wall (via absorption) into the body fluids (lymph fluid and blood), which transport them to the body cells, where they are utilized in metabolic processes (assimilation). The unabsorbed parts of food, together with some waste products secreted into the alimentary canal, are eliminated. Thus, the functions of the GI tract may be summarized as, first, to reduce food to small particles and to move it forward by muscle contractions (peristalsis); second, to secrete digestive juices that break down food particles into their constituent small nutrient molecules; third, to absorb nutrients from the GI lumen into the body fluids; and fourth, to eliminate wastes.

The GI system in humans consists of the mouth, the pharynx, the esophagus, the stomach, the small intestine, the large intestine, and the anus. In addition, there are the accessory organs: the liver, with its gallbladder, and the pancreas. The digestive process starts in the oral cavity (mouth) when food is ingested. The food is broken down by chewing; the tongue mixes the chewed particles with saliva from three pairs of salivary glands situated in the walls of the lower jaw. The lubricated food mass, formed into a bolus by the tongue, is easily swallowed. Saliva contains water, inorganic salts, salivary amylase (an enzyme breaking down starch), and mucus. Chewing a piece of bread for some time without swallowing it turns the taste of bread sweet, a result of the amylase having transformed starch into glucose.

Through the act of swallowing, the bolus is pushed backward into the pharynx and from there into the esophagus. The esophagus is a muscular tube made up in large part of smooth (involuntary) muscle, which contracts slowly by peristaltic movement. The wave of contraction moves the bolus toward the stomach. At the point where the esophagus reaches the stomach, there is a circular muscle known as the cardiac or gastroesophageal sphincter. During rest it contracts and, usually, prevents the reflux of gastric contents into the esophagus. Sometimes, however, the sphincter does not close completely, which results in "heartburn."

The stomach has basically three functions: It stores food; it mixes food mechanically and moves it forward toward the small intestine by repetitive peristaltic contractions; and it secretes pepsinogen, hydrochloric acid, and mucus. Pepsinogen, in contact with hydrochloric acid, is converted into the active enzyme pepsin, which reduces the long protein chains into shorter chains of polypeptides and some amino acids (the building blocks of proteins). Numerous stomach cells secrete copious amounts of alkaline mucus that, normally, is evenly coating the inner lining of the stomach, preventing pepsin and hydrochloric acid from coming in contact with the stomach wall. When, through a malfunction of the distribution process, parts of the stomach lining are exposed to the corroding effects of the enzyme and acid, so-called peptic ulcers result.

The end result of gastric (stomach) digestion is a pastelike mass called chyme. When chyme accumulates in the terminal portion of the stomach, exerting increased pressure, the circular muscle (pyloric sphincter) separating the stomach from the small intestine relaxes for a short time and admits a small portion of chyme into the upper part of the small intestine. The small intestine, which has a length of about 6 meters, is made up of three parts. The first part is called the duodenum. Although only 25 centimeters in length, it is the most important section of the GI tract, because in it takes place most of the digestive process. The second part of the small intestine is the jejunum, and the last part is the ileum.

Into the duodenum opens the duodenal papilla, the common orifice of the pancreatic duct and the bile duct. During meals, pancreatic juice flows into the duodenum through the pancreatic duct. The alkaline pancreatic juice contains mainly sodium bicarbonate and enzymes. Among the enzymes are trypsin and chymotrypsin, which break down proteins and polypeptides (derived from the activity of pepsin) into amino acids; amylase, which breaks down starch into glucose; and lipase, which reduces fat molecules to their constituent glycerol and fatty acids. Bicarbonate assures that the acidic chyme is neutralized so that the duodenal environment stays alkaline and, thus, pancreatic enzymes, which can work only in an alkaline medium, can be activated.

The main contribution of the liver to the digestive process is its secretion of bile through the bile duct into the duodenum. Although this secretion is continuous, between meals (or if no fatty meals are ingested) bile will not be released into the duodenum but will rather be stored in the gallbladder. Thus, the gallbladder has the function to store bile for the eventual ingestion of a large fatty meal. During storage, the gallbladder concentrates bile by reabsorbing water into the blood. Therefore, bile, which is light yellow in color when secreted by the liver, could become dark green or almost black when stored for a lengthy time in the bladder. Concentrated, stagnating bile may cause the formation of gallstones by the precipitation of cholesterol. Bile does not contain enzymes but is rather an alkaline solution of bile salts, which act as detergents; that is, they emulsify lipids, breaking large fat globules into smaller ones and, thus, facilitating the action of lipase as well as the absorption of fats from the small intestine. Nevertheless, the gallbladder has only a limited role in the digestive process as such. That is made obvious by the fact that patients, after surgical removal of the gallbladder, can lead a completely normal life, not even necessitating a special diet.

In the wall of the duodenum are a number of glands that secrete the final complement of digestive enzymes, together with alkaline fluid and mucus. These enzymes help to finish the breakdown of peptides and fats as well as that of some sugars, such as cane and milk sugar. The rest of the small intestine (the jejunum and ileum) is mainly concerned with the absorption of the digested nutrient molecules. The wall of the small intestine is not smooth but contains a large number of folds (villi) made up of cells with fingerlike projections (microvilli), which result in a very much increased intestinal surface area (about 300 square meters). This large surface area facilitates the absorption of the nutrient molecules through the epithelial cells of the intestinal lining into the body fluids.

The functions of the stomach, duodenum, pancreas, and gallbladder are coordinated by nervous as well as hormonal mechanisms, which control and regulate the timing of the various secretions and their amounts, thus ensuring the efficiency of the digestive processes.

Where the end portion of the ileum meets the large intestine is a sphincter muscle called the ileocecal valve. This valve, which is closed most of the time, opens about two hours after an ingested meal, allowing the nonabsorbed portion of the chyme to flow from the ileum into the large intestine (colon). The large intestine, which is about 1 meter long, has the shape of an inverted U. The ascending section, which extends upward on the right side of the abdominal cavity, starts with a blind pouch (the cecum), from which projects the ill-reputed, wormlike appendix. If, for some reason, the appendix gets infected and inflamed, its emergency surgical removal is lifesaving. The descending colon extends down on the left side of the abdomen, whereas the transverse colon connects the other two parts. The descending part of the colon ends in the shape of an S (sigmoid), which continues with a short tube, the rectum, closed by the anal sphincter. The function of the colon is mainly water and electrolyte reabsorption as well as the formation of solid fecal matter from sloughed-off cells of the gut, from bacteria, and from undigested remnants of food. In contrast to what is usually assumed, the bacteria living in the human colon are beneficial in that they break down substances that have escaped digestion. The bacteria use the energy from this process to manufacture amino acids and some vitamins (such as vitamin K) which can be absorbed and utilized by the body.

Methods of Study

Research on digestion started quite early in the history of the life sciences. Knowledge about the structure of the digestive system was gained by dissections. In the beginning, it was assumed that digestion was a physical process involving the grinding action of the stomach. Later, in the seventeenth century, it was suggested that digestion was a chemical process involving changes similar to those taking place during fermentation. A way of testing this suggestion was to place meat in small metal cylinders with open ends covered by wire gauze and to feed these to various animal species. When the animals regurgitated the cylinders, the meat was found to be partially dissolved. Similarly, animals were made to swallow and regurgitate sponges. The juice squeezed from the sponges was then mixed with meat. When the meat dissolved, scientists concluded that digestion was a chemical process. These experiments were later extended to humans. Further proof of the chemical nature of digestion was gained in the eighteenth century, when hydrochloric acid was isolated from stomach juices and used in test tubes to break down starch to the simple sugar glucose.

Subsequently, an extract was obtained from stomach juice that did not contain hydrochloric acid but decomposed meat even more efficiently than the acid did. This true ferment was called pepsin. By surgically producing tubes (fistulas) leading from the body surface into the duodenum of experimental animals, it was shown that the fats, starch, and proteins of the stomach contents, when discharged into the duodenum, were decomposed by pancreatic juice that contained the respective enzymes.

Most of what is known about stomach digestion was gained from the findings published by the American army surgeon William Beaumont, who observed the digestive process with the help of the Canadian Alexis St. Martin, who, as a consequence of a gunshot wound, had developed a gastric fistula (a permanent hole through the abdominal wall into the interior of the stomach). Thus, Beaumont found that the gastric juice is poured out only when food is present in the stomach. He also recognized that the elements of the gastric juice and those of mucus are different secretions. He studied the motions of the stomach and determined the digestibility of different dietary components in the stomach. Furthermore, he established the fact that mental disturbances directly affect the secretion of gastric juice and of digestion, and he refuted many erroneous opinions about gastric digestion. Later, scientists distinguished among and made a detailed study of fats, proteins, and carbohydrates. After the discovery of X rays, the radiological study of the alimentary canal became possible. Using radio-opaque substances (such as bismuth and barium sulfate), scientists were able to study the peristaltic movements of the digestive system and diagnose diseases of the alimentary canal, such as tumors and ulcers. In the meantime, endoscopic methods started to undergo improvements. With the invention of fiber optics, the functioning of the digestive tract could be studied by direct visualization of the stomach and intestine (using gastroscopy and colonoscopy, for example).

The study of the process of absorption involved the experimental tying-off of loops of the small intestine from the rest of the digestive tract and the placing of various solutions of different concentrations into the loops. Radioactive tracers were used to study not only the process of absorption but also the functions of the large intestine (elimination and excretion).

Context

The human body is a complex system made up of cells. All the cells need energy to survive. This energy is derived from nutrients that the body obtains from food. Almost all the organ systems of the human body cooperate in the procurement of energy. Blood and lymph fluids transport the nutrients to the cells; oxygen, needed to metabolize the nutrients, is provided through the gas exchange system; the kidneys excrete the waste products of the metabolic processes; but, foremost, the digestive system supplies the nutrients needed for metabolic processes in the first place. Therefore, it is obvious that the process of digestion is one of the most important functions of the human physiology. Life depends on the energy derived from foodstuffs, and only by the digestive process are humans able to extract the energy from food.

What is not always realized, however, is the fact that, as long as the food is still inside the lumen of the digestive tract—that is, before it passes through the walls of the alimentary canal into the bloodstream—it is from a physiological point of view still a part of the environment rather than part of the body; being in continuity with the external medium by taking in and eliminating matter, the alimentary canal is not included in the "internal medium" proper of the body. The process of absorption, occurring through the cells making up the walls of the digestive system, determines the form and the amount of nutrients that will reach the body cells where they are assimilated. Only through the process of assimilation can the nutrients become part of the cell structure of the body.

The discovery of how the body breaks down foods and how it gains the nutrients necessary for survival and growth cleared the way not only for scientifically sound nutrition but also for the medical management and treatment of diseases of the digestive system: from disturbances of salivary secretion to the failure of the anal sphincter, as well as malformations such as ulcers and tumors of the alimentary canal and of its accessory glands, the liver and the pancreas. Thus, treatments were devised for the management of ulcers, starting with the prescription of specific diets and proceeding to surgical interventions. Today, it is assumed that ulcers are not a disease of the stomach or duodenum per se but rather are a consequence of stress-induced nervous disorders that result in faulty signals reaching the digestive tract. Therefore, stress management is paramount in ulcer patients. Nevertheless, the most modern treatment consists of medication that inhibits acid production by the stomach, allowing the ulcers to heal. Celiac-sprue, a disease of the small intestine in which the mucosal lining atrophies, results in the inability of the patients to absorb fats from the intestine. The consequence is a deficiency in both fat-soluble vitamins and essential fatty acids, leading to malnutrition. It was discovered that the disease was caused by an allergy to gluten, a protein in flour. A strict diet that excludes gluten leads to a dramatic improvement, and often even a cure, with the restoration of the normal structure of the intestinal mucosa. Other applications of the knowledge gained from the study of the digestive system include the treatment of liver and gallbladder diseases: gallstones, cirrhosis of the liver (destruction of the liver tissue), and hepatitis (inflammation of the liver), as well as liver cancer.

The tools used to diagnose polyps and cancer of the colon are constantly improving, so that increasingly direct visualization by fiber optics is used instead of X rays, thus minimizing the risk of radiation to patients. Also, the finding that a high-fiber diet may protect against colon cancer is a direct result of the in-depth study of the function of the GI tract.

Bibliography

Davenport, Horace Willard. *A Digest of Digestion*. Chicago: Year Book Medical Publishers, 1975. An abbreviated text for beginning students. All references are omitted, and there are many helpful illustrations. The text conducts the reader on a journey through the alimentary canal, first showing the mechanism of propulsion and secretion, then following food in the process of being digested and absorbed. Clearly written, with a minimum of technical terms.

_____. *Physiology of the Digestive Tract*. 4th ed. Chicago: Year Book Medical Publishers, 1977. A textbook covering in a clear but concise style the functions of the alimentary canal. It contains a large number of references that allow the gathering of additional, detailed information on parts of particular interest to the reader. Although the text is geared toward college students, most of it can be understood by the general reader.

Hui, Y. H. *Essentials of Nutrition and Diet Therapy.* Monterey, Calif.: Wadsworth Health Sciences Division, 1985. A condensed version of *Human Nutrition and Diet Therapy* by the same author. Chapter 8, "The Physiology of Ingested Foodstuffs," covers in brief the functions of the digestive system, including the characteristics of the enzymatic system of digestion, followed by the process of absorption, transport, and metabolism of nutrients. Chapter 18, "Diet and Gastrointestinal Diseases," emphasizes various diseases of the digestive system (such as malabsorption, cystic fibrosis, lactose intolerance, celiac disease, ulcerative colitis, diverticular diseases, and liver cirrhosis) and their management.

_____. *Principles and Issues in Nutrition.* Monterey, Calif.: Wadsworth Health Sciences Division, 1985. Chapter 14, "Metabolism," is a nontechnical discussion of digestion leading to the fate of nutrients subsequent to their absorption into the body fluids. Some health problems, such as heartburn, constipation, and gas, are correlated with the digestive process.

Sanford, Paul A. *Digestive System Physiology.* Baltimore: University Park Press, 1982. A very good, short introduction to the digestive system, including food intake and its control, the structure and function of the alimentary canal, and the absorption and fate of nutrients. An extensive bibliography is offered after each chapter.

Sernka, Thomas J., and Eugene D. Jacobson. *Gastrointestinal Physiology: The Essentials.* 2d ed. Baltimore: Williams and Wilkins, 1983. An introduction, for beginning students, to the physiology of the alimentary canal. The authors place a premium on essentials and brevity. Structural and biochemical details have been omitted. Nevertheless, the discussion is somewhat more technical than Sanford's text.

René R. Roth

Cross-References

Digestion of Carbohydrates, 629; Digestion of Fats, 636; Digestion of Proteins, 644; Digestion Regulation, 650; Digestion Strategies, 656; The Digestive Tract, 670; Enzymes and Ribozymes, 851; Ingestion, 1414; Macronutrients and Micronutrients, 1642; Metabolic Pathways, 1691; Vitamins and Minerals, 2688.

THE DIGESTIVE TRACT

Type of life science: Animal anatomy
Other fields of study: Animal physiology, cell biology (cytology), and histology

The digestive tract is the group of organs where nutrients brought into the animal from the environment are broken down to molecules that can be absorbed into the animal's body. Knowledge of the digestive tract and its functions allows an appreciation of the importance of correct diet and the causes of gastrointestinal diseases.

Principal terms

ABSORPTION: the movement of nutrients out of the lumen of the gut into the body
BILE SALTS: organic compounds derived from cholesterol that are secreted by the liver into the gut lumen and that emulsify fats
DIGESTION: the process by which larger organic nutrients are broken down to smaller molecules in the lumen of the gut
DUODENUM: the first part of the small intestine, where it joins the stomach
ENTEROCYTES: the cells that line the lumen of the small intestine
LIVER: an organ derived from the gut that secretes bile; it is connected to the gut by a duct through which its secretions enter the gut
LUMEN: the central opening through the digestive tract, which is continuous from the mouth to the anus
LYMPHATIC VESSELS: very thin tubes that carry water, proteins, and fats from the gut to the bloodstream
MUCOSA: the lining of the inner wall of the gut facing the lumen
PANCREAS: an organ derived from the gut that secretes digestive enzymes; it is connected to the gut by a duct through which its secretions enter the gut
PLEXUS: a group of nerve cells and their connections to one another
SPHINCTER: a ring of muscle that can close off a portion of the gut

Summary of the Phenomenon

Digestion is the process by which food is broken down into molecules that are small enough to be absorbed into the body. Digestion takes place in the digestive tract of animals. The digestive tract is a continuous tube that acts on ingested food in a sequential manner. Each part of the digestive tract is adapted to reduce the size of food particles, either mechanically or enzymatically, until they are small enough to be absorbed into the body. Consideration of the mechanisms of food intake in lower animals will illustrate the evolution of complexity as an adaptation to the changing environments of these animals.

Sponges are primitive water-dwelling animals that are attached to a fixed point in the water. They bring food into their bodies from currents of water containing particulate food passing through openings in their outer wall. These currents are created by movements of flagella on cells called choanocytes. Food enters the choanocytes by phagocytosis. Phagocytosis is the process in which a cell surrounds a particle with extensions of its cell membrane until the particle is completely surrounded and thus becomes enclosed within a small sac, or vesicle, within the cell. Intracellular enzymes then digest the food particles dissolved in the fluid into their component molecules, which then become available to the metabolic systems in the cytoplasm of the cell. Some cells, called amoebocytes, carry the food particles to other cells in the sponge by crawling through the spaces between the cells. Their travel is by amoeboid motion, in which the cell sends out an extension, called a pseudopod, and then follows it.

This method of feeding and digestion is adequate for a sponge because most of the sponge cells are in close contact with the water currents in which it lives. Thus, these cells can have direct access to food carried in the water currents. The cells that are not in close contact with water currents can be adequately supplied by the amoebocytes. The digestion, or breakdown, must be carried on inside the cells by cytoplasmic enzymes because if these enzymes were released to the extracellular surface, they would be washed away.

The coelenterates, such as jellyfishes or hydras, are more advanced than sponges and require a more-elaborate digestive mechanism. These water-dwelling animals are either attached to a surface or float in the water currents. Thus, as are sponges, they are dependent on food carried in the water. These animals, however, can eat live prey as well as particulate food. They are equipped with tentacles that can reach out and trap smaller animals and paralyze them with poisoned darts called nematocysts. The tentacles then bring the food into a distinct body cavity, the gastrovascular cavity, through its one opening. The digestive cavity is, at least partially, not in direct contact with the water currents around the animal. Digestion can take place through extracellular enzymes secreted by the cells lining this cavity. The resulting molecules are then absorbed through the cell membranes. Amoebocytes also function in these animals. These animals have limited motion through musclelike cells and this motion moves fluid within the gastrovascular cavity, thus carrying fluid to all parts of the animal.

Flatworms are more advanced than sponges and coelenterates and live in a moist, but not watery, environment. They have a distinct nervous and muscular system and can move to search for food. Their digestive tract, as that of sponges, has only a single opening. Food is pushed into this opening by the muscle action of the first part of the digestive tract, which can be protruded to the outside of the animal. Digestion is extracellular and carried to the rest of the animal through muscle contractions of the digestive tract. The digestive tract is highly branched and extends to all parts of the animal.

Animals more highly evolved than flatworms, including roundworms, insects, fish, mammals, and birds, have a functionally similar digestive tract. These animals all have similar requirements, which have necessitated further, more-efficient digestion. These animals are more active and thus must ingest more food. Their digestive tracts have two openings, allowing a continuous digestion: Food enters at one end and is excreted at the other. In contrast, an animal with only one digestive opening cannot excrete and ingest at the same time. The greater size of these more-evolved animals also requires that digested food be absorbed into the circulatory system so that distribution to the rest of the body cells is quick. The absorbing portion of the gut is therefore surrounded by blood vessels.

Further adaptations have required sophisticated specializations of the digestive tract. These include initial chewing devices that can mechanically reduce the size of food so that it can be swallowed. Parts of the digestive system have evolved to store food until it can be efficiently digested. This adaptation allows animals to eat sporadically, when food is available, and allows time for other activities, such as hunting or hiding. Other portions of the digestive tract have become specialized to secrete powerful enzymes that sequentially break down the molecules in food to smaller and smaller molecules. Last, the terminal portions of the digestive tract retain food and extract any remaining nutritional value and eliminate the rest at a convenient time. Many of these adaptations required the formation of a space, called a coelom, between the digestive tract and the rest of the body. This space allows the gut to coil and thus become much longer than the animal, with a resulting increase in the surface area available for digestion and absorption.

The mouth, or buccal cavity, is designed for the entry of food into the digestive tract. The lips and tongue are highly sensitive to the texture and taste of food. They are capable of very precise movements because their musculature is supplied with an extensive nerve supply. The tongue can move laterally, up and down, and in and out, because it has both longitudinal and circular muscles. Movements of the jaws during chewing (mastication) cause the teeth to crush and tear food in the mouth. The teeth have an outer covering of very tough enamel, which protects them against abrasion. Some animals have teeth that grow throughout their life and replace the worn-out ends. Salivary glands in the sides or base of the jaw secrete saliva through ducts that empty into the mouth at the sides of or under the tongue. Saliva has the primary function of lubricating and wetting chewed food. Saliva contains an enzyme, called salivary amylase, which begins the digestion of starch, although the digestion is greatly slowed after the food enters the acidic stomach lumen.

After the food has been reduced to small particles and mixed with saliva, it is swallowed (deglutition). Swallowing is partly a reflex action, controlled by a center in the base of the brain. The tongue rises to the roof of the mouth, pushing the rounded mass of chewed food, called a bolus, into the opening of the esophagus. Further propulsion is created by contraction of the area between the mouth and the esophagus, called the pharynx. The esophagus is a muscular tube leading to the stomach. Contractions of muscles which encircle the esophagus cause a moving ring of contraction, called peristalsis, which propels the bolus into the stomach.

The wall of the gastrointestinal tract is similar throughout its length. The layers, from lumen outward, are the mucosa, submucosa, submucosal nerve plexus, circular muscle, myenteric nerve plexus, longitudinal muscle, and the thin connective tissue covering called the serosa. The stomach and intestines are suspended from the back wall of the abdominal cavity by a sheet of connective tissue called the mesentery. Nerves, blood vessels, and lymphatic vessels reach the gut in the mesentery.

The cavity of the gut, or lumen, is lined by a single sheet of cells called the mucosa. The mucosa contains a wide variety of cell types. Most of the mucosa is composed of a cell type which is called columnar epithelium because the cells are longer than their diameter. Mucous, or goblet, cells secrete mucus, which is the viscous slippery material that protects the cells of the gut against mechanical abrasion and chemical attack. Other cells secrete enzymes into the lumen. Hydrochloric acid is secreted by parietal cells in the stomach. Other cells in the small intestine secrete basic bicarbonate ion. These cells provide the degree of acidity or basicity appropriate to the different regions of the gut. Other cells are adapted to absorb nutrients from or to secrete fluid into the lumen of the gut.

There are also many endocrine cells in the mucosa. These cells secrete hormones into the blood when they are stimulated by nerves or by the contents of the gut. These hormones control the degree of motility or secretion of the gut and the metabolic and physiological responses of the body following feeding. Indeed, the digestive system is the largest endocrine gland in the body. These same hormones are found in the brain, where they act as neurotransmitters, and in other endocrine glands. They have numerous functions revolving around the digestive tract. Some of these hormones can increase or decrease hunger. Others prepare the body for the nutrients that will be absorbed from the digestive tract so that the nutrients can be efficiently utilized. Certain hormones can be released by different types of nutrients in the lumen of the digestive tract. Other hormones can be released through the action of nerves when food is eaten.

The layer next to the mucosa, called the submucosa, is composed of fibrous connective tissue. It provides a mechanical support for the mucosa and also contains the nerve and blood supply leading to and from the mucosa. The lymphatic vessels draining the mucosa also travel through the submucosa.

The next, more external layer, is a sheet of nerves, called the submucous (Meissner) plexus. These nerves send fibers inward to the mucosa and also outward to the other layers. They respond to the luminal contents and to other nerves and hormones. There are as many nerves in the gut as there are in the spinal cord. They are an intrinsic nervous system of the gut—that is, they begin and end in the gut. They are considered a separate category along with the autonomic (involuntary) and somatic (voluntary) nervous systems.

The next layer of the gut wall is a layer of visceral smooth muscle oriented circularly around the circumference of the gut. Contraction of these muscles causes a ring of contraction that may or may not move down the intestine. Next, there is another layer of nerves called the myenteric (Auerbach) plexus. Both nerve plexuses are responsible for controlling and integrating the functions of the intestine. Motility of the muscles of the gut, absorption of salt, water, and nutrients, and blood flow are all regulated by these nerves. The outermost layer of the gut is composed of visceral smooth muscle oriented longitudinally along the gut. Contractions of these muscles shortens the length of the gut.

There are also rings of smooth muscle, called sphincters, which control the movement from one part of the gut to the adjacent part. These sphincters are found between the esophagus and the stomach, the stomach and small intestine, the small and large intestine, and the large intestine and the outside.

Food that enters the stomach is partially digested by the enzyme pepsin, which is secreted by the chief cells of the gastric mucosa. Pepsin begins the digestion of protein. The hydrochloric acid secreted by the parietal cells has the functions of activating the pepsin and killing bacteria. The most necessary function of the stomach is storage of food (now reduced to a semiliquid state called acid chyme, or chyme) and slowly propelling it into the small intestine. Additionally, the stomach secretes a substance called intrinsic factor, required for absorption of vitamin B_{12}, which promotes red blood cell formation.

Ruminants, such as cattle and sheep, have the end of the esophagus and the beginning of the stomach modified into large chambers, called the rumen and reticulum, in which food is stored. These portions of the stomach are alkaline because of the enormous volume of basic saliva secreted by the animal. Bacterial digestion of the chyme occurs in these chambers. In addition, the contents can be regurgitated into the mouth and this cud then chewed further. After the cud is chewed and reswallowed, it bypasses the previous chambers and enters a third chamber, called the omasum, where it is churned by muscular contractions. Finally, it enters the abomasum, which is similar to the stomach of other animals.

Birds have specialized adaptations of the stomach, called the crop and gizzard. The crop is a large structure at the beginning of the stomach that stores food until it enters the stomach. The gizzard is a muscular portion of the stomach that grinds the food. This grinding by the gizzard is necessary because birds have no teeth. Frequently, birds will ingest small stones, which are stored in the gizzard and help grind the food.

The stomach empties into the small intestine. The first portion of the small intestine is called the duodenum, the middle portion the jejunum, and the terminal portion the ileum. There are two large organs that are connected to the duodenum through ducts that empty into its lumen. These organs are the liver and the pancreas. The liver secretes bile salts, which are necessary to emulsify fats into small particles for absorption. Bile salts are stored in the gall bladder between meals. The gall bladder is connected, by a branch, to the duct leading from the liver to the duodenum. The pancreas secretes basic bicarbonate, which helps neutralize stomach acids that enter the duodenum. The pancreas also secretes many different digestive enzymes, which break down proteins, fats, carbohydrates, nucleic acids, and other large molecules. Thus, as soon as chyme enters the duodenum, it is immediately mixed with digestive enzymes and bile salts that entered the lumen from the pancreatic and bile ducts.

The chyme is mixed and propelled along the small intestine by longitudinal and circular muscle contractions. These contractions continually mix the chyme with the pancreatic enzymes and bile salts and present the digested molecules to the mucosal surface, where further digestion takes place. Most of the mucosal cells, called enterocytes, produce enzymes and absorb nutrients. Enterocytes are continuously formed in mucosal pits, called crypts. They migrate up tiny fingerlike projections, called villi, which protrude into the lumen of the gut. It takes about three days for the enterocyte to travel from the base of the crypt to the tip of the villi, and then it is sloughed into the lumen. The villi are thought to increase the surface area of the gut on which digestion and absorption take place. The enterocytes produce enzymes that are attached to the mucosal surface of the cells. These enzymes are responsible for the final stages of digestion, producing the smallest molecules, which are now in a form that can be absorbed by the intestine. Because the digestion takes place on the cells' surface, it is called contact digestion.

After molecules are in their completely digested form, they are absorbed by enterocytes, which transport them from the lumen of the gut to the circulatory or the lymphatic system. Most organic nutrients, such as amino acids, fats, and glucose are absorbed in the first half of the small intestine, the duodenum and jejunum. Salt, water, and bile salts are absorbed primarily in the ileum. Absorption is virtually complete as long as the digestive system is functioning normally. Usually, the main problems that arise during gastrointestinal disorders are associated with malabsorption of fats. Fats require bile salts to be emulsified. Emulsification is necessary for enzymes to break down fats and also to reduce the final size of the fat microdroplet that results. If any step in this process is not functioning well, then the fats come out of suspension in the intestine and are excreted.

The final contents of the small intestine consist mostly of salts, water, indigestible fiber, and the debris from sloughed enterocytes. The small intestine empties into the large intestine, where some bacterial digestion occurs, which produces mostly small fatty acid molecules. The debris from these bacteria add to the bulk of the undigested material. Muscle contraction propels the material through the large intestine until it is eliminated by defecation. Sphincters control the final evacuation.

Methods of Study

The structural features of the digestive tract can be determined by classical techniques of anatomical dissection and histological examination of the cellular characteristics of the different sections of the digestive tract. The secretions and the digestive steps can be determined by sampling the luminal contents. The sampling can be done by passing a tube through the digestive tract until the end reaches the desired portion and then withdrawing a sample for biochemical analyses.

Motility can be measured by attaching a balloon to a tube passed into the digestive tract and measuring the changes in pressure from muscle contractions. Absorption can be measured by perfusing a solution of known composition from one opening in a double tube and collecting the solution remaining after it has passed through the gut lumen from a second opening.

The presence of abnormal structures or pathologic changes, such as tumors or ulcers, can be directly visualized by means of endoscopy. This procedure involves passing a thin tube, called an endoscope, into the gastrointestinal tract. The endoscope can be inserted either through the esophagus or through the rectum. The tube contains fiber optics, which can carry light toward the tip of the endoscope for illumination of the mucosal lining. The reflected light is carried by fiber optics back to an eyepiece or video camera, which is used to magnify and observe the features of the intestine. The tip of the endoscope can be controlled and rotated to observe all parts of the region where it is located. Endoscopes can be modified so that a small sample of tissue, a biopsy, can be cut from the gastrointestinal tract and removed for examination for pathologic changes by microscopy or biochemical techniques. In a similar manner, minor surgery, such as the removal of small growths, can be undertaken.

Motility of the intestine or the presence of obstructions that prevent the passage of food along the gastrointestinal tract can be observed by X-ray techniques. A liquid substance, such as a barium suspension, which is opaque to X rays, is swallowed. A series of X rays is taken, or continuous monitoring by an X-ray camera is used. Obstructions can be visualized from the buildup of barium above the blockade. The speed of movement can be estimated to determine if the overall motility of the gastrointestinal tract is abnormal. X rays can also be used to determine directly the presence of abnormal structures such as gallstones, which form in the bile ducts, or tumors. The bile duct and gallbladder system can be visualized with X rays by administering a radiopaque dye that is secreted by the liver into the duct system.

The overall integrity of the gastrointestinal tract can be determined by ingesting inert substances of different molecular sizes and determining if they appear in the blood. Normally, only relatively small molecules can penetrate the very tight mucosal lining of the gut, unless they are nutrients of the body. The penetration of larger molecules across the mucosa indicates leaks resulting from damage to the gastrointestinal lining.

Context

The digestive tract and its functions have become subjects of everyday consideration in society. Obesity is a major aesthetic and health-related concern. Knowledge of the function of the digestive tract and its relationship to body metabolism can allow one to evaluate intelligently the claims of the numerous diet regimens that are advertised. For example, since proteins are initially digested in the stomach, they will not be intact when they are absorbed. Hence, claims that specific ingested proteins will have hormonelike effects on the body are unlikely to be true. Anorexia and bulimia are a frequently encountered phenomenon, at least in the popular press. Control mechanisms over food ingestion may be a useful means to control these eating disorders. Gastrointestinal disturbances, such as ulcers, diarrhea, constipation, and vomiting, may be better controlled and their causes better appreciated by knowing how the digestive tract functions.

Medical disorders involving the digestive tract are more frequent than those involving almost any other system in the body. The functions of this system are, therefore, a major area of clinical research. Infant diarrhea is a significant concern because it is relatively common and infants can easily become dehydrated, with fatal results. Tumors of the digestive tract can release pathologic amounts of hormones into the body, with severe consequences to body function. Another clinical concern involves reduced blood flow to the digestive tract. This impairment can occur when the movements of the intestines twist the arteries leading to them or when there is a blockage of the blood vessels within the intestine. The cells of the mucosa begin to die, and there is no longer an effective barrier between the contents of the lumen and the body. Bacteria, or their toxins, and the powerful digestive enzymes can then enter the blood and begin to attack other cells.

Bibliography

Arms, Karen, and Pamela S. Camp. *Biology.* 3d ed. Philadelphia: Saunders College Publishing, 1987. A clear and well-illustrated general biology text. The functions of the digestive tract in different phyla of animals and specifically of higher animals is presented.

Ganong, William F. *Review of Medical Physiology.* 14th ed. East Norwalk, Conn.: Appleton and Lange, 1989. An advanced text, but has well-illustrated and concise explanations of digestive functions and structures. The structures of the digestive tract, their functions, and the control mechanisms are thoroughly covered. The text is very useful because the topics are presented in small sections and subsections. Well indexed for locating information.

Guyton, Arthur C. *Human Physiology and Mechanisms of Disease.* Philadelphia: W. B. Saunders, 1982. An intermediate-level animal physiology text. Several general and specific chapters on the structure and function of the digestive tract are presented. Also included is a section on diseases. Well written and verbally oriented.

_____. *Textbook of Medical Physiology.* 7th ed. Philadelphia: W B. Saunders, 1986. An advanced-level medically oriented physiology text. Strong emphasis on disease mechanisms as well as normal structure and function.

Rhoades, Rodney, and Richard Pflanzer. *Human Physiology.* Philadelphia: Saunders College Publishing, 1989. A well-written intermediate-level animal physiology text. Excellent illustrations and clear, direct, and pertinent writing.

Tortora, Gerard J., and Nicholas P. Anagnostakos. *Principles of Anatomy and Physiology.* 5th ed. New York: Harper & Row, 1987. An introductory-level text. Includes detailed illustrations of anatomy and cellular structures of the digestive tract and simple explanations of function. Points out the relationship to normal life and pathologic events.

David Mailman

Cross-References

Digestion of Carbohydrates, 629; Digestion of Fats, 636; Digestion of Proteins, 644; Digestion Regulation, 650; Digestion Strategies, 656; Digestive Processes in Humans, 663; Excretion of Nitrogenous Wastes, 932; Ingestion, 1414; Macronutrients and Micronutrients, 1642; Vitamins and Minerals, 2688.

DNA BENDING IN REGULATION

Type of life science: Genetic regulation in prokaryotes
Other fields of study: Biochemistry, biophysics, and molecular biology

Regulation is the control of biochemical processes that occur within living cells. At the level of the gene, regulation involves the interaction of proteins with DNA. Some regulatory proteins recognize a region of the DNA molecule that is inherently bent. After binding to the DNA, other regulatory proteins cause a nearby region of the DNA to bend.

Principal terms

BASE: one of several small nitrogen-containing organic molecules found in nucleic acids

DEOXYRIBONUCLEIC ACID (DNA) REPLICATION: the process whereby a molecule of DNA duplicates itself

ENZYME: a protein catalyst that speeds up a biochemical reaction without being consumed

NUCLEIC ACID: a macromolecule, either DNA or RNA, composed of many nucleotides joined together in a chainlike way

NUCLEOTIDE: a unit of a nucleic acid consisting of an organic base, a sugar molecule, and a phosphate group

PROTEIN: a macromolecule composed of one or more long chains of amino acids

TRANSCRIPTION: the process by which the information in DNA is transferred or copied into RNA

Summary of the Phenomenon

Deoxyribonucleic acid (DNA) bending is a localized alteration in the structure of a DNA molecule in which the curvature of the molecule is changed by about 30 degrees or even more. DNA bending is either inherent in the molecule or induced by interaction with a protein. Before examining the role of bent DNA in regulation, the nature of DNA and the control of cellular processes must be described briefly.

Regulation is the control of biochemical processes that occur within living cells. At the level of DNA, regulation includes the control of two fundamental processes, transcription and DNA replication. Transcription is the process whereby the sequence of nucleotides constituting the genetic information becomes encoded in ribonucleic acid (RNA). DNA replication is the process whereby DNA is duplicated within the cell. Regulation at the DNA level involves the interaction of a special class of proteins called regulatory proteins.

At the molecular level, the nucleic acids DNA and RNA are each made up of a series of nucleotides linked together. The nucleotides are joined together by a phosphate group, which connects the sugar of one nucleotide to that of another. In this manner millions of nucleotides can be connected to form a nucleic acid. The RNA that is copied or transcribed from the DNA of a gene is called messenger RNA (mRNA). This mRNA is in turn used to make the proteins that perform a variety of functions within living organisms. In addition to the lengthy sequence of nucleotides—a thousand or more—needed to form a gene, relatively short sequences of about five to twenty nucleotides act as target sites at which regulatory proteins bind to the DNA. These target sites are located at or near the genes.

The first example of gene regulation in prokaryotes was elucidated by François Jacob and Jacques Monod in the early 1960's. These two French scientists received the Nobel Prize in 1965 for their development of the operon theory. According to this theory, a cluster of genes called an operon is coordinately controlled by the interaction of certain proteins that bind to target sites situated in front of the gene cluster. These target sites are specific sequences of nucleotides. One of these sites is the promoter to which the enzyme RNA polymerase binds. Once bound, the RNA polymerase copies or transcribes the DNA of the operon and forms the corresponding mRNA. Between the promoter and the gene cluster is another target site called the operator. In the lac operon of *Escherichia coli*, the regulatory protein, known as the lac repressor, normally is bound to the operator. Since the lac repressor is a rather large protein, it covers a portion of the promoter and prevents the RNA polymerase from binding. In this manner, transcription is turned off.

Since the development of the operon theory, many regulatory gene systems have been discovered in both prokaryotic and eukaryotic systems. Regulatory proteins act by binding to the DNA at specific target regions within the chromosomal DNA. Some of these proteins, such as the lac repressor, recognize special sequences of nucleotides within the target region of the DNA molecule, while others recognize changes in the structure of the target region.

In order to visualize the protein-DNA interactions, a "poppet bead" analogy can be used. (Poppet beads are beads used for children's necklaces; the necklace can be varied in length by adding additional poppet beads.) The bacterial chromosome resembles a double-stranded necklace of poppet beads, with each bead representing a nucleotide. A typical bacterial chromosome consists of one gigantic molecule of DNA containing about 10 million nucleotides. The two strands of DNA (or poppet beads, in our analogy) are twisted around each other to form a double helix. In the DNA double helix, as well as in the poppet bead necklace, considerable flexibility exists. By twisting and rotating the beads, a variety of three-dimensional structures or shapes can be achieved, including localized bends of 90 degrees or more.

To continue the analogy, induced bending occurs when a protein, represented by a flexible "nerf" ball, comes into contact with the DNA. In some cases, the DNA molecule or poppet bead strands may literally surround the protein or "nerf" ball, causing considerable distortions or bends in the DNA molecule. Just like the flexible "nerf" ball, the regulatory protein may undergo subtle changes in its structure.

At the atomic level, atoms within the protein molecule interact with the atoms of the DNA molecule, causing portions of the protein molecule to become rather strongly attached to the DNA. In terms of another analogy, the double-helical DNA resembles a spiral staircase in which the paired organic bases, adenine-thymine and guanine-cytosine, form the steps of the staircase. The AT and GC pairs are held together by chemical bonds called hydrogen bonds. The phosphate portion of the DNA molecule serves as the frame and railings that connect the steps to each other.

The phosphate groups in the DNA molecule are negatively charged. Positively charged regions of the protein molecule are initially attracted to the negatively charged phosphate groups of the DNA. Since the phosphate groups forming the backbone of the DNA are on the outside of the spiral staircase, there are open areas of grooves that are not occupied by either the steps or the frame. By penetrating the grooves in the DNA double helix, portions of the protein molecule come into direct contact with the organic base pairs situated inside the double helix. More specifically, organic groups on the protein, such as amino groups and hydroxyl groups, will interact with similar groups on the DNA molecule, utilizing weak attractions called hydrogen bonds. As a result of these attractions, a rather tight complex of the protein and DNA is formed. In addition, the protein-DNA interactions are very specific, depending on the nucleotide sequence of the individual target site.

One of the first examples of induced DNA bending to be examined involves the cyclic adenosine monophosphate (cyclic AMP) receptor protein known as the catabolite activator protein (CAP). The target site of this regulatory protein is located about sixty nucleotides from the operator site of the lac operon. In 1984, Hen-Ming Wu and Donald M. Crothers showed that the binding of CAP to its target site causes the DNA in the vicinity to bend. The extent of bending of the DNA in this thirty-nucleotide-pair region is dramatic, being more than 90 degrees but less than 180 degrees. Bending of this magnitude causes the DNA double helix in the region of the lac promoter to open up or unwind. This permits the RNA polymerase to bind to the promoter region. Consequently, the efficient transcription of the mRNA of the lac operon can take place. The involvement of cyclic AMP in regulation has important ramifications in the control of certain eukaryotic processes. Cyclic AMP is involved as a "second messenger" that initiates cellular metabolic processes induced by a variety of hormones.

In contrast to the induced bending caused by CAP and certain other regulatory proteins involved in transcription, some regulatory proteins recognize intrinsic DNA bending, sometimes called sequence-directed bending. Intrinsic bending was first discovered in 1982 by Paul Englund and others in kinetoplast DNA, the mitochondrial DNA of parasitic protozoa. The bent region of DNA is recognized by a nicking enzyme that cuts the mitochondrial DNA and is believed to be involved in the replication of kinetoplast DNA.

Intrinsic DNA bending has been found at or near the origins of DNA replication of a variety of organisms, most notably those of the bacterial virus lambda and the eukaryotic viruses SV40 and adenovirus. Intrinsic DNA bending arises from the presence of stretches of adenine-thymine (AT) base pairs called AT tracts. These AT tracts consist of roughly three to seven AT pairs distributed at regular intervals of about eleven base pairs. Each of these tracts can bend the DNA about 10 degrees. Depending on the number of tracts, the DNA molecule is bent by 40 or 50 degrees or more.

The lambda replication origin is perhaps the most well-studied replication origin. In this system, the lambda O protein, a regulatory protein involved in DNA replication, recognizes the bent DNA and attaches to it. The attachment of the O protein further bends the DNA in the origin region. Bending in this region apparently causes DNA strand separation, which is a prerequisite for DNA replication. Once a localized region of the double helix is unwound, other proteins involved in DNA replication are able to interact with the DNA to promote its replication.

Methods of Study

The identification and details of various regulated gene systems have been worked out by geneticists using classical genetic techniques similar to those employed by Jacob and Monod. Important technical developments in the 1970's and 1980's, however, have allowed life scientists to examine the interaction of proteins with DNA at the molecular level. Techniques such as electron microscopy and X-ray crystallography have been used to study DNA-protein interactions. Gel electrophoresis, however, because of its ready availability and its great analytical capabilities, has become the most widely used technique to study DNA-protein interactions at the molecular level. Electrophoresis is the separation of electrically charged molecules in an electric field. Gel electrophoresis can separate molecules not only on the basis of their net electrical charge but also on the basis of their size. Large molecules move more slowly through the gel than do smaller molecules, because they are more likely to be trapped within the pores of the gel.

A modification of gel electrophoresis is the band-shift assay, or gel-retention assay, developed in the early 1980's. This technique is used to study the binding of proteins to a fragment of DNA believed to contain the target site. If the protein does bind to the DNA fragment, then the DNA-protein complex will be larger than the DNA fragment itself. Upon electrophoresis, the DNA-protein complex will move more slowly than the DNA fragment alone. After electrophoresis, the DNA complexed with the protein appears as a band that has been retained, or shifted, compared to the band of the DNA fragment alone.

The band-shift assay has also been used by scientists to demonstrate both protein-induced bending and sequence-directed DNA bending. Researcher Donald M. Crothers and his coworkers measured the relative stabilities of the cyclic AMP receptor protein bound to fragments of DNA containing its target site. From these measurements, the extent of bending induced by the cyclic AMP receptor protein was determined. In the case of sequence directed DNA bending, the DNA fragment suspected of being bent is compared with a DNA fragment known not to be bent. The bent DNA will move more slowly than the DNA that is not bent. Crothers, Paul Englund, and their coworkers demonstrated the presence of sequence-directed bent DNA in fragments from kinetoplasts by using this assay.

Two additional gel electrophoretic techniques used to study protein-DNA interactions are nucleotide sequencing and DNA footprinting. In the first technique, the banding pattern, or sequencing ladder, of a protein-free DNA fragment containing the protein-binding site to be examined is analyzed, and the sequence of nucleotides determined. In footprinting, the banding pattern of the protein-free DNA is compared with the banding pattern of the DNA after interaction with the binding protein. The banding pattern will be obscured wherever the protein has come into contact with the DNA. In this way the sequence of nucleotides at the target site is determined.

By using electrophoretic techniques, the molecular biologist can gain insight into the mechanism by which regulatory proteins interact with DNA. The band shift, or gel retention, assay is particularly useful in detecting both protein-induced bending of DNA and sequence-directed DNA bending.

Context

Regulation or control of gene expression is essential to the survival not only of the individual cell but also of the organism itself. What protein(s) and enzyme(s) are produced by an individual gene or a cluster of genes depends on signals received by the cell. These signals cause gene systems to be turned on or off. Since these systems depend on DNA-protein interactions, it is important to understand how these regulatory systems operate.

Regulation is particularly important during development. It must control whether certain genes are to be turned on or off during the lifetime of an organism. Certain genes may be turned on in liver cells, for example, but not in skin cells. Regulatory genes may have a crucial role in the aging process. Although the role of protein-induced bending in these processes is not fully understood, some regulatory systems depend on it.

The exact role of sequence-directed DNA bending is not clear; however, it apparently plays a role in the initiation of DNA replication. It is essential that an organism be able to reproduce itself and that multicellular organisms be able to replace individual cells periodically. This reproductive process involves DNA replication.

The details of bacterial DNA replication are reasonably well understood because of the pioneering work of Arthur Kornberg, who received the Nobel Prize in 1959, primarily for his work on DNA polymerase, the key enzyme in DNA replication. About a dozen separate proteins and enzymes are involved in bacterial DNA replication. How these proteins recognize the origin of DNA replication and interact with one another is still being elucidated.

For the *Escherichia coli* chromosome, which consists of about 10 million nucleotide pairs, DNA replication begins within an origin region consisting of about four hundred nucleotide pairs. How do the proteins and enzymes involved in replication recognize this relatively small portion of chromosomal DNA? Possibly sequence-directed bent DNA provides the key.

In eukaryotic DNA, the mechanism is even more complex. It is likely that the recognition of sequence-directed bent DNA again provides a key step in the process. Quite possibly an essential protein binds to the bent DNA and induces further DNA bending to provide the opportunity for other proteins to come into proper orientation to initiate DNA replication.

One of the greatest challenges facing medical scientists continues to be understanding the causes of cancer. At a very elementary level, it is clear that DNA replication in cancer cells is unregulated and out of control as compared to DNA replication in normal cells. It could be that one or more of the regulatory proteins engaged in DNA replication is absent or is not functioning properly. Further research should help to answer that question. Basic research into the mechanisms of gene regulation should help scientists understand essential biological processes such as transcription, DNA replication, and developmental processes, including aging.

Bibliography

Alberts, Bruce, Dennis Bray, Julian Lewis, Martin Raff, Keith Roberts, and James D. Watson. *Molecular Biology of the Cell.* 2d ed. New York: Garland, 1989. Chapter 10, "Control of Gene Expression," describes the nature of gene regulation in general terms. Written at the college level but suitable for high school as well. It is well illustrated and extensively referenced.

Berridge, Michael J. "The Molecular Basis of Communications Within the Cell." *Scientific American* 253 (October, 1985): 48-57. This article describes several "second messengers," including cyclic AMP. The article explains how the organism uses these signals to respond to its needs.

Doolittle, Russell F. "Proteins." *Scientific American* 253 (October, 1985): 88-99. This article discusses the basics of protein structure and function.

Felsenfeld, Gary. "DNA." *Scientific American* 253 (October, 1985): 58-67. An excellent article that describes DNA structure, including the A, B, and Z forms. Emphasis is placed not only on the importance of the nucleotide sequence but also on the fact that the DNA molecule is flexible. The interaction of regulatory proteins with DNA and the nature of DNA bending are described.

Gehring, Walter J. "The Molecular Basis of Development." *Scientific American* 253 (October, 1985): 153-162. This article describes certain aspects of development and the importance of a short stretch of nucleotides called the homeobox.

Moses, Phyllis M., and Nam-Hai Chua. "Light Switches for Plant Genes." *Scientific American* 258 (April, 1988): 88-93. The author explains how light can interact with stretches of plant DNA so that certain genes are turned on and off. Light tells plants when to sprout, how to grow, and how to age.

Rothwell, Norman V. *Understanding Genetics.* 4th ed. New York: Oxford University Press, 1988. Chapter 17, "Control Mechanisms and Differentiation," discusses enzyme induction and repression, gene regulation and the plasticity of DNA, differentiation in relation to time and aging, and control mechanisms and the cancer cell. Written at the college level but suitable for high school as well. The chapter is well illustrated and has more than fifty references.

Sachs, Leo. "Growth, Differentiation, and the Reversal of Malignancy." *Scientific American* 254 (January, 1986): 40-47. This article describes how the processes of growth and differentiation are regulated in normal cells and how this information makes it possible to answer several questions about cancer.

Alan D. Cooper

Cross-References

Aging in Humans, 42; Central Metabolism Regulation, 411; DNA Replication, 692; DNA Sequencing, 698; DNA's Molecular Structure, 706; Positive and Negative Eukaryotic Transcriptional Control, 895; Homeotic Genes and Homeoboxes, 1314; Nucleic Acid Structure, 1987; Transcription of DNA to Form RNA, 2632.

DNA HYBRIDIZATION ANALYSIS OF RELATEDNESS

Types of life science: Evolutionary biology and molecular biology
Other fields of study: Biochemistry, genetics, and systematics (taxonomy)

DNA hybridization estimates the genetic similarity between the DNA of various organisms. Radioactively labeled DNA that has been separated into strands is reacted with DNA from different species, and the results can be used to reconstruct evolutionary histories of species or groups of species.

Principal terms

COMPLEMENTARY BASE PAIRING: the hydrogen bonding between a
   particular purine base and a particular pyrimidine base in double-
   strand nucleic acid molecules (DNA or RNA); the specific pairings
   are adenine with thymine, or uracil and guanine with cytosine
CONVERGENCE: the appearance of similar characters in genetically
   dissimilar species
DELTA T_m: the difference between the temperature at which half the
   heteroduplex molecules separate into their individual strands and the
   temperature at which half the homoduplex molecules separate
DEOXYRIBONUCLEIC ACID (DNA): the genetic material of living things;
   the functional constituent of chromosomes
GENOME: all the genes contained in a single set of chromosomes
HETERODUPLEX DNA: DNA in which the two strands are from two
   different sources, such as two different species
HOMODUPLEX DNA: DNA in which both strands are derived from the
   same source, usually from the same population of a species
NUCLEASE: an enzyme that cuts nucleic acids, such as DNA, by
   specifically breaking certain bonds while allowing other bonds to
   remain
NUCLEOTIDE: a molecule consisting of a pentose sugar (deoxyribose in
   DNA, ribose in RNA), a nitrogenous base, and a phosphate group;
   DNA and RNA are made up of nucleotides
PHYLOGENY: the evolutionary history of taxa (such as species or groups
   of species) that depicts the order of descent and the relationships
   among the groups
REPETITIVE DNA: a DNA sequence that is repeated many times in the
   genome
SINGLE-COPY DNA: a DNA sequence that is included only once in the
   genome

Summary of the Methodology

Deoxyribonucleic acid (DNA)—the substance of genes and heredity in all living things—is the major constituent of the chromosomes, which determine all the organism's individual characteristics. Nucleic acids, of which DNA is the most important representative, are the only chemicals that can direct their own reproduction. They also direct protein synthesis, which is the chemical combination of series of amino acids to form protein. Protein is the chemical basis of the cellular material of which all life is composed.

DNA consists of two long chains of nucleotides—organic compounds that consist of a nitrogen-containing purine or pyramidine base that is connected to the sugar deoxyribose and a phosphate group. DNA usually exists as a double-stranded helix.

Under normal physiological conditions, DNA can rarely come apart. If the double helix is exposed to near-boiling temperatures or to extremes of acidity or alkalinity, it rapidly denatures (separates). In DNA hybridization, DNA molecules from two organisms are first extracted from cells. Most of the DNA is found in the nuclei, which are isolated by high-speed centrifugation. After purification, the DNA is separated into individual strands at high temperature. The strands are sheared into five-hundred- to one-thousand-nucleotide segments.

The DNA from one species is then made radioactive, usually by a method known as nick-translation. In this method, the DNA strand is "nicked" at various intervals by means of an enzyme, and DNA components are labeled with radioactive phosphorus. The DNA strands from two species are then combined under conditions that permit joining of the strands to form molecules that contain one strand from each organism. Strands combined from two species in this way are referred to as heteroduplex strands; strands that are combined from members of the same or closely related species are referred to as homoduplex. Excess single strands are removed via the addition of nuclease enzymes that digest single-, but not double-strand, DNA. Sequences forming duplexes need not be complementary for every nucleotide. In most cases, imperfect double helixes are formed where the heteroduplex molecules between different species (and to a lesser extent between individuals of the same species) contain nucleotide mismatches. The extent of mismatch (because of noncomplementary nucleotides) is measured by the difference in melting temperature. The temperature at which the strands separate is determined principally by how closely the bases pair, and this can be used to show the relative degree of affinity between the species from which the samples of DNA were taken. The extent of melting is determined by the percentage of DNA that is found as a single-strand form compared to that existing as the double-strand form. The single-strand form is susceptible to digestion by certain nucleases, which, following digestion, results in soluble fragments. The protected double-strand form can be precipitated. The ratio of radioactivity in the soluble fraction versus the precipitated fraction will therefore give an estimate of the degree of bonding at various temperatures.

The greater the similarity between the two sets of DNA, the greater the strength of the bonds within the DNA duplex. DNA strands that have high homology (similarity) will melt at a higher temperature than strands that have a greater number of nucleotide mismatches (low homology). Organisms that are genetically more distant from one another will therefore have a lower melting point than those that are genetically closer. Homoduplexes (duplex DNA in which both strands are derived from the same source) melt at a higher temperature than do heteroduplexes (duplex DNA in which the strands are from different sources).

Median melting temperatures are commonly used to measure the degree of thermal stability of DNA complexes. Thermal stability is the temperature at which 50 percent of the single-copy DNA that hybridizes is dissociated. Thermal stability is usually indicated as T_m, for median melting temperature. The difference between the T_m of the homoduplex and the T_m of the heteroduplex (the difference is known as delta T_m) is used to estimate the difference in nucleotide sequences between the two species. In general, a change of one delta T_m represents about a 1 percent difference in nucleotide sequence. The overall level of evolutionary divergence between two species is indicated by the delta T_m figure.

A phylogeny is the evolutionary history of a species or groups of species in terms of their derivations and relationships with one another. Phylogenies reconstructed from DNA-DNA hybridizations are based on the assumption that the delta T_m value is linearly related to the proportion of nucleotides that differ between the two DNA sequences. The data from a number of studies appear to support this assumption.

Applications of the Method

This method of DNA-DNA hybridization has been used for inference of phylogenetic relations between many sets of species. For example, DNA-DNA hybridization profiles of three species of *Drosophila* (the fruit fly) have been examined. The T_m where both strands were from *Drosophila melanogaster* was 78 degrees Celsius. The T_m where one strand was from *Drosophila melanogaster* and the other strand from *Drosophila simulans* was 75 degrees Celsius. When one strand was from *Drosophila melanogaster* and the second strand was from *Drosophila funebris*, the T_m was 65 degrees Celsius. Since a delta T_m of 1 degree Celsius corresponds to approximately 1 percent of the nucleotides being mismatched, the estimated genetic distance between *Drosophila melanogaster* and *Drosophila simulans* is 3 percent and between *Drosophila melanogaster* and *Drosophila funebris* is 13 percent.

Charles Sibley and Jon Ahlquist have conducted more than twenty thousand DNA-DNA hybridization tests on sixteen hundred species of birds that were drawn from 168 of the 171 traditionally recognized bird families. Their data were found to be useful in determining phylogenies that had formerly been judged difficult or impossible to determine because convergent evolution had selected for morphological similarities that were not based on common ancestry. The problem of convergence is especially pronounced in birds. Sibley and Ahlquist's work led to several major revisions in classical bird taxonomy. One of the unexpected discoveries was that the Corvivi, which include ravens, jays, and crows, originated from Australia and then subsequently spread throughout the world.

The best-known and perhaps most controversial use of the DNA-DNA hybridization technique involves primates. In 1984, Sibley and Ahlquist began conducting a series of DNA hybridization tests. As with birds, they believed that DNA-DNA hybridizations could be used to clarify previously obscure primate relationships, such as those concerning humans, gorillas, and chimpanzees. In contrast to earlier work, they concluded that humans and chimpanzees are genetically closer to one another than either are to gorillas. Based upon molecular clock techniques, the following approximate divergence dates were estimated: Old World monkeys, 30 million years ago; gibbons, 20 million; orangutan, 15 million; gorilla, 7.7 to 11 million; and chimpanzee-human, 5.5 to 7.7 million years ago.

DNA-DNA hybridization can also be used with other techniques for estimating phylogenies and divergence time. For example, the extent of evolutionary divergence among North American cave cricket populations has been estimated using both DNA hybridization and isozyme analysis. In this case, the phylogenies generated from the two techniques were in general agreement.

Context

The DNA-DNA hybridization technique is attractive because it effectively compares very large numbers of sites (nucleotides) on DNA obtained from different samples. Each site is effectively a single bit of information. In contrast, phylogenies based on other molecular techniques compare much smaller amounts of data. Phylogenies based on an alternative method of determining changes in amino acid sequences in proteins utilize comparisons of approximately a thousand nucleotides between species. Another common technique, known as direct DNA sequencing, involves the comparison of approximately seventeen thousand nucleotides. In DNA-DNA hybridizations, however, millions of base pairs of nucleotides can be compared. For example, if mammal species are being compared, each set of chromosomes (one from each species) contains approximately 2 billion nucleotides. A set of chromosomes from a sample of a species is called a genome. Even if only single base pairs are considered, approximately 1.2 billion nucleotide pairs can be used in the comparison.

DNA-DNA hybridization has been used principally by evolutionary biologists to infer phylogenetic relationship in evolutionary studies. DNA-DNA hybridization is a very powerful technique for reconstructing phylogenies because divergence can be estimated using almost the entire genome. In addition, convergence, the result of both selection and chance, can lead to inaccurate phylogenies; this technique eliminates that possibility. Although convergence could occur at particular parts of the genome, those parts would still represent only a very small part of the DNA that had been hybridized. Since DNA-DNA hybridization techniques average across the total genome, these effects are nearly inconsequential.

DNA-DNA hybridization can also serve as a molecular clock, because it involves most of the homologous DNA between the two compared species. By averaging many changes that might occur throughout virtually the entire genome, a more uniform rate of change is obtained. In other molecular clocks, much smaller pieces of the genome are examined. For these smaller units, in which only a particular gene or DNA sequence is examined, it is unlikely that the "ticking" of the clock will be uniform for long periods of time, because the mutation rate for any particular gene may be slow during some periods and fast during others. The result presents the potential for highly inaccurate assumptions about the time required for various mutations to occur.

The phylogenetic tree derived from DNA-DNA comparisons gives branching order and, with proper calibration of the molecular clock, branching times. DNA-DNA hybridization permits time estimates to be made with some degree of accuracy. This had not been possible for phylogenies based on classical taxonomic techniques such as morphological changes.

Bibliography

Ayala, Francisco J. "Molecular Genetics and Evolution." In *Molecular Evolution*, edited by F. J. Ayala. Sunderland, Mass.: Sinauer Associates, 1976. A well-written, short introduction that covers the basic concepts of the structure of DNA, the genetic code, estimating genetic variation in natural populations, and phylogenetics.

_____. *Population and Evolutionary Genetics: A Primer*. Menlo Park, Calif.: Benjamin/Cummings, 1982. This book introduces the concepts and theories that account for evolutionary processes at the genetic level. It does so with brevity and clarity. Francisco Ayala not only writes clearly, he is also a prominent researcher in the field. Some of the examples are from his own work. An overview of DNA-DNA hybridization and its use in phylogenetic reconstruction is presented on pages 197-198.

Caccone, Adalgisa, and Jeffrey R. Powell. "Molecular Evolutionary Divergence Among North American Cave Cricket Populations. II. DNA-DNA Hybridization." *Evolution* 41 (1987): 1215-1238. Although this is an article from a specialized journal, it contains a step-by-step description of the techniques involved in DNA-DNA hybridization.

Dobzhansky, Theodosius, Francisco J. Ayala, G. Ledyard Stebbins, and James W. Valentine. *Evolution*. San Francisco: W. H. Freeman, 1977. Although dated, this book offers a broad perspective. The four authors are among the most prominent in the field of evolutionary studies. The text is aimed at beginning majors and is more interdisciplinary in approach than most other texts. Chapter 2 is a good treatment of the genetic structure of populations. It includes a brief overview of molecular techniques for quantifying genetic variation. More detailed treatments of isozyme electrophoresis, DNA-DNA hybridization, sequence analysis proteins, phylogenetic reconstructions, and the use of molecular-clock data are presented in chapter 9.

Hartl, Daniel L., and Andrew G. Clark. *Principles of Population Genetics*. 2d ed. Sunderland, Mass.: Sinauer Associates, 1989. An advanced text that covers the topic in detail. The book is aimed at third- and fourth-year undergraduates as well as graduate students. It includes most of the new concepts and data emerging from molecular genetics. The first chapter gives an overview of different molecular techniques that are used to address evolutionary questions. More detailed descriptions, including those concerning DNA-DNA hybridization, are covered in chapter 7.

Lewin, Roger. "DNA Reveals Surprises in Human Family Tree." *Science* 226 (December 7, 1984); 1179-1182. A short, easy-to-read article on how DNA studies have forced reexamination of primate phylogeny.

Nei, Masatoshi. *Molecular Evolutionary Genetics*. New York: Columbia University Press, 1987. An advanced text that summarizes and reviews developments in the field. The author is a prominent theorist. The book is very useful for those with a solid foundation in population genetics.

Strickberger, Monroe W. *Evolution*. Boston: Jones and Bartlett, 1989. An intermediate-level text that presents a detailed overview of evolution and evolutionary processes. Chapter 12 describes the numerous techniques that are used to reconstruct molecular phylogenies, including amino acid and nucleic acid sequence comparisons, DNA-DNA hybridizations, and molecular clocks. The numerous diagrams are especially useful.

Wilson, Allan C. "The Molecular Basis of Evolution." *Scientific American* 253 (October, 1985) 164-172. Describes the various techniques that are used to construct molecular-based phylogenies. The approach is general, and numerous diagrams illustrate the major points.

Robert A. Browne

Cross-References

DNA REPLICATION

Type of life science: Molecular biology
Other fields of study: Biochemistry, cell biology (cytology), genetics, and microbiology

*The process of DNA replication makes two new molecules of DNA using an orig-
inal molecule as a template. This process preserves the genetic information contained in the original molecule.*

Principal terms
ADENINE, CYTOSINE, GUANINE, and THYMINE: the four bases found in
DNA, which code genetic information
DENSITY GRADIENT CENTRIFUGATION: a technique for separating
molecules according to their density
EUKARYOTIC CELLS: cells of higher organisms such as plants and
animals; these cells have nuclei and other internal structures
GENE: the basic unit of inheritance; at the molecular level, a gene
consists of a segment of DNA that codes for a particular protein
HELIX: a spiral shape often likened to a spiral staircase; the DNA
molecule is normally this shape
HYDROGEN BOND: a relatively weak attraction between molecules or
parts of a molecule
MEIOSIS: a special kind of cell division in which four cells are produced
and each cell has only half the original number of chromosomes;
meiosis produces the sex cells (eggs and sperm)
NUCLEOTIDES: the subunits from which DNA is made
PROKARYOTIC CELL: a simple cell whose DNA is not contained in a
nucleus; bacterial cells are prokaryotic

Summary of the Phenomenon
The most exciting feature of the structure of the deoxyribonucleic acid (DNA)
molecule as proposed by James Watson and Francis Crick was that it suggested a
simple method of copying itself. Since DNA contains the genetic information for an
organism, it is crucial that the information in that molecule is copied exactly. Once
the structure of the molecule was known, the method of replication seemed obvious
to most biologists. Proving it, however, required some sophisticated experimentation.
The information in a DNA molecule is contained in the sequence of the pairs of
bases in the middle of the double helical structure. The bases, which can form
pairs, are determined by their shape and hydrogen bonding properties. This forms
the basis of the accuracy with which the molecule replicates. The original molecule
unwinds from its helical structure. The two strands separate and a new, complemen-

tary strand forms on each of the original strands. The order of bases on the new strand is determined by the original strand and the base pairing rules: Adenine (A) pairs with thymine (T), and guanine (G) pairs with cytosine (C). Where there is an adenine base in the old strand, there must be a thymine in the new one. None of the other three bases will fit, because they do not have the correct shape or hydrogen bonding properties. Similarly, if the old strand has a cytosine base, the new one must have a guanine. Each base is attached to a deoxyribose sugar and a phosphate group, forming a nucleotide. Once these nucleotides are linked together, the new strand is complete, and there are now two molecules where there was one. This method of replication has been called "semiconservative," indicating that one-half of each new DNA molecule is a completely conserved strand from the original molecule.

In principle, the replication of DNA is easy. In practice, the cell requires a large number of enzymes and other proteins in order to accomplish it. The process is somewhat more involved in eukaryotic cells, since their DNA is surrounded by protein molecules. Bacteria and other prokaryotic cells have "naked" DNA, and much less of it. In a bacterial cell, DNA replication starts at only one point on the chromosome and proceeds in both directions from that point. In higher forms of life, replication begins at many points on a chromosome and proceeds in both directions from each point. This way the massive amount of DNA in a cell of a human being can be copied in a reasonable amount of time.

Other than the amount of DNA and the protein coat, the process is the same in prokaryotic and eukaryotic cells. Enzymes called helicases unwind the DNA molecule. Single-strand binding proteins attach to the separate strands and help keep them apart. An analogy is the unwound strands of a rope or piece of string: the strands tend to loop and kink into a tangled mess. Additional enzymes prevent this from happening to the DNA strands. They can temporarily break a strand and allow it to spin around and untangle itself. Once the strands are separated, the new strand cannot simply begin to form. Nucleotides must be attached to an existing strand to start the process. This existing strand is a short piece (about five nucleotides) of ribonucleic acid (RNA), which is chemically similar to DNA but normally occurs as single strands.

Another complication arises because the two strands of the DNA molecule have a directionality. If one imagines each strand as an arrow, then the double-stranded molecule would have the two arrows pointing in opposite directions. The reason for the problem is that the enzyme which hooks nucleotides together can operate in only one direction. Then how are both new strands synthesized at the same time? The enzyme works fine for synthesizing one new strand. The nucleotides of the new strand line up using the old strand for a template. The base-pairing rules ensure that the order is correct. Then the DNA polymerase can simply proceed along the new strand, connecting the nucleotides together. The same enzyme works on the other strand as well; however, since it must work in the direction opposite to the way the molecule is replicating, it can make only short segments of a new strand. Each of these segments is then linked together to make a complete molecule by another enzyme, DNA ligase. The segments are from one thousand to two thousand nucleotides long in bacteria but only one hundred to three hundred nucleotides long in eukaryotes.

The accuracy of copying the DNA template is impressive. Replication of DNA is a chemical process, and chemical processes rely on random movements of molecules to put the correct ones together for a reaction to take place. There are enzymatic systems to make sure that only the correct nucleotides become part of the new DNA strand. Chance determines which nucleotide will move into the growing point of the new molecule. DNA polymerase, however, is much more likely to connect it to the chain if its shape is a good fit. It has been estimated that one nucleotide in 100,000 added to the chain is incorrect. If this happens, DNA polymerase is significantly inhibited in its actions. In fact, its takes so long to add the next nucleotide under these circumstances that the polymerase is likely to disconnect the previous, wrong one first. That is not as surprising as it may seem. Most enzymes are capable of catalyzing their specific reaction in both directions. Which way the reaction goes usually depends on whether the raw materials or products have more energy. DNA polymerase, then, can add new nucleotides to the growing strand and can also recognize an incorrect nucleotide. In this sense, it operates like a correcting typewriter and removes the wrong letter so that the correct one can be inserted.

Even DNA polymerase is not perfect. It has been estimated that it makes a mistake in one in ten million nucleotides. As good as that may seem, it is not good enough. The human genetic information is coded in about three billion nucleotides. A further error-coding mechanism cuts the chance of a mistake down to one in ten billion nucleotides.

Detecting a mistake is relatively easy. The double helix will have a wrinkle where there is a mismatched pair of nucleotides. The wrinkle exists because the pair of bases do not match in size. Correcting the error is more difficult to explain, since the mechanism has to make sure that it corrects the proper strand. Is there some difference between the original DNA strand and the newly created one? It appears that, in some bacteria at least, there is. In these bacteria, a small group of atoms (a methyl group) is added to some adenine bases. The ones modified are those that are found in the sequence GATC (guanine-adenine-thymine-cytosine). Since it takes some time to make this change, an error-correcting mechanism could tell which was the old strand by the presence of methyl groups. The current model suggests that enzymes then chop out a section of the new strand, including the mismatched nucleotide. DNA polymerase then replaces the missing section with the correct sequence of nucleotides. There is ample evidence of error-correcting mechanisms in organisms which do not add methyl groups to their DNA. Exactly how the mechanism distinguishes between old DNA and new DNA is not clear.

Mistakes in copying DNA are not all bad. If DNA were copied exactly every time, then the information would never change. Changes in DNA are mutations.

Although mutations are normally thought to be harmful, a few can be beneficial. Mutations giving rise to new characteristics that are beneficial to an organism may, through the process of natural selection, enhance a species' ability to survive.

Methods of Study

The method of replication of DNA was suggested by the architecture of the molecule itself. The experiments that confirmed it were an elegant example of science at its best. Matthew Meselson and Franklin W. Stahl attacked the problem in the late 1950's. Before they could prove that DNA replication was semiconservative, they had to devise a way of differentiating the old and new strands. Their method was simple in principle and elegant in execution.

Working with bacteria, Meselson and Stahl cultured their organisms in a medium containing a heavy isotope of nitrogen, nitrogen 15. Chemically, heavy nitrogen behaves exactly as the more usual lighter isotope, nitrogen 14. After careful extraction from the bacteria, DNA containing the heavy or light isotope of nitrogen could be distinguished by density gradient centrifugation. In this technique, a solution of the salt cesium chloride is spun in a centrifuge at a very high speed for several days. The large cesium ions are dragged to the bottom of the tube by centrifugal force, in the same way that water is dragged out of clothes in the spin cycle of a washer. The solution eventually acquires a density gradient, being denser near the bottom of the tube. When DNA is placed in the tube and centrifuged again, the DNA is dragged down the tube until it reaches solution of its own density. DNA with heavy nitrogen is denser and so goes farther down the tube than DNA with the lighter isotope.

A sample of bacteria was transferred to a normal culture medium, containing the normal (lighter) isotope of nitrogen. The bacteria were given enough time to reproduce once. Their DNA was quickly extracted and centrifuged in a cesium chloride gradient. As expected, the DNA formed a band about halfway between that containing nitrogen 15 and that containing nitrogen 14. The only logical explanation is that this DNA consists of one old strand (with nitrogen 15) and one new strand (with the lighter isotope). When the bacteria was cultured in the normal medium for two generations, two bands of DNA were found. One band was at the halfway mark, as before. This band consisted of one original heavy strand and one brand-new light one. The other band was nearer the top of the tube. It consisted of a first-generation light strand and its brand-new complementary, light strand.

Investigating the proofreading and error-correcting mechanism is proving more challenging. In the simpler prokaryotic systems, bacterial strains with higher-than-normal mutation rates have proved useful. It is believed that the mutation rates are high because these strains lack one or more of the error-correcting mechanisms. Eukaryotic organisms frequently have multiple copies of their genetic information in each cell. This makes investigation much more complicated; most of the mechanisms suggested for higher organisms are in the realm of educated speculation. This is one of the many challenges remaining in the area of molecular biology.

Context

Since the DNA molecule contains the genetic information for an organism, it must be copied frequently. Multicellular organisms such as animals and plants start life as a single cell. In order to grow, that cell has to divide many millions of times. Each descendant of the original cell, with a few exceptions, must have its own copy of the genetic information. Therefore, the DNA has to be copied many millions of times. Even after adulthood is reached, a considerable amount of cell division is required for maintenance and repair. Before a cell can divide, its DNA has to replicate. If the replication were not extremely accurate, the human body might have cells containing different genetic information, resulting in chaos.

When it comes time for the adult to reproduce, the DNA has to be copied again. A special type of cell division, meiosis, produces the eggs and sperm which will unite to form the single cell of the next generation. Each of the sex cells contributes half of the genetic information of the next generation. The DNA of a sex cell must be a faithful copy of the parent's DNA in order to pass along its genetic qualities.

The only reason an organism might have for producing DNA containing different information would be to produce new experimental information. When this happens, it is referred to as mutation. Most mutations result in individuals that are inferior to previous generations. A prime example would be sickle-cell anemia. A change of one nucleotide in the DNA that codes for one protein is disastrous. The protein is hemoglobin, which carries oxygen in the red blood cells. The sickle-cell form of the molecule does not dissolve properly. As a result, the hemoglobin clumps to one side of the red blood cell and does not carry oxygen. An individual with only this form of hemoglobin cannot survive. However, since an individual receives one complete copy of all his genetic information from each parent, he will usually have a "good" copy of the hemoglobin gene as well. The individual can make enough normal hemoglobin to survive under most conditions. The frequency of mistakes in copying DNA, although very low, is still high enough to produce the mutations that add variety to the genetic information. Some mutations will confer an advantage on the individual that has it. In the natural world, an individual with an advantage will be able to live longer and produce more young. Thus, the "better" genetic information will increase in frequency in the population, resulting in adaptive evolution.

Bibliography

Camp, Pamela S., and Karen Arms. *Exploring Biology*. 2d ed. Philadelphia: W. B. Saunders, 1984. A lighter introductory biology text. Chapter 14, "DNA," describes the evidence that DNA is the genetic material as well as its quantity in various types of organisms. Replication is concisely described. The pronunciation guide in the margin is a unique feature.

Campbell, Neil. *Biology*. Menlo Park, Calif.: Benjamin/Cummings, 1987. A thorough and complete introductory biology text. Chapter 15, "The Molecular Basis of Inheritance," provides a detailed but readable account of the structure of the molecule and its method of replication. While aimed at college students, the text is readable, and many diagrams stand by themselves.

Kornberg, Arthur. "The Synthesis of DNA." In *The Chemical Basis of Life: An Introduction to Molecular and Cell Biology*, edited by P. C. Hanawalt and R. H. Haynes. San Francisco: W. H. Freeman, 1973. Kornberg's article "The Synthesis of DNA," which appeared originally in *Scientific American*, is one of many dealing with the biology of the most important molecule in living systems. Like most *Scientific American* articles, it is clearly written and profusely illustrated.

Meselson, Matthew, and Franklin W. Stahl. "The Replication of DNA in *Escherichia coli*." *Proceedings of the National Academy of Sciences* 44 (1958): 671. A more technical description of a classic experiment in molecular biology. It describes the proof of the semiconservative method of replication.

Radman, Mirislav, and Robert Wagner. "The High Fidelity of DNA Duplication." *Scientific American* 259 (August, 1988): 40-46. Provides a readable account of the proofreading and error-correcting mechanisms that make the process as accurate as it is. The authors are careful to point out what is known and what is speculation. The bibliography refers to more technical articles on the subject.

Watson, James D. *The Double Helix*. New York: Atheneum, 1968. While this book only briefly suggests the method of replication, it is a lively and readable account of the persons and personalities involved in discovering the structure of the molecule. Written from the viewpoint of one of the discoverers, it provides an insight into how science sometimes works.

_____. *Molecular Biology of the Gene*. 3d ed. Menlo Park, Calif.: W. A. Benjamin, 1976. This volume could be considered the definitive text on molecular biology, written by one of the discoverers of the structure of DNA. Chapter 9, "The Replication of DNA," covers the subject thoroughly, discussing the enzymes involved.

James Waddell

Cross-References

Chromosomes, 462; DNA Sequencing, 698; DNA's Molecular Structure, 706; Eukaryotic Gene Organization, 871; Evolution: A Historical Perspective, 903; Gene Mutation and Repair, 1103; Genes and Nucleic Acids, 1134; Mitosis and Meiosis, 1753; Neutral Mutations and Evolutionary Clocks, 1944; Nuclear Structure, 1972; Nucleic Acid Structure, 1987.

DNA SEQUENCING

Type of life science: Molecular biology
Other fields of study: Biochemistry and genetics

DNA sequencing is an experimental technique by which the nucleotide order (guanine, thymine . . .) of a gene is determined. DNA sequencing techniques have contributed much to the understanding of gene structure and organization and in locating regulatory and control regions on the genes.

Principal terms

DIDEOXYNUCLEOTIDE: a type of nucleotide, 2', 3'-dideoxynucleotide triphosphate, that prematurely inhibits further growth of a DNA polynucleotide chain when it is incorporated into that chain

DIMETHYL SULFATE: a chemical that methylates (adds a methyl group—CH_3) to adenine and guanine nucleotides in DNA

ELECTROPHORESIS: a technique that separates molecules in an electric field; the electrophoresis of DNA by subjecting it to negative and positive electrodes separates each molecule on the basis of size, shape, and electrical charge

HYDRAZINE: a chemical that reacts with and modifies cytosine and thymine nucleotides in DNA

NUCLEOTIDE: the basic chemical unit of DNA, repeated over and over, that consists of a deoxyribose sugar, a phosphate, and a nitrogenous base consisting of adenine, guanine, cytosine, or thymine

PIPERIDINE: a chemical that breaks DNA nucleotide chains at the points of cytosine and thymine nucleotides

POLYACRYLAMIDE: a type of gel used in DNA sequencing electrophoresis; prolonged exposure to skin or ingestion/inhalation can be toxic to nerve cells

PURINE: a type of DNA nitrogenous base consisting of a five-atom carbon-nitrogen ring structure and a six-atom carbon-nitrogen ring; adenine and guanine are examples

PYRIMIDINE: a type of DNA nitrogenous base consisting of a single six-atom carbon-nitrogen ring structure, such as cytosine and thymine

RADIOACTIVE ISOTOPE: an unstable atom, having extra or fewer neutrons, that tends to disintegrate into more stable atoms while emitting radioactive particles

Summary of the Methodology

DNA sequencing is a valuable tool for determining the nucleotide sequence of deoxyribonucleic acid (DNA). Two principal techniques exist: dideoxy chain-terminating nucleotide sequencing, developed by Frederick Sanger, who won the Nobel Prize in Chemistry in both 1958 and 1980, and diagnostic chemical DNA sequencing, developed by Allan M. Maxam and Walter Gilbert. Gilbert shared the 1980 Nobel Prize in Chemistry with Sanger. The two techniques are very similar in overall format, such as the use of radioactive isotope DNA labels and electrophoresis of the DNA through polyacrylamide gels. The major difference between the two techniques lies in how the DNA is chemically treated in order to break the DNA polynucleotide chain.

DNA consists of two parallel polynucleotide chains, each polynucleotide consisting of tens of thousands of nucleotides. Each nucleotide is composed of a sugar (that is, deoxyribose), a phosphate, and one of four nitrogenous bases: adenine (A), guanine (G), cytosine (C), or thymine (T). An adenine nucleotide on one polynucleotide chain always pairs with a thymine nucleotide on its companion polynucleotide chain; a cytosine nucleotide on one chain always pairs with a guanine nucleotide on its companion chain. The order of nitrogenous bases from nucleotide to nucleotide (ACTCCGATGC . . .) on a single polynucleotide chain serves as the genetic code. A typical gene (DNA molecule) is approximately one thousand nucleotides long. During ribonucleic (RNA) transcription, an enzyme called RNA polymerase reads the DNA nucleotide sequence to manufacture a complementary messenger RNA nucleotide sequence. During protein translation, a multienzyme ribosome reads the RNA nucleotide sequence to manufacture an appropriate protein, a long chain of amino acids. A specific DNA nucleotide sequence (a gene) encodes a specific messenger RNA nucleotide sequence, which encodes a specific protein.

The Sanger dideoxy sequencing technique uses altered DNA nucleotides, dideoxynucleotides, to stop the growth of DNA polynucleotide chains during DNA replication, a process by which the enzyme DNA polymerase manufactures a new DNA copy. Normally, DNA contains deoxynucleotides, nucleotides containing the sugar deoxyribose (that is, one deoxygenated carbon). Dideoxynucleotides contain dideoxyribose, a sugar containing two deoxygenated carbons. The deoxygenation of a second carbon on a dideoxynucleotide terminates further growth of a DNA chain in which that dideoxynucleotide is located because there will be no attachment for the phosphate of the next nucleotide.

In the Sanger dideoxy sequencing experiment, a single DNA polynucleotide chain of the gene to be sequenced is used as a template, or mold, for constructing complementary DNA polynucleotide chains. Many copies of this single-chain nucleotide template are placed in the test tube, along with the enzyme DNA polymerase and deoxyadenosine triphosphate (dATP) that has been labeled with radioactive isotope phosphorus 32; also included are deoxyguanosine triphosphate (dGTP), deoxycytosine triphosphate (dCTP), and deoxythymosine triphosphate (dTTP). With this mixture, complete complementary DNA polynucleotide chains can be produced:

> DNA template: TCGCCAGCTTTGAC . . .
> Complement 1: AGCGGTCGAAACTG . . .
> Complement 2: AGCGGTCGAAACTG . . .
>   etc.

Additional incorporation of the dideoxynucleotides dideoxyadenosine triphosphate (ddATP) dideoxyguanosine triphosphate (ddGTP), dideoxycytosine triphosphate (ddCTP), and dideoxythymosine triphosphate (ddTTP) results in premature termination of DNA chains at random sites wherever adenine, guanine, cytosine, and thymine occur. For example, given the sample DNA template and the incorporation of ddGTP into complementary DNA molecules, the following interrupted DNA chains would result:

> DNA template: TCGCCAGCTTTGAC . . .
> Complement 1: AGCGGTCGAAACTG . . .
> Complement 2: AGCGGTCGAAACTddG . . .
> Complement 3: AGCGGTCddG . . .
> Complement 4: AGCGddG . . .
> Complement 5: AGCddG . . .
> Complement 6: AddG . . .

For each experiment, an array of incomplete DNA chains is generated. The chains vary in length because of the location of the particular dideoxynucleotide which terminates the sequence when it is incorporated into the molecule. Knowing which dideoxynucleotide is incorporated, the experimenter can obtain an estimate of where this particular nucleotide is located in the total DNA sequence.

To obtain the exact DNA nucleotide sequence, the variable-length chains from each of the four dideoxy reactions (the ddATP reaction, ddGTP reaction, ddCTP reaction, and the ddTTP reaction) are separated based upon size in an electric field on a polyacrylamide gel, a process called polyacrylamide gel electrophoresis. Once electrophoresis is completed, the radioactive DNA chains are imprinted onto nitrocellulose paper, a process called Southern blotting. The radioactive DNA chains are revealed by autoradiography, a technique by which the nitrocellulose paper is exposed to X-ray film.

The Maxam and Gilbert sequencing technique involves taking a phosphorus-32 radioactive isotope-labeled DNA polynucleotide chain, chemically breaking the chain at specific nucleotides (adenine, guanine, cytosine, thymine), electrophoresing the variable-length DNA fragments on polyacrylamide gels, Southern blotting the gels, autoradiographing the DNA fragments from the Southern blot, and interpreting the banding pattern to sequence the gene. This technique, derived independently of Sanger's work, is almost identical. The only difference is that existing DNA chains are chemically modified and broken.

Among nucleotide nitrogenous bases, adenine and guanine belong to a class called "purines," whereas thymine and cytosine are "pyrimidines." When dimethyl sulfate is added to a DNA polynucleotide chain, methyl groups ($—CH_3$) attach to adenines and guanines, making these purines unstable; subsequent heating breaks the DNA chains precisely at adenines and guanines. The experimenter therefore knows that these DNA fragments end with adenine or guanine. To be more specific, a second set of reactions can be performed, where the same ingredients and conditions (dimethyl sulfate and heat) are supplemented by dilute acid and alkali treatment. This second approach preferentially breaks DNA at adenines instead of guanines.

For pyrimidines, a third series of reactions breaks the DNA polynucleotide chain at cytosines and thymines. The chemical hydrazine modifies cytosine and thymine nucleotides, making them unstable. Subsequent treatment with the chemical piperidine breaks the DNA chain at cytosine and thymine nucleotides. To be more specific, a fourth series of reactions includes hydrazine, piperidine, and sodium chloride; this reaction preferentially breaks DNA at cytosine nucleotides instead of thymines.

Once these four reactions are performed, the DNA fragments from each reaction set are separated by size in a polyacrylamide electrophoretic gel, which is then Southern blotted and autoradiographed. Fragments are ranked according to size. The end nucleotide of each fragment is identified by the size ordering of fragments in each reaction column. Judging the reaction classes is slightly more complicated than in the Sanger method, because adenines and cytosines must each be read from two different reaction columns.

Applications of the Method

The Sanger and Maxam and Gilbert DNA sequencing methods are cornerstone experiments of molecular biology, genetics, and biotechnology. The study of any gene system is incomplete without DNA sequencing, which has been used to determine the nucleotide sequences of many genes; identify the control regions of genes; study mutations and their effects upon genes; and compare the genes from different species for evolutionary studies. DNA sequencing is indispensable to molecular biology.

The DNA polynucleotide sequences of many genes have been identified since the development of the DNA sequencing techniques in 1977. Among the major sequenced genes from various species are human and other mammalian hemoglobin genes, cytochrome genes, transfer RNA genes, immunoglobulin genes, ribosomal RNA genes, oncogenes (that is, cancer-stimulating genes), and entire viral genomes (such as bacteriophage MS2).

DNA sequencing enables molecular biologists to understand all aspects of gene organization. Coding regions of a gene can be identified as can those nucleotide sequences (exons) that encode messenger RNA for encoding protein. Noncoding regions, which are removed from messenger RNA before protein translation, are called introns. Sequencing studies of DNA and RNA from each gene have enabled biologists to identify coding and noncoding regions. Some noncoding introns can serve as exons, and some genes can produce more than one protein type by rearranging the coding-noncoding status of introns and exons.

Preceding each gene, DNA nucleotide sequences have been identified that control the gene's ability to encode messenger RNA; messenger RNA, in turn, encodes the order of amino acids in protein synthesis. Control regions prior to the gene coding region are access points for the enzyme RNA polymerase. RNA polymerase recognizes specific nucleotide control regions and aligns itself with the DNA so that it can move down the DNA polynucleotide, read the coding region, and manufacture a messenger RNA molecule for subsequent protein translation. Stimulatory hormones are chemicals, either protein or steroid in content, that interact with the precoding nucleotide control regions, modifying these nucleotides so that RNA polymerase can gain access to a gene's coding region, allowing the gene to be turned on; messenger RNA and protein can then be manufactured. Inhibitory hormones block the control nucleotides so that RNA polymerase cannot gain access to the gene coding region; the gene is then turned off and no protein is made.

The DNA control nucleotides are conserved, or remain the same, from species to species. Consequently, they are referred to as consensus sequences. Much work is directed toward how RNA polymerase and hormones interact with the control consensus sequence nucleotides. These studies include X-ray crystallography to study the three-dimensional structure of DNA control regions, antibody binding to DNA nucleotides and other control molecules, and chemical binding of control molecules to DNA nucleotides. In addition to control molecules, structural molecules such as histone proteins interact directly with DNA nucleotides in a specific, but as yet undetermined way.

Numerous DNA nucleotides, specifically highly repetitive and moderately repetitive DNA, are short nucleotide stretches repeated over and over again in the DNA of eukaryotic chromosomes. Some of these DNA stretches are repeated tens upon thousands of times. They may provide structural or regulatory roles, or both, in eukaryotic chromosomes.

When genes are mutated, there are slight alterations in the nucleotides of the gene. These changes in the DNA, caused by ionizing radiation or mutagenic chemicals, are reflected in the corresponding messenger RNA nucleotides and protein amino acid sequences. DNA sequencing plays an important role in identifying the exact locations and possible causes of the mutation in a given gene. For example, sickle-cell anemia and related blood disorders known as "thallasemias" are caused by changes in a single nucleotide in the human beta hemoglobin gene. These changes give rise to a single amino acid change in the beta hemoglobin protein, a protein having more than 250 amino acids. A single nucleotide change can nevertheless make the difference between life and death. DNA sequencing may be useful in helping to treat mutations and genetic disease in the future.

The determination of DNA sequencing for every human gene on every human chromosome is a major objective of the Human Genome Project, an endeavor being pursued by the National Institutes of Health in the United States, as well as by other countries, such as the Soviet Union, Japan, and some countries of Western Europe. The project, which could cost up to one trillion U.S. dollars, is expected to expand scientific knowledge of human genes, where they are located, what they encode, and how they are controlled in coordination with one another. The treatment of genetic disease, cancer, and aging-related processes will be major beneficiaries of this program, which will utilize both the Sanger and the Maxam and Gilbert DNA nucleotide sequencing methods.

Finally, comparative nucleotide sequencing of DNA molecules from different species is a useful tool for constructing possible evolutionary phylogenies. If genes encoding similar proteins are compared between species, closely related species such as humans and chimpanzees should have very few differences between their respective DNA nucleotide sequences. More distantly related species (humans and sponges, for example) should have more differences between their respective nucleotide sequences for genes that they share. The increased nucleotide differences in these genes are the result of the accumulated mutations that have occurred during the evolution of different species.

> Species A: AGC CCC TGG AGG GTC CAG . . . } Close
> Species B: AGC CCC TAG AGG GTC CAG . . . }
> Species C: ATA CCA TCG AGG GAC CAG . . . } Distant

DNA sequence comparisons of various subcellular components taken from different species, such as mammalian hemoglobins, is of tremendous value in understanding evolution as well as the function of various gene products in these species.

Context

DNA sequencing techniques provide biotechnologists with a powerful tool for understanding gene structure, organization, control, and function. A gene is a long chain of approximately one thousand DNA nucleotide pairs. The information content of the DNA four nucleotides (adenine, guanine, cytosine, and thymine) is used to encode messenger RNA during RNA transcription. Subsequently, the complementary nucleotide sequence of the messenger RNA is used to encode a long chain of amino acids during protein translation. DNA therefore encodes RNA, which encodes protein. In the cells of all living organisms, DNA is the information storage molecule, while protein is a catalyst.

Within a gene's internal structure, there are different nucleotide regions encompassing a number of functions. Some DNA nucleotides serve as control regions where hormones, RNA polymerase, and other regulatory molecules operate. Other DNA nucleotides are coding regions, such as exons for the amino acids of proteins. Still other DNA nucleotides are noncoding regions, such as introns, whose functions are uncertain.

DNA sequencing has also been useful in deciphering gene mutations and has been a powerful tool in evolutionary studies. Gene mutations are changes in the nucleotide sequence of a gene's DNA caused by ionizing radiation or chemicals or both. Gene mutations are responsible for a variety of human genetic disorders, including hemophilia, cystic fibrosis, Tay-Sachs disease, sickle-cell anemia, and various cancers. Scientists' understanding of the DNA sequence changes in these disorders may one day be useful for diagnoses and treatment of genetic diseases. Also, mutations are stimuli for evolutionary change. DNA sequencing allows for comparisons of nucleotide sequences for genes from various species; closely related species have few nucleotide differences, whereas distantly related species have many differences.

The simultaneous developments of methods of determining DNA nucleotide sequencing by Frederick Sanger, Allan N. Maxam, and Walter Gilbert in 1977 reflected the need at the time for a methodology which delved into the basic structure of genes. DNA sequencing is indispensable to molecular biology; it is intricately involved in gene cloning. Once a gene has been cloned, the next step is always the determination of its nucleotide sequence.

Both the Sanger and the Maxam and Gilbert techniques use many of the same experimental protocols, such as polyacrylamide gel electrophoresis, Southern blotting, and autoradiography. The primary difference between the two techniques is the chemical treatment of the DNA. Neither method has a distinct advantage over the other. Various biochemical laboratories use one or the other or both in their studies of gene structure and organization. The Sanger and Maxam and Gilbert DNA nucleotide sequencing techniques have had a major impact on molecular biology.

Bibliography

Alberts, Bruce, Dennis Bray, Julian Lewis, Martin Raff, Keith Roberts, and James D. Watson. *Molecular Biology of the Cell*. 2d ed. New York: Garland, 1989. This work is an excellent intermediate-level undergraduate textbook in cell biology and developmental genetics, written by major authorities in these fields. The book is clearly written and includes many good photographs and diagrams. Chapter 4, "How Cells Are Studied," provides a good discussion of DNA nucleotide sequencing techniques.

Felsenfeld, Gary. "DNA." *Scientific American* 253 (October, 1985): 58-67. As part of a special *Scientific American* issue, "The Molecules of Life," this article describes clearly the structure of DNA, how it is organized into genes, and how DNA folds up to form a chromosome. The article includes excellent diagrams, relevant experiments, and a summary of gene regulation mechanisms.

Gardner, E. J., and D. P. Snustad. *Principals of Genetics*. 7th ed. New York: John Wiley & Sons, 1984. Gardner and Snustad's book is an excellent beginning textbook in genetics for undergraduate biology majors. It is well illustrated and provides in-depth coverage of the subject. Chapter 10, "Genetic Fine Structure," describes DNA and the nucleotide sequencing techniques.

Goodenough, Ursula. *Genetics*. 2d ed. New York: Holt, Rinehart and Winston, 1978. This is a fine genetics textbook for undergraduate biology majors. It is clear, contains good diagrams, and includes extensive reference lists at the end of each chapter. Chapter 7, "Molecular Biology of Chromosomes," discusses Maxam and Gilbert's DNA sequencing method.

Lewin, Benjamin. *Genes II*. New York: John Wiley & Sons, 1985. As a sequel to

Genes, this advanced textbook is a readable, comprehensive summary of current advances in molecular biology. The text includes many chapters covering gene organization and regulation. Chapter 5, "Isolating the Gene," describes nucleotide sequencing.

Maniatis, T., E. F. Fritsch, and J. Sambrook. *Molecular Cloning: A Laboratory Manual*. Cold Spring Harbor, N.Y.: Cold Spring Harbor Laboratory, 1982. This information-packed laboratory manual is a must for molecular biology and biotechnology laboratories. It includes protocols and material needs for numerous experiments aimed at studying DNA, RNA, and protein. Chapter 5, "Electrophoresis," and appendix A include important information on Maxam and Gilbert's nucleotide sequencing.

Stryer, Lubert. *Biochemistry*. 2d ed. San Francisco: W. H. Freeman, 1981. Stryer's classic work is an outstanding textbook for advanced undergraduate students in biology, biochemistry, and physiology. The book is clearly written, and much of it is understandable to the generalist. It is very well illustrated. Chapter 24, "DNA," discusses Sanger's dideoxynucleotide sequencing technique.

Wallace, Robert A., Jack L. King, and Gerald P. Sanders. *Biosphere: The Realm of Life*. 2d ed. Glenview, Ill.: Scott, Foresman, 1988. This is an excellent introductory biology textbook for both science and nonscience majors. It is written clearly and intended for the general reader. Chapter 16, "Frontiers in Molecular Biology," provides an excellent discussion of the two nucleotide sequencing methods.

Zubay, Geoffrey. *Biochemistry*. Reading, Mass.: Addison-Wesley, 1983. A graduate biochemistry textbook, this work is very detailed. The illustrations and data tables are excellent. Chapter 20, "DNA Metabolism," is a comprehensive discussion of gene structure, organization, and biochemistry. DNA nucleotide sequencing techniques are described.

David Wason Hollar, Jr.

Cross-References

DNA Replication, 692; DNA's Molecular Structure, 706; Genes and Nucleic Acids, 1134; Genes and Polypeptide Chains, 1141; The Genetic Code, 1148; Deciphering the Genetic Code, 1155; Transcription of DNA to Form RNA, 2632.

DNA'S MOLECULAR STRUCTURE

Types of life science: Biochemistry and molecular biology
Other field of study: Genetics

The discovery that the three-dimensional structure of deoxyribonucleic acid (DNA) consists of two long strands of nucleotides twisted, in ropelike fashion, into a double helix has been of pivotal significance in elucidating the replication of genes and in initiating an explosion of knowledge in molecular biology.

Principal terms

DEOXYRIBOSE: DNA's sugar component, made up of five carbon atoms, four of which are combined with one oxygen atom in a ring; the second carbon lacks the hydroxyl (hydrogen-oxygen) group present in ribose

NUCLEOTIDE: the basic building block of the nucleic acids, consisting of three essential parts: a nitrogen-containing purine or pyrimidine derivative, called a base; a five-carbon sugar (either ribose or deoxyribose); and a phosphoric-acid group

PHOSPHODIESTER BOND: a phosphate group which joins the third carbon on one sugar to the fifth carbon of the adjacent sugar

PHOSPHORIC ACID: a weak acid whose principal structural feature is a central phosphorous atom surrounded by four oxygen atoms; it bridges, by means of phosphodiester bonds, adjacent nucleotides in DNA and RNA

POLYNUCLEOTIDE: a very long chain of many nucleotides linked together by phosphodiester bonds that give the polymer a polarity or directionality

PURINE: an organic base formed from fused five- and six-membered heterocyclic rings (ring compounds containing nitrogen as well as carbon atoms); adenine and guanine are purine bases found in DNA and RNA

PYRIMIDINE: an organic base formed on a single heterocyclic ring; DNA contains the pyrimidines cytosine and thymine, whereas in RNA, the pyrimidine uracil replaces thymine

RIBONUCLEIC ACID (RNA): a polynucleotide composed of ribose (sugar) and phosphate groups, along with the purines adenine and guanine and the pyrimidines cytosine and uracil

RIBOSE: RNA's five-carbon sugar, containing four hydroxyl groups, three of which are attached to the heterocyclic ring of one oxygen and four carbon atoms

Summary of the Phenomenon

Deoxyribonucleic acid (DNA), a molecule at the core of life itself, has existed in the universe for at least a few billion years, but it was not until 1869 that Friedrich Miescher, a Swiss biochemist, was able to isolate it, though in a highly impure form. He discovered this material in Tübingen, where he had gone, as a young postdoctoral student, to do research on the chemistry of white blood cells. Through a series of chemical operations performed on pus cells, with their particularly large nuclei, he isolated a previously unobserved gelatinous substance. Further analysis revealed that the new material contained phosphorus and nitrogen; Miescher named it "nuclein," because of its origin in cell nuclei. He recognized that the new substance's acidity was attributable to phosphoric acid.

During the last two decades of the nineteenth century, Albrecht Kossel, a German physiological chemist, discovered that nuclein contained purines, nitrogenous compounds with two rings, and pyrimidines, nitrogenous compounds with single rings. Furthermore, he showed that these nucleic acids were made of two different purines, adenine and guanine (A and G), and two different pyrimidines, thymine and cytosine (T and C). He also found a sugar among nucleic acid's decomposition products, but he was unable to identify it. Indeed, because nucleic acids were difficult to analyze, it was not until the first decade of the twentieth century that scientists realized that there are two types of nucleic acid: the thymus type, which is now known to be rich in DNA, and the yeast type, which is rich in ribonucleic acid (RNA).

Phoebus Levene, a Russian-American chemist who studied for a time with Kossel, was able to identify the sugar in yeast nucleic acid as ribose in 1908, but he did not definitively identify deoxyribose in thymus nucleic acid until 1929. He established that thymus nucleic acid contains the bases adenine, guanine, cytosine, and thymine and that yeast nucleic acid contains the bases adenine, guanine, cytosine, and uracil. He also isolated, from various nucleic acids, sugar-base fragments (called nucleosides) and base-sugar-phosphate groups (called nucleotides). In the 1920's, he developed a theory that nucleic acids are linear chains of purines and pyrimidines joined to one another by means of the sugar-phosphate group. He took the simplest route and proposed that nucleic acids are composed of repeated sets of four nucleotides (the tetranucleotide hypothesis). Since this monotonous sequence could convey little information, most scientists believed that proteins, with their more than twenty amino acid building blocks, were more likely than nucleic acids to be the purveyors of the cell's genetic messages.

By World War II, scientists knew that DNA was an extremely long molecule, but most continued to believe that proteins were the sole carriers of genetic information and that nucleic acids played, at the most, a facilitating role. That DNA was the true source of genetic information was shown by Oswald T. Avery and his coworkers at the Rockefeller Institute for Medical Research. In a laboratory near Levene's, they discovered that protein-free DNA carried genetic information from a nonvirulent form of *Pneumococcus* bacterial cells to a virulent form. Avery stated that his work meant that DNA is not merely structurally important but is a functionally active substance in determining a cell's specific characteristics and biochemical activity.

His discovery, which was published in a 1944 paper, greatly surprised those geneticists and biochemists who had long believed that genes, in order to perform their complex tasks, had to be made of proteins. As a matter of fact, many of them continued to believe that protein contaminants in Avery's experiments must be the transforming agents, not the DNA itself. Avery's work endured, however, and the realization that DNA is the genetic molecule focused attention on its structure.

Only by understanding how covalent bonds link together the atoms of DNA and then by establishing their three-dimensional arrangement in space could scientists learn how this molecule carries genetic information. The British organic chemist Alexander Todd decided to clarify the chemical bonding of the nucleic acids by starting with the simplest units, the nucleosides. By the early 1950's, he was able to show that the nucleic acids are linear, rather than branched, polymers and to specify exactly how the sugar ring (ribose or deoxyribose) is bonded to the various bases and to the phosphate group.

During the 1940's, while Todd was working out the detailed bonding of the nucleic acids, Erwin Chargaff, a biochemist at the College of Physicians and Surgeons in New York, was exploring the chemical differences in the base compositions of DNAs from different sources. By 1950, his careful analyses of the base compositions of DNA samples from many plants and animals had revealed that the compositions varied widely, but his data also yielded the significant result that the ratios of adenine to thymine, and guanine to cytosine, were always close to one. Chargaff's work disproved the theory that DNA was made of repeating tetranucleotide units, but he did not attach any meaning to the one-to-one base ratios (now known as Chargaff's ratios), since, along with other scientists, he continued to think of DNA as a single polynucleotide chain.

Linus Pauling, along with many other American chemists, was slow to accept DNA as the genetic material. Since the 1930's, Pauling had done important work on hemoglobin and the structure of proteins. In 1948, he discovered the structure of the protein alpha keratin by using only a pen, a ruler, and a piece of paper: The alpha helix held together in its twisting turns by hydrogen bonds (in which a hydrogen atom served as a bridge between neighboring atoms).

In the early 1950's, James Watson and Francis Crick, both of whom had become interested in DNA, were deeply impressed by Pauling's work, not so much because of the helical structure he had discovered ("helices were in the air," according to Crick), but because Pauling had the correct approach to biological problems, since he believed that the chemists' knowledge of atomic sizes, bond distances, and bond angles would allow biologists to build accurate models of the three-dimensional structures of the complex molecules in living things. Crick, then in his mid-thirties, was a physicist working on the theory of the X-ray diffraction of proteins. Watson, in his early twenties, was a biologist, whose interest in genes had led him to the Cavendish Laboratory of Cambridge University. At first glance, Watson and Crick made an odd team: Crick had expertise in crystallography and Watson in genetics, but neither had much knowledge of chemistry. Nevertheless, they were determined to discover the structure of DNA.

Work going on in three groups ultimately led to the formulation of DNA's three-dimensional structure: Pauling and Robert Corey at the California Institute of Technology; Maurice Wilkins and Rosalind Franklin in John Randall's laboratory at King's College, London; and Watson and Crick at the Cavendish Laboratory. Particularly important were Franklin's X-ray studies of DNA. She showed that DNA existed in two forms, each with a distinctive X-ray picture: The wetter form (called the B form) gave an X-shaped pattern, and the slightly drier form (the A form) gave a more detailed array of spots. From these X-ray pictures, the workers in Randall's laboratory found that DNA had two periodicities in its B form: a major one of 3.4 angstroms and a secondary one of 34 angstroms. Gradually, their studies also began to suggest that DNA had a helical structure.

Watson and Crick decided to approach DNA's structure using Pauling's model-building approach. As did other scientists, they knew that DNA's chemical formula, with its many single bonds that allowed free rotation of various groups, meant that the molecule could assume many different configurations. In their early research, Watson and Crick had to make some assumptions. For example, they assumed that the polynucleotide chain was coiled in a helix, somewhat like a vine winding around a cylinder. They reasoned that the different sizes and shapes of the bases probably led to their irregular sequence along the chain, whereas the orderly sugar-phosphate backbone must be responsible for the regular molecular features predicted from the X-ray photographs. Because of the high density of DNA, Watson and Crick proposed, as their first model, a triple helix. The three polynucleotide strands were arranged with the sugar-phosphate groups on the inside of the molecule and the bases on the outside. Wilkins, Franklin, and others came to Cambridge to see this model, but they thought it was ridiculous. Watson and Crick had understood neither the X-ray data nor the water content of the various forms of DNA.

In the latter part of 1952, Pauling, relying on poor X-ray photographs of DNA and faulty information about the density of its two forms, also proposed a triple helix. He had decided that packing the extremely bulky bases in the center of the molecule would be too difficult, and so, like Watson and Crick, he situated them on the periphery of his three-strand model. Before this work, Pauling had speculated, in some of his papers and talks, that the genetic material in living things had to be composed of two complementary strands, but in studying the actual density determinations and X-ray photographs, he was led to the conclusion that this DNA, the product of laboratory manipulations, must be a triple helix.

Watson and Crick quickly abandoned their triple helix. Their search for another model of DNA was aided by a visit to Cambridge in the summer of 1952 by Erwin Chargaff. After talking with them, he was shocked that neither had precise knowledge of the chemical differences among the four bases. He explained to them his findings about the base ratios, which eventually suggested to them that these bases might be paired in the DNA structure. Watson, in fact, started manipulating paper models of the bases, in an attempt to mate them, but he did not understand which base forms actually existed in DNA (chemists had found that these nitrogenous bases could exist, depending on conditions, in two forms, the keto and the enol). Fortunately, an American crystallographer (and Pauling protégé), Jerry Donohue, had an excellent knowledge of these base forms, which he communicated to Watson, who was still mired in like-with-like schemes. At Donohue's insistence, Watson began matching adenine with thymine, and guanine with cytosine. This proved to be the key to the structure, for when these base pairs were joined with hydrogen bonds, their combinations were almost identical in size and shape. Thus, these base pairs could be fit, like Astbury's pile of plates, into the interior of the helix, whereas the regular sugar-phosphate backbone at the molecule's exterior could account for its acidity and its interactions with water.

In the Watson-Crick model, DNA's structure consists of two strands, which may contain several million nucleotide units, that run in opposite directions (because of the asymmetry of the sugar-phosphate linkage):

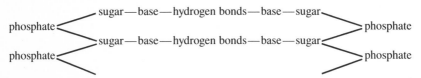

Although the hydrogen bonds that hold the chains together are much weaker than normal chemical bonds, they are so numerous that the union is tight. The two strands are not straight, as they appear in the above diagram; rather, they wind around an imaginary axis in a helical fashion, as if wrapped around a cylinder. The sugar-phosphate groups form the coil, with their attached bases extending inward toward the helix's axis. In this double helix (which represents the B form of DNA), a single turn repeats itself every ten base pairs. More specifically, the space between one base pair and the next is 3.4 angstroms, and the helix makes one complete turn every 34 angstroms. (Scientists later determined that the A form has eleven base pairs per turn and that the pairs are tilted about 25 degrees away from the perpendicular to the helix axis.)

The double helix is a right-hand helix, which means that an observer looking down the axis of the helix sees each strand, as it goes away from him, moving in a clockwise direction. This helix, which is about 20 angstroms in diameter, has a deep groove on its surface, winding parallel to a much shallower groove. The structure is stabilized by the hydrogen bonding of the complementary base pairs. The purine adenine (A) is always hydrogen-bonded to the pyrimidine thymine (T), while the purine guanine (G) is always hydrogen-bonded to the pyrimidine cytosine (C). Because of this base-pairing scheme, each chain's sequence, for example, TACGCAT, determines its partner's sequence, in this case, ATGCGTA. The complementary nature of these opposing sequences accounts for Chargaff's ratios and, as Watson and Crick cleverly noted in their famous 1953 paper in *Nature*, provides a natural explanation for the replication of the molecule. Because of the specific phosphodiester bonding between the sugars, each strand has a top and bottom end, making the two strands antiparallel—that is, positioned relative to each other like two swimmers heading in opposite directions.

In the decades after the discovery of the double helix, scientists found that DNA could exist in structures other than the B form double helix. For example, the chromosomes of some small viruses have single-stranded DNA molecules. Furthermore, some DNA molecules from living organisms turned out to be circular, which means that the polynucleotide chain formed a closed loop. In fact, the DNA molecule of some viruses interconvert between linear and circular forms, the linear being present inside the virus particle, the circular form existing in the host cell. While studying the conversion of the linear to the circular form of DNA, Jerome Vinograd, a physical chemist, discovered that the axis of the double helix can be twisted to form a superhelix, which can be right- or left-handed.

In the late 1970's and early 1980's, Alexander Rich at the Massachusetts Institute of Technology discovered a left-handed double helix containing about twelve nucleotides per turn. Because the backbones follow a zigzag path, this left-handed structure was called Z-DNA. Instead of the major and minor grooves of B-DNA, only a single groove winds around Z-DNA. Scientists have found the Z form of DNA in nature, specifically in regions of the DNA molecule where G and C bases form an alternating sequence.

Methods of Study

The DNA molecule has proved difficult to study. Even today, with greatly advanced techniques and instruments, it is challenging to obtain unmodified and unadulterated DNA from any organism other than very simple viruses. The reason lies in the nature of the molecule itself. DNA is extremely long and thin, though the length of laboratory-generated DNA depends somewhat on the method of preparation. A good sample may reach a length of 30,000 angstrom units, so that the structure is more than a thousand times as long as it is thick. The length of DNA inside the cell is probably much greater than this, because various extraction and purification techniques inevitably cause breaks in the molecule. Inside a cell, the DNA helix is surrounded by various proteins, and in separating the molecule from their proteins, random damage almost always occurs. Even a naked DNA chain, because it is so long and thin, is not immune to various shearing forces, both physical and chemical.

In very early investigations into the nature of DNA (when it was known as nuclein), scientists used chemical methods to establish its basic composition. In the late nineteenth century, Miescher, for example, used salt solutions, alcohol, acids, and alkalies to extract nuclei from pus cells and from salmon sperm. When he added hydrochloric acid to pus cells, he obtained pure nuclei; when he added alkali, then acid, to the nuclei, he obtained the grey precipitate known as nuclein. Miescher failed to obtain DNA in a pure form, but he did obtain evidence that nuclein must consist of very large molecules, since it would not pass through a parchment filter. In

1899, Richard Altmann, a student of Miescher's, improved the preparation of pure nuclein. Using standard techniques, he obtained nucleoprotein, a combination of protein and nucleic acid, from calf thymus and then used salt to precipitate the protein component, which was removed. The addition of ethyl alcohol to the remaining solution caused the precipitation of the nucleic acid in the form of fibers. Albrecht Kossel, an organic chemist who improved Altmann's extraction techniques, established the basic techniques for isolating purines and pyrimidines from nucleic acids obtained from yeast cells and calf thymus, for which he received the 1910 Nobel Prize in Physiology or Medicine.

Phoebus Levene and Alexander Todd approached the nucleic acids from the perspective of organic chemistry. Using techniques originated by Emil Fischer, the great German chemist, Levene gently split apart the nucleic acids and analyzed the structures of their fragments by such chemical techniques as methylation (various methyl compounds were useful in discovering functional groups attached to the sugar and base rings). He discovered both ribose and deoxyribose. Todd, building on Levene's work, used both analytic and synthetic organic chemical techniques in elucidating the structures of the mononucleotide building blocks of nucleic acids. Like Levene, he broke the nucleic acids into many fragments, whose structures he then analyzed.

All the groups that worked on the structure of DNA—those of Astbury and Bell, Pauling and Corey, Wilkins and Franklin, and Watson and Crick—made use of X-ray diffraction. In this technique, discovered by Max von Laue in 1912, a beam of X rays, in passing through a crystal, interacts with its regular array of atoms. These interactions result in a complex group of diffracted beams, whose intensities, angles of exit, and phases are directly related to the atomic structure of the repeating unit of the crystal. Rosalind Franklin, in particular, made great improvements in the quality of X-ray photographs of DNA fibers. Her pictures of both the A and B forms contained a large number of sharp spots that yielded valuable information about the size and configuration of the DNA molecule.

The scientist most responsible for making model-building an important part of molecular biology was Linus Pauling. Early in his career, he had developed a coordination theory of crystal structure, in which he provided ways to predict the structures of various substances by first deciding which possible atomic arrangements were chemically reasonable and were in agreement with the interatomic distances and ionic sizes that had already been established. Then he selected the most likely arrangements and examined their agreement with the X-ray data. Watson and Crick were so impressed by Pauling's method that they made substantial use of it in their research leading to the double helix. They also made use of organic chemistry (to clarify the tautomeric forms of the bases), physical chemistry (to make sure that DNA's atoms were properly situated in terms of atomic sizes, bond distances, and bond angles), and X-ray crystallography (to determine the overall size and shape of the structure as well as the spacings between the bases and its helical form).

Since Watson and Crick proposed their DNA model, actual images of the double helix have been obtained with a scanning tunneling electron microscope (STM). In this instrument, a computer monitors a tunneling current—a miniscule flow of electrons that jumps between the microscope and the molecular surface being mapped—which changes in proportion to the gap distance. As the microscope scans the molecule, a computer generates a three-dimensional image of its surface. The STM has produced amazingly detailed three-dimensional images of DNA magnified one million times that confirm not only the Watson-Crick structure of DNA's B form but also those DNAs that exist in several different helical conformations.

Context

DNA has been called the master key of life, and the discovery of its structure has been called the most influential event in twentieth century biology. DNA is certainly the most renowned of all molecules. Its double-stranded structure has appeared on the covers of *Time*, *Newsweek*, and other magazines, and rightly so, for this molecule, from its perch in the chromosomes of every cell, directs the reproduction and development of all living organisms. Man and monkey, rose and rat, micro-organisms and macro-organisms, all share a DNA kinship. Its exquisite structure contains genetic messages that make eyes blue, peacock feathers iridescent, and lilacs fragrant. Although the unique experiences of human lives are caused by much more than genes, it is nevertheless DNA that sets the physical limits on what human beings, as well as other living things, can or cannot become.

Watson and Crick's discovery of the double helix led to an avalanche of significant discoveries in molecular biology. The most important feature of their model was that it suggested how DNA might produce an exact copy of itself. Since the model consists of two chains, each of which is the complement of the other, either chain may act as a mold or template on which a complementary chain can be synthesized. As the two chains of DNA unwind and separate, each strand begins to construct a new complement onto itself. When the process is finished, two pairs of double helices exist where there was one before. Thus, the Watson-Crick model explained, at the molecular level, how genes duplicate themselves with great fidelity.

The Watson-Crick model also contributed to the solution of the pivotal problem of genetics: how genes control the making of proteins in cells. Though this problem was not solved directly by the double helix, the study of the interactions between DNA and the proteins it indirectly produces revealed that its structure contains, in the sequences of its bases, an intricate code that supervises the construction of the thousands of proteins used by cells. In working out this genetic code, scientists discovered little similarity between DNA's three-nucleotide sequences that code for particular amino acids and the structures of the amino acids themselves. Indeed, the transfer of information from DNA to the cellular mechanisms overseeing protein construction turned out to be quite complex, involving various types of RNA.

Watson and Crick, the originators of the revolution in molecular biology, also played important parts in its evolution. They helped formulate its "central dogma," which explains how genetic information passes from DNA to the cell's proteins. In the first part of the process, DNA serves as the template for its self-replication (duplication). Then, RNA molecules are made on a DNA template (transcription). Finally, RNA templates determine all proteins (translation). Although DNA can therefore act on itself, the processes of transcription and translation were seen as moving in one direction only: DNA sequences are never made on protein templates, and DNA sequences are never made on RNA templates. In the course of time, some exceptions to these rules have been discovered, but the central dogma remains essentially valid, as does the double helix. Watson and Crick, along with many other scientists, solved, by means of ideas drawn from physics and chemistry, the basic mysteries of the gene.

Bibliography

Alberts, Bruce, Dennis Bray, Julian Lewis, Martin Raff, Keith Roberts, and James D. Watson. *Molecular Biology of the Cell.* 2d ed. New York: Garland, 1989. The first edition established this textbook as a classic, and the second edition makes improvements in this "Gospel for all serious students in the biomedical sciences." Intended for students taking a first course in cell biology, this textbook has wider appeal, since the authors, all of whom are experts in their fields, have written their chapters by first explaining fundamental concepts. Copiously illustrated with photographs as well as two-color figures and diagrams, this book has excellent sets of references at the ends of chapters and a comprehensive index.

Crick, Francis. *What Mad Pursuit: A Personal View of Scientific Discovery.* New York: Basic Books, 1988. This memoir focuses on Crick's experiences before, during, and after the discovery of the double helix. Though he does have a short prologue outlining a few details of his upbringing and education, his auto-biographical account centers on the fascinating combination of choice and chance that led to the epochal discovery of DNA's structure and how the genetic code was broken. The book has a packet of photographs, two scientific appendices, and an index.

Freifelder, David. *The DNA Molecule, Structure and Properties: Original Papers, Analyses, and Problems.* San Francisco: W. H. Freeman, 1978. The author intends this collection of the most important papers on DNA structure for undergraduate students in molecular biology. The papers are complemented by his own narrative, in which he summarizes important papers not reprinted, describes the conceptual context behind the papers that are reprinted, and analyzes how the scientific community reacted to all these papers. His hope is to communicate to beginners in the field both the intellectual and emotional excitement surrounding great scientific discoveries. For those unfamiliar with basic molecular biology, there are several scientific appendices. Index.

Judson, Horace Freeland. *The Eighth Day of Creation: The Makers of Revolution in Biology.* New York: Simon & Schuster, 1979. Judson was a science journalist when he wrote this popular account of how DNA's structure was determined and how the genetic code was worked out. Based on more than a hundred interviews with the scientists involved, Judson's book communicates both a sense of wonder about scientific discovery and a clear understanding of many of the principal scientific ideas behind the revolution in biology. The book contains a large number of notes, many of which have detailed bibliographical information, and an extensive index.

Olby, Robert. *The Path to the Double Helix*. Seattle: University of Washington Press, 1974. Olby, whose specialty is the history of biology, presents the first detailed account of the intellectual and institutional evolution in biology and allied sciences that led to a chemical understanding of the gene. His book explores how the concept of the macromolecular was developed, how the nucleic acids came to be seen as the hereditary material, and how the double helix was discovered. Illustrated with figures and a packet of photographs; it has an extensive bibliography of over fifty pages and an extensive index.

Watson, James D. *The Double Helix: A Personal Account of the Discovery of the Structure of DNA*. New York: W. W. Norton, 1980. *The Double Helix* was first published by Athenaeum in 1968. This version, edited by Gunther S. Stent, contains, in addition to the full text of the original edition, extensive commentaries, reviews, and related scientific papers. Figures and photographs are part of Watson's book and of some of the other material. Contains an index of names.

Watson, James D., Nancy H. Hopkins, Jeffrey W. Roberts, Joan Argetsinger Steitz, and Alan M. Weiner. *The Molecular Biology of the Gene*. 4th ed. Menlo Park, Calif.: Benjamin/Cummings, 1987. Through the successive editions of Watson's classic text, one can follow the explosive development of molecular biology. This fourth edition, which has two volumes (*Volume I: General Principles* and *Volume II: Specialized Aspects*), is aimed at undergraduates taking their first course in molecular biology. Each section is written by an expert in the field. Two-color diagrams, photographs, and multicolored computer images populate the text. Extensive bibliographies at the ends of chapters and a comprehensive index.

Robert J. Paradowski

Cross-References

DNA Bending in Regulation, 679; DNA Hybridization Analysis of Relatedness, 686; DNA Replication, 692; DNA Sequencing, 698; Genes and Nucleic Acids, 1134; Genes and Polypeptide Chains, 1141; The Genetic Code, 1148; Deciphering the Genetic Code, 1155; Neutral Mutations and Evolutionary Clocks, 1944; Nucleic Acid Structure, 1987; Proteins, 2272; Sequence Comparisons for Proteins and Nucleic Acids, 2466; Transcription of DNA to Form RNA, 2632; Translation of Messenger RNA to Form Protein, 2647.

DORMANCY

Type of life science: Plant physiology
Other field of study: Botany

Dormancy refers to a condition in plants in which there is little or no growth and in which most, if not all, metabolic processes either cease or are greatly reduced. A large number of environmental and chemical factors can either induce or release dormancy, and knowledge of these factors can be used to improve plant growth.

Principal terms

DECIDUOUS: a term applied to plants that shed their leaves annually
GERMINATION: the onset of growth of a dormant structure, such as a seed or a spore
HERBACEOUS: a general term for nonwoody plants
PHENOLICS: a group of biochemical compounds associated with the basic structure of phenol
PHOTOPERIOD: a term referring to the relative lengths of day and night
SENESCENCE: the aging and ultimate death of a plant part, accompanied by breakdown of cellular components
TEMPERATE ZONE: that region of the earth with moderate temperatures and rainfall that also has a winter and summer change of seasons

Summary of the Phenomenon

Dormancy is the state in which a plant or plant part exhibits little or no growth and in which most, if not all, metabolic activity ceases for a period of time. Both genetic and environmental factors play a role in determining the type and duration of the dormant period.

The vast majority of plant life on this planet functions best at temperatures well above freezing. Except for those in the tropical regions, however, plants are exposed to temperatures below freezing for varying lengths of time during the year. Plants, unlike animals, do not have the luxury of body insulation or locomotion. Hence, the plants cannot seek shelter, hibernate, or do the other things animals do to survive cold weather. In order to survive these periods of freezing temperature, many plants become dormant. In other words, metabolic activity either ceases or is drastically reduced.

The type of dormant response depends on the plant's pattern of growth and death. Perennials are those plants that live year after year; each year, these plants undergo a period of dormancy during the cold season. In the herbaceous species, the aboveground portion dies, but the plants survive as specialized underground stems. Woody shrubs and trees remain alive aboveground. The deciduous species shed their leaves in winter, while the gymnosperms, which keep their leaves year round, dramatically reduce their metabolic rates. Biennial species live for two years. The first year is devoted to vegetative growth and the formation of underground storage tissues. After the plant lies dormant through the winter months, its second year of growth results in the stored food supply being utilized to produce flowers and seed. Annuals are plants that complete an entire life cycle in one growing season. The plants die; seeds, which normally remain dormant until the following growing season, are produced.

Most perennial trees and shrubs in temperate regions produce buds in the summer. These buds, which can eventually develop into leaves, stems, or flowers, exhibit reduced metabolic activity even before leaves begin to senesce (age). As temperatures decrease in the fall, complete dormancy sets in. Specialized leaves called bud scales cover the dormant tissue. These scales block the diffusion of oxygen into the bud; they also prevent the loss of water from the tissue.

Almost all flowering plants produce seeds. The seeds develop as ovules within a structural component of the flower called the ovary. As the ovary ripens to form the fruit, the ovules mature into seeds. Each seed is composed of a reserved food supply and a new plant with embryonic root, leaf, and stem tissue. The embryonic plant and reserve food supply are surrounded by a tough seed coat. The seeds of many species, especially trees in the temperate zones, do not germinate immediately after maturing even under ideal moisture, temperature, and nutritional conditions because there is a built-in period of dormancy.

A number of environmental factors appear to induce bud dormancy. In many species, bud dormancy occurs in response to low temperatures; among other species, the proper short-day photoperiod is responsible for initiating dormancy, while in still other species, both low temperature and short days are required to trigger the onset of dormancy. Hence, dormancy is generally initiated with the onset of the short and/or cold days of winter. In addition, dormancy in buds has been shown to occur under situations of limited supply of nutrients or drought conditions. Dormancy can therefore be seen as a survival mechanism. When temperature, water, or nutritional conditions are no longer favorable, the buds become dormant.

Seed dormancy can also be caused by a number of different factors. For several reasons, the presence of a hard seed coat will very often result in dormancy of the seed. In many cases, the seed coat is impermeable to water. Since water is required for the germination process, the impermeable nature of the seed coat will serve as an effective inducer of dormancy. In some instances, the seed coat may be impermeable to certain gases. Both carbon dioxide and oxygen are required for germination; some seed coats prevent the diffusion of oxygen into the seed, while others are impermeable to carbon dioxide. In a few species, the seed coat physically restricts the growth of the embryo. A growing embryo must develop sufficient thrust to break through a seed coat, and in some instances the seed coat prevents this from happening. Seed germination is also dependent on temperature. The seeds of almost all species have a minimal temperature below which the seeds will not germinate. The exact mechanism by which low temperature causes dormancy is poorly understood, but it appears that the temperature alters membrane structure, which somehow prevents the seed from germinating. Light is also a factor in the dormancy of many seeds. In many species, light is required for germination; in some cases, however, the exposure to light will induce dormancy. Also, some species exhibit a sensitivity to the photoperiod. Certain species are dormant under short days and germinate under long days, while others remain dormant when exposed to long days and germinate under short days. The light apparently activates a plant regulator that blocks the metabolic reactions necessary for germination.

Although it is environmental conditions that most often induce dormancy, the process is almost always under genetic and chemical control. Numerous studies show that bud dormancy is induced in some varieties of certain species but not in other varieties of the same species. This difference strongly suggests a genetic variation in the control mechanism. In addition, many buds and seeds will remain dormant even when exposed to the ideal temperature, moisture, and amount of light. This obviously indicates that something other than only the environment is involved in the control of dormancy. The exact mechanism of genetic control is not clearly understood, but there is some information relating to the chemical control. There is some suggestion that the plant hormone abscisic acid may be associated with bud dormancy, but the evidence is inconclusive. With seed dormancy, however, the involvement of abscisic acid is fairly certain. A number of studies have shown that abscisic acid, when applied to the seed, will block the activity of enzymes necessary for germination.

A number of germination-inhibiting substances are present in dormant seeds. Respiratory inhibitors, such as cyanide, are produced in some seeds. High concentrations of various inorganic salts prevent germination in some species, while an assortment of phenolic compounds are known to prevent the process in others. A compound known as coumarin is particularly widespread in seeds and is known to be an effective inhibitor of germination. A number of these germination-inhibiting substances are present in both fruit and seed. These chemicals prevent the seeds from germinating within the fruit itself. In addition, the substances will cause the seeds to lie dormant in nature until sufficient rain has fallen to leach the chemical from the seeds. This not only releases dormancy but also ensures that sufficient moisture will be available to support the young seedlings.

Methods of Study

One major aspect of the study of dormancy involves subjecting plants to a wide variety of environmental conditions. In some instances, the phenomenon can be studied under natural conditions. This involves observing the buds, seeds, or other plant parts during the different seasons to determine when development or germination occurs. Natural environments are not always constant from year to year, however, and critical studies often require the presence of an unchanging environment. Most often, these experiments are conducted in controlled environmental chambers. For studying bud dormancy, the plants are placed in the chamber and then exposed to various temperatures, photoperiods, or other environmental parameters to determine which conditions will cause the buds to remain dormant and which ones will induce development. The investigation of seed dormancy is performed under conditions very similar to those used to study bud dormancy, but smaller (and sometimes less sophisticated) equipment can often be used. Generally, specific numbers of seeds are placed in appropriate containers and exposed to various conditions for different lengths of time. Subsequently, germination tests are run on each batch of seeds to determine the effect of the treatment.

The effect of a wide variety of chemicals on dormancy can be studied in various ways. The substances are sometimes placed directly on the buds or, in some instances, sprayed on the entire plant. The buds are then observed to determine the influence of the chemical on dormancy. Seeds are most often soaked in the chemical being studied and then subjected to germination tests. Usually, the chemical studies are conducted in conjunction with investigations of a variety of environmental conditions. Studies of the chemicals present within the buds or seeds usually require sophisticated biochemical methods. The specific technique will depend on which group of chemicals are being investigated.

Several plant hormones appear to be involved in either the induction or release of dormancy. Enzyme activity is associated with the metabolic reactions necessary for bud development or seed germination. Since dormancy is obviously under genetic control, molecular investigations are necessary to understand this control. Hence, studies of the mechanisms responsible for dormancy usually include techniques used in plant hormone studies, enzymology, and molecular biology.

Context

Dormancy obviously evolved as an effective means of surviving unfavorable environmental conditions. In the temperate zones, buds normally form from spring to midsummer. While there may be a little growth in the late summer, the process virtually ceases in the fall in preparation for the forthcoming winter. This dormant state protects the buds from freezing temperatures. A mature seed contains a complete embryo along with a reserve food supply; this mature seed is formed within the ripened fruit. If it were not for the germination inhibitors present in the fruit and/or seed, the seeds would begin to germinate while still in the fruit. In addition, the seeds of plants in the temperate regions most often reach the soil in late summer or early fall, at which times the plants are most often faced with low moisture availability and future cold weather. Were the seeds to germinate at this time, survival would be difficult.

From a practical standpoint, methods of releasing this dormancy are often of more concern than the induction of dormancy. In nature, plants must overcome this dormancy when environmental conditions are suitable for growth. It is often desirable to break dormancy artificially in the laboratory or commercial plant operations in order to obtain faster results or increase plant production. Hence, it is advantageous to know what conditions are necessary to induce the development of a dormant bud or the germination of a dormant seed. Treatments to release bud dormancy can be categorized as either temperature-, light-, or chemical-related.

Just as low temperature will induce bud dormancy in many plants, extended exposure to temperatures between 4 and 10 degrees Celsius can break dormancy. The amount of time required at low temperature varies from species to species and can range from days to months. Blueberries, for example require about twenty-nine days at 7 degrees Celsius, while apples require approximately fifty days. On the other hand, in plants such as gladiolus, heat is required to release dormancy. The length of the photoperiod is also important in overcoming dormancy in many buds. Since short days induce bud dormancy in many plants, one would expect long days to release it, and in many cases that is what is observed. As the days grow longer in the spring, the buds will begin to open. Some buds require a combination: subjection to low temperatures followed by exposure to long days. A number of chemicals will also break bud dormancy. Ethylene chlorohydrin has been used for years to release dormancy in many fruit trees, and natural hormones known as gibberellins will break dormancy in most cold-requiring plants when applied directly to the buds.

Treatments for the release of seed dormancy fall into the same three categories of light, temperature, and chemicals, plus a forth category referred to as mechanical. The scarification (mechanical breaking) of the seed coat has proven to be an effective means of overcoming dormancy in many seeds. The broken seed coats allow the seeds to take up the water and gases necessary for germination. Just as with buds, the exposure of seeds to temperatures between 4 and 10 degrees Celsius will break dormancy in numerous species. Again, the time at low temperature necessary to cause germination varies—from a few days to as long as two winter seasons for some species. Light stimulates germination in a number of seeds. In some species, both the presence of light and the proper photoperiod are necessary to break dormancy. Most species require a long day regime, but a few must be exposed to short days. A wide variety of chemicals will release seed dormancy. Gibberellins, cytokinins, and ethylene, all natural plant hormones, have been shown to be involved in breaking seed dormancy, and the gibberellins and other substances, such as thiourea, are used to germinate seeds commercially.

The exact molecular mechanisms associated with breaking dormancy are not known. It is apparent that the various environmental conditions and chemicals involved with releasing dormancy somehow cause the production of growth-regulating substances. These substances, in turn, control the various genes required to code for the proteins necessary for seed germination or bud growth.

Bibliography

Campbell, Neil A. *Biology*. 2d ed. Menlo Park, Calif.: Benjamin/Cummings, 1990. An introductory college-level textbook for science students. Chapter 34, "Plant Reproduction," provides a clear, concise description of seed dormancy. The well-written text and superb graphics furnish the reader with a clear understanding of dormancy. List of suggested readings at the end of the chapter. Glossary.

Curtis, Helena, and N. Sue Barnes. *Biology*. 5th ed. New York: Worth, 1989. An introductory college-level textbook for science students. Chapter 29, "The Flowering Plants: An Introduction," provides a general discussion of the concept of dormancy. A very readable text and well-done graphics make the phenomenon understandable even to the novice. List of suggested readings at the end of the chapter. Glossary.

Leopold, A. Carl, and P. E. Kriedman. *Plant Growth and Development.* 2d ed. New York: McGraw-Hill, 1975. An intermediate college-level textbook for science students. Chapter 19, "Dormancy," provides an in-depth view of both bud and seed dormancy. The mechanisms are discussed in detail, and accompanying research data are presented. List of somewhat technical references cited at the end of the chapter.

Mayer, A. M., and A. Poljakoff-Mayber. *The Germination of Seeds.* 4th ed. New York: Permagon, 1989. An excellent, though somewhat technical, in-depth discussion of the various aspects of seed germination and dormancy. For the more advanced student. Extensive bibliography with primarily technical papers cited at the end of the chapter.

Raven, R. H., P. F. Evert, and S. E. Eichorn. *Biology of Plants.* 4th ed. New York: Worth, 1986. An introductory college textbook for science students. Chapter 26, "External Factors and Plant Growth," provides a good discussion of dormancy. The profusely illustrated text furnishes an excellent general overview of the phenomenon in both buds and seeds. Glossary.

Salisbury, Frank B., and Cleon Ross. *Plant Physiology.* 3d ed. Belmont, Calif.: Wadsworth, 1985. An intermediate college-level textbook for science students. Chapter 21, "Growth Response to Temperature," gives an in-depth view of the physiological role of dormancy. An excellent explanation of the phenomenon is provided in text and graphics. Detailed bibliography at the end of the chapter.

Samish, Rudolf. "Dormancy in Woody Plants." *Annual Review of Plant Physiology* 5 (1954): 183-204. A detailed review outlining much of the early work done in the area of plant dormancy. A very informative discussion of the woody plants, with a detailed list of somewhat technical literature citations.

Vegis, Augeklis. "Dormancy in Higher Plants." *Annual Review of Plant Physiology* 15 (1964): 185-224. A detailed review outlining much of the pertinent information related to the overall phenomenon of dormancy in plants. A very informative overview, with a detailed list of somewhat technical literature citations.

D. R. Gossett

Cross-References

The Biosphere, Biomes, and Habitats, 210; Flowering Regulation, 1010; Germination and Seedling Development, 1205; Leaf-Fall Regulation, 1542; Plant Hormones, 2103; Plant Life Spans, 2110; Seeds, 2452.

ECOLOGICAL INTERACTIONS BETWEEN PLANTS AND ANIMALS

Type of life science: Ecology
Other fields of study: Animal physiology, botany, plant physiology, and zoology

Interactions between plants and animals in natural environments often revolve around either food acquisition or pollination and seed dispersal. By studying such processes, scientists have discovered strategies to increase agricultural production and to duplicate naturally produced pesticides.

Principal terms

CELLULAR RESPIRATION: the release of energy in organisms at the cell level, primarily by the use of oxygen

CHLOROPHYLL: one of several forms of photoactive green pigments in plant cells that is necessary for photosynthesis to occur

COEVOLUTION: a mutualistic relationship between two different organisms in which, as a result of natural selection, the organisms become interdependent

CROSS-POLLINATION: the transfer of pollen grains and their enclosed sperm cells from the male portion of a flower to a female portion of another flower within the same species

FOOD CHAIN (FOOD WEB): a diagram illustrating the movement of food materials from green plants (producers) through various levels of animals (consumers) within natural environments

NATURAL SELECTION: the survival of variant types of organisms as a result of adaptability to environmental stresses

PISTIL: a female portion of a flower that produces unfertilized egg cells

STAMEN: a male portion of a flower that produces pollen grains and their enclosed sperm cells

Summary of the Phenomenon

Ecology represents the organized body of knowledge that deals with the interrelationships between living organisms and their nonliving environments. Increasingly, the realm of ecology involves a systematic analysis of plant-animal interactions through the considerations of nutrient flow in food chains and food webs, exchange of such important gases as oxygen and carbon dioxide between plants and animals, and strategies of mutual survival between plant and animal species through the processes of pollination and seed dispersal.

Ecologists study both abiotic and biotic features of such plant and animal interactions. The abiotic aspects of any environment consist of nonliving, physical variables, such as temperature and moisture, that determine where species can survive and reproduce. The biotic (living) environment includes all other plants, animals, and microorganisms with which a particular species interacts. Certainly, two examples of plant and animal interactions involve the continual processes of photosynthesis and cellular respiration. Green plants are often classified as ecological producers and have the unique ability to carry out both these important chemical reactions. Animals, for the most part, can act only as consumers, taking the products of photosynthesis and chemically releasing them at the cellular level to produce energy for all life activities.

One topic that has captured the attention of ecologists involves the phenomenon of mutualism, in which two different species of organisms beneficially reside together in close association, usually revolving around nutritional needs. One such example demonstrating a plant and animal association is a certain species of small aquatic flatworm that absorbs microscopic green plants called algae into its tissues. The benefit to the animal is one of added food supply; the adaptation to this alga has been so complete that the flatworm does not actively feed as an adult. The algae, in turn, receive adequate supplies of nitrogen and carbon dioxide and are literally transported throughout tidal flats in marine habitats as the flatworm migrates, thus exposing the algae favorably to increased sunlight. A similar example of mutualism has been reported by ecologists studying various types of reef-building corals, which are actually marine, colonial animals that grow single-celled green algae called zooxanthellae within their bodies. The coral organisms use the nutrients produced by these algae as additional energy supplies, enabling them to build more easily the massive coral reefs associated with tropical waters. In 1987, William B. Rudman reported a similar situation while researching the formation of such coral reefs in East African coastal waters. He discovered a type of sea slug called a nudibranch that absorbs green algae into its transparent digestive tract, producing an excellent camouflage as it moves about on the coral reefs in search of prey. In turn, the algae growing within both the coral and sea slugs receive important gases from these organisms for their own life necessities.

An example of plant-animal mutualism that has been documented as a classic example of coevolution involves the yucca plant and a species of small, white moth common throughout the southwestern United States. The concept of coevolution builds upon Charles Darwin's theories of natural selection, reported in 1859, and describes situations in which two decidedly different organisms have evolved into a close ecological relationship characterized by compatible structures in both. Thus, coevolution is a mutualistic relationship between two different species that, as a result of natural selection, have become intimately interdependent. The yucca plant and yucca moth reflect such a relationship. The female moth collects pollen grains bearing sperm cells from the stamens of one flower on the plant and transports these pollen loads to the pistil of another flower, thereby ensuring cross-pollination and fertilization. During this process, the moth will lay her own fertilized eggs in the flower's undeveloped seed pods. The developing moth larvae have a secure residence for growth and a steady food supply. These larvae will rarely consume all the developing plant seeds; thus, both species (plant and animal) benefit.

Although these examples demonstrate the evolution of structures and secretions that reflect mutual associations between plants and animals, other interactions are not so self-supportive. Plant-eating animals, called herbivores, have always been able to consume large quantities of green plants with little "fear of reprisal." Yet, some types of carnivorous plants have evolved that capture and digest small insects and crustaceans as nutritional supplements to their normal photosynthetic activities. Many of these plants grow abundantly in marshlike environments, such as bogs and swamps, where many insects congregate to reproduce. Such famous plants as the Venus's-flytrap, sundews, butterworts, and pitcher plants have modified stems and leaves to capture and consume insects and spiders rich in protein. On a smaller scale, in freshwater ponds and lakes, a submerged green plant commonly known as the bladderwort partially satisfies its protein requirements by snaring and digesting small crustaceans, such as the water flea, within its modified leaves.

A form of ecological interaction commonly classified as mimicry can be found worldwide in diverse environments. In such situations, an animal or plant has evolved structures or behavior patterns that allow it to mimic either its surroundings or another organism as a defensive or offensive strategy. Certain types of insects, such as leafhoppers, walking sticks, praying mantids, and katydids (a type of grass-hopper), often duplicate plant structures in environments ranging from the tropical rain forests to the northern coniferous forests of the United States. Such exact mimicry of their plant hosts affords these insects protection from their own predators as well as camouflage that enables them to capture their own prey readily. In other examples of mimicry, some insects will absorb unpalatable plant substances in their larval stages and retain these chemicals in their adult form, making them undesirable to birds as food sources. The monarch butterfly demonstrates this type of interaction with the milkweed plant. The viceroy butterfly has evolved similar colorations and markings to that of the monarch, thereby ensuring its own survival against bird predators. Certain species of ambush bugs and crab spiders have evolved coloration patterns that allow them to hide within flower heads of such common plants as goldenrod, enabling them to grasp better the bees and flies that visit these flowers.

Many ecologists have been studying the phenomenon known as nonsymbiotic mutualism: different plants and animals that have coevolved morphological structures and behavior patterns by which they benefit each other but that do not have to live physically together. This type of mutualism can be demonstrated in the often unusual and bizarre shapes, patterns, and colorations that more advanced flowering plants have developed to attract various insects, birds, and small mammals for pollination and seed dispersal purposes. Pollination essentially is the transfer of pollen grains (and their enclosed sperm cells) from the male portion of a flower to the egg cells within the female portion of a flower. Pollination can be accomplished by the wind, by heavy dew or rains, or by animals, and it results in the plant's sexual production of seeds that represent the next generation of new embryo plants. Accessory structures, called fruits, often form around seeds and are usually tasty and brightly marked to attract animals for seed dispersal. Although the fruits themselves become biological bribes for animals to consume, often the seeds within these fruits are not easily digested and thus pass through the animals' digestive tracts unharmed, sometimes great distances from the original plant. Other types of seed disperal mechanisms involve the evolution of hooks, barbs, and sticky substances on seeds that enable them to be easily transported by animals' fur, feet, feathers, or beaks to new regions for possible plant colonization. Such strategies of dispersal reduce competition between the parent plant and its new seedlings for moisture, living space, and nutritional requirements.

The evolution of flowering plants and their resulting use of animals in pollination and seed dispersal probably began in dense, tropical rain forests, where pollination by the wind would be cumbersome. Because insects are the most abundant form of animal life in rain forests, strategies based upon insect transport of pollen probably originated there. Because structural specialization increases the possibility that a flower's pollen will be transferred to a plant of the same species, many plants have evolved a vast array of scents, colors, and nutritional products to attract many insects, some birds, and a few mammals. Not only does pollen include the plant's sperm cells, but it is also rich in food for these animals. Another source of animal nutrition is a substance called nectar, a sugar-rich fluid often produced in specialized structures called nectaries within the flower itself or on adjacent stems and leaves. Assorted waxes and oils are also produced by plants to ensure plant-animal interactions. As species of bees, flies, wasps, butterflies, and hawkmoths are attracted to flower heads for these nutritional rewards, they unwittingly become agents of pollination by transferring pollen from male portions of flowers (stamens) to the appropriate female portion (pistils). Some flowers have evolved distinctive, unpleasant odors reminiscent of rotting flesh or feces, thereby attracting carrion beetles and flesh flies in search of places to reproduce and deposit their own fertilized eggs. As these animals consummate their own relationships, they often become agents of pollination for the plant itself. Some tropical plants such as orchids even mimic a female bee, wasp, or beetle, so that its male counterpart will attempt to mate with it, thereby ensuring precise pollination.

Among the bird species, probably the hummingbirds are the best examples of plant pollinators. Various types of flowers with bright, red colors, tubular shapes, and strong, sweet odors have evolved in tropical and temperate regions to take advantage of the hummingbirds' long beaks and tongues as an aid to pollination.

Because most mammals, such as small rodents and bats, do not detect colors as well as bees and butterflies, flowers that use them as pollinators do not rely upon color cues in their petals but instead focus upon the production of strong, fermenting or fruitlike odors and abundant pollen rich in protein to attract them. In certain environments, bats and mice that are primarily nocturnal have replaced day-flying insects and birds in these important interactions between plants and animals.

Methods of Study

Contemporary ecologists have gone beyond the purely descriptive observations of plant-animal interactions (initially within the realm of natural history) and have designed controlled experiments that are crucial to the development of such basic concepts as coevolution. For example, the use of radioactive isotopes and the marking of pollen with dye and fluorescent material in field settings have allowed ecologists to demonstrate precise distances and patterns of pollen dispersal. Ecologists and insect physiologists have cooperatively studied how certain insects, such as bees, are sensitive to ultraviolet light. When some flowers are viewed under ultraviolet light, distinct floral patterns become evident to guide these insects to nectar pollen sources. Through basic research, Carolyn Dickerman reported in 1986 that animal color preferences vary throughout the season. Insect pollinators, who must feed every day, will adapt to these changes by shifting their foraging behavior. Research in the field has demonstrated that some species of flowers, such as the scarlet gilia, will produce differently colored flowers to accommodate shifts in pollinator species. Early in the growing season, this plant will produce long, red, tubular-shaped flowers to attract hummingbirds. As the hummingbirds migrate later, the flowers will become lighter in hue and are pollinated primarily by nocturnal hawkmoths.

In the laboratory, ecologists and biochemists have cooperatively analyzed the chemical composition of plant secretions and products. The chemical analysis of nectar indicates great variation in composition, correlating with the type of pollinator. Flowers pollinated by beetles generally have high amino acid content. The nectar associated with hummingbird-pollinated flowers is rich in sugar. Pollen also varies widely in chemical composition within plant species. Oils and waxes are major chemical products in the pollen of plants visited primarily by bees and flies. For bat-pollinated flowers, the protein content is quite high.

Research has also successfully analyzed how certain plants have been able to develop toxins as chemical defenses against animals. These protective devices include such poisons as nicotine and rotenone that help prevent insect and small mammal attacks. A more remarkable group of protective compounds recently isolated from some plants are known as juvocimines. These chemicals actually mimic juvenile insect hormones. Insect larvae feeding on leaves containing juvocimines are prevented from undergoing their normal development into functional, breeding adults. Thus, the specific insect population that could cause extensive plant damage is locally reduced.

Ecological interactions between plants and animals are diverse and varied. These plant-animal interactions can be viewed as absolute necessities for developing food chains and food webs and for maintaining the global balances of such important gases as oxygen and carbon dioxide. The interactions can also be very precise, limited, and crucial for determining species survival or extinction. By analyzing varied plant-animal interactions, from the microscopic level to the global perspective, one can more fully appreciate all the ecological relationships that exist on the earth.

Context

The ecological importance of plant-animal interactions cannot be stressed enough. Modern-day agriculture owes its existence to the activities of such insect pollinators as honeybees for the production of domestic fruits, vegetables, and honey. It is becoming increasingly evident to many ecologists and forestry scientists how important certain bird species, such as blue jays and cedar waxwings, are in natural reforestation of burned and blighted areas through their seed dispersal strategies. The plant horticulture and floral industries also are developing an appreciation of specific plant-animal interactions that produce more viable natural strains of flowers and ornamental shrubbery. The study of natural chemical defenses produced by some plants against animal invasions is most promising. The renewed interest in earlier efforts to extract such plant products as nicotine, rotenone, pyrethrum, and caffeine may produce natural compounds that can be effective insecticides without the long-term, environmental hazards associated with such man-made pesticides as malathion, chlordane, and dichlorodiphenyltrichloroethane (DDT).

Finally, humankind is realizing that it is important to understand and protect certain plant-animal interactions associated with the tropical regions of the earth; otherwise, the global balance of oxygen and carbon dioxide could be seriously disrupted. Also, these tropical areas represent the last natural environments for the continuation of important plant species that produce secretions and products that have favorable medicinal qualities for humans and domestic livestock. By maintaining these populations and understanding how certain animals interact with them, humans can be guaranteed a viable supply of beneficial plant species whose medicinal values can be duplicated within the laboratory.

Bibliography

Barth, Frederick G. *Insects and Flowers: The Biology of a Partnership*. Princeton, N.J.: Princeton University Press, 1985. This beautifully illustrated book, rich in both color photographs and electron micrographs, describes all aspects of flower-insect interactions. Includes bibliography and index. The writing style is appropriate for both general readers and introductory-level biology students.

Buchsbaum, Ralph, and Mildred Buchsbaum. *Basic Ecology*. Pacific Grove, Calif.: Boxwood Press, 1974. Although this paperback text is somewhat dated, it still ranks as an excellent introduction to all descriptive aspects of ecology. The husband-wife author team writes with a clear, concise style. The black-and-white photographs, in conjunction with the glossary and index, nicely reinforce the chapter presentations.

Dickerman, Carolyn. "Pollination: Strategies for Survival." *Ward's Natural Science Bulletin* (Summer, 1986): 1-4. This article traces the coevolution of flowering plants with their animal pollinators, especially the beetles, butterflies, and hawkmoths. An excellent introduction to both strategies of pollination and seed dispersal. The author also outlines some current research techniques and includes a simplified biological key that focuses upon flower structures that will help determine which animals pollinate them.

Horne, Henry F., and Lynne C. Westley. *Ecological Relationships of Plants and Animals*. New York: Oxford University Press, 1988. Offers introductory students in botany, zoology, and ecology a comprehensive summary of both field and experimental studies on the ecology and evolution of plant and animal interactions. Excellent black-and-white photographs, illustrations, charts, and tables are found throughout its 270 pages. This textbook is written with clarity but is not only for the casual reader.

Meeuse, Bastian, and Sean Morris. *The Sex Life of Flowers*. New York: Facts on File, 1984. This well-written text includes beautiful photographs and illustrations, and it appeals to readers with varied scientific backgrounds. It describes the evolution of the flower as an organ of sexual reproduction and portrays selected animal adaptations in structure and behavior to accommodate pollination and seed dispersal. Includes a chapter-by-chapter listing of further reading sources. The photographs and writing are based upon the Public Broadcasting Service series entitled "Sexual Encounters of the Floral Kind."

Norstag, Knut, and Andrew J. Meyerriecks. *Biology*. 2d ed. Columbus, Ohio: Charles E. Merrill, 1985. A textbook written with exceptional clarity and organization. Excellent photographs and diagrams are distributed throughout its six hundred pages. Chapter 24 discusses ecology and coevolution of plants and animals. Includes a glossary and index. This is a college-level textbook but is also suitable for advanced high school students.

Rudman, William B. "Solar-Powered Animals." *Natural History* 96 (October, 1987): 50-53. A well-written article for all readers interested in plant-animal interactions, especially focusing upon mutualism involving marine corals, sea slugs, and their green algae allies. The undersea photography is excellent.

Thomas C. Moon

Cross-References

Adaptations and Their Mechanisms, 22; The Biosphere, Biomes, and Habitats, 210; Coevolution, 512; Digestion Strategies, 656; Ecological Niches, 729; Ecological Principles, 736; Flower Structure, 999; Insect Societies, 1430; Predation, 2178; Rhythms and Behavior, 2398; Symbiosis, Commensalism, and Parasitism, 2572.

ECOLOGICAL NICHES

Type of life science: Ecology
Other field of study: Evolutionary biology

An ecological niche is the physical space in which a plant or animal lives and all the interactions with the other living organisms and components of its environment. Ecological niches are important in the preservation of organisms that are vulnerable to certain activities of human beings.

Principal terms

COMMUNITY: all the populations of plant and animal species living and interacting in a given habitat or area at a given time

ENVIRONMENT: all the external conditions that affect an organism or other specified system during its lifetime

FOOD PYRAMID: diagram representing organisms of a particular type that can be supported at each trophic level from a given input of solar energy in food chains and food webs

HABITAT: place or type of place where an organism or community of organisms naturally thrives

ORGANISM: any form of life

TROPHIC LEVEL: a level in a food chain or food web at which all organisms consume the same general types of food

Summary of the Phenomenon

The idea of the niche probably had its first roots in ecology in 1910. At that time, Roswell Johnson wrote that different species utilize different niches in the environment. He theorized that individuals of a particular species are only in certain places because of food supply and environmental factors that limit their distribution in an area. Later, in 1924, Joseph Grinnel developed his concept of niche that centered on an organism's distribution having limits set on it by climatic and physical barriers. At the same time, Charles Elton was defining his own idea of niche. His description of niche involved the way an organism makes its living—in particular, how it gathers food.

For many years, ecologists focused on Elton's definition and referred to niche in terms of an organism's place in the food pyramid. The food pyramid is a simplified scheme in which organisms interact with one another while obtaining food. The food pyramid is represented as a triangle, often with four horizontal divisions, each division being a different trophic level.

The base of the food pyramid is the first trophic level and contains the primary producers: photosynthetic plants. At the second trophic level are the primary consumers. These are the herbivores, such as deer and rabbits, which feed directly on the primary producers. Secondary consumers are found at the third trophic level. This third trophic level contains carnivores, such as the mountain lion. The members of the uppermost trophic level are the scavengers and decomposers, including hyenas, buzzards, fungi, and bacteria. The organisms in this trophic level break down all the nutrients (such as carbon and nitrogen) in the bodies of plants and animals and return them to the soil to be absorbed and used by plants.

It should be noted that no ecosystem actually has a simple and well-defined food pyramid. Many organisms interact with more than only the organisms at the adjacent trophic levels. For example, a coyote could be considered to belong to the third trophic level with the carnivores, but the coyote also feeds on occasional fruits and other primary producers. Basically, all living things are dependent on the first trophic level, because it alone has the capability to convert solar energy to energy found in, for example, glucose and starch. The food pyramid takes the geometric form of a triangle to show the flow of energy through a system.

Photosynthetic plants lose 10 percent of the energy they absorb from the sun as they convert solar energy into glucose and starch. In turn, the herbivores can convert and use only 90 percent of the energy they obtain by eating plants. Hence, less energy is found at each higher trophic level. Because of this reduced energy, fewer organisms can be supported by each higher trophic level. Consequently, the sections of the pyramid get smaller at each higher trophic level, representing the decreasing levels of energy and number of members.

Through the years, two concepts of niche have evolved in ecology. The first is the place niche, the physical space in which an organism lives. The second is the ecological niche, and it encompasses the particular location occupied by an organism and its functional role in the community.

The functional role of a species is not limited to its placement along a food pyramid; it also includes the interactions of a species with other organisms while obtaining food. For example, the methods used to tolerate the physical factors of its environment, such as climate, water, nutrients, soils, parasites, and the like, are all part of its functional role. In other words, the ecological niche of an organism is its natural history: all the interactions and interrelationships of the species with other organisms and the environment.

The study of the interrelationships among organisms has been the focus of ecological studies since the 1960's. Before this time, researchers had focused on the food pyramid and its effect on population changes of merely a single species. One example, the classic population study of the lynx and the snowshoe hare of Canada, originally focused on the interactions of the species in the food pyramid. It was discovered that the lynx had a ten-year population cycle closely following the population cycle of its prey, the snowshoe hare. The lynx population appeared to rise, causing a decline in the population of the snowshoe hare. In the investigations that followed, however, studies diverted the focus from the food pyramid to other elements of the niche of the two species. For example, the reproductive nature of the hare provided a contradiction to the simple predator-prey explanation. The hare has a faster rate of reproduction than the lynx. It seemed impossible that the significantly lower population of lynx could effectively place sufficient predator pressure on the hare to cause its drastic decline in numbers. Therefore, it appeared that the population dynamics of the hare and lynx were regulated by more than simply a predator-prey relationship.

Later studies of the lynx and hare suggested that the peaks and dives in the two populations may also be a factor of parasites of the hare that are carried by the lynx. A rise in the lynx population increases the carriers of parasites of the hare. Therefore, it is thought that, although the hare has a much greater reproduction rate than the lynx, the population of hares will still decline because of the combination of predation by the lynx and the increased frequency of parasites of the hare. This study involved looking at more than one dimension of the ecological niche of a species and broke away from concentrating on only the interactions between organisms in the food pyramid.

The goal of understanding how species interact with one another can also be better accomplished by defining the degree of niche overlap, the degree of the sharing of resources between two species. When two species use one or more of the same elements of an ecological niche, they exhibit interspecific competition. It was once believed that interspecific competition would always lead to survival of only the better competitor of the two species. That was the original concept of the principle of the competition exclusion law of ecology: No two species can utilize the same ecological niche. It was conjectured that the weaker competitor would either migrate, begin using another resource not used by the stronger competitor, or become extinct. It is now believed that the end result of two species sharing elements of ecological niches may not always be exclusion.

Ecologists theorize that similar species do, in fact, coexist, despite the sharing of elements of their ecological niches, because of character displacement, which leads to a decrease in niche overlap. Character displacement involves a change in the morphological, behavioral, or physiological state of a species without geographical isolation. Character displacement occurs as a result of natural selection arising from competition between one or more ecologically similar species. Examples might be changes in mouth sizes so that they begin to feed on different sizes of the same food type, thereby decreasing competition.

The more specialized a species, the more rigid it will be in terms of its ecological niche. A species that is general in terms of its ecological niche needs will be better able to find and use an alternative for the common element of the niche. Since a highly specialized species cannot substitute whatever is being used, it cannot compete as well as the other species. Therefore, a specialized species is more likely to become extinct.

For example, a panda is a very specialized feeder, eating mainly bamboo. If a pest is introduced into the environment that destroys bamboo, the panda will probably starve, being unable to switch to another food source. On the other hand, the coyote is a generalized feeder. It has a broad variety of food types that make up its diet. If humans initiate a pest-control program, killing the population of rabbits, the coyote will not fall victim to starvation, because it can switch to feeding predominantly on rodents, insects, fruits, and domesticated animals (including cats, dogs, and chickens). Hence, species with specialized ecological niche demands (specialists) are more in danger of extinction than those with generalized needs (generalists). Although this fundamental difference in survival can be seen between specialists and generalists, it must be noted again that exclusion is not an inevitable result of competition. There are many cases of ecologically similar species that coexist.

When individuals of the same species compete for the same elements of the ecological niche, it is referred to as intraspecific competition. Intraspecific competition has the opposite effect of interspecific competition: niche generalizations. In increasing populations, the first inhabitants will have access to optimal resources. The opportunity for optimal resources decreases as the population increases; hence, intraspecific competition increases. Deviant individuals using marginal resources may slowly begin to use less-optimal resources that are in less demand. That can lead to an increase in the diversity of ecological niches used by the species as a whole. In other words, the species may become more generalized and exploit wider varieties of niche elements.

Representing a situation on the opposite end of the spectrum from that of two organisms competing for the same dimension of an ecological niche is the vacant niche theory. This ecological principle states that when an organism is removed from its ecological niche, space, or any other dimension of the niche, another organism of the same or similar species will reinvade.

Methods of Study

Theoretical studies of ecological niches are abstract, since humans are limited to three-dimensional diagrams, and there are more dimensions than three to an ecological niche. This multidimensionality is referred to as the n-dimensional niche. This abstract n-dimensional niche can be studied mathematically and statistically, but ecology is mainly a field science. Therefore, the focus of techniques are those used for field research of the ecological niche.

Research that attempts to describe all the elements of the n-dimensional ecological niche would require extensive observations. Yet, ecological niches are difficult to measure not only because of the plethora of data that would have to be collected but also because of the element of change in nature. The internal and external environment of an organism is always dynamic. Nothing in life is static, even if equilibrium is established.

These constant fluctuations create daily and seasonal changes in space and ecological niches. Therefore, because of the constant fluctuations, any merely descriptive field observations would not be reliable depictions of an organism's ecological niche. Ecologists must also resort to quantitative data of measurable features of an organism's ecological niche. For example, the temperature, pH, light intensity, algae makeup, predators, and activity level of the organism are measurable features of an ecological niche in a pond community. The difficulty is in the collection of each of the necessary measurements making up an ecological niche. The ecologist would have to limit the data to a manageable number of specific dimensions of the niche based on conjecture and basic intuition. Such limitations often lead to incomplete and disconnected measurements that can at best only partially describe a few of the dimensions of the ecological niche.

Ecologists realize that complete observations and measurements of all the dimensions of an organism's ecological niche are unattainable. The focus in understanding how a species interacts with its community centers on determining the degree of niche overlap between any two species. In other words, the level of competition for space niche and resources. Studies of this niche overlap are typically limited to dimensions that can be quantitatively measured. Yet, there is still the problem of deciding which of the dimensions are involved in the competition between the two species. Again, the ecologist must usually rely on inherent knowledge about the two species in question. Often, researchers investigating niche competition measure no more than four ecological niche dimensions to determine the niche overlap in an attempt to understand how two individuals competing for the same space, resources, or other ecological niche features can coexist.

Field methods for observations and quantitative measurements of elements of ecological niches, niche overlap, and niche competition are probably endless. To name a few, describing an organism's niche may involve fecal samples to determine its diet, fecal samples of possible predators to identify its primary predator, animal and plant species checklists of its space niche along with soil components, climatic trends, and the like. Niche competition and overlap often can be studied first in the laboratory under controlled situations. One method might involve recording the population dynamics of the species as different elements in the ecological niche are manipulated to determine which is the better competitor and what is the resource that is most responsible for limiting the population size.

Context

The shift in meaning and study from merely space and trophic level placement in the food pyramid to ecological niche of n dimensions has been beneficial for the field of ecology and for humankind's daily activities. This focus on community ecology is obviously much more productive for the goal of ecology, the understanding of how all living organisms interact with one another, and with the nonliving elements in the environment.

Perhaps more important is the attempt to describe niches in terms of community ecology, which can be essential for some of humankind's confrontations with nature. For example, it becomes more and more apparent that synthetic chemicals are often too costly and too hazardous to continue using for control of crop pests and carriers of diseases. The goal is to control pests effectively with biological controls. Biological controls can involve the introduction of natural predators of the undesirable pest or the introduction of a virus or bacteria that eliminates the pest and is harmless to humans and wildlife.

The success of a biological control is directly proportional to the knowledge of the pest's n-dimensional ecological niche and the other organisms with which it comes in contact. A classic example of the havoc that can result from manipulations of nature without adequate ecological information is when Hawaii attempted to use biological controls to eradicate a population of snakes, which man accidentally introduced. The biological control used was the snake's natural predator, the mongoose. One very important dimension of the ecological niche of both species was ignored. One species was active only at night, while the other was active only during the day. Needless to say, this particular venture with a biological control was not a success.

Another relevant function of community-oriented studies of ecological niches involves endangered species. In addition to having aesthetic and potential medicinal values, an endangered organism may be a keystone species, a species on which the entire community depends. A keystone species is so integral to keeping a community healthy and functioning that if obliterated the community no longer operates properly and is not productive.

Habitat destruction has become the commonest cause of drastic population declines of endangered species. To enhance the habitat of the endangered species, it is undeniably beneficial to know what attracts a species to its particular preferred habitat. This knowledge involves the details of many of the dimensions of its ecological niche integral to its population distribution. Another common cause of endangering the survival of a species is when an introduced organism competes for the same resources and displaces the native species. Solving such competition between native and introduced species would first involve determining niche overlap.

It is often stated that an ounce of prevention is worth a pound of cure. Thus, the researching and understanding of all the dimensions of ecological niches are integral components for preventing environmental manipulations by humankind that might lead to species extinction. Many science authorities have agreed that future research in ecology and related fields should focus on solving three main problems: species endangerment, soil erosion, and solid waste management.

This focus on research in ecology often means that studies of pristine communities, those undisturbed, will be the most helpful for future restoration projects. Although quantitative and qualitative descriptions of pristine areas seem to be unscientific at the time they are made, because there is no control or experimental group, they are often the most helpful for later investigations. For example, after a species has shown a drastic decline in its population, the information from the observations of the once-pristine area may help to uncover what niche dimension was altered, causing the significant population decrease.

Bibliography

Ehrlich, Paul R. *The Machinery of Nature*. New York: Simon & Schuster, 1986. Chapter 6, "Who Lives Together, and How," cites many examples of interactions between species in terms of community ecology. Includes several photographs of animals in their habitat and a list for further reading at the end of the book.

Giller, Paul S. *Community Structure and the Niche*. New York: Chapman and Hall, 1984. This excellent book is intended to give an introduction to the current theories and ideals on community structure and to provide an opening into the vast and detailed information available. It contains many charts and diagrams detailing topics under discussion. An extensive list of references is found at the back of the book.

Knight, Clifford B. *Basic Concepts of Ecology*. New York: Macmillan, 1965. This general ecology book covers a broad range of topics. Ecological niche is discussed in chapter 6, with several photographs and tables supporting the text. An ample list of references is provided at the end of the chapter.

National Science Foundation Staff. *Ecology: Impacts and Implications*. Garden City Park, N.J.: Avery Publishing Group, 1982. A collection of articles that describe the ecology in nontechnical terms. Habitats discussed range from Antarctic waters to tropical forests, and emphasis is on the relationships between organisms and their environment. Includes photographs of habitats and diagrams of ecological processes.

Ricklefs, Robert E. *Ecology*. 2d ed. New York: Chiron Press, 1979. A textbook written with exceptional clarity. Chapter 39, "The Niche Concept in Community Ecology," gives an in-depth discussion of the ecological niche and the principles involved. Many charts, figures, tables, and mathematical equations are used, further enhancing the topic. Chapter 41 describes the food pyramid and its relevance to the ecological niche. Glossary and bibliography are found at the end of the book.

Smith, Robert L. *Ecology and Field Biology*. 3d ed. New York: Harper & Row, 1980. A text easily readable by college and senior-level high school students. It has many informative illustrations, and the extensive appendices make the book a useful source. Includes an excellent index and glossary.

Whittaker, Robert H., and Simon A. Levin, eds. *Niche: Theory and Application*. Stroudsburg, Pa.: Dowden, Hutchinson & Ross, 1975. A compilation of papers written on various elements of the ecological niche. Essays 5 through 8 deal with the competitive exclusion principle. The authors' comments preceding the papers are excellent summarizations. The papers do tend to be technical and might be more suitable for the college-level reader.

Jessica O. Ellison

Cross-References

Adaptations and Their Mechanisms, 22; The Biosphere, Biomes, and Habitats, 210; Coevolution, 512; Competition, 541; Demographics, 597; Ecological Principles, 736; Mark, Release, and Recapture Methods for Population Analysis, 1668; Population Fluctuations, 2154; Predation, 2178; Sessile Community Sampling, 2473; Speciation and the Species Concept, 2521.

ECOLOGICAL PRINCIPLES

Type of life science: Ecology
Other fields of study: Evolutionary biology and systematics (taxonomy)

Ecology is the study of the relationships of organisms to their environments. By examining those relationships in natural ecosystems, principles can be discovered which may help humankind understand its own role on this planet.

Principal terms
ADAPTATION: a genetic (intrinsic) feature of an organism which, through natural selection, enhances its fitness in a given environment
COMMUNITY: all the populations that exist in a given habitat
ECOSYSTEM: the biological community in a given habitat combined with all the physical properties of the environment in that habitat
ENVIRONMENT: all the forces (heat, light, and so on) and things (food, water, other organisms) external to an oganism which directly affect it
FITNESS: the contribution of an organism to future generations; the perpetuation of its genes through reproduction
HABITAT: the place where an organism lives; for example, a pond or forest
NATURAL SELECTION: a change in the genetic makeup of a population as a result of different survival and reproduction (fitness) among its members
NICHE: the role of an organism in its environment; the sum of all factors that define its existence (temperature, energy requirements, and so on)
POPULATION: all the individuals in a habitat which are of the same species
RESOURCE: a requirement for life, such as space for living, food (for animals), or light (for plants), not including conditions such as temperature or salinity

Summary of the Phenomenon

Ecology is the study of how organisms relate to their natural environments. The two principal concerns of ecologists are the distribution and abundance of organisms: Why are animals, plants, and other organisms found where they are, and why are some common and others rare? These questions have their roots in the theory of evolution. In fact, it is difficult (and not often worthwhile) to separate modern ecological matters from the concerns of evolutionary biologists. Ecology can be divided according to several levels of organization: the individual organism, the population, the community, and the ecosystem.

An ecologist views organisms as consequences of past natural selection brought about by their environments. That is, each organism represents an array of adaptations that can provide insight into the environmental pressures that resulted in its present form. Adaptations of organisms are also revealed by other features, such as the range of temperature an organism can tolerate, the amount of moisture it requires, or the variety of food it can exploit. Food and space for living are considered resources; factors such as temperature, light, and moisture are conditions which determine the rate of resource utilization. When ecologists have discovered the full range of resources and conditions necessary for an organism's existence, they have discovered its niche.

Many species, such as many insects and plants, have a large reproductive output. This compensates for high mortality imposed by natural selection. Other species, such as large mammals and birds, have fewer offspring. Many of these animals care for their young, thus increasing the chances that their offspring will survive to reproduce. These are two different strategies for success, based upon the principle that organisms have a finite energy budget. Energy acquired from food (animals) or sunlight (plants) must be partitioned among growth, maintenance, and reproduction. The greater the energy allocated to the care of offspring, for example, the fewer the offspring that can be produced.

The concept of an energy budget is a key to understanding evolutionary strategies of organisms, as well as the energetics of ecosystems. The amount of energy fixed and stored by an organism is called net production; this is the energy used for growth and reproduction. Net production is the difference between gross production (the amount of energy assimilated) and respiration (metabolic maintenance cost). The greater the respiration, the less energy will be left over for growth and reproduction. Endothermic animals, which physiologically regulate their body heat (mammals and birds), have a very high respiration rate relative to ectotherms (reptiles, amphibians, fish, and invertebrates), which cannot. Among endotherms, smaller animals have higher respiration rates than larger ones, because the ratio of body surface area (the area over which heat is exchanged with the environment) to volume (the size of the "furnace") decreases with increasing body size.

Although single organisms can be studied with regard to adaptations, in nature most organisms exist in populations rather than as individuals. Some organisms reproduce asexually (that is, by forming clones), so that a single individual may spawn an entire population of genetically identical individuals. Populations of sexually reproducing organisms, however, have the property of genetic variability, since not all individuals are identical. That is, members of a population have slightly different niches and will therefore not all be equally capable of living in a given environment. This is the property upon which Charles Darwin's theory of natural selection depends: Because not all individuals are identical, some will have greater fitness than others. Those with superior fitness will reproduce in greater numbers and therefore will contribute more genes to successive generations. In nature, many species consist of populations occupying more than a single habitat.

This constitutes a buffer against extinction: If one habitat is destroyed, the species will not go extinct, because it exists in other habitats.

Two dynamic features of populations are growth and regulation. Growth is simply the difference between birth and death rates, which can be positive (growing), negative (declining), or zero (in equilibrium). Every species has a genetic capacity for exponential (continuously accelerating) increase, which will express itself to varying degrees depending on environmental conditions: A population in its "ideal" environment will express this capacity more nearly than one in a less favorable environment. The rate of growth of a population is affected by its age structure— the proportion of individuals of different ages. For example, a population which is growing rapidly will have a higher proportion of juvenile individuals than one which is growing more slowly.

Populations may be regulated (so that they have equal birth and death rates) by a number of factors, all of which are sensitive to changes in population size. A population may be regulated by competition among its members for the resource that is in shortest supply (limiting). The largest population that can be sustained by the available resources is called the carrying capacity of the environment. A population of rodents, for example, might be limited by its food supply such that as the population grows and food runs out, the reproductive rates declines. Thus, the effect of food on population growth depends upon the population size relative to the limiting resource. Similarly, parasites that cause disease spread faster in large, dense populations than in smaller ones (for humans, plague spreads faster in cities than in rural areas). Predators can also regulate populations of their prey by responding to changes in prey availability. Climate and catastrophic events such as storms may severely affect populations, but their effect is not dependent upon density and is thus not considered regulatory.

Competition occurs between, as well as within, species. Two species are said to be in competition with each other if and only if they share a resource that is in short supply. If, however, they merely share a resource that is plentiful, then they are not really competing for it. Competition is thought to be a major force in determining how many species can coexist in natural communities. There are a number of alternative hypotheses, however, which involve such factors as evolutionary time, productivity (the energy base for a community), heterogeneity of the habitat, and physical harshness of the environment.

Predator-prey interactions are those in which the predator benefits from killing and consuming its prey. These differ from most parasite-host interactions in that parasites usually do not kill their hosts (a form of suicide for creatures that live inside other creatures). Similarly, most plant-eating animals (herbivores) do not kill the plants on which they feed. Many ecologists classify herbivores as parasites for this reason. There are exceptions, such as birds and rodents that eat seeds, and these can be classified as legitimate predator-prey interactions. Predators can influence the number of species in a community by affecting competition among their prey: If populations of competing species are lowered by predators so that they are below their carrying capacities, then there may be enough resources to support colonization by new species.

In many cases, the interaction between two species is mutually beneficial. Mutualism is often thought to arise as a result of closely linked evolutionary histories (coevolution) of different species. Termites harbor protozoans in their guts that produce an enzyme which can break down cellulose in wood. The protozoans thus are provided with a habitat, and termites are able to derive nourishment from wood. Some *Acacia* trees in the tropics have hollow thorns which provide a habitat for ants. In return, the ants defend the trees from other insects which would otherwise damage or defoliate them.

Communities of organisms are composed of many populations that may interact with one another in a variety of ways: predation, competition, mutualism, parasitism, and so on. The composition of communities changes over time through the process of succession. In terrestrial communities, bare rock may be weathered and broken down by bacteria and other organisms until it becomes soil. Plants can then invade and colonize this newly formed soil, which in turn provides food and habitat for animals. The developing community goes through a series of stages, the nature of which depends on local climatic conditions, until it reaches a kind of equilibrium. In many cases this equilibrium stage, called climax, is a mature forest. Aquatic succession essentially is a process of becoming a terrestrial community. The basin of a lake, for example, will gradually be filled with silt from terrestrial run off and accumulated dead organic material from populations of organisms within the lake itself.

Ecosystems consist of several trophic levels, or levels at which energy is acquired: primary producers, consumers, and decomposers. Primary producers are green plants that capture solar energy and transform it, through the process of photosynthesis, into chemical energy. Organisms that eat plants (herbivores) or animals (carnivores) to obtain their enegy are collectively called consumers. Decomposers are those consumers, such as bacteria and fungi, that obtain energy by breaking down dead bodies of plants and animals. These trophic levels are linked together into a structure called a food web, in which energy is transferred from primary producers to consumers and decomposers, until finally all is lost as heat. Each transfer of energy entails a loss (as heat) of at least 90 percent, which means that the total amount of energy available to carnivores in an ecosystem is substantially less than that available to herbivores.

As with individual organisms, ecosystems and their trophic levels have energy budgets. The net production of one trophic level is available to the next-higher trophic level as biomass (mass of biological material). Plants have higher net productivity (rates of production) than animals because their metabolic maintenance cost is lower relative to gross productivity; herbivores often have higher net productivity than predators for the same reason. For the community as a whole, net productivity is highest during early successional stages, since biomass is being added more rapidly than later on, when the community is closer to climax equilibrium.

In contrast to the unidirectional flow of energy, materials are conserved and recycled from dead organisms by decomposers to support productivity at higher trophic levels. Carbon, water, and mineral nutrients required for plant growth are cycled through various organisms within an ecosystem. Materials and energy are also exchanged among ecosystems: There is no such thing in nature as a "closed" ecosystem that is entirely self-contained.

Methods of Study

The science of ecology is necessarily more broadly based than most biological disciplines; consequently, there is more than one approach to it. Ecological studies fall into three categories: descriptive, experimental, and mathematical.

Descriptive ecology is concerned with describing natural history, usually in qualitative terms. The study of adaptations, for example, is descriptive in that one can measure the present "value" of an adaptive feature, but one can only conjecture as to the history of natural selection that was responsible for it. On the other hand, there are some patterns discernible in nature for which hypotheses can be constructed and tested by statistical inference. For example, the spatial distribution (dispersion) of birds on an island may be random, indicating no biological interaction among them. If the birds are more evenly spaced (uniform dispersion) than predicted assuming randomness, however, then it might be inferred that the birds are competing for space; they are exhibiting territorial exclusion of one another. Such "natural experiments," as they are called, depend heavily upon the careful design of statistical tests.

Experimental ecology is no different from any other experimental discipline; hypotheses are constructed from observations of nature, controlled experiments are designed to test them, and conclusions are drawn from the results of the experiments. The basic laboratory for an ecologist is the field. Experiments in the field are difficult because it is hard to isolate and manipulate variable factors one at a time, which is a requisite for any good experiment in science. A common experiment that is performed to test for resource limitation in an organism is enhancement of that resource. If food, for example, is thought to be in short supply (implying competition), one section of the habitat is provided more food than is already present; another section is left alone as a control. If survivorship, growth, or reproductive output is higher in the enhanced portion of the habitat than in the control area, the researcher may infer that the organisms therein were food-limited. Alternatively, an ecologist might have decreased the density of organisms in one portion of the habitat, which might seem equivalent to increasing food supply for the remaining organisms, except that it represents a change in population density as well. Therefore, this second design will not allow the researcher to differentiate between the possibly separate effects of food level and simple population density on organisms in the habitat.

Mathematical ecology relies heavily upon computers to generate models of nature. A model is simply a formalized, quantitative set of hypotheses constructed from sets of assumptions of how things happen in nature. A model of population growth might contain assumptions about the age structure of a population, its genetic capacity for increase, and the average rate of resource utilization by its members. By changing these assumptions, scientists can cause the model population to behave in different ways over time. The utility of such modeling is limited to the accuracy of the assumptions employed.

Modern ecology is concerned with integrating these different approaches, all of which have in common the goal of predicting the way nature will behave in the future, based upon how it behaves in the present. Description of natural history leads to hypotheses that can be tested experimentally, which in turn may allow the construction of realistic mathematical (quantitative) models of how nature works.

Context

People historically have viewed nature as an adversary. The "conquest of nature" has traditionally meant human encroachment on natural ecosystems, usually without benefit of predictive knowledge. Such environmental problems as pollution, species extinction, and overpopulation can be viewed as experiments performed on a grand scale without appropriate controls. The problem with such experiments is that the outcomes might be irreversible. A major lesson of ecology is that humans are not separate from nature; we are constrained by the same principles as are other organisms on the planet Earth. One object of ecology, then, is to learn these principles so that they can be applied to our portion of the earth's ecosystem.

Populations that are not regulated by predators, disease, or food limitation grow exponentially. The human population, on a global scale, grows this way. All the wars and famines in history have scarcely made a dent in this growth pattern. Humankind has yet to identify its carrying capacity on a global scale, although regional famines certainly have provided insights into what happens when local carrying capacity is exceeded. The human carrying capacity needs to be defined in realistic ecological terms, and such constraints as energy, food, and space must be incorporated into the calculations. For example, knowledge of energy flow teaches that there is more energy at the bottom of a food web (producers) than at successively higher trophic levels (consumers), which means that more people could be supported as herbivores than as carnivores.

The study of disease transmisson, epidemiology, relies heavily on ecological principles. Population density, rates of migration among epidemic centers, physiological tolerance of the host, and rates of evolution of disease-causing parasites are all the subjects of ecological study.

An obvious application of ecological principles is conservation. Before habitats for endangered species can be set aside, for example, their ecological requirements, such as migratory routes, breeding, and feeding habits, must be known. This also applies to the introduction (intentional or accidental) of exotic species into habitats. History is filled with examples of introduced species that caused the extinction of native species. Application of ecological knowledge in a timely fashion, therefore, might prevent species from becoming endangered in the first place.

One of the greatest challenges we face is the loss of habitats worldwide. This is especially true of the tropics, which contain most of the earth's species of plants and animals. Species in the tropics have narrow niches, which means that they are more restricted in range and less tolerant of change than are many temperate species. Therefore, destruction of tropical habitats, such as rain forests, leads to rapid species extinction. These species are the potential sources of many pharmaceutically valuable drugs; further, they are a genetic record of millions of years of evolutionary history. Tropical rain forests also are prime sources of oxygen and act as a buffer against carbon dioxide accumulation in the atmosphere. Ecological knowledge of global carbon cycles permits the prediction that destruction of these forests will have a profound impact on the quality of the air.

Bibliography

Carson, Rachel. *Silent Spring*. Boston: Houghton Mifflin, 1962. This book often has been credited with launching the environmental movement in the United States. Carson presents a chilling look at what can happen when we cause our environment to deteriorate. As timely today as when it was written, this book will appeal to concerned members of the general populace; no scientific training is required to understand its message.

Elton, Charles. *Animal Ecology*. New York: Macmillan, 1927. Written by one of the founders of the field, Elton's book is not only of historical interest but also surprisingly timely. Much of the philosophy behind modern approaches to ecology stems from this work. Especially noteworthy is Elton's development of the niche concept.

Hutchinson, G. Evelyn. *The Ecological Theater and the Evolutionary Play*. New Haven, Conn.: Yale University Press, 1969. The author, arguably the father of modern ecology, writes lucidly and incisively about the interplay between ecology and evolution. His approach is strongly historical, and his accounts of "the naturalist as art critic" are both informative and entertaining. Hutchinson's philosophy of science, well detailed herein, has influenced generations of ecologists and evolutionary biologists.

Krebs, Charles J. *The Message of Ecology*. New York: Harper & Row, 1987. As the author notes in his preface, this book was designed to introduce readers to the scope of modern ecology without "all the detail that is necessary in a more conventional textbook." The subject matter includes all levels of ecology: individuals, populations, communities, and ecosystems. While not exhaustive in any of these areas, this small book is sufficient to give the novice reader a feeling for the ecologist's world.

Odum, Eugene P. *Basic Ecology*. Philadelphia: W. B. Saunders, 1983. This is a thoughtfully down-scaled and less technical version of the author's classic text, *Fundamentals of Ecology*. As such, it can be read by anyone with a high school background in biology and chemistry. It covers all the levels of ecology and includes a brief "epilogue," in which Odum makes some predictions about humans' future on earth, drawing on his considerable expertise.

Ricklefs, Robert E. *Ecology*. 3d ed. New York: Chiron Press, 1988. This is one of the best general texts in the field; it covers more ground more thoroughly than many other texts do. Suitable for a college-level course, it requires some background in general biology and genetics at the college level. The writing style is clear enough, however, that even the reader with less background can glean much from Ricklefs' discussion of adaptations of organisms to their environments.

Wilson, Edward O., and William H. Bossert. *A Primer of Population Biology*. Sunderland, Mass.: Sinauer Associates, 1971. This is a self-teaching guide to basic mathematical population biology that can profit anyone familiar with basic algebra. It leads the reader step-by-step through basic population growth and ecological genetics (a course in basic genetics would be useful background), with clearly defined terms at each step.

L. E. Hurd

Cross-References

Adaptations and Their Mechanisms, 22; Biomass Related to Energy, 203; The Biosphere, Biomes, and Habitats, 210; Coevolution, 512; Community Structure and Stability, 533; Competition, 541; Demographics, 597; Ecological Niches, 729; The Greenhouse Effect, 1225; Mark, Release, and Recapture Methods for Population Analysis, 1668; The Nitrogen and Phosphorus Cycles, 1951; Population Fluctuations, 2154; Exponential and Logistic Population Growth, 2161; Predation, 2178; Reproductive Strategies, 2339; Sessile Community Sampling, 2473; Succession, 2566; Symbiosis, Commensalism, and Parasitism, 2572; The Water Cycle, 2695.

ELECTRON MICROSCOPY

Type of life science: Cell biology (cytology)
Other fields of study: Biophysics and histology

The electron microscope has revolutionized biology since its invention in 1931.
Electron microscopy has provided views of cells, bacteria, proteins, and other bio-
logical systems that could not have been obtained by any other method.

Principal terms

ELECTROMAGNETIC WAVE: a phenomenon involving oscillating electric
and magnetic fields capable of transferring energy

ELECTRON: a negatively charged subatomic particle

ELECTRON MICROSCOPE: any of the family of instruments that form
images using electrons instead of light

LIGHT MICROSCOPE: a microscope that forms images using light waves

RESOLVED IMAGE: an image of an object which is distinctly separated
from the images of other objects

SCANNING ELECTRON MICROSCOPE (SEM): an electron microscope that
operates by use of a beam of electrons that are scanned over a
specimen; most useful for studying a specimen's surface

TRANSMISSION ELECTRON MICROSCOPE (TEM): an electron microscope
that operates by aiming a beam of electrons through a specimen;
most useful for studying the internal structure of cells

WAVE: a traveling disturbance which transports energy without
transporting matter

WAVELENGTH: the distance between the adjacent peaks (or troughs) of a
wave

Summary of the Methodology

The electron microscope was invented in 1931 by Ernst Ruska (who, in 1986, won
the Nobel Prize in Physics for this effort); since the time of its invention, several
different types of electron microscope have been developed. Electron microscopy
uses a beam of electrons instead of a beam of light to form an image. Light is a
form of electromagnetic radiation; electromagnetic radiation is a process that transfers energy as a wave without transferring matter. An electromagnetic wave can be
visualized in terms of a wave traveling on the surface of a pool of water: The
undulating pattern of peaks and troughs constitutes the wave. In the case of electromagnetic radiation, the undulations that constitute the wave occur in electric and
magnetic fields that are perpendicular to each other. The properties of waves that
are of interest in electron microscopy can be described in terms of the wavelength
of a wave. The wavelength of a wave is the distance between adjacent peaks (or
adjacent troughs) in the waveform. Wavelength is important because when a wave

interacts with matter, any structures that are smaller than one-quarter of a wavelength are "invisible" to the wave. In approximate terms, the smallest object that a wave can be used to image is equal in size to the wavelength of the wave used to form the image. The wavelength of visible light is approximately between 400 nanometers and 700 nanometers (a nanometer is one billionth of a meter).

It is usual to consider light as a wave, or a ray, and to consider electrons as particles. According to quantum physics, however, waves and particles are two aspects of the same phenomenon: Light can be considered as a stream of particles, and a stream of electrons can be considered as a wave. This behavior is usually referred to as wave-particle duality. A stream of electrons has a smaller wavelength than a beam of light, and electrons can therefore be used to form images of small objects — such as cells. If distinct images of separate objects are formed, the images are said to be resolved. Because the wavelength of an electron is much smaller than the wavelength of light, the electron microscope can resolve images of objects that are a million times smaller than the objects seen in traditional optical microscopes. The resolving power of a scanning tunneling microscope (STM) is sufficient to render it capable of determining the positions of individual atoms in the surface layer of a material. There is a variety of different types of electron microscope. The basic types include the transmission electron microscope, the scanning electron microscope, and the scanning tunneling microscope. The specimen in an electron microscope is usually observed in a vacuum in order to prevent scattering of the electrons by air molecules; the need for a vacuum presents the greatest difficulty in the application of electron microscopy to biological systems.

The simplest electron microscope is the transmission electron microscope (TEM). Electrons are produced by an electron gun and are accelerated by a potential difference (voltage). The electrons from the electron gun pass through a condenser lens and are then used to illuminate the specimen. The electrons which pass through the specimen are then allowed to pass through an electron lens objective. The objective magnifies the image, and then a second electron lens, which plays the role of the eyepiece in the standard microscope, is used to focus the image for observation. (The "lenses" used in electron microscopes are not lenses in the usual sense; instead, they are electric and magnetic fields, and they are accordingly referred to as electrostatic or magnetic lenses.) The image can then be formed on a photographic plate or observed on a fluorescent screen, or the electrons can be collected by a charge-sensitive device to produce an image on a cathode-ray tube. Higher magnification can be achieved by using more lenses.

The sample thickness will affect the resolving ability of the TEM. Usually, at least in the case of biological samples, the sample should be no more than ten times thicker than the structures that are to be analyzed. The resolving power of the TEM is such that it can observe structures that are slightly larger than atoms, but since the development of other systems, it has become less used, even though its resolution often exceeds that of the SEM. Typical resolutions are in the subnanometer range, with magnifications of up to 500,000 times.

The interpretation of the electron micrographs produced by a TEM is sometimes difficult. The major source of difficulty is that the image is produced by transmitted radiation. The eye is accustomed to interpreting images that are produced by reflection. In the absence of a sample, a TEM beam would saturate a film plate used to record an image. The sample prevents some of the electrons from reaching the film plate; the image produced by a TEM is somewhat similar to a negative produced in a normal camera. Much of the difficulty can be removed by photographing the micrograph and converting it to a positive image—there are, however, some residual interpretation difficulties caused by shadows.

The high-voltage electron microscope (HVEM) is a variant of the TEM. The conventional TEM works best on particles less than 0.5 nanometers thick; electrons of higher speed can be produced by increasing the voltage used to accelerate them, and thicker samples can then be analyzed. The wavelength of the electrons decreases as their speed (hence, their kinetic energy) increases. These short-wavelength electrons are less likely to collide with atoms as they pass through the specimen, and they are therefore able to render a sharper image of a thicker sample.

The scanning electron microscope (SEM) works on a different principle. Electrons are again produced and accelerated by an electron gun, but in an SEM the beam is focused by electron lenses and used to scan a sample. The scanning will result in two different electron beams being emitted by the sample, a primary beam of backscattered electrons produced by reflection and a secondary beam of electrons emitted by the atoms of the sample. By scanning the entire sample and collecting the primary and secondary electrons, the operator can produce an image of a sample on a cathode-ray tube.

The scanning tunneling electron microscope (STM) works on a completely different principle. It was developed by Gerd Binnig and Heinrich Rohrer at an International Business Machines (IBM) research laboratory in the 1980's; Binnig and Rohrer shared the 1986 Nobel Prize in Physics with Ernst Ruska for their work. The STM uses quantum tunneling. Quantum tunneling is the penetration of a barrier by a particle that, when analyzed by classical physics, does not have enough energy to pass through the barrier. Quantum mechanics predicts that there is a finite probability of a particle passing through a barrier, even if it lacks the energy to pass over it. The number of particles passing through the barrier will vary with the barrier thickness and the particle energy. This principle is used in the STM by allowing electrons to tunnel across a vacuum, from a stylus to a sample. The quantum tunneling of electrons sets up a "tunneling current" that increases as the vacuum gap between the stylus and the sample decreases. The variation in tunneling current can be used to map the surface of the sample as the stylus moves across its surface. The STM is capable of detecting structures 0.1 nanometer in size in the direction parallel to the motion of the scanning stylus. This means that atoms can be easily detected. The performance in the vertical direction is even more impressive: The STM can detect irregularities on the order of 0.01 nanometer. Thus, the STM, with its higher resolving power than the SEM or TEM, has little difficulty in the imaging of atoms.

The principal accommodations that must be made in the examination of biological samples using electron microscopy occur in the preparation of the sample. A commonly used method is the construction of replicas, made by the the vacuum deposition of thin layers of carbon, metals, or alloys on the surface of the sample. These films provide a replica of the surface, which can be scanned. Another useful technique, which is the standard technique of sample preparation used in optical microscopy, is the sectioning of samples and their impregnation with stains. The stains that are useful in electron microscopy are usually chemical compounds of heavy metals. These are effective stains because they strongly scatter electrons.

Many methods of sample preparation have been developed to enable electron microscopy to be more widely used on biological samples. Freeze-fracture and freeze-etch are methods of sample preparation that have been widely used. Freeze-fracture involves the freezing and splitting of a water-containing sample. Freeze-etch is a second step, in which ice is allowed to sublime (vaporize without forming a liquid) before the sample is analyzed in an electron microscope. Both techniques are used to examine the internal structure of materials without subjecting them to chemical changes. Freeze-fracture and freeze-etch allow the interior layers of water-containing samples to be investigated without the straining and chemical preparations that are needed to render internal structures visible in a standard light microscope. In particular, these techniques allow the observation of cell walls and cell membranes in a state which is as close as possible to the living state.

Applications of the Method

The electron microscope has revolutionized scientists' understanding of the microscopic world in the biological, medical, and physical sciences. Although it is not possible to observe living materials using electron microscopy, freeze-fracture and freeze-etch have allowed the observation of biological materials in an almost natural state.

Each of the different types of electron microscopes has proved to be useful in the biological sciences. The practice of correlative microscopy is being used increasingly. Correlative microscopy involves the the examination of a sample using both light microscopy and electron microscopy; this method allows the acquisition of a variety of views of the same structure, and it allows the ambiguities that may result from views produced by a single microscope to be removed. Light microscopy, scanning electron microscopy, and transmission electron microscopy are most effective on samples of different sizes. Light microscopy is usually reserved for the observation of large numbers of cells or for the location of single cells. Scanning electron microscopy is used in the examination of the surface profiles of cells. Transmission electron microscopy is used to probe the interiors of cells to elucidate their structures. The scanning tunneling microscope can be used to examine still smaller structures. Each of the techniques described has been used extensively in the biological sciences.

The transmission electron microscope (TEM) was the first electron microscope to be developed, and it is the most common type. The TEM has more in common with light microscopes than it does with any other electron microscope; in fact, it shares the chief disadvantage of the optical microscope—that is, it gives little impression of the vertical scale of the specimen under observation. This means that the structures present in the specimen are imaged, but the subtleties of the surface of the specimen are lost. Furthermore, the TEM imposes severe constraints on the type of specimens which can be analyzed. The sample must be thin enough to permit the beam of electrons to pass through it, and it must be resilient enough to resist being damaged by the imaging electrons.

Most biological materials are too thick to be observed under the TEM, so it is necessary to prepare ultrathin sections of samples prior to their analysis. Both plant and animal samples have been examined using the TEM, and their analysis has led to the discovery of a variety of internal structures. In the cytoplasms of animal cells, lamellae, membranes, microsomes, and spores were discovered by the TEM. The internal structure of the mitochondria, which had previously been discovered with light microscopy, has been probed. The TEM has also been used to examine the interiors of the nuclei of cells. The examination of the cell nuclei has enabled the investigation of chromosome organization and gene structure. This examination of the microstructure of cells has contributed to the development of molecular biology and genetic engineering.

The TEM has also been used to examine bacteria and viruses. The TEM detected the presence of nucleic acids in bacteria and produced the first images of viruses; most viruses are too small to be resolved in light microscopes. In plants, the TEM has been used in the study of chloroplasts, and the walls of cells. The observation of chloroplasts led to the discovery of the internal membranes called thylakoids, which absorb light for the process of photosynthesis. The discovery of the thylakoids has enhanced the understanding of photosynthesis.

The scanning electron microscope (SEM) has been widely used in the biological sciences. Physical laws impose no constraints on the size of the sample to be examined—they are, instead, imposed by the available sample chambers. The SEM is usually used in the magnification range of 10 to 100,000 times. When compared with the light microscope, the main advantage of the SEM is that it is able to produce three-dimensional images. These images are possible because the entire sample can be observed in focus at the same time, and the sample can be observed from a variety of angles.

The SEM has allowed images to be formed of algae, bacteria, spores, molds, and fungi. These images have enabled the structure and function of these samples to be determined. The xylem and phloem cells that transport water through the stems of plants have been examined in the SEM, thus allowing the water transportation process to be better understood. The SEM has also been used on human samples—the structures of blood, skin, and bone have been examined The SEM also has applications in exploring the pathology of cells. Many structures formed by living cells are better understood because sample preparation techniques such as freeze-fracture and freeze-etch have allowed the examination of lifelike samples under the SEM.

Context

Electron microscopy allows both greater resolution and greater magnification than light microscopy. In fact, the views are so spectacular that there is a tendency to use the electron microscope to observe objects large enough to be imaged satisfactorily in a low-power light microscope. The invention of the electron microscope has allowed biologist to look at—and inside—cells and has enabled the examination of biologically important molecules such as deoxyribonucleic acid (DNA) and proteins. The recognition of the cell as the basic unit of life predates the electron microscope, but the understanding of cellular structure has advanced in parallel with the development of electron microscopy.

Electron microscopes have also been useful in promoting public health and industrial safety. One of the major hazards of an industrialized society is the existence of airborne particulate pollutants. Particles in the range of 3 microns (three-millionths of a meter) have a tendency to collect in the lungs, where they remain to irritate the lining of the lungs. In the modern world, the principal contaminants are carbon particles and asbestos fibers. The electron microscope allows scientists to ensure that the atmosphere is free of such contaminants; conversely, it can alert scientists to their presence.

In all electron microscopes, biological applications are limited by the techniques available for sample preparation. The high resolution of the scanning tunneling microscope (STM) offers the scientist the ability to observe materials on the atomic scale. Unfortunately for biologists, the STM (like the SEM) requires a sample to be an electrical conductor, and few materials of biological interest are electrical conductors. Nevertheless, the biological applications of electron microscopy are still in their infancy, and improvements in sample preparation will increase its usefulness in future biological applications.

Bibliography

Hey, Tony, and Patrick Walters. *The Quantum Universe*. Cambridge, England: Cambridge University Press, 1987. This work, written for the layman, is devoted to quantum physics. All physical processes necessary for a good understanding of electron microscopy are covered, and there is a section devoted to microscopy. The main ideas are developed pictorially rather than through the use of mathematical equations.

Koehler, James K. *Advanced Techniques in Biological Electron Microscopy*. New York: Springer-Verlag, 1973. As the title suggests, this is an advanced work; it is intended for the reader who wishes to learn to use the electron microscope. An invaluable reference for those who wish to know how samples are prepared for use in an electron microscope.

Scanga, Franco, ed. *Atlas of Electron Microscopy: Biological Applications*. Rev. ed.

New York: American Elsevier, 1964. An excellent place to begin studying electron mircographs of biological systems. The micrographs pictured in this volume provide the reader with an extensive understanding of the range of applicability of electron microscopy and an appreciation of the relative merits of electron and optical spectroscopy.

Shipman, James T., and Jerry D. Wilson. *An Introduction to Physical Science*. 6th ed. Lexington, Mass.: D. C. Heath, 1990. This book is recommended for those readers who lack an understanding of wave-particle duality and quantum physics. It is an elementary college-level text requiring no mathematical prerequisites. Recommended for those who wish to develop a thorough understanding of the advantages of electron microscopy.

Tribe, Michael A., Michael R. Eraut, and Robert K. Snook. *Electron Microscopy and Cell Structure*. Cambridge, England: Cambridge University Press, 1975. A companion volume to *Light Microscopy* in the Cambridge Basic Biology series. Presents a good discussion of the relative merits of traditional light microscopy and electron microscopy. Contains several photographs of the views of cells provided by electron microscopes.

_____. *Light Microscopy*. Cambridge, England: Cambridge University Press, 1975. This work is part of the Cambridge Basic Biology series and provides the basic knowledge of light microscopy necessary to appreciate the benefits of electron microscopy. Recommended to readers not familiar with technical concepts, such as magnification and resolution. Written for college freshmen but suitable for the high school reader.

Watt, Ian M. *The Principles and Practice of Electron Microscopy*. Cambridge, England: Cambridge University Press, 1985. An easily understood survey of the entire field of electron microscopy. This book is a good resource for those who need more information about the field. Many references for further study are provided.

Stephen R. Addison

Cross-References

Autoradiography and Subcellular Fractionation of Radioactive Tracer Molecules, 148; Cell Sizes and Capabilities, 368; The Cytoskeleton, 582; Microbial Diseases, 1714; Microbiology: Scope and Methodology, 1729; Applied Microbiology, 1737; Nuclear Structure, 1972; Prokaryotic Cell Structure, 2210; Self-Replicating Molecules, 2459; Subcellular Fractionation Using Centrifugation, 2552.

ELECTRON TRANSPORT AND OXIDATIVE PHOSPHORYLATION

Types of life science: Biochemistry and respiration
Other field of study: Biophysics

Oxidative phosphorylation includes the reactions taking place in mitochondria to produce adenosine triphosphate (ATP), which functions as the primary energy currency of cells. A key part to this process is the electron transport system, which converts the energy resulting from the breakdown of fuel molecules into a form that the cell can use to make ATP.

Principal terms

ADENOSINE TRIPHOSPHATE (ATP): a molecule forming the principal currency in the cell's energy economy; ATP contains two phosphate groups that store energy in the molecule, and removal of each of these phosphate groups releases energy

ATP SYNTHETASE: an enzyme in mitochondria that can use a proton concentration gradient to drive the synthesis of ATP from ADP and phosphate

CHEMIOSMOTIC HYPOTHESIS: a model stating that ATP synthesis in mitchondria is driven by a mechanism using energy released from the stepwise transfer of electrons and from a proton gradient in mitochondria

ELECTRON CARRIER (ELECTRON ACCEPTOR): a compound that can pick up and then release electrons between two different molecules in the cell; two common ones are nicotinamide adenine dinucleotide (NAD^+) and flavin adenine dinucleotide (FAD)

GLYCOLYSIS: the chemical oxidation of sugars such as glucose to yield smaller fuel molecules

KREBS CYCLE (CITRIC ACID CYCLE): the final sequence of chemical reactions in the breakdown of cellular fuel molecules; these reactions take place in the matrix of the mitochondrion

MITOCHONDRION: a cellular structure consisting of two membranes that surround a space called the matrix (the inner membrane contains the electron transport system); mitochondria change the energy from food into ATP

PHOSPHORYLATION: the addition of a phosphate group to a molecule; many cellular molecules are phosphorylated

Summary of the Phenomenon

The ability to convert the energy from food molecules into cellular energy efficiently is crucial to the survival of a cell and therefore to the survival of the whole organism. Oxidative phosphorylation is the precise sequence of reactions in mitochondria that result in the synthesis of adenosine triphosphate (ATP), the primary energy currency of cells. These reactions begin with obtaining the electrons that will provide a source of energy and end in the conversion of this energy into ATP from adenosine diphosphate (ADP) and phosphate. The name "oxidative phosphorylation" derives from the facts that fuel substances are oxidized to provide the electrons and that adenosine diphosphate (ADP) gets a third phosphate attached to it (or is phosphorylated) to become ATP.

Oxidative phosphorylation may be divided into four general steps. The first involves getting the electrons that will contribute energy for the entire process. In the second step, the large amount of energy in these electrons is changed into a form manageable by the cell. This is accomplished via a series of chemical reactions known as the electron transport system. Third, the energy is used to create a stockpile of hydrogen ions, or protons. Finally, the stockpile of protons is used to drive the synthesis of ATP.

The first step in oxidative phosphorylation is to obtain energy in the form of electrons. The main source of these electrons is the chemical oxidation reactions of fuel molecules, such as carbohydrates and fats, performed by the cell. These reactions include glycolysis, fatty acid oxidation, and the Krebs cycle (citric acid cycle). Chemical oxidation results in a loss of electrons by the oxidized molecule; when the electrons are removed from a fuel molecule they are picked up by an electron acceptor, or electron carrier. Electron carriers are molecules that can transport electrons between molecules in the cell, much as a package delivery service will carry a box between two addresses. The most common electron carriers are nicotinamide adenine dinucleotide (NAD^+) and flavin adenine dinucleotide (FAD). Each one of these molecules can carry two electrons at a time. Once the NAD^+ or FAD accepts the electrons, it is said to be chemically reduced and is symbolized as NADH or $FADH_2$.

In the second step in oxidation phosphorylation, the energy associated with the electrons is converted into a form manageable by the cell. This is accomplished by transferring the electrons to another electron carrier. Every time one carrier gives a pair of electrons to another, a small amount of energy is released. This energy is captured by the mitochondrion and used in a later step of oxidative phosphorylation to make ATP. The electron pair continues to be transferred through a series of electron carriers until any extra energy they carry has been given off. At that point they are delivered to oxygen, which is the final electron acceptor in the series. (The source of this oxygen is the earth's atmosphere.) When the electrons are accepted by the oxygen, it combines with two hydrogen ions to form a molecule of water.

This orderly sequence of electron transfers makes up the electron transport system. The components of the electron transport system are located in the inner of the two membranes in mitochrondria, and they are arranged in four large complexes called complex I, complex II, complex III, and complex IV. Each complex contains a component responsible for picking up the electrons and a protein portion that delivers the electrons to the next carrier in the chain. Each complex also contains additional proteins—in some cases as many as twenty—that attach the complex to the inner mitochondrial membrane.

In addition to these four complexes, there are two smaller electron carriers that can transport electrons between the larger complexes. One of these, cytochrome c, is a small protein. The other electron carrier is called ubiquinone, or coenzyme Q. It is made up of a ring of carbon atoms attached to a long chain of carbon and hydrogen atoms. Every time the electron pair is delivered to a new carrier, it loses a certain amount of energy, and each of the carriers can only pick up electrons that have a particular energy value. Therefore, an electron pair moves through the electron transport system in an exact order, going only into carriers that are able to accommodate the precise amount of energy the electron brings along.

The order in which electrons move through all the components of the electron transport system has been worked out by Britton Chance and several other investigators. Complex I takes electrons from NADH, then gives them to ubiquinone. Complex III transfers electrons from ubiquinone to cytochrome c. Finally, complex IV transports electrons from cytochrome c to oxygen (O_2). So an electron pair entering the system would proceed: NADH $\rightarrow$ complex I $\rightarrow$ ubiquinone $\rightarrow$ complex III $\rightarrow$ cytochrome c $\rightarrow$ complex IV $\rightarrow$ oxygen. Complex II accepts electrons directly from a small fuel molecule found inside the mitochondrion, then gives them to ubiquinone.

The excess energy given off during each transfer of electrons is used in the third step of the process to create a proton gradient. This is done by three of the complexes (I, III, and IV), which contain an additional protein component that is able to use this excess energy to move protons across the membrane. The protons are moved from inside the mitochondrion, through the inner membrane, into the space between the inner and outer membranes of the mitochrondrion. The accumulation of protons in this intermembrane space results in the buildup of a large difference in the proton concentration. Thus, proton concentration will be relatively high in the intermembrane space and relatively low inside the mitochondrion.

Finally, in the fourth and final step of oxidative phosphorylation, the proton stockpile is used to drive the synthesis of ATP. The conversion of the energy from the proton gradient into ATP is catalyzed by an ATP-synthesizing enzyme also found in the inner membrane of the mitochondrion. This enzyme is called ATP synthetase, or ATP synthase. ATP synthase is a very large molecule. Its large size has enabled researchers to visualize it using the electron microscope. At very high magnification, the ATP synthase molecule looks like a lollipop sticking out from the inner membrane into the inside of the mitochrondrion.

Work from the laboratory of Efraim Racker has demonstrated that there are different functions for the two parts of the lollipop. The spherical part of the lollipop can be removed by mechanical shaking and has been found still to be able to synthesize ATP. Racker called the sphere F_1, or coupling factor 1. The "stick" portion of the lollipop is embedded in the inner mitochondrial membrane. This part of the enzyme acts as a tunnel for protons to travel back into the mitochondrion.

The stick portion of the enzyme can be inactivated by the antibiotic oligomycin, so it is called the F_o, or oligomycin-sensitive factor. Another name for the ATP synthase is thus $F_oF_1ATPase$.

The fine details of how the movement of protons through the channel in the stick derives ATP synthesis have not been completely worked out. The spherical portion of the molecule can make ATP without the proton gradient. Once synthesized, however, the ATP remains tightly attached, so no additional ATP can be made by the enzyme. The large concentration of protons in the intermembrane space will tend to push protons back into the matrix through the tunnel provided by the ATP synthase. Paul Boyer has suggested that when protons move through the lollipop stick into the mitochondrion, the sphere changes its shape. This shape change, in turn, causes the enzyme to release newly synthesized ATP. One obvious advantage of this process is that the ATP can now be used by the cell. The process also lets the enzyme make more ATP. Boyer's proposal, which has gradually gained acceptance among researchers, is reasonable. Many biological enzyme reactions work by using similar shape changes to attach and release the substrates. A molecule of ATP is released for every three hydrogen ions that are returned to the matrix.

In 1961, Peter Mitchell proposed that the stepwise transfer of electrons by the electron transport system and the proton gradient worked together to synthesize ATP. His proposal, called the chemiosmotic hypothesis, represented a radical departure from other ideas at the time. At first the chemiosmotic hypothesis found little support among scientists, but the chemiosmotic hypothesis has stood the test of time. Although some details remain to be worked out, the experimental evidence accumulated by Mitchell, as well as by many other investigators since 1961, overwhelmingly supports this model. Mitchell received the Nobel Prize in Chemistry in 1978 for his proposal of the chemiosmotic hypothesis and the elegant research he performed in its support.

Methods of Study

The general processes that are included in oxidative phosphorylation were first described by scientists such as Otto Warburg, Herman Kalckar, and Fritz Lipmann in the first forty years of the twentieth century. Oxidative phosphorylation was initially called cellular respiration, since it required the utilization of oxygen. It was not until the late 1940's that Eugene Kennedy and Albert Lehninger showed that respiration took place in mitochondria. Once the location of respiration in cells was identified, scientists were able to focus their studies on the identification of the molecules involved in the process and on understanding in detail how they work together to make ATP. In the next decade, advances in the isolation of individual cellular structures made it possible to obtain large quantities of isolated mitochondria. Researchers used these isolated mitochondria to work out the types of enzymes involved in the process. Much of their work focused on identifying the electron carriers, as well as working out a "balance sheet" of electrons required for every ATP molecule produced.

One of the most intellectually and experimentally challenging problems in modern biochemistry involved identifying the sequence in which the electron carriers operate in the electron transport system. Initially, each carrier was purified from isolated mitochondria. Then the energy potential, or voltage, of each purified carrier was measured by researchers using standard procedures developed by physicists to measure voltage. Because electrons are transferred "downhill"—that is, from a carrier of higher voltage to a carrier of lower voltage—the approximate order of the carriers in the sequence could be determined.

To carry out these measurements, scientists had to remove the carriers from their natural environment in the mitochondrion, and this was known to reduce the accuracy of the data. The fine details of the sequence were worked out by Chance and his colleagues in an elegant series of experiments that combined two powerful methodologies. These investigators devised techniques that allowed them to make precise measurements of the chemical and physical characteristics of the electron carriers while they were still in the mitochondrial membrane. They then used drugs that inhibit the function of specific carriers and looked at the effects the drugs had on electron transport and on each carrier. The combined results from these two kinds of experiments allowed them to work out the sequence of carriers in detail.

A variety of these inhibitory drugs was used in these studies. Since they inhibit electron transport, and therefore ATP synthesis, they are powerful metabolic poisons. Some of these substances include the antibiotic antimycin A, rotenone, Amytal, cyanide, and carbon monoxide.

An equally challenging area of study has focused on understanding how the energy from the electrons is converted into ATP. Many years of research were spent trying to understand this process. Mitchell's proposal of the chemiosmotic hypothesis, suggesting that the link between the movement of electrons and ATP synthesis was the formation of a proton gradient, pointed the way for a productive direction of investigation. The research group headed by Racker isolated inner mitochondrial membranes and showed that they were capable of transporting, or pumping, protons in one direction. If the inner membranes were treated with drugs that interfere with formation of the proton gradient, ATP synthesis stopped. This demonstrated that the proton gradient was necessary for making ATP. Drugs that can destroy the proton gradient are called "uncouplers" of oxidation phosphorylation, because they completely break the link between the electron transport system and ATP synthesis. Subsequent to this work, other investigators showed that the protons were transported into the intermembrane space by specific protein components of complexes I, III, and IV of the electron transport system.

Context

Cells depend on energy in the form of ATP to carry out virtually every cellular function. In nearly all living organisms, and certainly in humans, 95 percent of all the ATP in cells is made through the process of oxidative phosphorylation. Mutations affecting components of the electron transport system or the ATP synthesizing mechanism have been documented. These defects lower the efficiency of ATP synthesis in mitchondria and can seriously handicap body tissues that need an abundant supply of ATP for their everyday function, such as the heart muscle and the brain. Individuals carrying these mutations may suffer from heart irregularities or, in some cases, some types of epilepsy.

As discussed above, some drugs can uncouple the electron transport system from ATP synthesis. In mitochondria that are uncoupled, the electron transport system continues to carry electrons to oxygen, but no ATP is made because the proton gradient is destroyed. The uncoupler 2,4-dinitrophenol (DNP) was used at one time to treat obesity. The mitochondria in a patient taking the DNP were uncoupled, so little ATP was made from the oxidation of food molecules. After several deaths were traced to the treatment, however, it was discontinued.

Under controlled conditions, uncoupling can be put to good use by the organism. Many animals, such as newborns (including humans), some mammals that live in very cold climates, and mammals that hibernate, use the uncoupling mechanism as a way of generating body heat. This process takes place in a special type of fat tissue called brown fat. The mitochondria in brown fat contain a large amount of a protein called thermogenin (the name means "heat maker") that is able to uncouple the mitochondria. In this way the energy from the transfer of electrons is given off as heat, without additional synthesis of ATP. Thus, the thermogenin turns the mitochondrion into an effective furnace. By regulating the amount of thermogenin made, the organism is able to control its temperature effectively under demanding conditions.

A comparable type of coupling mechanism is used by the skunk cabbage plant. The mitochondria in the flowers of this plant are able to uncouple, resulting in heat generation. This increases the rate of evaporation of strongly scented attractant molecules that lure insects to the flowers. The insects then can help in pollination of the flowers.

Bibliography

Ernster, L., and G. Schatz. "Mitochondria: A Historical Review." *Journal of Cell Biology* 91 (1981): 227s-255s. An information-packed chronology of the events surrounding the discovery of mitochondria and the energy-producing reactions. This is a very clearly organized review. Background in college level biology would be useful.

Garland, Peter. "A Man Driven by Proticity." *Nature* 276 (1978): 8-9. This brief news article summarizes Peter Mitchell's work at the time he was awarded the Nobel Prize; it also describes some of the earlier theories of ATP synthesis. The article includes a short historical review of Mitchell's interest in membranes as well as the author's insights on Mitchell as a scientist.

Harold, Franklin M. "The 1978 Nobel Prize in Chemistry." *Science* 202 (1978): 1174-1175. This is a very straightforward, excellent historical perspective of the work that led Mitchell to propose the chemiosmotic hypothesis. The article also describes the skepticism encountered by Mitchell following his proposal and the subsequent research from several groups that resulted in acceptance of the chemiosmotic hypothesis. There is also a useful biographical note on Mitchell.

Mitchell, Peter. "Keilin's Respiratory Chain Concept and Its Chemiosmotic Consequences." *Science* 206 (1979): 1148-1159. This is the lecture that Peter Mitchell delivered in Stockholm at the Nobel Prize ceremonies. Mitchell summarizes the work that led him to propose the hypothesis, as well as subsequent work in its support.

Stryer, Lubert. *Biochemistry.* 3d ed. New York: W. H. Freeman, 1988. Chapter 17 of this text contains very good descriptions of oxidative phosphorylation and the electron transport system. There are many full-color diagrams that will aid in understanding what is known about the structure and function of the components of the electron transport system. This is a college-level biochemistry textbook, and background in chemistry will be useful; however, many of the figures provide useful illustrative material for all levels.

Wolfe, Stephen L. *Biology: The Foundations.* Belmont, Calif.: Wadsworth, 1983. This is an introductory biology text. Chapter 7 includes an excellent description of oxidative phosphorylation as well as of the chemical reactions that provide energy to drive the process. Contains numerous simple diagrams of the process as well as several information boxes and supplements relating oxidative phosphorylation to the whole organism.

Alina C. Lopo

Cross-References

ATP and Other Energetic Molecules, 134; Catabolism of Fats and Proteins, 337; Glycolysis and Fermentation, 1219; The Krebs Cycle, 1520; Mitochondria, 1745; Prokaryotic Cell Structure, 2210; Respiration: Oxidation-Reduction, 2376; Submitochondrial Fractionation, 2559; Temperature Regulation, 2609.

ELECTROPHORESIS: AN OVERVIEW

Type of life science: Biochemistry
Other fields of study: Biophysics, cell biology (cytology), developmental biology (embryology), evolutionary biology, genetic regulation, immunology, microbiology, and molecular biology

Electrophoresis is the migration of electrically charged particles in an electric field. It is widely used to separate, isolate, and characterize macromolecules. Among the many applications of electrophoresis are clinical tests for inherited diseases, DNA profiling (employed in legal cases), and the determination of evolutionary relationships among organisms.

Principal terms

AMINO ACID: a small organic molecule, twenty types of which can combine to form various proteins

BASE: a small nitrogen-containing organic molecule, several of which are found in nucleic acids

CONCENTRATION: the amount of substance dissolved in a given volume of solution

ELECTRODE: the conductor through which the current of electricity enters or leaves the electrophoresis apparatus

MOLECULAR WEIGHT: the size of a molecule, measured in daltons; one dalton equals the weight of one hydrogen atom

NUCLEIC ACID: a macromolecule, either DNA or RNA, composed of many nucleotides joined together

NUCLEOTIDE: a unit of a nucleic acid, consisting of an organic base, a sugar molecule, and a phosphate group

PROTEIN: a macromolecule composed of one or more long chains of amino acids

Summary of the Methodology

Electrophoresis, a technique widely used in the life sciences, is the migration of electrically charged particles in an electric field. The technique may be used to separate small particles, such as amino acids, from one another or to separate extremely large macromolecules, such as proteins and nucleic acids. It is used both as an analytical technique to separate the components of a complex mixture and as a preparative technique to isolate a specific component. Because of its ease of operation, the small sample size needed, and its ability to separate closely related macromolecules, electrophoresis is a more powerful analytical tool than other separation techniques, such as chromatography and centrifugation.

The velocity at which the particle moves is directly proportional to the strength of the electric field (measured in volts per centimeter) and to the net charge of the particle. The velocity is inversely proportional to the size of the particle. Since the electric field is directly related to the voltage, increasing the voltage increases the velocity at which the particle moves. If the voltage and, hence, the electric field are kept constant, the velocity of the particle depends on its net charge and its size. If two particles have the same charge, then the smaller one moves more rapidly and has a higher velocity.

Arne Tiselius, a Swedish chemist who won the Nobel Prize in 1948, is generally credited with the development of electrophoresis in the late 1920's. Early applications of this method involved moving-boundary electrophoresis, in which the particles to be separated migrate freely in an aqueous solution toward one of two electrodes. A simple apparatus consists of a U-shaped tube with electrodes at either end. The positively charged molecules migrate through the fluid environment toward the negative electrode, and the negatively charged particles move toward the positive electrode. The migration of the molecules as a band or boundary can be followed visually or by using a suitable spectrophotometric system that measures the refractive index or the absorption of light.

Zone electrophoresis, introduced in the 1930's, has largely replaced moving-boundary electrophoresis as the method of choice for separating molecules on the basis of charge. Rather than being allowed to separate in a liquid medium, the molecules are separated on a solid or semisolid support that connects the two electrodes. Zone electrophoresis employs a solid support such as paper and cellulose acetate or a semisolid support such as the gels of starch, agarose, and polyacrylamide. The molecules to be separated migrate as bands or zones within the support. The characteristics of the support, particularly pore size, aid in the separation of the components of complex mixtures.

Paper electrophoresis and cellulose acetate electrophoresis, two techniques developed in the 1950's, have been widely used to separate molecules of small to medium size—that is, those with molecular weights of about ten thousand daltons or less. The apparatus used for these separations consists of two troughs filled with an aqueous solution; they are connected by either paper or cellulose acetate strips. The entire unit is covered to prevent evaporation of the liquid. The samples are applied to the center of the strip, the electric current is turned on, and the components in the sample are separated. The positive particles migrate to the negative electrode immersed in one trough, and the negative particles migrate to the positive electrode immersed in the other trough. Neutral particles stay at the point of application (called the origin). In both paper electrophoresis and cellulose acetate electrophoresis, the supporting medium adsorbs the particles to various degrees, thus aiding in the separation of the particles. Following the electrophoretic run, the separated bands can be visualized by using appropriate dyes. Amino acids can be visualized by ninhydrin spray reagent, which colors the bands purple, and proteins by Coomassie blue stain, which colors the bands blue. In 1958, Vernon Ingram, of the Massachusetts Institute of Technology, used paper electrophoresis to differentiate between normal hemoglobin and sickle-cell hemoglobin, proteins that differ by a net electrical charge of one.

The net electrical charge on a molecule depends on the types of organic groups present and on the molecule's environment. Particularly important for amino acids and proteins are the carboxyl group and the amino group. In the proper environment, the acidic carboxyl group loses a proton (that is, a hydrogen ion) and becomes negatively charged. The amino group accepts a proton to become positively charged. The net electrical charge on the amino acid or protein molecule depends on the relative number of the positively charged amino groups and the number of negatively charged carboxyl groups. The aqueous environment may be acidic, basic, or neutral depending on the relative concentrations of hydrogen ions in the aqueous solution.

Since the environment plays a role in determining the charge of the molecule, it is important that a constant acidity, basicity, or neutrality be maintained in the aqueous environment so that the velocity of the particle remains constant during the electrophoretic run. To accomplish this, special solutions called buffers are used.

In the 1960's and 1970's, better support systems were developed, including agarose gels and polyacrylamide gels. These systems utilize the pores within the gels to restrict the migration of larger molecules in the electric field. These methods are used in the separation of macromolecules, particularly nucleic acids and proteins. Depending on the pore size of the gel, the components of a particular macromolecular preparation can be separated on the basis of size. Agarose at 1 or 2 percent concentration is used to separate DNA molecules with molecular weights ranging up to several million. Polyacrylamide gel electrophoresis (PAGE), developed in the early 1960's, is widely used for separating proteins as well as nucleic acids. In the 1960's, electrophoresis equipment for holding the gel consisted of tubes, but in later years they were largely replaced by vertical slabs consisting of glass plates. Another innovation was the flat-bed system, in which the gel electrophoresis is carried out horizontally.

Polyacrylamide gels have two advantages over agarose gels: They are not as fragile and are consequently easier to handle and store, and the pore size can be varied over a much wider range. Hence, under certain conditions, very small molecules can be separated from one another. This procedure is important in the analysis of the base sequences of nucleic acids. On the other hand, huge molecules, such as certain proteins and certain deoxyribonucleic acid (DNA) molecules, can be separated from one another under a different set of conditions.

In both agarose and polyacrylamide gel electrophoresis, the components of the sample placed in each well separate and form bands that are visualized by various staining procedures. The series of bands associated with each well is called a lane. Up to twenty or more samples may be placed on a single gel and run simultaneously. After the run, the banding patterns in each lane can be compared.

Applications of the Method

Electrophoresis has been applied to biophysics, biochemistry, cell biology, developmental biology, evolutionary biology, genetics, immunology, microbiology, and molecular biology. Among the special techniques employing electrophoresis are SDS-PAGE, DNA sequencing, footprinting, the gel retention assay, and Southern, Northern, and Western blotting.

In SDS-PAGE, a detergent, sodium dodecylsulfate (SDS), is used to treat proteins so that all the protein molecules in the sample have a net negative charge. Depending on the concentration of acrylamide used (and, hence, on the size of the pores formed), proteins ranging in size from molecular weights of about ten thousand to several hundred thousand daltons can be separated. The SDS-PAGE system, developed by U. K. Laemmli in 1970, provides a discontinuous (DISC) gel separation that gives narrower bands than continuous gel systems and is therefore a more powerful analytical tool.

SDS-PAGE is usually used by scientists to identify the molecular weights of proteins that have been isolated from biological sources. By running several proteins of known molecular weight and comparing them to the sample, molecular weights of individual proteins in the sample can be determined. It is a common practice to monitor the purity of the protein isolations by analyzing the contents of the sample or fraction obtained at each step of the isolation procedure. If the isolation is successful, each fraction should have fewer proteins in it, as exhibited by fewer bands on the SDS-PAGE gel. A single band appearing on the gel is usually taken as evidence that the protein has indeed been purified.

DNA sequencing (nucleotide sequencing) depends on the ability of polyacrylamide electrophoresis to separate DNA molecules on the basis of size. First, the fragment of DNA to be sequenced is labeled with radioactive phosphorus. In the chemical method, the DNA, labeled with the radioactive phosphorus in a time-dependent reaction, is electrophoresed at high voltage. A series of bands called a sequencing ladder is visualized by a technique called autoradiography. The radiation given off by the labeled DNA bands is detected on X-ray film. Remarkably, the bands in the sequencing ladder consist of a series of fragments that differ from one another by only one nucleotide. Sequences of up to three hundred nucleotides can usually be determined from one electrophoretic run.

DNA footprinting is a modification of DNA sequencing that is used to study protein-DNA interactions. A sequencing ladder of a DNA fragment believed to contain the protein binding site is compared to that of the DNA fragment after it has been allowed to interact with the DNA-binding protein. Open spaces rather than bands are seen on the sequencing ladder wherever the protein has made contact with DNA. In this way, the exact nucleotide sequence of the protein binding site can be determined.

Restriction mapping is a technique often used in conjunction with sequencing. This technique is used to characterize, or otherwise identify, rather large pieces of DNA of about one thousand nucleotides or more. Specialized proteins called restriction enzymes cut the DNA molecule at specific sites by recognizing particular sequences of nucleotides. The resulting DNA fragments can be separated by gel electrophoresis. The DNA fragments are visualized as bands by the use of a dye called ethidium bromide that binds to the DNA. The ethidium bromide-bound DNA bands produce an orange-pink color when exposed to ultraviolet light. The size of the resulting restriction fragments can be determined by comparing the positions of the bands with the positions of bands of DNA fragments of known size. Since more than one hundred restriction enzymes with specific sites for cutting DNA are known, rather detailed restriction maps of DNA molecules can be constructed.

By combining the techniques of restriction mapping and DNA sequencing, rather large stretches of DNA containing one or more genes can be determined. In 1980, only a few genes had been sequenced; by 1990, more than a thousand genes had been sequenced, including the globulin genes and muscle actin genes from a variety of organisms. By comparing the sequences of genes, biologists can determine the evolutionary relationships of various organisms.

Three related techniques, known as Southern, Northern, and Western blotting employ gel electrophoresis followed by the transfer of the separated biological molecules from the gel to a suitable material, such as a sheet of nitrocellulose paper or nylon membrane, to which the biological molecules become attached. In Southern blotting, developed by E. M. Southern in 1975, DNA is transferred; in Northern blotting, ribonucleic acid (RNA) is transferred; in Western blotting, proteins are transferred. In all three procedures, the resulting blot on the nitrocellulose or nylon sheet exhibits the same banding as in the original gel.

In order to identify the components that have been separated from a mixture by electrophoresis and transferred to the nitrocellulose paper, the components are made to react with specific molecules called probes. These probes may be tagged with radioactive atoms, and the nitrocellulose sheets can then be analyzed by autoradiography. This is usually done in Southern and Northern blotting, in which radioactive DNA probes or radioactive RNA probes are specifically bound to the DNA or RNA molecules that have been transferred. Alternatively, the probe may be a macromolecule that has a small dye molecule attached to it. This is the case in Western blotting, in which specific protein probes called antibodies specifically bind to certain proteins called antigens that have been transferred to the nitrocellulose paper following electrophoresis.

Southern and Northern blotting have been used in embryology and developmental biology to study how genes are "turned on and off" during transcription. Western blotting is used in characterizing proteins and in analyzing their relatedness to other proteins. This technique has applications in the clinical laboratory in diagnosing diseases in which a particular protein is abnormal or absent in affected individuals. Southern blotting is used in forensic laboratories to analyze biological samples containing DNA by a technique known as DNA profiling or DNA fingerprinting.

Context

Electrophoresis allows the scientist to separate and isolate molecules found in living cells that are very similar to one another. Biological molecules differing only slightly in terms of size and/or electrical charge can be separated. In order to determine and understand the exact sequence of events occurring in a biological process at the molecular level, each component of the process must be isolated and characterized. For example, the isolation and characterization of specific proteins, such as DNA polymerase and topoisomerases (involved in DNA replication) and RNA polymerase (involved in transcription), as well as many others, depend on electrophoresis. Electrophoresis therefore provides a method by which biochemists and molecular biologists can unravel the complexities of cellular processes, such as DNA replication, gene regulation, and genetic recombination.

In the clinical laboratory, many diagnostic procedures are dependent on electrophoresis. Genetic diseases such as aglobulinemia, muscular dystrophy, and sickle-cell anemia can be detected because a particular protein, the end product of a gene, is not produced by the individual or because an altered protein, differing from the normal protein, is produced. In immunology, electrophoresis is used to isolate and characterize antibodies, which are proteins, and to study antigen-antibody interactions.

In the field of recombinant DNA technology, electrophoresis is an essential and powerful technique. Electrophoresis is used to separate the recombinant DNA molecules from one another and from any uncombined DNA molecules that may be present. Following its isolation, the nucleotide sequences of the recombinant DNA can be elucidated. The sequences of numerous genes have been determined in this way. Electrophoresis is also employed in the emerging biotechnology industry. Important proteins, such as insulin and growth hormone, can be produced by recombinant DNA techniques.

The legal field accepts as evidence data obtained by electrophoresis. A particular technique known as DNA profiling or fingerprinting is used to verify whether an individual could have fathered a particular child by comparing DNA samples taken from the father and child. In criminal cases, tiny samples of semen, blood, or tissue found at the scene of a crime can be analyzed and the DNA profile compared to that of the suspect.

Electrophoresis is a technique that is commonly used by scientists to isolate components of living cells and to study basic cellular mechanisms. Most of the major advances in molecular biology and biochemistry that have taken place since the 1960's have utilized the technique of electrophoresis.

Bibliography

Alberts, Bruce, Dennis Bray, Julian Lewis, Martin Raff, Keith Roberts, and James D. Watson. *Molecular Biology of the Cell.* 2d ed. New York: Garland, 1989. Chapter 4, "How Cells Are Studied," describes in general terms the methods and techniques used to study cells. Techniques employing electrophoresis, such as isoelectric focusing, Southern blotting, restriction mapping, and DNA sequencing, are discussed with ample illustrations. Written at the college level but suitable for high school as well.

Brewer, J. M., A. J. Pesce, and R. B. Ashworth. *Experimental Techniques in Biochemistry*. Englewood Cliffs, N.J.: Prentice-Hall, 1974. Chapter 5, "Electrophoresis," describes electrophoresis in terms of theory and practical aspects. Numerous diagrams are helpful. Written at the college level. More than forty references are cited, but they are highly technical.

Freifelder, David. *Physical Biochemistry: Applications to Biochemistry and Molecular Biology*. San Francisco: W. H. Freeman, 1976. Chapter 9, "Electrophoresis," describes in a clear manner using illustrations and several electrophoretic techniques, including isoelectric focusing and immunoelectrophoresis. Written at the college level. It includes eleven references.

Robyt, John F., and Bernard J. White. *Biochemical Techniques: Theory and Practice*. Monterey, Calif.: Brooks/Cole, 1987. Chapter 5, "Electrophoretic Techniques," describes electrophoresis in terms of theory, historical perspective, and applications. Written at the college level, it explains a variety of electrophoretic techniques, including two-dimensional electrophoresis, isoelectric focusing, and immunoelectrophoresis. It includes more than twenty references.

Weinberg, Robert A. "The Molecules of Life." *Scientific American* 253 (October, 1985): 48-57. This article introduces a whole issue that is devoted to modern biology. It describes the relationship of recent discoveries of biology to the new field of biotechnology.

White, Ray, and Jean-Marc Lalouel. "Chromosome Mapping with DNA Markers." *Scientific American* 258 (February, 1988): 40-49. This article describes how markers called restriction fragment length polymorphisms (RFLP) can be used to locate genes that cause certain diseases. The RFLP's can be used to detect genetic carriers of certain diseases, such as muscular dystrophy. Extensive mapping of human chromosomes by using RFLP's is needed before the entire human genome can be sequenced.

Alan D. Cooper

Cross-References

EMOTIONS

Type of life science: Ethology
Other fields of study: Animal physiology and neurobiology

Emotions cover a range of inherited physical responses triggered by personal experiences. Scientific interest in emotions involves describing both the objective and subjective nature of emotions, locating the neurological and biochemical sources within an organism, and investigating the biological basis for emotions.

Principal terms
 BEHAVIORALISM: a method of studying behavior that is based on objective standards which can be predicted and controlled
 ETHOLOGY: a branch of biology that studies behavior
 HYPOTHALAMUS: an organ in the lower part of the brain that contains nerve centers and helps coordinate the endocrine and nervous systems
 INSTINCTS: a range of inherited (not learned) behavior patterns that are predictable for a species
 NEUROBIOLOGY: the study of the biology of the brain
 NEUROETHOLOGY: the study of behavior through brain functions
 PEPTIDE: a chemical consisting of a short chain of amino acids; a neuropeptide is a peptide that functions in the brain
 PHYSIOLOGY: a branch of biology that deals with the process and activities of an organism through the functions of its organic parts
 STEREOTYPED BEHAVIOR: an unlearned and unchanging behavioral pattern that is unique to a species
 THALAMUS: a central nervous system relay center located in the lower portions of the brain

Summary of the Phenomenon

The study of human emotional behavior and related emotional patterns in animals has been the subject of many writers since the beginning of written records. Emotions and feelings have been the subject of poetry, have been included in discourses concerning the good life, and have been found within philosophical tracts on inner harmony and in a variety of self-help books that date back to the classical antiquity of both East and West. Sources from the distant past, however, offered few scientific contributions toward an understanding of the source, role, and mechanism of emotions. In the seventeenth century, the philosopher René Descartes began to account for the separate functions of the body and the soul. He included emotions such as fear, joy, love, and hate as parts of the soul. One century later, David Hume would continue this line of philosophical inquiry with his great work *A Treatise of Human Nature*, in which emotions are described as arising from the human perception of the world. For example, joy is the result of the impression of pleasure associated with something in the world.

By the nineteenth century, with the beginnings of psychology, the focus on emotional behavior began to shift toward qualification and experimentation. Wilhelm Wundt formed a theory of emotions based on having people report their feelings after being subjected to sensory stimulation. This investigation was based on a series of dichotomies such as pleasant-unpleasant and tension-release. More complex and subtle theories of emotions were developed that were based on Wundt's work. These theories were of limited value because of the constraints of the original concept: The terms were vague, and responses could not be accurately measured. At this stage, psychology proved to be a useful tool for the observation of emotions, but it could not account for the mechanism within the mind.

Charles Darwin gave the scientific world a theory of evolution, but he was also an avid observer of instinctive behavior. He observed domesticated pigeons (in 1868), described how emotions were expressed by humans and animals (1871), and even kept a detailed journal on both the physical and behavioral growth of his children. His major contribution toward a study of emotions can be found in *The Expression of the Emotions in Man and Animals*, published in 1872. It suggested, for example, that the sneer may be derived from a snarl that was a sign of aggression. He believed that emotions were remnants of earlier evolutionary adaptive behavior. Consequently, Darwin was one of the first to remove human emotions from the mind and soul and to think of them as biological functions of the organism.

One early derivative of Darwin's work was extensive studies of facial expressions and body movements that express emotions. Of the numerous attempts to classify and categorize human expression, none has had lasting scientific value, although the recent popular studies in "body language" are derived from this tradition. As it turned out, Darwin's contributions to the study of emotions were not as important to psychology as to a branch of zoology known as ethology. Ethology is the comparative study of animal behavior.

Over the course of the twentieth century, this discipline studied instinctive behaviors involving a broad range of animal life. In recognition of the growing maturity of the field and the successes of ethology, the 1973 Nobel Prize in Physiology or Medicine was awarded to Karl von Frisch, Konrad Lorenz, and Niko Tinbergen. Of the three, Lorenz alone would attempt to link the broad range of instinctive animal behavior with human emotions. In a widely acknowledged work entitled *On Aggression* (1966), Lorenz assumed a close link between instinct and emotion. For example, Lorenz believed that the instinct to defend a territory can produce emotions such as pride, fear, and rage.

Four major schools of thought or classical theories of emotions exist. The concept of a physiological basis for emotions was developed by American psychologist William James and independently by Danish physician Carl Georg Lange. James showed that emotions were the result of physiological changes and disturbances, such as changes in brain functions and alterations in the nervous system. Similarly,

Lange's work described changes in the circulatory systems during emotional reactions. The James and Lange theories of emotions came to be linked as a result of a celebrated attempt on the part of Walter B. Cannon to refute their theories collectively. In place of the James-Lange theory, Cannon proposed an alternative physiological model that claimed emotions to be a physical mechanism that resisted stress and alerted the defensive faculties of the organism.

The behavioralists, particularly those in the United States, took a different approach to emotions. From this perspective, John B. Watson wrote one of the classic texts on psychology. He thought that emotions were part of an overall pattern of behavior that was inherited rather than acquired. He attempted to establish the basic emotions of fear, rage, and love by testing the emotional responses of newborn babies, rabbits, and other animals. The major difference between the approaches of behavioralists and ethologists lies in the difficulty Watson encountered in distinguishing between the patterns of emotional and nonemotional responses. Subsequently, Watson began to focus his studies on the stimulus situation rather than on the nature of the response. By the 1950's, B. F. Skinner, a later representative of the behavioralist tradition, began to argue that a pattern of behavior itself defines an emotion. For example, a person pounding a table shows the emotional condition of anger.

The psychoanalytical theory of emotions can be traced to the works of Sigmund Freud. Although there was no systematic accounting of emotions, Freud could not escape from the presence of emotional behavior in his work. Anxiety and fear, for example, were common patterns in his patients, and he explained these conditions as the result of earlier traumatic events that became a part of an individual's unconscious and repressed memory. Later Freudians, beginning with this initial concern with emotions, provided more complex and sophisticated theories. For example, in 1967, David Rapaport suggested that when energies of instinctive drives become blocked in the unconscious and cannot be discharged in the normal fashion, these energies then become expressed via emotions.

A fourth school attempted to deal with the subjective problems of emotion either by changing its designation or by arguing that emotion did not deserve a special designation at all. The first approach occurred in the 1930's, when the two terms emotion and instinct were subsumed under the word "motivation" or "drive." This tack of changing the term failed to remove some of the earlier problems associated with the investigations of emotions attributable to the interposition of learned behavior between stimulus and response. Accepting such limits, later experiments were designed to uncover systematically the role of learning in motivational studies. For example, Elizabeth Duffy demonstrated that emotions and drives concern specific changes in the energy levels of an organism. Slow, low-level changes in energy produce certain feelings, whereas quick and high-level changes produce a range of effects that were once described as emotions.

A common denominator for all these theories of emotions is the assumed location of an organic source for these responses. Since an emotion is a response to an external condition, these theories assume, perceptions of stimuli trigger a specific response. Therefore, one internal organ or a network of organs must be responsible for the response. The work of Cannon was associated with the thalamus, an organ that serves as a nerve relay center. Damage to the thalamus produces a range of results that include changes in the intensity of experiences and extreme emotional responses. Other studies focused on the cerebral cortex and the neural patterns of the brain. In 1951, Donald B. Lindsey found that he could measure an entire range of electrical responses, from initial awareness, to full attention, and finally to signs of emotional response. Similar studies of emotions have followed the continuing explorations in neuroscience and have produced an approximate (yet still crudely organized) emotional map of the brain.

By the 1970's, studies of the brain had yielded significant results that characterized motivation and emotions as the result of neurological and biochemical changes that are similar to other comparable changes in an organism. These results include a better understanding of how the more than 100 billion neurons function in the brain and how each neuron can connect, by way of synapses, to several thousand other neurons. A synapse functions by way of a chemical agent, which transmits a piece of information, and several peptides (short chains of amino acids), which facilitate the reception of the information. From these realizations it is only a few steps toward discovering the means by which genes control all the chemical and neurological developments of the brain. In a sense, the journey toward an understanding of emotions and behaviors in general leads back to the work of Darwin. It becomes necessary to address the question of what selective advantage emotions confer on an individual of a species. Although there are tantalizing hypotheses offered for the role of emotions, continuing research on understanding the brain will offer a more definitive answer.

Methods of Study

The early students of emotion began their work by observation. In the nineteenth century, these studies resulted in drawings, and later photographs, of facial expressions. The failure to identify universal norms of expression led scientists in turn to experiments with specific stimuli, which they attempted to categorize by the range of responses. By the first half of the twentieth century, research in emotions benefited from an increased understanding of biochemical functions in organisms. This understanding included findings that explained fright as the result of an adrenalin activity that produces increasing levels of blood sugar. Fear also causes increased amounts of gastric acids in the stomach and decreased mucous secretions in the mouth and nose (the "dry mouth" experienced during moments of fear).

Extensive research materials have been compiled on the measurement and detection of emotions based on external physiological changes. For example, the electrical resistance of the skin fluctuates during emotional responses. This is called galvanic skin response, and it provides an indication of changing moods and feeling. The rate and pattern of respiration, the blinking rate of eyes, and the contraction of muscles have all been explored in terms of emotional shifts in an organism. The most commonly known application of these sets of emotional indicators is the lie detector test, which uses a polygraph device to monitor physiological changes. The accuracy of such tests, however, is often open to question.

Major contributions to the studies of emotions often come from attempts to treat and normalize extreme emotional states. For example, aggressive behavior in its extreme forms can result in physical harm to the individual afflicted with the problem and to others. It was discovered that the level of violence in laboratory rats is reduced through specific lesions of the hypothalamus. Beginning in the 1950's, refinements of this technique, called psychosurgery, were performed on people suffering from epileptic fits as well as other violent disorders. There appeared to be "switches" in the brain that could turn specific emotional states on and off. Similarly, psychoactive drugs were found to act directly on the neurological circuits of the brain to increase or decrease aggressive behavior. Hormones, such as adrenalin and cortisol (in several of its forms in the body), are secreted during either a fighting response or a retreating posture.

Research into other psychological and behavioral disorders, such as depression, eating dysfunctions, and sexual disorders, has produced a more complete map of the complex neurological and biochemical makeup of emotional behaviors. As the search for the causes of instinctive behavior moved further into the organism, the necessary methodologies followed—into the areas of brain function (neuroethology), the chemistry of innate behavior, and the genetic component of behavior. For example, attempting to discover the source of the egg-laying behavior of a species of a large marine snail (*Aplysia*), Richard Scheller and Richard Axel found three genes that produce a number of peptides that govern this behavior.

The scientific methods for the study of emotions, which began with the drawings of facial expression and simple stimulus-response techniques, have evolved into a highly technical field of study. Whether the term used is emotions, motivations, or drives, the mechanism involved consists of a chain that goes from sensory reaction to brain response to chemical motor function and finally to organic activity. Beyond the individual organism, there are the evolutionary developments of a species, which carry a specific past or present selective advantage as a result of a set of emotional behaviors.

Context

Emotions are a part of all higher organisms, and observable instinctive responses are only a small part of an intricate pattern. The genetic makeup of an organism dictates both specific and unlearned patterns of responses and allows variations on the patterns; all these responses are factors in determining evolutionary selection of individuals within a species. Clearly, emotions such as aggression, fear, lust, and grief can all play a role in the area of sexual selection, reproduction, food gathering, and other basic needs which are the most critical for survival. In higher animals, emotions and motivations are often overshadowed and disguised by learned patterns of responses. For example, in dogs, the pulling back of facial muscles and the showing of teeth is a response to fear and attack. In humans, laughter is a similar response to surprise, embarrassment, and uneasiness. Through social adaptation, however, laughter has taken on additional behavioral conventions.

Until the early part of the twentieth century, emotions and instincts were thought to be learned responses to specific situations. Consequently, if aggression is learned, then it could be modified, changed, and unlearned. With the establishment of a genetic and biochemical foundation for instincts, however, research in stereotyped behavior has become part of a heated debate. In 1975, Edward O. Wilson published *Sociobiology: The New Synthesis*. This highly technical work found a surprisingly large audience; in it, Wilson attempted to place all social behavior on a biological basis. Although the work emphasized animal behavior, Wilson implied that all human history was also part of evolutionary biology and that his work would synthesize all the social sciences with biology. Since behavior patterns such as aggression, selection of sexual partners, and the care of the young play a prominent part in cultural activities, Wilson seems to suggest that in the future the true science of society will originate from neurobiology and sociology.

While the concept of total biological determinism has been accepted by only a few recognized scholars, significant portions of this idea have been intergrated into biological and social research. The degree of biological determination of behavior and the component of learning varies in different organisms. Even if genetics controls only half of all human behavior and learned responses the other half, these conclusions can be seen to alter the outlook on human culture profoundly.

Bibliography

Gray, Jeffrey A. *The Psychology of Fear and Stress*. New York: McGraw-Hill, 1971. This book offers a thorough and comprehensive treatment of the subject. A valuable reference, since Gray has brought together many pertinent studies on the subject in a single volume. Recommended as a reference for specific aspects of fear and stress rather than as a book for general reading.

Hamburg, David A. "Psychobiological Studies of Aggressive Behavior." *Nature* 230 (1971): 19-23. This is one of a series of articles written by Hamburg during the 1970's. He was a psychiatrist who began to look in the evolutionary and anthropological literature for a biological basis of aggression. His articles are fairly technical.

Konner, Melvin. *The Tangled Wing: Biological Constraints on the Human Spirit*. New York: Harper & Row, 1983. Although Konner has his own thesis to prove in this work, part 2 (more than two hundred pages) offers an excellent overview of work on human emotions and motivations. A few sections are technical, but a determined reader will be well rewarded.

Lewontin, R. C., Steve Rose, and Leon J. Kamin. *Not in Our Genes: Biology, Ideology, and Human Nature*. New York: Random House, 1984. Presents a thorough review of and arguments against biological determinism. Topics include human equality, the IQ controversy, schizophrenia, and sociobiology. Bibliographies are found in the footnotes of the chapters. A few sections require specialized knowledge, but it is usually accessible for the general reader.

Lorenz, Konrad. *On Aggression.* New York: Harcourt Brace Jovanovich, 1966. This was one of the first attempts to introduce an ethological link to the study of human aggression. Although the book contains some technical terms, large segments of the work remain available for the nontechnical reader.

Masters, William H., and Virginia E. Johnson. *Human Sexual Responses.* Boston: Little, Brown, 1966. This volume represents a critical turning point in the study of human sexuality and offers information on sexual research not previously available. Since the publication of this book, an extensive body of literature has appeared. Subsequent articles and books, however, tend to be more technical and specialized.

Scheller, Richard H., and Richard Axel. "How Genes Control an Innate Behavior." *Scientific American* 250 (March, 1984): 54-63. Describes how methods of recombinant DNA are used to find a set of genes that encode a neuropeptide and result in specific egg-laying behavior in a marine snail. Beyond its opening page, the article does require a background in college biochemistry and genetics.

Victor W. Chen

Cross-References

Communication, 526; Ethology, 858; Habituation and Sensitization, 1254; Imprinting, 1400; Instincts, 1438; Learning, 1548; Memory, 1683; Reflexes, 2301; Reproductive Behavior and Mating, 2333; Rhythms and Behavior, 2398; Territoriality and Aggression, 2617.

TESTING FOR ENDOCRINE FUNCTIONS
OF GLANDS AND ORGANS

Type of life science: Animal physiology
Other fields of study: Animal anatomy and biochemistry

Testing to determine whether an organ has an endocrine function involves conducting a series of experiments to learn if it produces one or more substances that meet the definition of a hormone. The research in this field has brought about important medical and technological breakthroughs.

Principal terms

ANTAGONIST: a chemical that binds to a hormone receptor and blocks the action of the hormone itself

BIOLOGICAL ASSAY: a means of measuring the relative amount of hormone activity by observing the magnitude of some physiological response that has previously been determined to be stimulated by the hormone

CHEMICAL ISOLATION: the step-by-step purification of a single chemical from a larger mix of chemicals

CHEMICAL PRECURSOR: a chemical that is changed by reactions within the body into some final compound

CRUDE EXTRACT: a liquid homogenate of a gland or organ; it contains all the hormones found in that organ

HORMONE: a chemical messenger that is carried by the blood from its site of production to its target site; hormones alter the functions of their target sites in specific ways

HORMONE RECEPTOR: the submicroscopic area on a hormone target site that receives the hormone and allows the target site to respond to the hormone

IN VITRO: refers to any procedure for maintaining living tissues in a laboratory dish after removal from the body

NATIVE: refers to the natural hormone found in the animal

PHYSIOLOGICAL PARAMETER: any bodily response that might be measurable, such as heart rate, blood pressure, sodium excretion, reproductive capability

Summary of the Methodology

An endocrine gland is one that produces and secretes hormones into the blood. Hormones are chemicals that have specific effects on certain parts of the body, called target sites. Establishing that a particular anatomical structure functions as an endocrine gland implies that information must also be available on the possible hormonal effects of that structure's chemical products. Scientists seek to establish that a particular gland or organ has an endocrine function by posing a series of questions that are designed to determine whether substances produced by that structure meet the definition of a hormone.

The function of the suspected gland is the basic question that scientists seek to answer, but the possible function sometimes can be understood by observing what physiological abnormalities can be seen in test animals in the absence of the organ. The traditional experimental approach has been to remove the gland from the body (surgical ablation). The next step, that of observing the test animals for abnormal functioning, is fraught with difficulty in the case of a possible endocrine gland whose target site is completely unknown. Researchers must decide which physiological parameters should be measured. If the target site of the hormones from the suspected endocrine gland is the reproductive system, it will be useless to measure parameters like blood pressure and heart rate. The initial description of the role of an endocrine gland usually requires scientists to measure all possible effects and to eliminate them, one by one, from consideration.

Can extracts made from the suspected gland restore normal functions in animals that have undergone ablation? At this stage, the chemical identity of the suspected hormonal products may not yet have been established, so a crude extract of the structure may be made by grinding or homogenizing small pieces of the tissue in some neutral liquid. The homogenate is then injected or otherwise administered to the animals that have previously undergone ablation, as a way of replacing the chemical products of the suspected gland. This approach is referred to as ablation and replacement. A successful reversal of all physiological effects of the ablation itself has important implications. First, it means that the effects of the ablation result from the loss of the structure's chemical products, and not only because of some anatomical role that the structure may play. Second, it implies that the products of the structure are capable, when freely distributed in the body, of causing predictable physiological effects; that is, they function as hormones do.

As an example of the power of this type of replacement experiment, consider testing for the possible function of a leg muscle. A researcher observes that animals that have this muscle removed have difficulty walking. One hypothesis might be that the muscle acts as an endocrine gland, producing a hormone necessary for walking. This is tested by injecting muscle extracts into previously operated animals. Because an improvement in locomotion is not observed, it can be correctly concluded that the effect of the muscle is not by way of a hormone.

What specific chemical compounds that may function as hormones can be identified in the tissue of the structure? Answering this question usually begins with making a crude extract, as described above, and then treating it with certain solvents to remove specific classes of chemicals. For example, a crude tissue extract can be washed with ether; many fat-soluble substances will dissolve into the ether, while other classes of compounds may remain in the aqueous phase of the solution. In this way the chemicals present in the crude extract are partitioned into specific solutions. These steps can be repeated until each solution contains only one chemical from the original mixture in the tissue; this process is referred to as chemical isolation. The isolated chemicals can then be analyzed by various means to deduce their chemical structures.

Can administration of compounds isolated from the suspected gland produce the same physiological effects in test animals as extracts of the structure? The isolated chemicals must be individually administered to test animals, and then the appropriate physiological measurements must be made. This step is important in assuring that all physiological effects of the secretions of a gland are accounted for by the hormones that it produces.

Do the suspected hormones appear in the blood of test animals? An affirmative answer to this question is essential to the labeling of a chemical as a hormone, since part of the definition of a hormone is that it is carried in the blood. Direct measurement of the putative hormone in the blood requires that some type of biological assay or chemical test be available. If there is no practical means of measuring the substance in the blood, an indirect approach to this question may be taken by performing transplants of the suspected endocrine gland from the usual site in the body to some other location. If all physiological functions in the animal bearing a transplant continue normally, then it may be tentatively assumed that the transplanted gland is assuming its usual function by virtue of the fact that its hormonal products are distributed by the blood, which circulates throughout the body. If normal physiological function is not restored by a transplant, then it may be assumed that the organ depends on its original anatomical location for its function, perhaps because of dependence on ducts that drain its secretions.

Can it be verified that the structure in question actually produces these suspected hormones? Today, one of the most common ways to verify that a particular tissue is capable of producing a certain hormone is to study a living sample of the tissue that has been removed from the animal and maintained in vitro in the laboratory. When this tissue is provided with the chemical precursors necessary for production of the putative hormone, it should in fact produce the substance.

A favorable answer to all of these experimental questions results in the general acceptance of an organ as an endocrine gland.

Applications of the Method

The experimental approach outlined here, or a modification of it, has been used to define about twenty mammalian structures as endocrine glands. Some of these structures, such as the thyroid and pituitary, appear to be solely endocrine in nature. When the organ being studied is exclusively endocrine in its function, the application of the ablation and replacement regime of experiments is straightforward. There are no additional functions of the organ that might confuse the interpretation of its endocrine role. Some endocrine glands exist as small patches of tissue in large organs that do serve other functions. For example, the intestine is usually defined as an organ of digestion, but is contains endocrine cells that secrete their hormones into the blood. Investigation of structures, such as the intestine, that serve more than one function has been a particular challenge to endocrinologists, who have had to modify the ablation and replacement approach.

Interestingly, the first hormone to be discovered was secretin, one of the intestinal hormones. The existence and function of secretin was inferred from results of experiments performed by William Bayliss and Ernest Henry Starling in 1902; they observed that extracts of the intestinal wall injected into the blood of test animals caused increased secretion of juices from the pancreas. This was the first indication that chemical messengers might carry information between several body parts. Bayliss and Starling correctly concluded that hormonal communication could be the basis of much information exchange within the body as a whole, and not only within the digestive system. It was this research team that proposed the definition of a hormone that is still in use today: a substance produced in one part of the body that is carried in the blood and affects the function of some distant organ. The importance of the definition provided by Bayliss and Starling cannot be underestimated. Their definition of a hormone has directly shaped the kinds of experiments that have been undertaken in endocrinology, since researchers have sought to demonstrate that a particular substance fits the requirements of a hormone, thereby qualifying the site of production as an endocrine gland.

Ironically, although other digestive hormones were discovered after secretin, the general progress in the field of gastrointestinal endocrinology was relatively slow. The lack of progress was caused, in part, by the fact that endocrine tissue is located all along the length of the digestive tract. It is not possible to remove the endocrine tissue while leaving the remainder of the digestive tract in place, so the classic ablation and replacement experiments were not possible. It is possible to synthesize chemicals that are similar, but not identical, to the native gastrointestinal hormones. These synthetic compounds, called antagonists, bind to the hormone receptors at their target sites, preventing the hormones from affecting the target sites in the usual manner. This approach has allowed better understanding of the effects of the gastrointestinal hormones and has offered essentially the same information as a surgical ablation experiment would have.

The inability to perform surgical ablation of the heart has also hampered study of the possible endocrine function of this organ. The heart produces a substance called atrial natriuretic peptide (ANP), which may be involved in regulation of the amount of sodium excreted by the kidney. ANP is also known as atrial natriuretic hormone; the disagreement in nomenclature reflects the fact that the scientific community is not yet certain whether this substance meets all the requirements for a hormone, and hence whether the heart should be considered an endocrine gland. Since surgical removal of the heart is not possible if one wishes to observe responses in living animals, researchers have tried to use other methods to study the possible role of ANP. For example, researchers have infused the substance into animals and measured changes in sodium excretion by the kidney. Results from different experiments suggest that the effects of ANP may be observed only when the animal is maintained in certain physiological states; some anesthetics may alter the responses, thus making interpretation even more difficult.

Another challenge has been to investigate the endocrine role of the hypothalamus, part of the brain that is involved in unconscious regulation of many body systems. Researchers suspected that the regulatory ability of the hypothalamus might depend at least partly on hormones. Removal of the entire hypothalamus was not a feasible approach to study its endocrine role, however, since the hypothalamus is necessary to life. Instead, researchers used biochemical techniques to determine what substances were produced by the cells of the hypothalamus. It was found that tiny but distinct areas are responsible for producing different compounds. Researchers were able to scale down the ablation approach by removing only small clusters of cells within the hypothalamus and then testing for abnormal functioning. This research demonstrated that the hypothalamus is indeed an endocrine gland that produces an assortment of hormones involved in reproduction, growth, and metabolism. The function of other substances produced within the hypothalamus is still being debated.

One of the most intriguing series of experiments in endocrinology has led to the acceptance of the pineal gland as an endocrine organ in mammals. The pineal gland is located above the top surface of the mammalian brain. Its microscopic structure in mammals is similar to that of other endocrine glands, a fact that led researchers to try to establish some endocrine function for it. For years, researchers performed pineal ablation experiments with disappointing results. Although many different physiological parameters were measured, not one single altered function could be found in animals that had undergone removal of the pineal (surgical removal of the pineal gland is called pinealectomy). Finally, a series of experiments by R. J. Reiter in the 1960's demonstrated that the seasonal changes in breeding typically exhibited by the golden hamster could be prevented by pinealectomy. Injections of melatonin, a hormone produced within the pineal, can restore the seasonal responses. Melatonin apparently acts a signal to the animal's reproductive system, but the details of how melatonin exerts its effects are still not known. It is now clear that previous failures to demonstrate an endocrine function for the pineal gland were caused by the choice of animal used in testing (not all animals are seasonal breeders) or by the fact that experimental animals are typically housed under controlled lighting that does not mimic seasonal changes in day length. When the appropriate animals and experimental conditions were used, the classic ablation and replacement approach proved to be useful in establishing that the pineal does indeed have an endocrine function.

Context

Understanding of the functions of the hormones and their sites of production has made possible rational therapies for a whole host of diseases. In many cases, the impetus to study a particular endocrine organ and its hormonal products is the existence of endocrine diseases in animals and humans.

Such is the case with the pioneering research on insulin, one of several hormones produced by scattered patches of endocrine cells within the pancreas. The most apparent function of insulin is to promote the uptake of glucose from the blood by several types of body cells. Since glucose provides the major form of energy used by most cells, insulin is critical to normal cell functioning and survival. An absence of insulin or a deficient response to it results in a set of characteristic symptoms that reflect the inability to function efficiently because of problems with energy levels. This is the situation in the disease diabetes mellitus, which can cause death if the symptoms are uncontrolled. Although complete control of diabetes symptoms is not always possible, since the isolation and identification of insulin in the 1920's many patients with diabetes have lived long, productive lives because of the availability of insulin therapy.

The medical benefits that arose from the research on the pancreas and insulin are easy to appreciate, but this research was also indirectly responsible for great improvements in the technological methods available to researchers. Because of its clinical importance, there was great motivation to study the insulin molecule, but often, appropriate methods were not available. Scientists thus developed new, more efficient techniques to study molecular structure and function. These techniques have since been widely applied in the fields of biology and chemistry, resulting in a great increase in our knowledge of molecular behavior.

Another milestone in endocrinology research also involved insulin, and that was the finding that some individuals produced antibodies to insulin. Previously, it was thought that insulin was too small a molecule to provoke antibody formation, so this observation caused scientists to reevaluate their theories on antibody production. In addition, the discovery of insulin antibodies allowed the development of a new technique for hormone measurement. This technique, radioimmunoassay (RIA), depends on a reaction between a hormone and antibodies specific to it; radioactive tracers added to the sample allow quantification of the reaction products. First applied to the measurement of insulin in 1960, RIA has since been extended to dozens of other hormones and biological substances. RIA is superior to methods previously available for hormone measurement because it is more reliable and can be used with small samples.

The availability of RIA has greatly expanded the information on hormones. One tangible benefit of RIA is the ease of screening for endocrine disorders or certain physiological conditions. In most cases, such testing requires only a small blood sample. Measurement of hormone levels by RIA is widely employed in the diagnosis of diseases involving the thyroid, adrenals, pancreas, gonads, and pituitary. RIA is also the basis for pregnancy tests performed in medical laboratories. A related technique that does not rely on radioactive tracers is used in pregnancy test kits designed for use in the home and in ovulation test kits that can be used to improve a woman's chance of conceiving a child.

Research on hormones and endocrine glands has been important not only because of the immediate benefits of medical therapy for endocrine diseases but also because of technological developments associated with the research. The broader application of these new technologies has allowed science in general to proceed at an ever-increasing pace in its discovery of basic knowledge.

Bibliography

Ariens Kappers, J. "A Survery of Advances in Pineal Research." In *The Pineal Gland*. Vol. 1, *Anatomy and Biochemistry*, edited by Russell Reiter. Boca Raton, Fla.: CRC Press, 1981. Although it contains technical language, this article by a pioneer in the field of pineal research includes a description of the earliest thoughts on the function of the pineal. It also documents the modern research that led to the definition of the pineal as an endocrine gland.

Borrell, Merriley Elaine. *Origins of the Hormone Concept: Internal Secretions and Physiological Research, 1889-1905*. Ann Arbor: University Microfilms International, 1984. Completed in 1976, this is a dissertation written by a doctoral candidate in the history of science at Yale University. It documents the early thinking that made the discovery of secretin in 1902 understandable. The experimental approach to endocrine research can be appreciated by understanding its roots.

Goldsworthy, Graham J., John Robinson, and William Mordue. *Endocrinology*. New York: John Wiley & Sons, 1981. Chapter 1, "Communication and Control Systems in Animals," includes information on how endocrine research is carried out. The text takes an unusual approach in that instead of devoting a chapter to each endocrine organ, the chapters each cover some common function of a group of hormones. An excellent glossary is included.

Hadley, Mac E. *Endocrinology*. Englewood Cliffs, N.J.: Prentice-Hall, 1984. This text is written for the beginning student of endocrinology. Chapter 1, "Introduction to Endocrinology," includes a historical perspective. Chapter 2, "The Vertebrate Endocrine System," gives an overview of what hormones are and how they work. The author's background is in comparative endocrinology (the study of hormones in different groups of animals), and this perspective is represented throughout the text.

Medvei, Victor Cornelius. *A History of Endocrinology*. Lancaster, England: MTP Press, 1982. A comprehensive history of the field, this book considers the earliest beginnings of endocrine research in prehistoric and ancient times. Also of interest are the biographies of eminent endocrinologists. One of the appendices is a complete chronology of significant discoveries for each gland.

Paxton, Mary Jean W. *Endocrinology: Biological and Medical Perspectives*. Dubuque, Iowa: Wm. C. Brown, 1986. This is a good text for the beginning student. Chapters on individual endocrine glands contain information on the techniques that have been used to investigate them. Chapter 13, "The Measurement of Hormones," gives detailed and well-organized information on measurement techniques.

Sawin, Clark T. *The Hormones: Endocrine Physiology*. Boston: Little, Brown, 1969. Although the text is now a bit out of date, the reader may be interested in chapter 1, "Approach to Endocrinology," which details the kinds of studies that are performed and the rationale for them. Chapter 2, "Recognized Endocrine Glands and Other Glands and Humors," is a general overview.

Sharpey-Schäfer, Edward A. *The Endocrine Organs: An Introduction to the Study of Internal Secretion.* 2d ed. 2 vols. New York: Longmans, Green, 1924-1926. The primary importance of this work is the historical perspective it provides. The reader will probably be surprised at the extent of knowledge at the time the book was written, only twenty-two years after the discovery of the first hormone.

Marcia Watson-Whitmyre

Cross-References

Blood Chemistry Analysis, 240; Endocrine Functions of the Kidneys and Heart, 780; Endocrine Functions of the Pancreas, 787; Endocrine Systems in Invertebrates, 793; Endocrinology of the Adrenal Glands, 800; Endocrinology of the Pituitary Gland, 807; Endocrinology of the Thyroid and Parathyroid Glands, 814; Histology, 1307; Hormonal Control of Blood Sugar and Fatty Acids, 1339; Hormonal Control of Protein Metabolism, 1347; Mammalian Hormones, 1368.

ENDOCRINE FUNCTIONS OF THE
KIDNEYS AND HEART

Type of life science: Animal physiology
Other fields of study: Animal anatomy and biochemistry

The kidney and heart function in concert to maintain a balance in the salt concentrations of the body. Kidney hormones promote salt retention, which results in an increase in water retention and blood pressure; hormones produced in the heart oppose these actions. An understanding of these mechanisms aids scientists in the development of agents to treat high blood pressure.

Principal terms
ATRIA: the upper chambers of the heart, which receive returning blood and transfer it to the lower chambers, the ventricles
ATRIOPEPTIN: the hormone synthesized and released from the right atrium of the heart; it has an important role in the regulation of blood pressure and in the excretion of water and sodium
DIURESIS: an increase in the production of urine
EXTRACELLULAR FLUID: the fluid that surrounds the cells, including the fluid portion of blood and the fluid in the spaces between the cells
HOMEOSTASIS: the maintenance of a relatively stable internal environment; each cell requires homeostasis for survival
HYPERTENSION: "high tension," specifically an increase in blood pressure in the ateries
JUXTAGLOMERULAR APPARATUS: a portion of the kidney that plays several imporant roles in regulating salt balance; its cells release renin, an enzymic hormone
MINERALOCORTICOID: a class of hormones synthesized in the adrenal cortex that affects the salt balance of the body; aldosterone is the most important mineralocorticoid
NEPHRON: the smallest functional unit in the kidney capable of forming urine
OSMOSIS: the driving force for the movement of water across a membrane; water moves from the area of higher water concentration (lower solute concentration) to the area of lower water concentration (higher solute concentration)

Summary of the Phenomenon

The individual cells of an animal live in a fluid environment similar to the composition of the sea. This salty internal environment bathes each cell of the animal and is called the extracellular fluid. Because of the ever-changing external environment, however, there is always the danger that the composition of this comparatively small "internal" sea could change quickly. The kidney functions as the ultimate organ to protect against any large fluctuations in an animal's internal environment. It is the role of the kidney to maintain both the stability of the extracellular fluid volume and the concentration of its essential electrolytes: sodium, potassium, and chloride. It is thus not surprising to find located in the kidney a collection of hormone-producing cells whose function is linked to the maintenance of the extracellular fluid via their actions on the fluid within the kidney tubules.

A brief description of the structural arrangement of an individual nephron of the kidney is essential for understanding kidney function and hormonal control of electrolyte homeostasis. Each nephron consists of its own blood supply coupled to a tubular component. The glomerulus is a saclike structure at the entrance to the nephron, and it consists of a ball of blood capillaries through which some of the water and solutes from the blood (the filtration fraction) are capable of passing. Approximately 20 percent of the blood plasma is filtered by the glomerulus in each pass through the kidney. The filtered fluid, which is almost identical in composition to blood, except for a lack of red and white blood cells and large-molecular-weight compounds, then passes into the tubular component of the nephron. Each tubule consists of a hollow, fluid-filled pipe surrounded by a single layer of cells. It is there that the fluid can be modified by various transport processes and converted into urine. Appropriately, the tubule is divided into various segments, based on the particular function that occurs along its length.

The tubular component begins with Bowman's capsule, a cuplike structure that collects the filtered fluid from the glomerular capillaries. From there the filtered fluid passes into the proximal tubule. In this portion, substances of value to the body, such as water, electrolytes, and nutrients can be reabsorbed, while waste products of the body can be secreted into the tubule for eventual removal from the body. The next segment, the loop of Henle, is found only in birds and mammals; it forms a sharp U-shaped loop. The descending limb is highly permeable to water, whereas the ascending limb is characterized by its ability to transport sodium out of the tube and into the surrounding fluid. This portion of the tubule, however, does not allow waste to escape from inside. As a consequence of this anatomical arrangement, the concentration of sodium chloride is very high at the bottom of the tubule and declines steadily up the ascending limb until it is actually lower than that measured in blood. This "countercurrent" flow between the two limbs is the means by which mammals and birds can produce a urine either more concentrated than body fluids or more dilute than normal body fluids. The composition of the urine is under the control of hormones that are released in response to changes in the concentrations of electrolytes in the blood and extracellular fluid. The ascending limb then returns to the glomerular region of its own nephron. At this point, the cells of the ascending limb lie next to the walls of the blood vessels supplying the glomerulus. This specialized combination of tubular cells and cells of the blood vessel form the juxtaglomerular apparatus ("juxta" means "next to"). It is this special anatomical arrangement that allows hormonal and physiological communication to occur between the distal tubule (containing the existing urine) and the blood vessel (containing the entering blood that will be filtered). Beyond this point, the tubule becomes highly coiled to form the distal convoluted tubule. The distal tubule and collecting duct are the sites where the concentration of electrolytes and water in the urine can be modified by their hormonal regulators. The distal tubule eventually empties into a collecting duct that drains the fluid from up to eight nephrons. The urine then empties into the renal pelvis, which drains the urine for temporary storage in the urinary bladder.

The sodium concentration in the body is reflected by the volume of the extracellular fluid. The body's principal electrolytes, sodium and chloride, account for more than 90 percent of the extracellular fluid's osmotic activity. Osmotic pressure can be thought of as a potentially powerful force that attracts and holds water. The greater the salt concentration, the greater its attractive force for water. If the sodium concentration is greater than normal, the extracellular fluid osmotic force is increased, the extra sodium "holds" extra water, and thus it increases the extracellular fluid volume. Conversely, if the sodium concentration is less than normal, the osmotic force of the extracellular fluid is decreased, so less water than normal is retained. This results in a lower blood volume. The volume of the extracellular fluid is very important. Because blood is a part of the extracellular fluid, the most critical result of a change in its volume is the corresponding change in blood pressure. If the volume is expanded, there is an increase in blood pressure, whereas, with a decline in the blood volume, there is a decrease in blood pressure.

Cells of the juxtaglomerular apparatus, in response to a decline in the concentration of sodium, in extracellular volume, or in blood pressure, secrete a hormone called renin into the blood. (Renin is, in fact, an enzyme.) Each of these interrelated signals for the release of renin will ultimately result in an increase in the blood volume, which restores blood pressure to normal.

Once released into the blood, renin acts as an enzyme to convert a blood protein, angiotensinogen, into angiotensin I. It does so by removing several of the amino acids from the inactive parent protein. Angiotensinogen is produced by the liver and is always present in the blood in high concentrations. This ensures that any changes in blood pressure can be responded to rapidly. Angiotensin I is then activated by cells of the lung into angiotensin II. Angiotensin II acts directly on the adrenal gland to stimulate the release of the hormone aldosterone. The adrenal gland is an endocrine gland (that is, it secretes hormones into the blood) that produces a number of different hormones in response to different stimuli.

Aldosterone is the principal mineralocorticoid that promotes the retention of sodium by stimulating the kidney tubules to transport sodium from the urinary filtrate back into the blood. This function is essential for the survival of an animal, because any deviations in its salt and water balance can rapidly result in unconsciousness and death. Aldosterone stimulates the recovery of sodium in both the distal and collecting tubule of the nephron. This is accomplished by the synthesis of a new protein that helps sodium pass through the membrane of these cells. Sodium moves passively from its higher concentration inside the kidney tubule into the comparatively lower concentration in the cell. Sodium pumps are located at the other end of the cell; they then pump the sodium ion into the extracellular fluid. From there it is taken up by the capillaries and returned to the blood system.

The renin-angiotensin-aldosterone system thus promotes salt retention and an increase in blood pressure. When the conditions that initially trigger the release of renin are corrected (sodium depletion, plasma volume reduction, or decreased blood pressure, for example), the release of renin is then inhibited. This is a classical example of negative feedback: The rate of secretion of the hormone is changed in response to information regarding the status of the response initiated by the hormone.

Angiotensin II performs several additional functions that contribute to raising blood pressure. Angiotensin II constricts the muscle cells surrounding the arterioles, making it harder for the blood to pump through these vessels. This increase in the resistance to the flow of blood directly increases blood pressure. Angiotensin II also has a feedback effect, partially suppressing renin secretion from the juxtaglomerular cells. The renin-angiotensin system is considered the most powerful influence on the retention of sodium by the kidney. There is also an opposing system that directly promotes sodium loss in the urine.

The heart is also an endocrine gland, which secretes a peptide hormone called atriopeptin. Atriopeptin is also involved in the regulation of blood pressure and blood volume, and it affects the excretion of water, sodium, and potassium into the urine. Atriopeptin is synthesized in cells near the surface of the right atrium of the heart. The primary trigger for its release is an increase in blood volume, which stretches nearby atrial muscle cells. In response to an increase in stretch, atriopeptin is released into the blood.

Once in the blood, atriopeptin directly inhibits the release of renin as well as the release of aldosterone from the adrenal gland. It is thought that atriopeptin causes the capillaries in the glomeruli to become more leaky (increase filtration fraction), with the result that more fluid enters the nephron through Bowman's capsule. Atriopeptin also acts on the distal kidney tubule to prevent the recovery of sodium into the blood, and hence it increases the volume of fluid in the urine. Finally, atriopeptin relaxes muscle cells throughout the blood system, which also helps to lower blood pressure.

Methods of Study

The classical method of identifying a putative endocrine gland is simply to remove it and observe what changes, if any, occur in its absence. If there are observable affects, the next step is to prevent these effects from occurring by injecting extracts of the gland. Finally, one would isolate and identify the active factor (hormone) from the extract.

This experimental approach is successful, however, on only those glands whose sole function is endocrine: thyroid, adrenal, and gonads. In situations in which the organ is essential for life, such as the heart or kidney, it is impossible to perform these types of experiments. For this reason, it was only recently discovered that organs such as the kidney and heart have an endocrine role in addition to their more important life-sustaining functions.

Removal of the adrenal gland can be accomplished, and the procedure has served as a model for studying the salt-retaining effects of aldosterone and its derivatives. The lives of animals without adrenal glands can be prolonged by feeding them large amounts of sodium chloride. The first potent salt-retaining hormone, a derivative of aldosterone, was actually synthesized in the laboratory before it was isolated from the adrenal gland. Normally, the derivative is found in very low concentrations and so is not physiologically important. Yet, from intensive studies of adrenalectomized dogs and rats, the administration of high concentrations of the derivative was found to correct the salt-losing defects of adrenal insufficiency and thus to prolong the animal's life markedly. The potency of the derivative could be determined by injecting the animal with the compound and measuring the sodium concentration of the urine four to six hours later. This method was then used to establish the potency of all the synthesized derivatives of aldosterone.

It was not until 1974 that it was noted that certain cells in the atrium of the heart had the appearance of endocrine (hormone-secreting) cells. The bulk of the heart is composed of muscle cells, which have a characteristic appearance under the electron microscope. These atrial cells contained granules, however, a structural characteristic of the endocrine cells of the pancreas and pituitary. When radioactively labeled amino acids were injected into these animals, they were rapidly taken up into these granules and synthesized into a protein—exactly as they would be in the granules of other endocrine cells.

The human atriopeptin gene has been cloned, making it possible to produce large quantities of the purified hormone for studies of its biological function. This was accomplished by isolating the gene from the atrium and inserting it into yeast or bacteria. Once a hormone is purified, specific antibodies can be produced by immunizing an animal against it. In this manner, sensitive assays (radioimmunoassays) have been developed for each of the hormones; the assays permit measurement of their concentrations in blood.

The ability of atriopeptin to relax muscle cells has been studied using cell-culture techniques in which strips of rabbit or rat kidney arteries are incubated. Various concentrations of atriopeptin can be added to each preparation, and its ability to prevent muscle contractions induced by angiotensin II can be measured. The potency of different analogues of atriopeptin synthesized in the laboratory can be tested by using such assays. One or more may possibly serve as a therapeutic treatment to control high blood pressure.

Context

Most people with high blood pressure have kidneys that basically function normally. These kidneys handle most minerals, electrolytes, nutrients, and waste products (and perform in function tests) exactly like a normal kidney. When it comes to the amount of salt in Western diets, however, the kidneys are simply not able to handle these excessive amounts. The average adult consumes more than 10 grams of salt per day. The kidneys evolved, in fact, to process approximately a tenth of this amount. Man originated in central Africa, far from the oceans and salty rains that provided a rich source of sodium for the soil and plants. Thus, man developed a salt appetite to aid in the search for dietary sources of sodium.

In the endocrine responses of the kidney and heart to their principal regulators, the primary factor controlling mineralocorticoid secretion is normally blood pressure. The juxtaglomerular cells of the kidney act as baroreceptors, monitoring blood pressure in the vessels supplying the nephron. An increase in the local blood pressure inhibits the release of renin, which results in a decrease in aldosterone release from the adrenal cortex. Blood pressure now begins to decline until the baroreceptors detect blood pressure levels below normal, which then reverses the process. Similarly, an increase in blood pressure increases the amount of pressure in the heart atrium. The increase in the strength of the muscle fibers signals the release of atriopeptin. Atriopeptin reverses the increase in blood pressure by enhancing the loss of sodium and water in the urine.

The sodium and potassium concentrations of the kidney distal tubules also play a role in the control of renin secretion. The macula densa, a group of specialized cells located in the juxtaglomerular apparatus, monitors their concentration. Whenever the sodium concentration is low or the potassium concentration is elevated, these cells trigger the release of renin into the bloodstream. In both of these situations, the corresponding change in aldosterone secretion tends to restore the electrolyte levels toward normal. Conversely, when sodium concentrations are increased, the release of atriopeptin somehow inhibits the secretion of renin and directly inhibits the adrenal secretion of aldosterone. The most striking effect of atriopeptin on the kidney is the increase in the amount of blood flow into the nephron. This leads to an increase in the amounts of urine formed and of sodium excreted from the body.

Abnormal function of any of these feedback systems can lead to changes in blood pressure. For example, an increase in the renin-angiotensin-aldosterone axis contributes to the development of hypertension. The sodium-retaining effects of aldosterone are lost within several days after aldosterone concentrations increase, although potassium continues to be excreted. The increase in angiotensin results in constriction of the blood vessels in the kidney, resulting in an increase in blood pressure. Agents that can block the formation or the effects of angiotension are thus useful in treating this form of hypertension.

Alternately, atriopeptin is being tested for use in treating hypertension. The administration of atriopeptin to rats with hypertension causes a reduction in blood pressure to normal levels. Because atriopeptin acts at so many different sites in the body, research is directed toward developing synthetic forms of atriopeptin that are specific to a particular organ. For example, one form of atriopeptin might specifically prevent the release of renin, while another might function as a muscle relaxant. The methodology for developing and testing these compounds is available.

Bibliography

Bennett, Cleaves. *Control Your High Blood Pressure Without Drugs*. Garden City, N.Y.: Doubleday, 1984. A popular book for those interested in the treatment of high blood pressure. Written from the physician-patient standpoint, the book examines the role of diet and exercise in the prevention and treatment of hypertension. Provides an extensive bibliography of journal articles related to salt metabolism and blood pressure. Chapter 25 specifically looks at nutrition, with an emphasis on identifying misconceptions about food quality.

Cantin, Marc, and Jacques Genest. "The Heart as an Endocrine Gland." *Scientific American* 254 (February, 1986): 76-81. Provides an excellent historical account of the discovery of atriopeptin by two of the researchers involved. The diagrams and figures help to illustrate the role of the heart as an endocrine gland and summarize the diverse functions of this new hormone.

Laragh, J., J. Sealey, A. Niarchus, and T. Pickering. "The Vasoconstriction-Volume Spectrum in Normotension and in the Pathogenesis of Hypertension." *Federation Proceedings* 41 (1982): 2415-2423. A review of the factors that contribute to the development of hypertension. Specifically profiles the renin-sodium axis and its role as a basic tool for identifying which components of the blood system are at fault. Results from the endocrine profile allow the appropriate therapeutic treatments to be applied successfully. Complex articles are cited in a detailed bibliography.

Norman, Anthony, and G. Litwack. *Hormones*. Orlando, Fla.: Academic Press, 1987. Chapters 10 and 15 provide a concise review of the adrenal cortex and endocrine kidney. The essential anatomy of each organ is presented, and the relationship of the hormonal secretions to their physiological events is fully documented at both the molecular and cellular level.

Sherwood, Lauralee. *Human Physiology: From Cells to Systems*. St. Paul, Minn.: West, 1989. Chapter 14 details the basic anatomy and physiology of the kidney, with reference to the dynamics of maintaining blood sodium and potassium concentrations. An excellent introductory textbook with clearly annotated diagrams that illustrate the essential function of the nephron.

Hillar Klandorf

Cross-References

ENDOCRINE FUNCTIONS OF THE PANCREAS

Type of life science: Animal physiology
Other fields of study: Animal anatomy and biochemistry

Small clusters of cells on the surface of the pancreas have been found to produce hormones that play vital roles in the regulation of carbohydrate metabolism. Discovery of these hormones and their functions has led to the saving of millions of lives.

Principal terms

DIABETES MELLITUS: a disorder characterized by hyperglycemia and disturbances in carbohydrate metabolism; commonly known as sugar diabetes

GLUCAGON: a hormone produced by the A cells in the pancreatic islets; it promotes the breakdown of glycogen to glucose and functions to increase blood sugar concentrations by promoting the conversion of glycogen to glucose

GLYCOGEN: a polysaccharide that functions as an important form of carbohydrate storage in the liver and muscles; it is sometimes referred to as "animal starch"

HYPERGLYCEMIA: a condition in which the blood sugar concentration is elevated and remains at levels higher than normal

HYPOGLYCEMIA: a condition in which the blood sugar concentration decreases to levels lower than normal

INSULIN: a hormone produced by the B cells in the pancreatic islets; its major function is to bring about a decrease in blood sugar levels by promoting the uptake of glucose by cells and its conversion into glycogen

PANCREATIC ISLETS: small clusters of cells located on the surface of the pancreas that produce hormones which play a vital role in the regulation of carbohydrate metabolism and the maintenance of blood sugar levels

Summary of the Phenomenon

The pancreas is a relatively large, flattened, elongated organ (about 15 centimeters long in the average adult human) that lies parallel to the stomach and is attached to the first section of small intestine. The pancreas functions both as a digestive organ and as an endocrine organ. As a digestive organ, it produces powerful enzymes that are released via the pancreatic duct into the small intestine to assist in food digestion. Its endocrine functions, on the other hand, are carried out by small clusters of cells called pancreatic islets (or islets of Langerhans), which are located on the surface of the pancreas. Although there are usually between one million and two million of these islets on a typical pancreas, they constitute only about 2 percent of its total weight. An extensive system of tiny blood vessels is associated with each pancreatic islet, enabling hormones produced within each islet to enter the bloodstream rapidly.

Based on differences in morphology and staining characteristics, several types of cells can be distinguished in the pancreatic islets. These include three major cell types that have been identified and classified as types A, B, and D. The A cells, which account for about 20 percent of the islet cells, secrete a hormone called glucagon; the B cells, which constitute about 70 percent of the islet cells, secrete a different hormone called insulin; and the D cells, approximately 10 percent, produce a third hormone called somatostatin. The arrangement of these different cells within each pancreatic islet is such that the A cells tend to be located around the islet periphery, the B cells are located toward its interior, and the D cells tend to lie between the A and B cells.

Glucagon, the hormone secreted by the A cells, is a polypeptide composed of twenty-nine amino acids with a total molecular weight of 3,482. After their release from the A cells, glucagon molecules attach to special receptors on cells in the liver, stimulating these cells to convert glycogen (animal starch) into glucose. Glucagon also stimulates the conversion of certain other molecules (such as amino acids) into glucose within these cells. The glucose produced within the liver cells is then re-leased into the bloodstream. Thus, the general effect of glucagon is to bring about a marked increase in the levels of sugar in the blood. One milligram of glucagon per kilogram body weight can elevate blood glucose concentrations by more than 20 milligrams per 100 milliliters of blood in about twenty minutes.

The secretion of glucagon by the A cells is stimulated by a number of factors, including low blood sugar levels (hypoglycemia), exercise, increased concentrations of amino acids, starvation, and certain stresses. Normally, the A cells will begin to secrete glucagon when blood sugar levels fall below 7 milligrams of glucose per 100 milliliters of blood. As the blood sugar concentration returns to normal levels in response to the effects of glucagon, further secretion of glucagon ceases, and the glucagon already present in the body is rapidly degraded and removed. This process helps the body to maintain and control the concentrations of sugar at normal levels in the blood during periods of high glucose demand.

The major effect of insulin, the hormone secreted by the B cells, is exactly opposite that of glucagon. This hormone, which is a polypeptide with a molecular weight of 5,808, causes the concentrations of sugar in the blood to decrease. Insulin molecules attach to special insulin receptors on cells in the liver, stimulating these cells to take up glucose from the blood and convert it to glycogen, a substance that functions as a form of carbohydrate storage. Insulin also causes certain other cells (muscle cells and adipose cells, for example) to increase their rates of uptake of glucose, amino acids, and fats from the blood. Because of its action in promoting the uptake and the storage of carbohydrates, protein, and fats, insulin has been called "the hormone of abundance." Additionally, insulin stimulates increased protein synthesis in many cells throughout the body, thus playing an important role in normal growth processes.

A variety of factors are involved in stimulating and inhibiting the secretion of insulin. The major stimulating factor is the concentration of glucose in the blood. When blood sugar concentrations are high, glucose enters the B cells and secretion of insulin commences. When blood sugar levels return to normal as a result of the effects of insulin, further secretion of insulin from the B cells is inhibited and the insulin remaining is rapidly degraded.

The role played by somatostatin, the hormone which is secreted from the D cells, is not well understood. Researchers have noted, however, that the D cells tend to be located in close proximity to both the A and B cells, and somatostatin has been shown to inhibit secretion of glucagon and insulin. Because of these observations, it is thought that the local release of somatostatin from the D cells may help to regulate and control the secretory activities of the A and B cells, thus preventing wild fluctuations of blood sugar levels between hypoglycemia and hyperglycemia.

Methods of Study

Early anatomical studies of the pancreas revealed the presence of many tiny clusters of cells associated with an extensive and copious blood supply, leading to suggestions that these cell clusters might have some kind of endocrine function. To prove that a particular structure or tissue has endocrine functions, however, the following three criteria must be first demonstrated: First, excision of the suspected tissue results in deficiency symptoms. Second, the deficiency symptoms are reversed by replacement of the excised tissue. Third, the deficiency symptoms are also reversed by extracts obtained from the excised tissues. After these criteria have been demonstrated, further studies can then be made with respect to determination of the specific active molecules in the extract, their chemical structure, and their mode of action. Many studies of this type over the past hundred years have led to a greater understanding of the endocrine functions of the cell clusters found on the pancreas. Thus, current knowledge in this area represents a blending of information drawn from anatomical observations, animal experiments, detailed studies of the modifying effects of various pancreatic extracts, and studies of the chemical structure of extracts.

Although disorders caused by diabetes mellitus (sugar diabetes) had been recognized for centuries, this disease was not associated with functional defects of the pancreas until 1889. At that time, experimenters first succeeded in causing diabetes in dogs by pancreatic excision. It was also noted in parallel studies that although sugar was normally absent in the urine of control animals, it was present in abundance in the urine of dogs from which the pancreas had been removed. Thus, it began to become clear that diabetes mellitus was a disorder of carbohydrate metabolism.

Following these discoveries, many experimenters attempted to obtain an extract from the pancreas that could reverse these symptoms, but these attempts met with repeated failures over a period of more than thirty years. These failures were attributable to the fact that the pancreas, as part of its exocrine functions, also produces powerful digestive enzymes which are involved in food digestion. The proteolytic activities of these enzymes tended to break down the molecules released from the endocrine cells, making it difficult to obtain active extracts.

Eventually, in 1921, techniques were developed enabling researchers for the first time to obtain active extracts for the pancreas which could reverse the diabetic symptoms. This active extract was called insulin. It was shown that insulin could restore blood sugar levels to normal in diabetic humans. Further detailed chemical studies indicated that insulin was a small protein molecule. Eventually, scientists succeeded in describing its molecular structure, and insulin became the first protein for which the molecular structure could be written.

In a similar manner, other active ingredients, such as glucagon and somatostatin, produced by cells in the pancreatic islets, have been isolated and chemically identified, and scientists' understanding of the vital endocrine functions of the pancreas has increased rapidly. Still, there is more to be learned. For example, the role of somatostatin is poorly understood, and even less is known about a fourth substance released from the pancreatic islets called pancreatic polypeptide. Thus, the endocrine functions of the pancreas continue to be the focus of intense research efforts.

Context

Although most tissues of the body can obtain energy from various types of nutrients (lipids, proteins, and carbohydrates, for example), glucose is the only nutrient that can be utilized by certain tissues, such as those of the brain and the retina of the eye. It is essential, therefore, that blood sugar concentrations be held at levels sufficient to meet the needs of these tissues. Normally, blood sugar concentrations should be higher than 45 milligrams per 100 milliliters of blood. Hypoglycemia is considered to be present when sugar concentrations fall below this critical level.

On the other hand, if blood sugar levels become too high, problems will arise from hyperosmolarity (increased concentration of osmotically active particles) of the blood. Such problems include various circulation disorders and excessive losses of water, ions, and nutrients in the urine.

The vital importance of the endocrine functions of the pancreas in controlling carbohydrate metabolism and maintaining normal blood sugar levels becomes evident when one considers the pathologic condition known as diabetes mellitus (sugar diabetes). There are two common forms of diabetes mellitus: type I (also called insulin-dependent diabetes), and type II (noninsulin-dependent diabetes). Type I diabetes usually occurs before the age of twenty and is characterized by damage to or destruction of the B cells in the pancreatic islets, so that their ability to secrete insulin is reduced or lost. Treatment for type I diabetes usually involves the regular administration by injection of sufficient insulin to control blood sugar levels. Type II diabetes, which usually appears in adulthood, is characterized by a reduction in the normal responses of the body to insulin. In individuals with type II diabetes, the

B cells function normally in their release of insulin, but apparently many of the insulin receptors on the target cells throughout the body lose their sensitivity to insulin. The normal treatment for this form of diabetes involves careful control of the diet and a program of regular exercise designed to maintain desirable blood sugar levels.

Sugar diabetes is characterized by a marked reduction in the uptake of glucose by muscle and adipose cells, and a rise in the blood sugar levels (hyperglycemia). As blood sugar levels rise, the body begins to excrete the excess sugar via the kidneys, and sugar appears in the urine, leading to excessive losses of water, ions, and nutrients from the body. Diabetes is also accompanied by decreases in protein synthesis and increased use of protein as an energy source by glucose-starved cells. Thus, tissues begin to waste away, and tissue repair abilities tend to be reduced in the affected person. Fat synthesis and storage within cells is also reduced in the diabetic, causing the accumulation of fatty acids and acidic ketone bodies in the blood. These acidic by-products, together with the effects of dehydration, can adversely affect neurons in the brain, leading to disorientation, coma, or death.

The life expectancy of diabetics has increased dramatically as medical science has learned about the endocrine functions of the pancreas. Before the discovery of insulin, a thirty-year-old diabetic could be expected to live less than four years, and diabetic children usually died within a year following the onset of the disease. Today, the death rate of diabetics is only 0.3 percent above that of the general population.

Bibliography

Banting, F. G., and C. Best. "The Internal Secretion of the Pancreas." *Journal of Laboratory and Clinical Medicine* 7 (1922): 251-266. This is the original paper in which Banting and Best describe the methods they used for the preparation of pancreatic extracts that could relieve the symptoms of experimentally produced diabetes. Banting won a Nobel Prize for these efforts. A classic and interesting example of early research in endocrine function of the pancreas.

DeGroot, Leslie, Jr. *Endocrinology*. New York: Grune & Stratton, 1979. A three-volume set covering a wide range of information on current knowledge of function, mechanism of action, and regulation of hormones. Respected authorities give detailed information in each area of endocrine physiology.

Esmann, Viggo, ed. *Regulatory Mechanisms of Carbohydrate Metabolism*. Elmsford, N.Y.: Pergamon Press, 1978. A clear and detailed description of the vital roles played by pancreatic islet hormones in control of carbohydrate metabolism. This book provides an excellent review for the student who is interested in delving deeper into this subject.

McCann, Samuel M. *Endocrine Physiology*. Baltimore: University Park Press, 1974. This textbook contains a comprehensive review of almost all aspects of endocrinology, including outstanding coverage of the endocrine functions of the pancreas.

Marieb, Elaine N. *Human Anatomy and Physiology*. Redwood City, Calif.:

Benjamin/Cummings, 1989. This section, in a textbook designed primarily for nursing students, contains a concise review of major features of the endocrine function of the pancreas, written for beginning college-level students. Clear, informative illustrations and diagrams.

Notkins, Abner L. "The Causes of Diabetes." *Scientific American* 241 (November, 1979): 17, 62-73. This article contains an outstanding description of the many symptoms of diabetes and their causes. It is highly recommended for the reader who is interested in understanding the causes of this disease in greater detail.

Podolsky, Stephen, ed. *Clinical Diabetes: Modern Management.* New York: Appleton-Century-Crofts, 1980. This textbook takes a clinical approach to the management of diabetes. It is recommended for the student who wants to understand the basis of recommended medical treatments for the diabetic.

Turner, C. D., and J. T. Bagnara. *General Endocrinology.* Philadelphia: W. B. Saunders, 1976. An excellent textbook, written at the intermediate college level, which provides a comprehensive introduction to endocrinology. References at the end of each chapter.

Unger, R. H., and R. E. Dobbs. "Insulin, Glucagon, and Somatostatin Secretion in the Regulation of Metabolism." *Annual Review of Physiology* 40 (1978): 307. This in-depth review provides useful and complete coverage of information about the vital roles played by hormones released from the pancreatic islets.

John M. Wakeman

Cross-References

Blood Chemistry Analysis, 240; Carbohydrates, 323; Testing for Endocrine Functions of Glands and Organs, 772; Endocrine Functions of the Kidneys and Heart, 780; Hormonal Control of Blood Sugar and Fatty Acids, 1339; Hormonal Control of Protein Metabolism, 1347; Hormone Mechanisms and Second Messengers, 1361; Osmosis, Free Diffusion, and Facilitated Diffusion, 2022; Water Retention and Excretion, 2709.

ENDOCRINE SYSTEMS IN INVERTEBRATES

Type of life science: Animal physiology
Other fields of study: Animal anatomy, biochemistry, and invertebrate biology

Many invertebrates have endocrine systems almost as complex as vertebrate endocrine systems. In most invertebrate phyla, the principal source of hormones is neurosecretory cells. Neurosecretory hormones have been found in all the larger invertebrate phyla.

Principal terms

BUDDING: a form of asexual reproduction that begins as an outpocketing of the parental body, resulting in either separation from or continued connection with the parent, forming a colony

DIAPAUSE: a resting phase in which metabolic activity is low and adverse conditions can be tolerated

MOLT: the process of replacing one exoskeleton with another

NEURONS: cells specialized for the conduction of electrical signals and the transmission of information (nerve cells)

NEUROSECRETORY CELLS: specialized neurons capable of manufacturing and releasing hormones (neurosecretions or neurosecretory hormones) and discharging them directly into circulation

PHOTOPERIOD: the measure of the relative length of daylight as it relates to the potential physiological responses that exposure to daylight evokes

TARGET ORGAN: a specific body part that a particular hormone directly affects

TROPHIC HORMONES: hormones that stimulate another endocrine gland

Summary of the Phenomenon

The endocrine systems of many invertebrates are nearly as complicated as vertebrate endocrine systems. The principal source of hormones in most invertebrate phyla is neurosecretory cells. These hormonal mechanisms have been found in arthropods, annelid worms, mollusks, and echinoderms. The physiological processes that are affected are generally fundamental, long-term ones that include such biological phenomena as growth, regeneration, reproduction and development, and certain metabolic processes.

The subkingdom of animals made up of all vertebrates and most invertebrates (protozoa and sponges are not included) is called the Metazoa, which is defined by the presence of nervous and endocrine systems in the animals in the group. These systems coordinate the activities of the animal so it can function as one. The nervous system is important in rapid communication, such as contraction of muscles for movement, while the endocrine system controls long-term processes within the body, such as the growth of organs or maintenance of appropriate metabolic concentrations. Chemical messengers released by the endocrine systems have to travel to a specific target organ to exert their effects. The means of travel is the circulatory system. Because it takes time for the chemicals to accumulate in effective concentrations, they must be stable enough to remain in the body without undergoing chemical charges and without being excreted. These chemical messengers— hormones—are, then, well suited to work over long periods of time. These two systems do not work independently of one another, however. It is probable that most animals' central nervous systems are strongly affected by hormones much of the time.

In 1928, German chemist Ernst Sharrar hypothesized that certain nerve cells have qualities of both nerve and endocrine gland cells. These neurosecretory cells are neurons which are cellularly like gland cells, but are widespread within the invertebrate body. They receive nervous impulses, but rather than communicating through synapses with other neurons or effector cells, they terminate close to the circulatory system and release substances which travel to act on organs or upon endocrine glands. These neurosecretory substances, therefore, are themselves hormones. Neurosecretory cells are usually found in clusters within the central nervous system. Extending from the cell bodies are axons that terminate in swollen knobs associated with blood spaces. Terminals that are aggregated into a body are called neurohemal organs. Neurosecretory material is produced by the cell bodies, transported down the axons, and stored in the swollen knobs. Release is accomplished by exocytosis.

To be classified as a neurosecretory cell, three criteria must be met: The cell must have the structural features of a neuron (cell body and axonlike fibers); the axons must not synapse with other cells but end in close association with an area of body fluid (generally a blood vessel or sinus, the combination making a neurohemal organ); the neuron must contain membrane-bound vesicles within the cytoplasm. There are, in addition, two physiological criteria: Destruction of these clustered cells, or the areas or organs where they are found, produces an alteration of existing internal conditions within the organism that can be restored by replacing the removed organ or injecting an extract from it; implantation of an organ thought to be neurosecretory into a normally functioning animal brings about a change in internal state by either prompting or inhibiting the occurrence of certain events.

Neurosecretions in invertebrates may influence behavior or target another endocrine gland by trophic neurosecretions or trophic hormones. For example, in many insects neurosecretions from neurosecretory cells in the brain exert a trophic effect on the prothoracic glands, which then produce and release the hormone ecdysone that controls molting, the developmental sequence of insects. There are other examples of how hormonal release is dependent on and dictated by the nervous system. Most animals respond developmentally to environmental changes, such as seasonal variations throughout the year. If unfavorable conditions develop, the animal may compensate by going into dormancy or migrating, or may overcome the conditions by other changes in habit or physiology. Even brief fluctuations, such as a temporary shortage of food or the absence of suitable mates, may dramatically affect development. The mating act in a female insect may speed up the development of her eggs; the changing day length may control when metamorphosis begins in annelids. Stimulation of sense organs sets up nervous messages that result in changes in the amounts of circulating hormones, which generate these "new" responses.

Invertebrate hormones play as many roles as there are invertebrate phyla. In the less highly organized invertebrates, endocrine glands are apparently absent; hormonal coordination depends on neurosecretions. Hormones released in the plant hydra are believed to come from the hypostomal region (the nerve ring around the oral opening) and from actively growing areas and are thought to regulate growth, regeneration, and the development of sexuality. Little is known about substances termed "wound hormones" in planarians, but their presence in wounded tissues has been inferred, even though its site of production is unclear.

All annelids possess neurosecretory cells in the brain that control growth, reproduction, and maturation. In nereids, reproductive body forms releasing eggs and sperm are controlled by at least one brain neurohormone, and normal reproductive development appears to depend on the gradual withdrawal of brain neurohormones with increasing age. Regeneration, too, is probably controlled by neurohormones.

In starfish and sea urchins, spawning of eggs is preceded by release of a "shedding hormone" found only in the radial nerves. This hormone, known as gonadstimulating substance, also stimulates the manufacture and secretion of a second substance by the gonads called meiosis-inducing substance (MIS). MIS causes the follicle cells to pull away from the gametes so the gametes can be expelled more easily; it induces meiosis within the oocytes, and, after diffusing into the coelomic fluid, stimulates muscle contractions which cause spawning.

Many mollusks have neurons resembling neurosecretory cells that change their apparent secretory activity with conditions such as reproductive state. In a few cases, evidence has been found for neurosecretory control of reproduction, water balance, or heart function. Cephalopods such as squids, however, are one of the few classes of animals that possess endocrine glands. The cephalopod brain is connected to the optic lobes by short optic stalks bearing optic glands. As the animal matures, the size of these glands increases. These glands function in the control of reproductive development. Glands on the gills, called mesodermal branchial glands, are also endocrine organs and are thought to function similarly to vertebrate adrenal glands.

Certainly the best-studied invertebrate system is that of insects. Insects possess discrete clusters of neurosecretory cells, well-developed neurohemal organs, and even nonneural endocrine glands. The insect endocrine system has four major components: the corpora cardiaca, a group of neurosecretory cells in the brain, the corpora allata, and the thoracic glands. The corpora cardiaca, closely associated with the heart, store and secrete hormones from the brain as well as producing their own inherent hormones. Along with the brain's neurosecretory cells, they compose the cerebral neurosecretory system. Molting is controlled by hormones called ecdysteroids produced under the brain's direction. Secretion of these ecdysteroids stimulates the release of ecdysone from the prothoracic gland. Ecdysone, also called the molting hormone, stimulates the development of adult structures but is held in check by juvenile hormone (JH), which favors the development of juvenile characteristics. During juvenile life, JH predominates and each molt yields a larger juvenile. High levels of JH are released by the corpus allatum during early stages of life. Its major function, then, is to ensure that when molting is triggered by ecdysone secretion, it results in the next larval stage. When the final stage is reached, ecdysone production dramatically falls, but sufficient levels are produced to induce a molt that will result in the adult stage. Similar systems are found in the crustaceans.

Because invertebrates make up about 95 percent of the species in the animal kingdom, one might anticipate a great diversity of invertebrate endocrine mechanisms. Eventually, this expectation may be confirmed; but knowledge of endocrine systems in many invertebrate groups is, for the most part, incomplete. What is known is that in most groups of invertebrates, neurosecretory systems are distinctly more prominent than nonneural endocrine glands, which occur in very few cases.

Methods of Study

Until the 1960's, the search for hormonal regulators in invertebrates was largely unsuccessful because early experiments of gonad transplantation from insects of one sex to those of the other and injection of vertebrate hormones into invertebrates yielded negative results. Strides made in the last twenty-five years are mostly the results of refinements of microscopic, operative, and analytical techniques, both chemical and physical. Arthropods have provided the most accessible material for study, and more is known about the phenomenon in crustaceans and insects than any other group. The range of investigation is expanding, however, and neurosecretion in invertebrates is not only accepted but recognized as widespread among them.

There are many problems generally associated with determining the functions of the neurosecretory system. The classical experimental method involves removal of the suspected endocrine gland and then reimplanting it at another location in the body. If the effects of removal are reversed and normal conditions return when the organ is relocated, then a hormonal mechanism is probably involved. The problem arises, however, because removing a neurohemal organ will leave behind the cut ends that may continue to release hormones, perhaps in an uncontrolled manner. A new neurohemal organ may be rapidly regenerated so that the effects of lessened amounts of neurosecretory hormones cannot be observed. In addition, reimplanting the organ may produce several hormones into the animal in abnormal concentrations or proportions. Hormonal deficiency may not be obvious immediately because stored hormones outside the neurohemal organ may be secreted or leached out for some time after the organ's removal. Yet another problem encountered is the lack of distinct neurohemal organs; instead, scattered neurosecretory cells may be found throughout the nervous system. It is therefore difficult to determine the exact function of the mechanisms because of the virtual impossibility of removing and testing these individual cells. In these cases, the neurosecretory nature of the cells is deduced based on their structural and chemical similarity to those in other animals whose function has been already verified.

Typical of the early work on insect growth hormones was the work done in the 1930's in England by V. B. Wigglesworth on the metamorphosis of a bloodsucking insect named *Rhodnius*. This insect goes through five immature stages, each separated by a molt, until it reaches adulthood. During each of these stages, it engorges and stretches its abdomen by ingesting a blood meal. This filling meal apparently stimulates the release of hormones that cause molting at the end of a specified time interval following the meal. Usually, the final molt (to adulthood) occurs about twenty-eight days after the blood meal. If the insect is decapitated during the first few days after its meal, molting does not occur, even though the animal may live for several months longer. Decapitation more than eight days after the blood meal does not interfere with molting, although a headless adult is produced. Wigglesworth further showed that joining the circulatory system of a later-decapitated insect to that of an earlier-decapitated insect allows both to molt into adults. It appears obvious that some stimulus passes via the blood from one insect to the other and induces molting; it is assumed that the stimulus is a hormone that is secreted about eight days after the blood meal.

Since Wigglesworth's time, studies typical of his work have shown evidence of hormonal activity and control of many other invertebrate phyla. Experimentation with insects still outweighs all other studies, however, since they are so available and easy to work with because of their size.

Context

The study of invertebrate hormones began as an attempt to draw parallels between invertebrate hormones and their similarity to known vertebrate hormones. Experimenters were virtually forced to look for these similarities because of legal restrictions placed on the use of vertebrates for experimental study. The end results, however, have shown that invertebrate hormones share little in common with vertebrate hormones.

One of the few similar hormones, in structure at least, is prothoracicotropic hormone (PTTH), isolated from the heads of adult silkworms. (PTTH stimulates the prothoracic gland to release ecdysone, which then regulates molting and growth.) Though structurally similar to vertebrate insulin, insect insulin has no functional link with vertebrate insulin.

The interaction of neurohormones and the nervous system has been studied using the lobster, tying the release of neurohormones to its behavior. By the introduction of neurohormones via injection, one can induce behavioral changes, such as increased aggression. By working with these crustaceans, the apparent relationship among neurohormones, the nervous system, and behavior modification may be used in observing and controlling animal behavior. It is not inconceivable that this same information could eventually be used as groundwork for helping patients with behavior problems.

There is, then, little to be learned about vertebrate hormones by studying the hormones of invertebrates. Perhaps this knowledge can be used to manipulate invertebrate populations, thus bettering the chance to feed the world. For example, discovery of JH-like substances which regulate growth and development in some crustaceans may allow their use in shrimp and lobster farming, as well as helping to eradicate crustacean predators and parasites from the sea.

Because of the widespread fear of using poisons as insecticides, time, research, and money have been invested in studying JH and its use as a "natural" pesticide. Because chemical poisons are often toxic to humans and because the insects often become tolerant or resistant to the poisons, a feasible solution involves conquering both drawbacks at once. The possible answer was suggested when it was found that some plants, including the balsam fir and the fiddleback fern, produce their own version of JH. Both insect-produced JH and plant-produced JH imitations (called juvenoids) arrest insect growth and prevent them from reaching reproductive age. These JH-like insecticides also have the benefits of being used in very small amounts with rapid breakdown (one week or less) and can be manipulated to target a specific pest or even families or groups of insects. Not only are these acceptable advantages, but the fact that the juvenoids do not kill the insect makes it a worthwhile idea for continued research.

Bibliography

Alexander, R. McNeill. *The Invertebrates*. Cambridge, England: Cambridge University Press, 1979. This textbook is a comprehensive look at each taxonomic group that makes up the invertebrates. It is designed primarily as a college textbook, but is good as a reference book also. There are limited descriptions of species. Hormones are addressed in two chapters: chapter 15, "Squids and Their Relatives," and chapter 18, "Insects in General." References follow each chapter.

Barnes, R. S. K., P. Calow, and P. J. W. Olive. *The Invertebrates: A New Synthesis*. Oxford, England: Blackwell Scientific Publications, 1988. An intermediate college-level text that endeavors to cover both the functional systems and diversity of invertebrates. Chapter 16, "Control Systems," details some of the research and methods, mostly concerning insects, but with some space given to lower invertebrates. Sources of further reading are noted following each chapter. Glossary.

Gardiner, Mary S. *The Biology of Invertebrates*. New York: McGraw-Hill, 1972. A lengthy and complex college text intended for students with some science or biology background. This book treats invertebrates functionally rather than systematically. Chapter 17, "Neurosecretion: Endocrine Regulation and Rhythms," is a detailed discussion of all that was known about invertebrate hormones at that time. General and special references given.

Hickman, Cleveland P., Larry S. Roberts, and Frances M. Hickman. *Biology of Ani-*

mals. 5th ed. St. Louis: Times Mirror/Mosby, 1990. The goal of this intermediate college text is to acquaint the major or nonmajor student with the various animal phyla. Also included is a section devoted to animal form and function. Chapter 11, "Chemical Coordination: Endocrine Systems," specifically, but briefly, defines the types of endocrine systems found in invertebrates. Selected references. Glossary.

Highnam, Kenneth C., and Leonard Hill. *The Comparative Endocrinology of the Invertebrates*. New York: Elsevier, 1969. This complex edition attempts to show the importance of hormonal control in invertebrates. Because, generally, invertebrates are easily suitable for classroom use, the authors have included some practical detail in hopes of stimulating the reader to do his own investigations. Some knowledge of structural organization and biology of animals is assumed. A lengthy bibliography concludes this volume.

Hill, Richard W., and Gordon A. Wyse. *Animal Physiology*. 2d ed. New York: Harper & Row, 1989. A very readable college-level text that provides a comprehensive introduction to comparative animal physiology. It places emphasis on animals' ecological relations to show their natural state. The book is written systematically, and chapter 21, "Endocrine and Neuroendocrine Physiology," is particularly helpful. Selected readings conclude each chapter.

Keeton, William T., and James L. Gould. *Biological Science*. 4th ed. New York: W. W. Norton, 1986. A textbook used for introductory biology in college, but even so, a complex edition. Much space is devoted to the cellular level of living organisms. Chapter 16, "Chemical Control in Animals," has a brief, up-to-date look at invertebrate hormones with emphasis on insects. Glossary.

Lee, Julius, and F. G. W. Knowles. *Animal Hormones*. London: Hutchinson University Library, 1965. A small volume used for reference, intermediately complex. It is intended to guide the reader rather than to provide a comprehensive account, so an extensive reference list is included. Most of the book is about vertebrate hormones, but four chapters are dedicated to invertebrate hormones, the controls they exert, and endocrine regulation of metabolism, development, and reproduction.

Iona C. Baldridge

Cross-References

Animal Cell Types, 105; Circulatory Systems of Invertebrates, 476; Testing for Endocrine Functions of Glands and Organs, 772; Mammalian Hormones, 1368; Hormones and Behavior, 1377; Higher Invertebrate Animals, 1475; Lower Invertebrate Animals, 1483; Metamorphosis Controls, 1706; Muscle Anatomy in Invertebrates, 1814; Pheromones, 2051.

ENDOCRINOLOGY OF THE ADRENAL GLANDS

Type of life science: Animal physiology
Other fields of study: Animal anatomy and biochemistry

The adrenal glands consist of two parts, the medulla and the cortex. The medulla produces epinephrine (adrenaline) and norepinephrine; the cortex produces steroidal hormones.

Principal terms

ANTIBODY: a substance produced by the immune system of an animal in response to a foreign substance; the antibody is specific for the substance that induced its production and can combine with it to inactivate it

AUTONOMIC NERVOUS SYSTEM: the portion of the peripheral nervous system responsible for the maintenance of homeostasis

HOMEOSTASIS: a state of equilibrium in the internal environment of living organisms that keeps within the narrow parameters that provide the optimum chance for survival

HORMONES: chemical messengers produced by endocrine glands

RECEPTORS: proteins on cell membranes or inside cells that serve as binding sites for chemical messengers; the receptor-messenger complex initiates a cellular response

TARGET CELLS: cells that have specific protein receptors for hormones

TISSUE: a group of cells of a similar type

Summary of the Phenomenon

Animal bodies house intricate systems of cells that require tight regulation and communication. The central nervous system is one regulating system that functions both to control various parameters and to put cells in rapid communication with one another. The endocrine system is another regulating system that serves the same purpose but that does so much more slowly than the nervous system. The endocrine system is a complex system of glands that communicate with the nervous system, with the other endocrine glands, and with various cells of the body. Endocrine glands communicate with cells by chemical messengers called hormones.

Endocrine glands release all of their hormones into the fluid surrounding cells; from there, the hormones diffuse into the bloodstream. Once in the bloodstream, they circulate to the various parts of the body. Not all cells are affected by a particular hormone; in fact, only a specific set of cells, called target cells, will be affected by any given hormone. Target cells are capable of being affected because they have a receptor for that particular hormone. The receptors may be located in the cell membrane, in the cell cytoplasm, or in the nucleus.

The central nervous system typically elicits a response that is very rapid but that lasts for only a short period of time. Most nervous communication is from cell to cell, and there is no general response—as there is in the endocrine system. The endocrine response to a stimulus takes much longer than the response of the nervous system; however, it also lasts much longer once it has been initiated.

The adrenal glands are endocrine glands that are found in all animals. They are composed of two distinct types of cells that differ not only in their embryological origin but also in the type of hormones they produce, in the factors that stimulate their release, and in the physiological effects they induce.

The adrenal glands are paired and are located above the kidneys in mammals. They have an inner region called the medulla that is derived during development from nervous tissue. It is composed of cells called chromaffin cells, which produce and secrete epinephrine (also called adrenaline) and norepinephrine. The outer region, called the cortex, is derived from mesodermal cells and produces a variety of steroidal hormones.

In most mammals, the cortex completely surrounds the medulla and is substantially larger than the medulla. In lower vertebrates, both the cortex and the medulla are present, but the arrangement of the two types of tissue varies in different animals. For example, in most fish, the tissues are completely separate and are located along blood vessels. In many amphibians, reptiles, and birds, the chromaffin cells are distributed in clusters throughout the medullary tissue. These tissues, then, demonstrate significant variation in arrangement and in size.

In humans, the medulla represents about 10 percent of the total adrenal gland. Epinephrine and norepinephrine are both synthesized from the amino acid tyrosine, although two distinct chromaffin cells produce and store the hormones. Under normal conditions, there is very little hormone from the adrenal medulla that is circulating in the body. The hormones are stored, awaiting a signal from the nervous system. In humans, norepinephrine represents less than 20 percent of the total hormone produced by the medulla.

The epinephrine and norepinephrine are released into the bloodstream in response to a stimulus from the sympathetic division of the autonomic nervous system. This response is also known as the fight or flight reaction. It prepares the body to defend itself from a predator or, in the case of humans, to maintain activity when there is a sustained increase in muscular work or when a stressful situation occurs. The autonomic nervous system release of hormones is restricted to a local effect on organs. The response of the adrenal medulla hormones is much more general, however, because the hormones are released into the bloodstream and circulate throughout the entire body.

Most cells, except nervous tissue, are target cells, with membrane receptors that bind the hormone and initiate an effect. These receptors on the surface of the cells activate an enzyme called adenylate cyclase that, in turn, causes the formation of cyclic adenosine monophosphate (cyclic AMP). Cyclic AMP is termed a second messenger, because it induces cellular activity for the primary messenger, in this case epinephrine.

Because of the large number of target cells that bind epinephrine, many diverse physiological effects may be observed. Epinephrine increases the rate and strength of contraction of heart muscles, increases blood pressure, increases blood flow to skeletal muscle, dilates the bronchial muscles, dilates the pupils of the eyes, and increases the availability of nutrients to the cells. The circulating medullary hormones are metabolized by monoamine oxidase or catechol—O—methyl transferase.

The adrenal cortex is necessary to life. Experimental animals that have had their adrenal glands removed die shortly after the surgery. Unlike the medulla, the cortex is highly organized structurally. The cells nearest the outer edge form the zona glomerulosa. The bulk of the organ is made up of highly organized columns of paired cells called the zona fasiculata. The region abutting the medulla is less well organized and is called the zona reticularis. Not only are these regions histologically different, but they also exhibit functional differences.

All the hormones of the adrenal cortex are steroids and are produced from cholesterol. As steroids, they affect target cells by diffusing through the membrane and binding to receptor proteins at an intracellular site. Once the hormone-receptor complex is formed, it enters the nucleus, where it stimulates the synthesis of specific proteins. It takes somewhat longer for cells to respond to steroidal hormones than to nonsteroidal hormones; however, the response is extended over a longer period of time. Adrenal cortex hormones fall into three categories: mineralocorticoids, glucocorticoids, and androgens.

The most important mineralocorticoid is aldosterone, which is produced by the zona glomerulosa. It stimulates the retention of sodium and the excretion of potassium in the collecting ducts of the kidney. In the event that there is a decrease in the body's blood volume or a decrease in blood pressure in the arterioles of the kidney, an effort will be made to conserve sodium. It is a three-step process, starting with the release of renin from the kidney. Renin is an enzyme that activates a protein circulating in the bloodsteam and converts it to angiotensin I. The angiotensin I is converted to angiotensin II, and the angiotensin II acts on the adrenal cortex to release aldosterone. The entire process may take about thirty minutes, but it generally remains effective for several hours.

The second group of hormones, the glucocorticoids, is produced in the zona fasiculata. There are many glucocorticoids, but cortisol and corticosterone are the most important to mammals. Glucocorticoids are released in response to a complex command system originating in the hypothalamus. The hypothalamus produces a neurohormone that acts on the pituitary gland to release adrenocorticotropic hormone (ACTH). The ACTH, in turn, acts on the cells of the adrenal cortex to initiate the release of cortisol and/or corticosterone.

The blood concentrations of cortisol follow a daily rhythm, with a low at midnight and a peak between 6 and 8 A.M., and they tend to fall slowly through the day. When an animal is under neurological or physical stress, the release of the neurohormone from the hypothalamus increases and so do concentrations of ACTH and cortisol.

Once in the blood, the glucocorticoids are active in most cells. They increase the formation of glucose in the liver and its release into the bloodstream, which in turn leads to an increased blood glucose concentration as well as an increased glycogen concentration in the liver. In addition, there is an increased mobilization of fat from the adipose tissue. In skeletal muscle cells, the glucocorticoids cause increased protein breakdown and decreased protein synthesis. The glucocorticoids are also known to block the inflammatory response. When an animal is injured, there is a series of specific events that occur at the site of the injury. Many of these inflammatory reactions are blocked by circulating cortisol.

The third group of hormones secreted by the adrenal cortex is the androgens, often referred to as the adrenal androgens. Androgens are male sex hormones. ACTH promotes the secretion of androgens throughout life, but the quantities are generally small. The commonest androgen from the adrenal gland is dehydroepiandrosterone, which is relatively weak compared with the androgens produced from the testes. The androgens produced in females probably have little effect when present under normal physiologic concentrations, except in terms of pubic and axillary (armpit) hair growth. In males, their presence in early life may contribute to the development of the male sex organs.

When the hormones are no longer of use to the cells, they are transported to the liver. The liver has a system to metabolize steroidal hormones and to break them down into their component parts or convert them to a water-soluble substance for excretion.

Methods of Study

The study of the physiological effects of endocrine glands is difficult in humans, because small changes in concentration can lead to dramatic changes in function. Most hormones are effective in very small concentrations, which are tightly regulated by the body. As research into normal body functions began, there were many substances isolated from cells, or from the fluids surrounding cells, for investigation. Scientists had to identify each of these chemicals and determine their role in the body. Many new substances are still being isolated from tissues. As technology improves, there will be more and more chemicals and possibly some new hormones identified. Once a hormone is isolated and identified, it is possible to determine its chemical structure and, in many cases, to synthesize the compound in the laboratory.

Most hormonal effects have been studied in laboratory animals, using one of two techniques. The first technique is to remove the entire gland and examine the effects on the animal. In the case of the endocrine system, if a gland is removed, death may follow within a few days, the necessary conclusion being that the gland is necessary for life. Yet, if the gland produces a number of hormones, the effects of each individual hormone loss may not be clear until they are studied individually.

The second technique involves supplying additional hormone, either synthetically prepared or extracted from the tissues of other animals. This technique can be used to increase the concentration of a specific hormone or the concentration of several hormones simultaneously. Physiological examination of the animals following the addition of varying quantities of the hormones has provided many insights into the role of the endocrine glands in normal function.

Since many of the hormones are present in the blood in extremely low concentrations, measuring them was a problem until the development of the radioimmunoassay. Radioimmunoassay requires that the hormone be isolated in a pure form and that an antibody against it be developed. Once the antibody is obtained, it will be specific for only one hormone. When the two are in contact, the antibody and the hormone bind tightly to each other and are not easily separated.

The radioimmunoassay is performed in a test tube that has a small quantity of the antibody. Two other substances are added to the tube: the test sample of the hormone and a known quantity of the same hormone that has a radioactive label. The two hormones will compete to bind the antibody. If they are present in equal quantities, then one-half of the antibody binding sites should contain unlabeled hormone and one-half of the binding sites should contain labeled hormone. Since the technician will always know how much labeled hormone is present in the tube, the quantity of unknown hormone in the sample can then be determined.

The concentration of the hormones is not the only factor that determines their physiological effect. In addition, the rate of excretion of the hormone and the number of receptors available to which the hormone can bind help determine its effectiveness. It has been discovered that the number of receptors for a specific hormone is not a constant. The differences in excretion and receptor number lead to differing physiological responses from the same quantity of a hormone. The role of, and control of, receptor number will be an area of active study in the future.

Context

The primary role of the adrenal gland is the maintenance of homeostasis. In the event that anything alters an organism's concentration of hormones, it will face serious consequences. Conditions that lead to deficiencies include genetic factors, inadequate quantities of the precursors needed for hormone synthesis, exposure to substances that injure the hormone-producing cells, too few hormone-producing cells, and problems in the regulation system. Causes of excessive production of hormones include errors in the regulation system and conditions that cause increased numbers of hormone-producing cells, such as tumors.

The adrenal medulla is not necessary for the survival of animals because it overlaps the function of the autonomic nervous system. Pheochromocytoma is a rare, usually nonmalignant tumor of the adrenal medulla that may be mild or serious. It can lead to hypertension, spasms of the retinal arteries, enlargement of the left ventricle of the heart, tremors, anxiety, or weakness. It is corrected by the removal of the tumor.

Adrenal cortex hormones are required for life. There are several possible causes of a loss of the hormones, including removal of or disease of the pituitary, resulting in lack of ACTH, or a disease of the adrenal gland. In either of the above cases, the patient must be treated quickly.

In the event of an insufficiency of glucocorticoids, the following symptoms may appear: generalized weakness that is associated with weight loss; abnormally low blood concentrations of glucose; dizziness, nausea, and vomiting.

An insufficiency of mineralocorticoids will lead to the excretion of sodium, which will cause decreased blood volume and low blood pressure. At the same time, there would be a decreased excretion of potassium, leading to excessive concentrations of that element. Patients with an underactive adrenal cortex also develop excessive skin pigmentation, often in blotches. This condition is probably a result of the fact that adrenal cortex hormones act to inhibit the release of hormones from the pituitary gland. If the adrenal hormones are not present in normal quantities, the pituitary is free to release its hormones, including the melanin-stimulating hormone that is responsible for the development of skin pigmentation.

Overproduction of adrenal cortex hormones is called Cushing's syndrome. It can be caused by overactivity of the hypothalamus, overactivity of the pituitary (resulting in high circulating concentrations of ACTH), or tumors of the adrenal cortex. The same symptoms would be observed in patients who receive overdoses of hydrocortisone. Symptoms include a round face (moon face), obesity in the trunk of the body, weakness from breakdown of muscle protein, bone weakness, increased concentrations of blood sugar, sodium retention and potassium loss, leading to hypertension, and decreased immune function.

Excessive quantities of the androgen hormones in males will, for the most part, go unnoticed, except if this condition occurs in a child, in which case there would be precocious development of male sexual characteristics. In females, there would also be masculinization, including growth of a beard, deepening of the voice, increased muscular growth, and excessive growth of the clitoris to resemble a penis.

Bibliography

Campbell, Neil. *Biology.* Menlo Park, Calif.: Benjamin/Cummings, 1987. A biology textbook written for college students that is easily understood. Includes a section on the adrenal glands, and the chapter on chemical coordination describes the role of the endocrine system in maintaining homeostasis.

Durham, Ross M. *Human Physiology: Functions of the Human Body.* Dubuque, Iowa: Wm. C. Brown, 1989. An easily read textbook of general physiology that is illustrated with clear diagrams and colorful pictures.

The Endocrine System: Miraculous Messengers. New York: Torstar Books, 1985. An excellent place for the reader with no biological background to begin. Examines the history, functions, and interactions of hormones. Beautifully illustrated.

Goodman, H. Maurice. *Basic Medical Endocrinology.* New York: Raven Press, 1988. A more advanced book, but readable by those that have done some previous background reading. The chapters on the adrenal glands, regulation of sodium and water balance, and regulation of fuel metabolism are particularly informative, but the entire book will be of interest to those studying endocrinology. Well illustrated.

Gordon, Malcolm S., George A. Bartholomew, Alan D. Grinell, C. Barker Jorgensen, and Fred N. White. *Animal Physiology: Principles and Adaptations*. 4th ed. New York: Macmillan, 1982. The physiology of various types of animals is described in this book, which covers a broad scope. The text is easily readable, and the role of the endocrine system in lower vertebrates is covered.

Vander, Arthur J., James H. Sherman, and Dorothy S. Luciano. *Human Physiology: The Mechanisms of Body Function*. New York: McGraw-Hill, 1985. A college-level general physiology text that can be easily understood by the high school student. A section on receptors is included in the chapter on homeostatic mechanisms.

West, John B., ed. *Best and Taylor's Physiological Basis of Medical Practice*. 11th ed. Baltimore: Williams & Wilkins, 1989. A classic text in the study of pathophysiology. It is clearly written and provides much detail on the physiologic function of the endocrine system and the medical problems when the glands are diseased. It assumes at least a basic knowledge of the subject matter. Includes an extensive bibliography.

Annette O'Connor

Cross-References

Testing for Endocrine Functions of Glands and Organs, 772; Endocrinology of the Pituitary Gland, 807; Endocrinology of the Thyroid and Parathyroid Glands, 814; Eukaryotic Transcriptional Control: Steroid Hormones, 887; Hormonal Control of Blood Sugar and Fatty Acids, 1339; Hormonal Control of Protein Metabolism, 1347; Hormone Mechanisms and Second Messengers, 1361; The Sympathetic and Parasympathetic Nervous Systems, 2580; Water Retention and Excretion, 2709.

ENDOCRINOLOGY OF THE PITUITARY GLAND

Type of life science: Neurobiology
Other fields of study: Animal anatomy, animal physiology, and biochemistry

The pituitary gland is an organ that releases hormones into the bloodstream. These hormones travel to all parts of the body, where they control growth, metabolism, water balance, and reproduction.

Principal terms

ANTERIOR PITUITARY: the part of the pituitary gland that secretes growth hormone, prolactin, follicle-stimulating hormone, luteinizing hormone, thyroid-stimulating hormone, adrenocorticotropic hormone, and melanocyte-stimulating hormone; controlled by hypothalamic hormones

ENDOCRINE GLAND: an organ that secretes a hormone into the bloodstream

HORMONE: a chemical messenger that is secreted by one cell that travels through the blood to affect cells elsewhere in the body

HYPOTHALAMUS: a region of the brain that controls secretion of hormones from the pituitary gland

NEGATIVE FEEDBACK: a mechanism by which the body regulates hormone levels within relatively narrow limits; pituitary hormones induce the release of other hormones which, in turn, prevent further pituitary hormone release

NEUROENDOCRINE CELL: a cell shaped like a nerve cell, with a cell body, axon, and nerve terminals; stimulation reaching the cell body is transmitted by the long axon to other terminals, which release hormones

POSTERIOR PITUITARY: the part of the pituitary gland that secretes antidiuretic hormone and oxytocin; controlled by neuronal messages from the hypothalamus

Summary of the Phenomenon

The pituitary is a small gland, about the size of a pea, lying just below the brain and above the roof of the mouth. Small blood vessels and nerve fibers connect it to the region of the brain called the hypothalamus. The hypothalamus sends hormonal and neural messages to the pituitary gland, thereby controlling its activity.

The pituitary gland releases at least nine different hormones into the bloodstream. Circulating in the blood, these hormones reach all parts of the body. They stimulate growth of the young, metabolic rate, the water content of the body, development of the ovaries and testes, contraction of the uterus, and lactation.

The pituitary is actually made of two glands joined together, which differ not only in the hormones they secrete but also in their cellular structure and their relationship to the hypothalamus. The posterior pituitary, or neurohypophysis, is made of axons and terminals of neuroendocrine cells. The cell bodies of these cells are located in the hypothalamus, and it is there that hormones are made. When neural messages stimulate these hypothalamic cells, hormones made in the cell bodies travel down the axon to the terminals in the posterior pituitary. The hormones are released by the posterior pituitary to adjacent blood vessels. The posterior pituitary secretes two such hormones, both of them small peptides of eight amino acids.

Antidiuretic hormone (ADH), also called vasopressin, is produced when the water content of the blood is low. Special cells in the brain sense the blood concentration and stimulate the ADH-containing neuroendocrine cells. The ADH released from the posterior pituitary reaches the kidneys, where it promotes the retention of water. With less water lost in the urine, the blood becomes less concentrated. The second hormone secreted by the posterior pituitary is oxytocin. It causes the uterus to contract at birth, helping to expel the infant and the placenta. Oxytocin is also produced when a mother nurses an infant; the infant stimulates nerves in the breast that send messages to the hypothalamic cells that contain oxytocin. The hormone leaves the pituitary and travels to the breast, where it causes small muscles surrounding the milk-producing tissue to contract and expel milk through the nipple. Neural messages from elsewhere in the brain may stimulate the hypothalamus directly. This occurs when a woman hears her infant cry and milk squirts from her nipples without an infant's sucking. In amphibians, reptiles, and birds, the posterior pituitary produces vasotocin. This hormone prevents water loss and stimulates contraction of the reproductive system during egg laying.

The anterior pituitary, or adenohypophysis, lies just in front of the posterior pituitary. The cells of the anterior pituitary are endocrine cells that produce several different hormones. The hypothalamus controls the anterior pituitary as well, but the control is hormonal, rather than neural, as is the case for the posterior pituitary. At least seven hormones are produced by the anterior pituitary. Growth hormone, or somatotropin, speeds up the rate of bone and muscle growth in young animals. It acts by increasing the rate at which amino acids enter cells and are built up into proteins. Growth hormone also provides the energy for this growth by stimulating the breakdown of fats and carbohydrates from cells where they are stored.

In mammals, the pituitary makes increasing amounts of prolactin during pregnancy. This hormone is released when an infant suckles at the breast. When it reaches the breast, prolactin induces the tissue to produce milk. The elevated prolactin level also suppresses activity of the ovaries, decreasing the probability that a female will become pregnant while nursing. Prolactin has a variety of effects in other species: It induces certain fish, birds, and mammals to show parental care, stimulates pigeons and doves to produce "crop milk," a compound they regurgitate to feed their young, and causes lizards to slough off their skin.

In addition to growth hormone and prolactin, the anterior pituitary secretes four tropic hormones, so called because they stimulate the activity of other endocrine glands. Follicle-stimulating hormone (FSH) and luteinizing hormone (LH) are known collectively as gonadotropins, because they stimulate the gonads (ovaries and testes). In the female, FSH initiates the development of an egg follicle in the ovary and stimulates the ovary to produce the hormone estrogen. LH induces ovulation, the process by which the ovary releases an egg. It also stimulates the ovary to produce the hormones estrogen and progesterone, which prepare the body for a possible pregnancy. The same two gonadotropic hormones are produced by males, where they influence the testes. FSH stimulates the testes to produce sperm, while LH induces the secretion of the hormone testosterone.

Thyroid-stimulating hormone (TSH) stimulates the thyroid gland to release the hormones thyroxine and triiodothyronine. These thyroid hormones are important for the development of the nervous system in young animals. In adults, they elevate the metabolic rate. When body temperature drops, TSH secretion increases. The increased metabolic rate that results helps raise body temperature.

Adrenocorticotropic hormone (ACTH) stimulates the adrenal gland to produce several hormones, particularly cortisol and corticosterone. These hormones are important for maintaining blood sugar levels and for combating inflammation and stress. In synthesizing ACTH, the cell first makes a large precursor protein, from which the thirty-nine-amino-acid sequence of ACTH is removed. Several other molecules are derived in this way from the precursor protein. It is not certain, however, if pituitary production of these molecules is of physiological significance in all species. These molecules include beta endorphin, an endogenous opiate that can decrease pain perception, beta lipotropin, which is able to promote breakdown of fat in fat cells, and melanocyte-stimulating hormone (MSH), which may be important for fetal growth. MSH is produced in a part of the pituitary called the intermediate lobe in reptiles and amphibians. The skin of these animals contains melanin, a dark pigment that is concentrated in small granules in cells known as melanocytes. When these cells are stimulated by MSH, the pigment disperses throughout the cells, which darkens the skin and allows the animal to blend in with the environment.

The secretion of the anterior pituitary hormones depends on chemical messages arriving from the hypothalamus by way of small blood vessels. These chemicals are called releasing hormones and inhibiting hormones, and they cause the pituitary to either secrete or stop secreting a particular hormone. To determine the amount of hormone to secrete, the hypothalamus must integrate information it receives from the blood and from elsewhere in the brain. For example, the hypothalamus secretes corticotropin-releasing hormone, which stimulates the pituitary to release ACTH. When ACTH reaches the adrenal gland, cortisol is secreted into the blood. When cortisol levels in the blood become high, the hypothalmus responds by decreasing its production of the releasing hormone, while the pituitary decreases its sensitivity to any releasing hormone that might arrive. As a result, less ACTH is secreted and cortisol levels fall. Since the increased cortisol goes back to the hypothalamus and pituitary to reverse the increased ACTH, the mechanism is termed negative feedback. This process ensures that cortisol remains within relatively narrow limits. Similar negative feedback mechanisms are involved in the regulation of the other anterior pituitary hormones.

The hypothalamus also receives neural input that may influence the rate at which it sends releasing hormones to the pituitary. For example, fright may cause a sudden release of ACTH, while the presence of a mate may induce release of the gonadotropins. The hypothalamic hormones are not released continually, but rather in regularly repeated bursts of secretion. As a result, pituitary hormones are released in a pulsatile fashion as well. This episodic secretion is necessary for pituitary function—if hypothalamic hormones are infused at a constant rate, the pituitary loses its ability to respond. Fluctuations in pituitary hormones are also seen when levels are measured at different times of day. ACTH levels are highest in the morning, while growth hormone is secreted mostly during sleep. On a larger time scale, fluctuations in the gonadotropins are seen during the reproductive cycle. It should also be noted that many pituitary hormones have been discovered in the brain and spinal cord, where they might act as neurotransmitters rather than as hormones.

Methods of Study

The earliest techniques for studying pituitary function made use of surgical removal of the gland and replacement of gland extracts. Rats whose pituitaries were removed showed many defects. They lost water, and they had shrunken thyroid glands, adrenal glands, and gonads; young rats stopped growing. This showed that many body systems are dependent on normal pituitary function. Crude extracts of the pituitary were injected to show that they could reverse the physiological defects. Finally, chemical and physical techniques were used to purify the pituitary extracts and to identify the chemical structure of the purified hormones.

The chemical components of the pituitary can be studied using various histological stains. Different endocrine cells take up different colored stains because of the different chemical natures of the hormones stored within them. For example, exposed to a particular stain, cells containing prolactin appear pink, whereas those containing gonadotropins appear blue. This technique allowed investigators to chart the changing levels of gonadotropins produced during different reproductive states.

Immunocytochemistry is a more accurate method of visualizing how hormones are distributed in a particular tissue. For example, a pituitary hormone is injected into a rabbit, which produces antibodies to that particular hormone. Those antibodies are then attached to a chemical that either fluoresces or produces a certain color, allowing the investigator to see the presence of the antibody. When these marked antibodies are added to a slice of pituitary tissue, they can be seen attached to those pituitary cells that produce that particular hormone. This method revealed that there are at least six types of cells in the anterior pituitary, each producing a different hormone. Immunocytochemistry has also been used to identify the hypothalamic cells that manufacture the hormones of the posterior pituitary.

Antibodies to pituitary hormones are also important in the technique known as radioimmunoassay, which allows precise measurement of hormone concentrations in the blood or in other tissue. Hormone levels may also be measured by bioassay, in which the physiological activity of the hormone is assessed. A bioassay for MSH consists of adding known quantities of the hormone to a piece of frog skin. In response to MSH, the melanocytes in the skin darken; the color change can be measured. A sample with an unknown amount of MSH is then added to frog skin, and the resultant darkening is compared to that which occurs with a known quantity of the hormone.

When a given substance has been shown to influence pituitary hormones in an experimental animal, scientists ask whether the substance affects the pituitary directly or if it acts by way of the hypothalamic hormones. This sort of question may be resolved by administering the substance to the pituitary after isolating it from hypothalamic influences. The pituitary of a rat will continue to function after it is removed and placed in a glass dish with appropriate nutrients. This technique showed that hormones from the adrenal gland and gonads can have direct effects on the pituitary gland.

Much knowledge of pituitary function comes from surgical studies, observation of the effects of hormone administration, and microscopic examination of pituitary tissue. Biochemical techniques are important for an understanding of the structure of pituitary hormones. Techniques of molecular biology are also being used to understand the function of pituitary hormones on a molecular level.

Context

A number of diseases are associated with a malfunction of the pituitary gland, and an understanding of the endocrinology of the pituitary has enabled physicians to devise treatments for these diseases. When the pituitary produces insufficient ADH, for example, a disease known as diabetes insipidus may develop. Individuals with this disorder are constantly thirsty, but the water they drink is quickly lost in their urine. The disease can be treated by administering ADH.

If growth hormone is lacking at a young age, dwarfism may result. Children with this condition may be treated by injections of human growth hormone. At one time, this hormone had to be extracted from the pituitary glands of cadavers, making it a rare and expensive treatment. Growth hormone is now produced commercially by gene-splicing techniques, a less costly procedure. These same techniques are being used to produce large amounts of the growth hormone of cattle. This hormone, when injected into beef cattle, increases the rate of protein synthesis and fat breakdown, resulting in leaner meat and dairy products.

Oxytocin is sometimes used to induce uterine contractions in women who are having a difficult labor. It also may be given to women after they give birth. The contractions that oxytocin induces in the uterus serve to minimize blood loss and help the uterus shrink to its original size. In some cases, it is possible to change the structure of a natural pituitary hormone to produce analogues of the hormone that have greater potency than the original hormone. Analogues of the gonadotropin-releasing hormone have been made that induce the pituitary to release FSH and LH. This treatment may be used to induce ovulation in women with certain kinds of infertility.

Bibliography

Durham, Ross. *Human Physiology: Functions of the Human Body.* Dubuque, Iowa: Wm. C. Brown, 1989. A lively text that presumes no previous knowledge of biology. Chapter 10, "The Endocrine System," is a clear overview of the pituitary and other endocrine glands. Illustrations, photographs, diagrams, and glossary are of especially high quality. Suitable for college or high school students.

Guillemin, Roger, and Robert Burgus. "The Hormones of the Hypothalamus." *Scientific American* 227 (November, 1972): 24-33. Describes the experimental evidence that led to the idea that the anterior pituitary gland is controlled by hypothalmic hormones. Diagrams show anatomical location of pituitary gland and its connections to the hypothalamus.

Hadley, Mac E. *Endocrinology.* 2d ed. Englewood Cliffs, N.J.: Prentice-Hall, 1988. An advanced college text in which the interested reader can find details about the chemical structure of pituitary hormones, cellular mechanisms of hormone action, and the effects of hormones in a broad range of species. Research is discussed and references given to original research papers. Chapter 8, "The Melanotropins," provides a particularly comprehensive overview of MSH effects. Richly illustrated.

Karsch, F. J. "The Hypothalamus and Anterior Pituitary Gland." In *Reproduction of Mammals*, edited by C. R. Austin and R. V. Short, vol. 3, *Hormonal Control of Reproduction.* 2d ed. Cambridge, England: Cambridge University Press, 1984. This chapter contains an exceptionally clear discussion of the relationship between the hypothalamus and pituitary, with a concentration on the gonadotropins. Emphasizes the importance of rhythmic release of pituitary hormones. A bibliography contains references for further reading.

Sherwood, Lauralee. *Human Physiology: From Cells to Systems.* St. Paul, Minn.: West, 1988. An intermediate-level college text, very clearly written. Chapter 18, "Principles of Endocrinology: Central Endocrine Organs," contains helpful diagrams of the hypothalamic-pituitary link and of negative feedback mechanisms. Actions of growth hormone are explained in detail. Illustrations.

Wade, Nicholas. *The Nobel Prize Duel.* Garden City, N.J.: Anchor Press, 1981. This popular account by a science journalist documents the race to elucidate the structure of the hormones that control the anterior pituitary gland. An insightful analysis of the personalities of Roger Guillemin and Andrew Schally, the scientists who won the 1977 Nobel Prize in Physiology or Medicine for their efforts.

Judith R. Gibber

Cross-References

Birth, 226; Endocrinology of the Adrenal Glands, 800; Endocrinology of the Thyroid and Parathyroid Glands, 814; Hormonal Control of Blood Sugar and Fatty Acids, 1339; Hormonal Control of Protein Metabolism, 1347; Hormone Mechanisms and Second Messengers, 1361; The Female Reproductive System, 2346; The Male Reproductive System, 2354; Water Retention and Excretion, 2709.

ENDOCRINOLOGY OF THE THYROID AND PARATHYROID GLANDS

Type of life science: Animal physiology
Other fields of study: Animal anatomy and biochemistry

The thyroid and parathyroid glands play a crucial role in the maintenance of homeostasis. The glands and their hormones interact with the nervous system, with other endocrine glands, and with target cells in the body.

Principal terms

AUTONOMIC NERVOUS SYSTEM: the portion of the peripheral nervous system responsible for the maintenance of homeostasis

BASAL METABOLIC RATE: the metabolic rate of an animal at rest and at moderate temperature after a twelve-hour fast

HOMEOSTASIS: the maintenance of the internal environment of living organisms within narrow parameters that provide the optimum chance for survival

HOMEOTHERM: an animal that maintains its internal temperature within a set range despite changes in external temperature

HORMONES: chemical messengers produced by endocrine glands

RECEPTORS: proteins on cell membranes or inside cells that serve as binding sites for chemical messengers; the receptor-messenger complex initiates a cellular response

TARGET CELLS: cells that have specific protein receptors for hormones

Summary of the Phenomenon

The internal environments of animals are regulated by two systems: the nervous system and the endocrine system. The endocrine system is a complex system of glands that interact with one another, with the nervous system, and with other organs. Endocrine glands communicate with other cells by chemical messengers called hormones. A study of the endocrine system involves an examination of the chemical nature of the hormones, the stimuli that promote the release of hormones into the bloodstream, the mechanism of action of the hormones at the target cell, the metabolism of the hormones, and the physiological effects of hormones and diseases caused by abnormal concentrations of hormones.

The thyroid gland is one of the endocrine glands found in vertebrates. In humans and other mammals, it is located at the base of the neck. It has two lobes, one on either side of the trachea, that are connected by a small band of tissue. An examination of the chemical nature of the thyroid messengers has revealed two major hormones: triiodothyronine and tetraiodothyronine, which is also known as thyroxine. Triiodothyronine is the only active form of the hormone, and thyroxine must be converted to triiodothyronine to be effective. In order to synthesize these hormones, the thyroid gland requires large quantities of the element iodine, which must be supplied in the diet.

Once produced, the hormones are stored in the glandular storage sites, called follicles, until they are released. The signal for the release of the thyroid hormones from the gland is a complex process that involves two other endocrine glands. The first step involves the release of a neurohormone from the region of the brain known as the hypothalamus. In this case, the neurohormone acts on an endocrine gland, the pituitary, to promote the release of the thyroid-stimulating hormone. The thyroid-stimulating hormone, as its name suggests, causes the release of triiodothyronine and tetraiodothyronine from the thyroid gland. When the concentrations of triiodothyronine and tetraiodothyronine rise in the blood, they inhibit any further release of hormones from the hypothalamus or pituitary. Unlike some other hormones, there is generally a constant concentration of circulating thyroid hormones that is not altered by daily fluctuations in the physiological state of the body.

The thyroid hormones, like other endocrine hormones, are transported by the bloodstream to their site of action, the target cells. Thyroid hormones are particularly important in the functioning of the heart, liver, kidney, nervous system, and skeletal muscle. At the target cell, they are able to cross the membrane and, once inside the cell, bind to specific receptors in the nucleus, where they stimulate the synthesis of new proteins that will increase the metabolic activity of the cell. Once they have performed their function, the thyroid hormones are metabolized by the target cells, and the products are then excreted by the kidneys.

The thyroid hormones have several diverse functions, including development and tissue differentiation, adaptation to the environment, metabolic activity of the cell, and temperature regulation. In addition, they act in conjunction with growth hormone and epinephrine to enhance the physiological responses that they generate.

The thyroid hormones are important in the physical growth and sexual maturation of the young. Normal growth is stimulated by growth hormone and other growth factors. The production of growth hormone in the pituitary is dependent upon the thyroid hormone. If levels of thyroid hormone are low, growth hormone will not be produced, resulting in smaller than normal stature and inhibition of sexual maturation.

The function of the sympathetic nervous system is also regulated by the thyroid hormone. Epinephrine, which is one of the major neurotransmitters of the autonomic nervous system, is potentiated (made more effective) by the thyroid hormones. The biological effects of epinephrine include increases in the rate and strength of the heartbeat and effects on blood pressure and respiration. Many of the symptoms experienced by organisms with excessively high levels of thyroid hormone reflect the action of epinephrine.

Thyroid hormones are responsible for determining the metabolic rate of cells. In the presence of thyroid hormone, there is an increase in oxygen consumption and heat production. Some of the increased activity can be attributed to the stimulation of metabolic pathways, and some of the increases are a result of a higher requirement for cellular energy in the form of adenosine triphosphate (ATP) in order to move molecules into cells by active transport. The heat generated by the increase in cellular metabolism is important in the regulation of the body temperature of homeotherms. The thyroid gland in mammals also produces another hormone, calcitonin, that does not contain iodine and whose function is not related to the function of triiodothyronine or tetraiodothyronine. Along with the parathyroid hormone, calcitonin regulates the plasma levels of calcium.

The parathyroid gland is closely associated with the thyroid gland. It consists of four small glands embedded in the posterior portion of the thyroid gland. The parathyroid glands are extremely small and are not easily visible during observation of the thyroid gland. The product of the parathyroid gland, known as the parathyroid hormone, is released in response to decreased calcium concentration in the blood. The element calcium can be found in many forms in the body. The most important form is ionized calcium. When present in bodily fluids, the concentration of ionized calcium must be tightly controlled. Calcitonin and parathyroid hormone have antagonistic actions that ensure that any small deviation of calcium concentration is immediately corrected.

Calcium and phosphate concentrations in the body are always in balance. If the level of calcium falls, the level of phosphate increases, and vice versa. The largest quantities of calcium and phosphate are found stored in the bone; the presence of calcium and phosphate gives bone its strength. Bone tissue is continually being broken down and rebuilt. Three cells are responsible for the formation and remodeling of bone: the osteoblasts (the bone-forming cells), the osteocytes (the mature cells of bone that are responsible for the formation of the bone matrix, which gives bone its hardness), and the osteoclasts (the cells capable of breaking down the bone matrix).

The parathyroid hormone is stored in the cells in which it is synthesized unless there is a decrease in the concentration of calcium in the plasma. If this event occurs, the parathyroid hormone is immediately released and is transported to its target cells, the osteocytes. The parathyroid hormone then triggers the release of calcium from these cells. In addition, the parathyroid hormone acts directly on the kidney to decrease the amount of calcium that is being excreted. In order to protect the kidney from the phosphate levels that increased while the calcium was falling, the parathyroid hormone promotes excretion of greater quantities of phosphate from the kidney.

These events occur relatively quickly and are followed, after about twelve hours, by increased osteoclastic activity, which leads to absorption of bone matrix and recycling of calcium. In order to restore calcium balance, there must be an increase of absorption of calcium from the intestine. The parathyroid hormone has no direct effect on the intestine, but it does stimulate the conversion of vitamin D to its active form; the vitamin D then promotes the active uptake of calcium from the intestine.

Calcitonin is released from the thyroid in response to elevated levels of ionized calcium in the blood. It acts on osteoclasts to prevent bone resorption and acts directly on the kidney to increase the excretion of calcium and phosphorus in the urine. Depletion of calcitonin from the body has little effect on the levels of calcium or phosphorus in the blood. This leads scientists to believe that the calcitonin's main function may not be regulation of calcium concentrations in plasma; rather, it may be more concerned with limiting the degree of bone resorption.

Methods of Study

Early studies in physiology described the criteria by which a substance was classified as a hormone. By definition, hormones are secreted into the fluids surrounding cells, then taken up by the bloodstream and transported to all parts of the body. The second criterion requires that if the gland is removed experimentally, specific symptoms of the loss should result. Finally, if the gland is replaced, or if the hormone is supplied by injection, the symptoms of the deficiency should be relieved. Since those early studies occurred, many hormones have been isolated and their chemical compositions defined. As a result of this research, synthetic forms of many of the hormones have been produced and are available for research or therapy.

Target cells are extremely sensitive to minute quantities of hormones. As a result, it is difficult to study endocrine effects in normal humans. Studies primarily involve the use of experimental animals or involve humans who have abnormally functioning glands, producing either too much or too little hormone. In experimental animals, removal of glands has been one technique that has been widely used to assess the physiological effects of the loss of endocrine glands or their specific hormones. Although it is possible to supply some hormones exogenously (from outside an organism), this is usually done only with experimental animals or with humans who receive the exogenous hormones as therapy to treat a deficiency disease.

On their surfaces, cells have proteins that are known as receptors. These receptors are usually specific for a particular compound. By localizing and determining the number of these receptors, scientists have been able to study the mechanism of action of hormones and the degree of response to a hormone based on the receptor numbers and on hormone concentration. Learning the location of the receptor and the action of the hormone-receptor complex has been helpful in determining how the hormone functions and has added to the basic knowledge of cellular mechanisms.

Since information is available regarding the chemical composition of hormones, detection of these hormones in the bloodstream at a precise moment or in a given time period (twenty-four hours, for example) provides accurate data regarding hormonal concentration. Information can also be gathered regarding the conversion of a hormone from an inactive to an active form. Other techniques for the determination of protein concentrations include measuring the metabolic by-products that appear in the urine. In the case of the thyroid and thyroid hormones, the uptake of radioactive iodine has been a useful measure of thyroid activity. Radioactive imaging is a method used to determine the location and size of organs and has been helpful in determining the occurrence of, or the extent of, tumors of the thyroid.

Context

The importance of the contribution of the thyroid and parathyroid glands in maintaining homeostasis becomes most evident when abnormalities in function are observed. In the thyroid, a deficiency in hormonal function, called hypothyroidism, prior to or at the time of birth leads to a child that suffers from cretinism. These children are obese and short in stature, and they suffer from mental retardation. If not treated promptly, the mental retardation may be permanent. Treatment in utero or at birth may significantly diminish or prevent the effects so that the individual may achieve normal size and mental capabilities.

In adulthood, inadequate quantities of thyroid hormones result in people with an appearance that typically includes an increase in weight, thin hair, scaly skin, and a husky voice. They also suffer from a proliferation of soft tissue and from edema, or swelling of tissues, which is most prominent around the eyes. Physiologically, they have a slow metabolic rate, decreased cardiac output, and decreased blood volume; they often feel cold. They are also likely to suffer from fatigue and drowsiness as well as poor memory or an inability to concentrate. The presence and extent of these symptoms are determined by the degree of hypothyroidism in any given individual. When the body suffers from low concentrations of thyroid hormone for an extended period of time, it tries to compensate by increasing the size of the thyroid gland. The gland growth is called a goiter and can grow to an extensive size without significantly increasing the output of thyroid hormone.

Hyperthyroidism is a condition in which there is too much circulating thyroid hormone. It results in an individual who suffers from weight loss in spite of eating large quantities of food, who feels constantly warm, and who demonstrates a nervous irritability, possibly with tremors. The individual may have muscular weakness, an increased heart rate, and fatigue, but an inability to sleep. Also, the person may have a protrusion of the eyeballs, and the size of the thyroid may increase to several times its normal size.

As with the thyroid, the parathyroid can produce symptoms of either hyperparathyroidism or hypoparathyroidism. Since these conditions involve the circulating concentration of ionized calcium, however, either condition is extremely dangerous. If the parathyroid glands are removed from an animal experimentally, the animal will die within forty-eight hours in a state of tetanic convulsions. In humans who have insufficient quantities of parathyroid hormone, the individual has hyperexcitability of the nervous system. The administration of vitamin D may successfully prevent the symptoms of hypoparathyroidism. Excess concentrations of parathyroid hormone result in high blood calcium, anorexia, polyuria, dehydration, headache, muscular weakness, and memory loss. This condition is usually treated by surgical removal of the diseased tissue that is producing the excessive quantities of hormone.

Bibliography

Campbell, Neil. *Biology.* Menlo Park, Calif.: Benjamin/Cummings, 1987. A biology textbook written for college students that is easily understood even by those with very little scientific background. The chapter on chemical coordination describes the role of the endocrine system in maintenance of homeostasis, and there is a specific section on the thyroid and parathyroid glands.

Cooke, B. A., R. J. B. King, and H. J. van der Moles, eds. *Hormones and Their Actions*. Amsterdam: Elsevier, 1988. Although a somewhat advanced book, it contains at least two articles that may be of particular interest to people studying the thyroid gland. Among them are "Mechanisms of Action of Thyroid Hormone," by J. Nunez, and "Metabolism of Thyroid Hormone," by T. J. Visser. An extensive bibliography is cited.

The Endocrine System: Miraculous Messengers. New York: Torstar Books, 1985. Written for the person with no scientific background, this 158-page book examines the history of hormones, their functions, and their interactions. It is beautifully illustrated and will provide even the casual reader with much valuable information. An excellent place for the person with no background in biology to begin.

Goodman, Maurice H. *Basic Medical Endocrinology*. New York: Raven Press, 1988. A readable but somewhat advanced book. The chapters on the thyroid gland and regulation of calcium homeostasis are particularly informative, but the entire book will be of interest to those studying endocrinology.

Gordon, Malcolm S., George A. Bartholomew, Alan D. Grinell, C. Barker Jorgensen, and Fred N. White. *Animal Physiology: Principles and Adaptations*. 4th ed. New York: Macmillan, 1982. The physiology of various types of animals is examined. The role of the endocrine system in lower vertebrates is included in this easily readable text. The role of the thyroid in the maintenance of body temperature is discussed. This book covers a broader scope than most books.

Guyton, Arthur C. *Textbook of Medical Physiology*. 7th ed. Philadelphia: W. B. Saunders, 1986. This text, written for medical students, presents a clear explanation of the physiology of the endocrines and the role of the endocrine glands in the healthy and diseased states. It is not too difficult to understand and provides an extensive bibliography for further reading.

Vander, Arthur J., James H. Sherman, and Dorothy S. Luciano. *Human Physiology: The Mechanisms of Body Function*. New York: McGraw-Hill, 1985. This general physiology text for college students can also be easily read by the high school student. The chapter on homeostatic mechanisms, which includes a section on receptors, will shed much light on the study of endocrinology. References are provided.

Annette O'Connor

Cross-References

Bone Growth and Dissolution Processes, 286; Testing for Endocrine Functions of Glands and Organs, 772; Endocrinology of the Adrenal Glands, 800; Endocrinology of the Pituitary Gland, 807; Mammalian Hormones, 1368; Metamorphosis Controls, 1706; Muscular Calcium Release and Reuptake, 1843; The Sympathetic and Parasympathetic Nervous Systems, 2580; Temperature Regulation, 2609.

ENDOCYTOSIS AND EXOCYTOSIS

Type of life science: Cell biology (cytology)
Other field of study: Biophysics

Endocytosis refers to the uptake of extracellular materials trapped in membranous vesicles that pinch off from the plasma membrane. It is important in feeding some cells and in bringing antibodies, enzymes, hormones, and toxins into the cell. Exocytosis is the ejection of specific secretion products by the fusion of a vesicle with the plasma membrane of a cell.

Principal terms

ENDOSOME: an uncoated, acidic sorting station in which endocytized materials undergo their first intracellular processing

LIGAND: a particular molecule present in the extracellular fluid that binds to specific receptors on the cell membrane

LYSOSOME: an intracellular digestive system that breaks down foreign materials brought into the cell as well as aiding in the recycling of intracellular organelles

MACROPHAGE: a large phagocytic cell capable of ingesting and digesting bacteria and cellular debris

NEUROTRANSMITTER: a substance used by neurons to transmit impulses across a synapse; also called a transmitter substance

PHAGOCYTE: any cell that engulfs and devours microorganisms or other particles

VACUOLE: a cavity enclosed by a membrane and found within the cytoplasm; it may function in storage, digestion, or water elimination

VESICLE: any small sac, especially a small spherical membrane-bound compartment within the cytoplasm

Summary of the Phenomenon

Endocytosis refers to the uptake of large molecules, such as antibodies, enzymes, hormones, toxins, and nutrients, that are brought into the cell across the cell membrane. Pieces of the membrane pinch off and form spherical vesicles that entrap these various substances. The functional significance of endocytosis varies among different cell types. In the amoeba, for example, endocytosis is a major route for the uptake of nutrients. White blood cells, however, employ this same process to capture and destroy invading bacteria. Just as materials can be brought into the cell by invagination (an inward folding of the cell membrane) and the formation of vesicles, the membrane of a vesicle can also fuse with the plasma membrane and thrust its contents out into the surrounding medium by the process of exocytosis. This process occurs in different cells to remove undigestible residues of substances brought in by endocytosis, to secrete substances such as hormones, and to transport substances completely across cellular borders; it results in the incorporation of the membrane of the secretory vesicle into the plasma (cell) membrane, providing a mechanism by which the plasma membranes can enlarge.

Endocytosis can occur in many forms, but it ultimately depends on the plasma membrane to provide the means of entry. Whatever object is taken in, it always enters the cell wrapped in a sealed membranous sac that began as a part of the plasma membrane that invaginated and broke free. In phagocytosis (from the Greek *phagein*, "to eat," plus *cytos*, "cell"), the cell ingests large solid particles such as bacteria or food. In the process, particles must first bind to the surface of the phagocyte. In this receptor-mediated endocytosis, the outside articles are "recognized," then bound by specific receptors. This substance bound to the receptor is the ligand. The region bearing the ligand complex then undergoes endocytosis. The same endocytic vesicle can be used for both receptor-mediated endocytosis (if it is bound to the specific surface receptor) and pinocytosis.

Receptor-mediated endocytosis is a highly selective method of bringing in proteins and small particles, because the receptors on the cell surface are highly specific. Once the bond between the receptor and molecule is made, the complex is internalized, usually clustering at coated pits—specialized depressions on the cell surface—because of lateral diffusion. The coating, found on the internal side of the membrane, is made of a visible protein called clathrin. Clathrin interacts with other proteins to encircle the ligand complex bound to the membrane. As the protein network finally closes, a vesicle has formed from the membrane and is imprisoned inside the network. Soon after, the cage disintegrates and disappears, releasing the vesicle. The clathrin coat is also lost from the vesicle, and this uncoated vesicle is known as an endosome.

In the form of endocytosis known as pinocytosis (from the Greek *pinien*, "to drink"), the cell takes in dissolved materials. Tiny droplets of fluid are trapped by folds in the plasma membrane, which pinch off into the cytoplasm as tiny vesicles. The liquid contents of the vesicles may be transferred into the cytoplasm, or the vesicles themselves may merge to form larger vacuoles called endosomes. Larger vesicles usually fuse with lysosomes, where the contents are degraded. Since extracellular components are taken in randomly as the dissolved contents of the engulfed droplets of fluid, it is a nonspecific process. Also called fluid-phase endocytosis, the process can lead to immense uptakes, since cells can easily "drink" the equivalent of their own volume every day.

Once food is gathered and vacuole formation is complete, the free-floating vacuole generally fuses with a lysosome (forming a phagolysosome), where the ingested material is degraded. The small breakdown products (such as amino acids, glucose, and nucleotides) that result are transported across the lysosomal membrane into the cytoplasm, where they can be used by the cell. Other products that result from the degradation process are incorporated into vesicles and released from the cell by exocytosis. The vesicles that do not undergo digestion may be either returned to the cell surface or moved to another destination. The main function of this activity is membrane retrieval, without which endocytosis could not keep occurring, because many cells may internalize as much as 50 percent of their plasma membrane each hour. Conversely, in cells that are constantly involved in secreting, an equivalent amount of membrane must be returned to the interior of the cell for each vesicle that fuses with the cell membrane; if it is not, the cell surface will keep expanding even though the growth of the cell itself may be retarded.

Inpocketing is affected by several factors. For example, the flexibility of the membrane determines the extent to which the plasma membrane can be bent; as invagination is complete, an adhesion must be formed between either side of the pocket before the vacuole breaks free from the membrane. As engulfment is completed, protons trapped inside the vesicle acidify the contents. These protons from the outside cytoplasm are discharged to the inside of the vesicle by an energy-dependent proton pump that probably exists in pits in the cell surface. The protons that this pump ejects are generally diluted and carried away by extracellular fluid, but as the pits form pockets, some protons are trapped inside. They accumulate rapidly, lowering the pH to about 4.7 (as opposed to the cytoplasm's pH of about 7). One important consequence of this process is that receptors lose their attraction for their ligands, thus causing them to fall off the membrane. Acidification of endocytic vesicles may serve a useful purpose in the cell: Any potentially hazardous endocytosed material stands a good chance of being inactivated.

Just as materials can be brought into the cell by invagination and formation of a vesicle, the membrane of a vesicle can fuse with the plasma membrane and extrude its contents into the surrounding medium by the process of exocytosis. Granules of secretory products (such as proteins) are dependent on exocytosis for discharge. Proteins, synthesized on ribosomes attached to the rough endoplasmic reticulum (ER), are transported to the Golgi complex for packaging as granules in vesicles. When the vesicle containing the granule reaches the cell surface, its internal contents are expelled into the extracellular space by exocytosis. The two cojoined membranes break open at their junction, releasing the contents of the granule into the external medium without disrupting the continuity of the cell membrane.

There are two recognized pathways of secretion. Molecules that follow the "constitutive" pathway of secretion are continuously secreted. They are the proteins that are synthesized on the rough endoplasmic recticulum and packaged in vesicles by the Golgi complex. In other cells, special secretory vesicles may store proteins and/ or small molecules. They fuse with the plasma membrane only when the cell is triggered by an extracellular signal and are said to follow the "regulated" pathway of secretion. The constitutive pathway operates in all cells, while the regulated pathway is used only by cells specialized for releasing products rapidly on demand, such as hormones, neurotransmitters, or digestive enzymes. In these specialized secretory cells, the signal to secrete is generally a chemical messenger, such as a hormone, that binds to receptors on the cell surface.

In exocytosis, the vesicle membrane becomes a part of the plasma membrane. In the case of the regulated pathway, the unique protein and lipid components of the secretory vesicle membrane are later recovered by endocytosis and reused in the formation of new secretory vesicles.

Methods of Study

Because endocytosis and exocytosis are cellular processes, the discovery and study of these phenomena could not occur before a fairly high-resolution microscope was developed. To find the earliest mention of exocytosis, one can go back about a hundred years to Messina, Sicily. Ilya Metchnikoff, a self-exiled Russian zoologist, observing a transparent starfish larva, noticed an amoeba-like wandering cell moving through the larval tissue. From that observation he determined that most organisms probably possess groups of these motile cells (cells capable of movement), whose job is to find, engulf, and digest unwanted trespassers such as microbes and viruses. Metchnikoff coined the term "phagocytosis."

With the advent of the electron microscope, investigators could visualize an endocytosis never detected with the light microscope. They noticed the presence of some sort of fuzzy contour outlining the profiles of certain membrane invaginations and closed vesicles, and they deduced that an organized structure might participate in receptor-mediated endocytosis. Further electron microscope studies of cultured cells exposed to different ligands have shown that a single coated pit may contain many kinds of receptors. The plasma membrane of one coated pit may accommodate as many as a thousand different receptors; all the receptor-ligand complexes that are enclosed in the clathrin coat are apparently delivered to the same endosomal compartment.

Endocytosis generally involves an interaction between the ingested substance and binding sites on the plasma membrane. Some of the earliest evidence for the significance of this binding was shown with microphage cells, demonstrating their uptake of soluble and insoluble forms of the protein horseradish peroxidase. Using horseradish peroxidase is advantageous because it is a highly visible protein that is easily traced using the electron microscope. Microphages incubated with insoluble peroxidase complexes, which bind to the plasma membrane surface, take up the peroxidase thousands of times faster than cells that are exposed to soluble peroxidase, which seldom binds to the microphage. Therefore, the binding of substances to the outer surface of the plasma membrane apparently stimulates their uptake by endocytosis.

Using horseradish peroxidase can also show the role of lysosomes in mediating the breakdown of products taken up by endocytosis. The location of this enzyme in tissue sections has been determined by a cytochemical procedure that yields a blue reaction product when it reacts with peroxidase. The same tissue sections are also stained by a procedure that stains red in the presence of acid phosphatase. As early as half an hour after exposure to the horseradish peroxidase, cells treated to stain show highly visible red and blue granules, an indication not only that the cells take up the peroxidase, but also that it is present in vesicles but not in lysosomes. Observations made at a later time, however, show purple granules instead of different red and blue granules, suggesting that the lysosomes and endosomes have fused. A day later, the color of the granules is again red: Apparently the lysosomal enzymes have broken down the peroxidase responsible for the blue color.

Virtually all methods used to study the phenomena of endocytosis and exocytosis depend on microscopy and biochemical analyses. Much of the work employs the electron microscope and uses traceable proteins to make the processes more obvious. The use of these methods shows the various roles that both endocytosis and exocytosis play in cells.

Context

Endocytosis is first and foremost a feeding mechanism for a variety of cell types. For example, many single-celled organisms, such as protozoa and lower invertebrates, depend on endocytosis as virtually their only feeding mechanism. Intracellular digestion is then completed with the aid of lysosomes.

A dramatic example of how impressive endocytosis can be is the ingestion and destruction of invading bacteria by macrophages. The cytoplasm of this cell type contains two kinds of granules: specific granules and a type similar to lysosomes. Although not lysosomes, these specific granules contain hydrolytic enzymes that are used in degrading foreign matter. When bacteria are taken up by phagocytosis, the specific granules discharge their contents into the vacuoles containing the ingested bacteria to start the digestive process. A few minutes later, the lysosome-like granules release their enzymes into the same vacuole to complete the breakdown of the ingested bacteria. So great is the destruction that the leukocytes themselves die in the process. Although this action is generally effective, some bacteria are still able to survive and even multiply inside these phagocytic cells.

In addition to mediating the breakdown of foreign particles, endocytosis is important for the uptake of normal extracellular substances. Developing egg cells, for example, use receptor-mediated endocytosis to accumulate yolk proteins from the bloodstream, storing these proteins for use as nutrients later in embryonic development. A hen's egg (a single cell) contains several grams of the protein precursor vitellogenin, all of which is imported into the yolk by endocytosis.

Another example of the role of endocytosis involves the low-density lipoproteins (LDL), which contain cholesterol and form a complex to carry cholesterol through the bloodstream. The LDL complex binds to specific plasma membrane receptors and is taken up because of the binding of LDL to specific LDL receptors present on the cell surface. The complex is then internalized in a coated pit, loses its clathrin coat, and forms endosomes. The LDL receptors are then recycled to the plasma membrane for reuse; cholesterol is secreted inside the cell and used for metabolic purposes. An unusual genetic disease, familial hypercholesterolemia, is caused by an inherited defect in cell-surface LDL receptors. Those with the deficiency cannot take up cholesterol; as a result, excessive amounts of cholesterol are secreted into the bloodstream, leading to severe circulatory disease.

The role of exocytosis is nearly always secretion. For example, in order to secrete insulin across their membranes, insulin-producing cells package insulin molecules in secretory vesicles; in response to extracellular signals, these vesicles fuse with the plasma membrane and open to the extracellular space, releasing insulin to the outside.

An equally common occurrence of exocytosis occurs each time an impulse is transmitted from neuron to neuron, or from neurons to other cells, at junctions called synapses. In chemical synapses, the arrival of an action potential in the presynaptic axon triggers the release of neurotransmitters into the synaptic cleft; from there they bind to receptors on the postsynaptic cell. Transmitters are stored in membrane-bound vesicles, and exocytosis of these vesicles is triggered by a rise in cytoplasmic calcium ions (Ca^{2+}).

The functional significance of endocytosis and exocytosis varies among different cell types. Endocytosis is important in bringing substances into a cell, while exocytosis makes secretion by a cell possible. Both processes also aid in regulating the size of the cell membrane.

Bibliography

Alberts, Bruce, Dennis Bray, Julian Lewis, Martin Raff, Keith Roberts, and James Watson. *Molecular Biology of the Cell*. 2d ed. New York: Garland, 1989. A college-level text meant as both an introduction to cell biology for the inexperienced biology student and an in-depth look at the functions of the eukaryotic cell. Chapter 6 includes a detailed description of endocytosis and exocytosis. An extremely thorough list of references is given after each chapter.

Anderson, Richard G. W., and Jerry Kaplan. "Receptor-Mediated Endocytosis." In *Modern Cell Biology*, edited by Birgit Satir. New York: Alan R. Liss, 1983. A set of four articles that extensively review the literature on specific aspects of the cell membrane. Because of the complexity of the writing, only a reader wishing an in-depth look at these topics would appreciate this volume. The first reading (chapter 1) is devoted to the phenomenon of receptor-mediated endocytosis. Each reference is cited in a lengthy and detailed bibliography.

Bretscher, Mark S. "The Molecules of the Cell Membrane." *Scientific American* 253 (October, 1985): 100-108. An article that redefines the composition of the cell membrane and establishes its roles and functions, especially regarding receptor-mediated endocytosis. Gives a detailed and illustrated description of the coated pit. Also describes how the membrane remains consistent in size because of endocytosis and exocytosis.

Curtis, A. S. G. "General Functions of the Cell Surface." In *Cell Biology in Medicine*, edited by E. Edward Bittar. New York: John Wiley & Sons, 1973. This article addresses the very general functions of the cell membrane, including phagocytosis and pinocytosis. The aim of the book, a compilation of chapters by different authors, is to show the student with a biological background who wants to tie the cellular level to medical science the relevance of cell biology to medical science. A useful source, although much of the information presented has since been updated. Bibliography.

Darnell, James, Harvey Lodish, and David Baltimore. *Molecular Cell Biology.* New York: Scientific American Books, 1986. Chapter 15, "Transport Across Cell Membranes," is rich with information given on a college level; it is well illustrated and particularly useful in explaining the experimental basis of the roles assigned to different molecules and structures. The shapes of different molecules are shown in both chemical and shape-revealing diagrams. Complex articles are cited in a detailed bibliography.

DeDuve, Christian. *A Guided Tour of the Living Cell.* 2 Vols. New York: Scientific American Books, 1984. Written on a high-school level, it "shrinks" the reader to the size of bacteria and takes him on a guided tour of the cell: its processes and its organelles and their functions. To aid in this imaginary trip, many drawings, pictures, and micrographs are used. The author includes a chapter on endocytosis that is particularly informative.

Kleinsmith, Lewis, and Valerie Kish. *Principles of Cell Biology.* New York: Harper & Row, 1988. An intermediate college-level text written as an introduction to cell biology. The goal is to acquaint the student with the fundamental principles that characterize cellular form and function. Chapter 6, "Function of Cytoplasmic Membranes," specifically discusses endocytosis, while exocytosis is mentioned with regard to membrane function. Suggested readings are included with each chapter.

Villee, Claude, Eldra Solomon, Charles Martin, Diana Martin, Linda Berg, and P. William Davis. *Biology.* 2d ed. Philadelphia: Saunders College Publishing, 1989. Written for beginning college students, it uses a comparative concept-oriented approach with the human as a model. Chapter 5, "Biological Membranes," tells of the structures and functions of the membranous organelles of the cells and describes methods of transport into and out of the cell. Recommended readings follow each chapter. Glossary.

Iona C. Baldridge

Cross-References

THE ENDOPLASMIC RETICULUM AND
THE GOLGI COMPLEX

Type of life science: Cell biology (cytology)
Other field of study: Biochemistry

The endoplasmic reticulum and the Golgi complex are very important components of the living cell. By studying these membranous structures, scientists have discovered how proteins are transported within human cells and secreted from human cells.

Principal terms

CISTERNA (*pl.* CISTERNAE): a flattened, membranous sac filled with fluid

ENDOPLASMIC RETICULUM (ER): an organelle composed of membranes, forming a system of tubes and flattened sacs

EUKARYOTIC CELL: a cell that has a true nucleus, with a membrane around it; the cells of all animals and plants fall into this category

GOLGI APPARATUS or GOLGI COMPLEX: a system of membranous sacs in the cell that packages molecules and sends them to the cell's surface

LYSOSOME: a small organelle containing powerful enzymes that are capable of digesting a variety of materials

MEMBRANE: a complex film of fatty molecules interspersed with proteins that covers the cell and many organelles, controlling what enters and leaves; it also makes up other organelles, such as the ER

ORGANELLE: a specialized structure having a definite function in a cell; for example, the nucleus, a ribosome, a mitochondrion

SECRETION: a chemical produced and given off by a cell to do its work outside that particular cell

SYNTHESIS: the combining of separate elements or small molecules to form larger chemical compounds

VESICLE: a small sphere made of membrane filled with protein in a watery medium

Summary of the Phenomenon

The endoplasmic reticulum (ER) and the Golgi complex are organelles composed of membrane that are very important to the functioning of living cells. The ER and Golgi apparatus apparently together play a crucial role in modifying, sorting, and dispatching many of the proteins newly synthesized by the cell. The ER may, in addition, act as a kind of circulatory system for the distribution throughout the cell of various substances. While doing so, its tubes provide a kind of skeleton or support for the entire cell.

All eukaryotic cells, that is, cells higher than bacteria (which are called prokaryotic cells), have extensive inner membranes. All eukaryotic cells, then, have an ER. Its highly folded single membrane is organized into a netlike mesh that extends throughout the cytoplasm. It is thought to form a continuous sheet enclosing a single internal space called the ER lumen or ER cisternal space. The ER membrane thus separates the ER lumen from the cytosol, or cytoplasm, the fluid material surrounding all the cell's organelles.

About half the total area of the membrane belonging to each cell is used to enclose the mazelike structure of the ER. Portions of the endoplasmic reticulum have many ribosomes bound to the side of the membrane facing the cytosol. These ribosomes are small structures engaged in the making of all the proteins which will become part of the cell's membranes, become part of various other organelles, or be exported from the cell. All these proteins are produced by a process called translation.

Since proteins are transported into the ER while they are still being manufactured (or translated), the ribosomes responsible must be attached to the ER. These membrane-bound ribosomes coat the surface of the ER, creating regions termed "rough endoplasmic reticulum" (RER). Rough regions of the ER seem to contain certain proteins responsible for making the ribosomes bind or attach there, but it is not clear to which of the many proteins in the RER membrane the ribosome binds.

Other regions of the ER, which lack bound ribosomes, are called "smooth endoplasmic reticulum" (SER). The great majority of cells contain little, if any, long stretches of true SER; instead, small regions of the ER are partly smooth and partly rough. Within these small regions of SER, the enzymes are found that produce all the various lipid molecules used in the rest of the cell. These may include lipids for stored energy as well as lipids that make up other membrane structures such as the plasma (cell) membrane. In certain specialized cells, however, SER is abundant—for example, in the cells that synthesize the hormones made from the chemical known as cholesterol. These hormones, or chemical messengers, are named steroids. The cells have an expanded SER containing the enzymes needed both to make the cholesterol and to modify it to form the hormones.

The development of the ER varies considerably in different cell types and is related to their function. It is often small and relatively undeveloped in eggs and in the cells of embryos, but it varies in size and complexity in the cells of human body organs. In cells whose major activity does not involve the production of proteins for export, the ER tends to remain poorly developed. When export of proteins, for example, hormones or digestive juices, is the major job of that organ, the RER is very extensive.

Many secreted proteins have been studied in a variety of cell types, and all of them follow a similar pathway: ribosome to ER to Golgi complex to cell exterior. Those other proteins destined to be part of the cell membrane or other organelles (for example, lysosomes, to perform digestion of food for the cell), are similarly initially imported into the ER, passing from there by means of the Golgi complex to their final location.

The Golgi complex or Golgi apparatus is usually located near the cell's nucleus and in animal cells is often close to the center of the cell. It consists of a collection of flattened, membrane-bound cisternae, which resemble stacks of plates. Each stack usually consists of four to six cisternae. The number of Golgi stacks per cell varies greatly, depending on the cell type. Some cells contain one large stack, while others contain hundreds of very small ones. These disklike compartments, the Golgi cisternae, receive lipids and proteins from the ER and dispatch these molecules to a variety of destinations within the cell, usually chemically modifying the compounds as they travel from one disk to another.

The Golgi complex was discovered in 1898 by Camillo Golgi, who used special dyes containing silver. Unlike the ER, these membrane sacs have no attached ribosomes. They exist in a so-called zone of exclusion with no ribosomes, no glycogen (stored starch), and no mitochondria (the organelle for energy production) nearby. The Golgi stacks are not flat. The side of each plate facing the nucleus is convex in shape and is called the entry or forming face. The other side of each hollow plate is concave in shape and is called the exit or maturing face. Chemicals are sent from the ER to the forming face of each cisterna in small bags of membrane called transition vesicles. After being modified by the addition or deletion of pieces to their molecules, chemicals are shipped away by secretory vesicles or sacs from the maturing face of the Golgi.

Swarms of these tiny vesicles are associated with the Golgi stacks, clustered on the side facing the ER and along the bulging rim of each cisterna. Each of these cisternae is a distinct compartment with its own set of processing enzymes, making a whole Golgi complex into a multistage processing unit. A steady stream of vesicles normally leaves the Golgi complex and moves toward the cell membrane. Some carry the new lipids and proteins that will become part of that plasma membrane itself. Others carry the many lipids and proteins destined to be secreted to the cell's exterior.

The interactions of these cell organelles can be briefly summarized as a process containing six basic steps. Proteins are synthesized on ribosomes of the rough endoplasmic reticulum. They enter the ER, sliding through its membrane into its cisterna, where they are separated and modified. They are transported to the Golgi apparatus. While within this Golgi complex, they are sorted, concentrated (like molecules are grouped together), and further modified or processed. The final products for export are stored in secretory vesicles or granules until needed outside the cell. Finally, they are discharged by secretion from the cell.

Methods of Study

Knowledge of the structure and functions of the endoplasmic reticulum and the Golgi complex was gained largely through three complementary techniques: the electron microscope, tissue fractionation, and autoradiography. Each has enabled scientists to learn part of the story; together they have provided a remarkably complete picture of these cell organelles.

In 1945, just as the electron microscope was becoming a useful research tool, Albert Claude and Keith Porter discovered the vast network of channels bounded by membranes that Porter named the endoplasmic reticulum. They were able to detect these minute cell structures because as high-speed electrons are passed through a tissue sample, different parts of cells absorb or scatter them in different ways to form an image on an electron-sensitive photographic plate. This technique enabled scientists to view objects magnified hundreds of thousands of times.

Aware of the existence and complexity of the ER and Golgi apparatus, scientists were curious to know their chemical composition and function within the cell. They used an instrument called an ultracentrifuge, which had been developed in 1925 by Theodor Svedberg. This machine spun its samples at such high speeds and with such force (it could attain hundreds of thousands of times the force of gravity) that many of the smaller and lighter components of the cell could be collected separately and studied for the first time.

When the ER is ruptured, the ends of fragments fuse and form roughly circular objects called microsomes. Various microsomes have been found that contain many enzymes used very specifically in the production of fats, phospholipids, and cholesterol. It is particularly helpful that these microsomes are still able to work exactly as they did within the cell, even after all these techniques to separate them have been applied. Scientists can use these fragments and acquire, within test tubes, the products they would normally make within undisturbed cells. Similarly, gentle methods of cell rupturing that preserve stacks of Golgi complex sacs or cisternae have permitted the isolation of the complex's various parts, containing the different enzymes that modify and process chemicals as they pass from section to section of the complex. Although the fractions obtained could show the chemical processes of the various parts, scientists had to return to intact cells to trace the traffic of proteins through the ER and Golgi. They used the technique called autoradiography to reveal this pathway from the ER eventually to the cell exterior.

Using the known facts that all proteins are built of amino acids and all amino acids contain the element hydrogen, scientists attached radioactive hydrogen to amino acids so the cells could incorporate them into their proteins. When the tissue was then covered with a thin layer of photographic emulsion (the same chemical used to develop snapshot negatives), the radioactive electrons emitted activated silver grains in the emulsion, which appear as dark squiggles in the electron microscope. With time, activated silver grains are found ever closer to the cell exterior, indicating the path followed by newly synthesized protein molecules destined for secretion.

Photographs taken through the electron microscope of these radioactive cells are called electron microscopic autoradiographs. They show, within the first few minutes, radioactive proteins clinging to the RER. Within ten minutes, those proteins have traveled to the beginning parts of the Golgi complex. In about thirty minutes, they are stored in the large Golgi cisternae. After about one hour, the radioactivity is found in vesicles on their way to the cell membrane or in vesicles already attached there and being emitted from the cell. The electron microscope can provide detailed pictures of the parts of a cell, but the pictures are frozen in time. Centrifugation and autoradiography help explain the dynamic sequence of events carried on in the ER, the Golgi complex, and its related organelles.

Context

The understanding of the pathways traveled by the many chemicals produced in human cells has given researchers clues to many diseases and the hope of treating them more effectively. Many diseases of the human body are actually defects in the cells that make up the body's organs. Many may be defects in the ER or Golgi apparatus' ability to transport and supply needed chemicals properly. Diseases as diverse as diabetes, cancer, arthritis, alcoholism, and deficiencies of the immune system are among those implicated. The extensive ER in pancreatic cells needed to produce properly the protein that can become insulin and the extensive Golgi complex needed to process the insulin precursor to a fully active hormone are of great interest to diabetes researchers.

Cells within connective tissues, called fibroblasts, are responsible for producing collagen, a protein made into tough, white fibers to give strength to those tissues. Perhaps the Golgi complex fails to secrete collagen correctly from those fibroblasts in diseases of the connective tissues. It is also suspected that defects of the immune system may be linked to the inability of those white blood cells called plasma cells to process and give off the antibodies needed to fight bacterial and viral infections effectively.

Many proteins made by human cells must be correctly transported to cell membranes and embedded there to act as receptors (recognition sites) for the hormones that must attach themselves there to work effectively. Certain hormone diseases may occur, even though a person has enough of that hormone, because there are not enough receptors on the cell membrane to receive it. It is also possible that an excess of receptors can cause too much hormone to be received; certain forms of high blood pressure and heart disease are suspected to be caused in this way.

Two other whole classes of diseases involve defects of the lysosomes. The Golgi apparatus wraps large numbers of concentrated digestive enzymes into these tiny but important organelles. More than thirty hereditary diseases have been linked to the absence of various digestive enzymes, because the substances that they are supposed to break down or destroy are being wrongly accumulated. Oppositely, in other diseases, lysosomes are not lacking in enzymes but are greatly overactive in cells. Arthritis is one such disease that seems to involve autodigestion; in several other known diseases, lysosomes also seem to turn against their own cells and begin to destroy them. Some lysosomes come directly from the ER, while others are produced by the Golgi complex. When it is known what stages they go through and what is necessary to keep the lysosome membrane intact, scientists will be much closer to effective prevention or cure of these diseases.

The significance of something as small as the ER and the Golgi complex could be easily overlooked, yet understanding their work within the cell promises to show researchers the way to understand and conquer many diseases of the human body.

Bibliography

Avers, Charlotte J. *Basic Cell Biology*. 2d ed. Boston: Willard Grant Press, 1982. Written for students with minimal background in biology or chemistry, at an introductory level. Gives dynamic sense of modern cell biology. Chapter 6, "Cellular Packaging: The ER and Its Derivatives," is especially well written. List of suggested readings includes several pointing to relationship between the ER, Golgi complex, and diseases related to defective lysosomes. Lengthy glossary.

DeDuve, Christian. *A Guided Tour of the Living Cell*. Vol. 1. New York: Scientific American Books, 1984. An imaginative, even humorous, yet accurate account by a Nobel Prize winner. High school students are the intended audience. Chapter 6, "The Cell's Export Industry: ER, Golgi Apparatus, and Secretion," includes fourteen very clear diagrams in its nineteen pages. Particularly good explanation of the Golgi complex and its work.

Dyson, Robert D. *Essentials of Cell Biology*. Boston: Allyn & Bacon, 1978. A very readable textbook. Gives unified description of cellular structure and function at the introductory level. Chapter 5 clearly explains the relationship of the ER and Golgi complex. Contains an unusually large number of photographs and diagrams. Glossary included.

Karp, Gerald. *Cell Biology*. 2d ed. New York: McGraw-Hill, 1984. Stresses the experimental approach. Assumes relatively little prior scientific knowledge. Has excellent and extensive photomicrographs and diagrams. Chapter 7, "Cytoplasmic Membrane Systems," presents a step-by-step development of the topic. Begins with a very clear explanation of research methods. Exceptionally long list of references.

Kleinsmith, Lewis J., and Valerie M. Kish. *Principles of Cell Biology*. New York: Harper & Row, 1988. Written as an introduction to the field of cell biology to acquaint undergraduates, encountering the subject for the first time, with fundamental principles. Chapter 6, "Functions of Cytoplasmic Membranes," provides great detail. Illustrations particularly helpful.

Novikoff, Alex B., and Eric Holtzman. *Cells and Organelles*. New York: Holt, Rinehart and Winston, 1976. Aimed at particularly gifted secondary students. Classic study giving a brief but quite complete description. Part 2, "Cell Organelles," includes a section on the ER and a section on the Golgi apparatus. Highly readable, with instructive illustrations.

Pines, Maya. *Inside the Cell: The New Frontier of Medical Science*. Hillside, New Jersey: Enslow, 1980. Very simple, very brief explanation, with illustrations, of each cell organelle. Excellent for relating ER and Golgi complex to all other cell organelles. Fine historical approach including earliest discoveries. Includes many quotes from famous cell biologists that put bare facts into interesting context. Glossary.

Rothman, James E. "The Compartmental Organization of the Golgi Apparatus." *Scientific American* 253 (September, 1985): 74-89. Explains in detail the processing of proteins as they pass from one Golgi cisterna to the next. The article is based on the author's original research, giving a personal flavor and excitement to the facts presented. Contains a good summary of the work that preceded his own. Well illustrated.

S. Grace Dominic Matzen

Cross-References

Autoradiography and Subcellular Fractionation of Radioactive Tracer Molecules, 148; The Origin of Different Cellular Membranes, 397; Endocytosis and Exocytosis, 820; Intracellular Trafficking, 1467; Lysosomes and Microbodies, 1635; Protein Synthesis: Locational Specificity and Targeting, 2266; Ribosomes, 2406; Secretion, 2445.

ENDORPHINS AND ENKEPHALINS

Types of life science: Neurobiology and biochemistry
Other field of study: Animal physiology

Specialized painkilling substances called endorphins and enkephalins can be released within the central nervous systems of higher animals. These neurochemicals can provide a temporary buffer from pain sensations; they can also induce a sense of well-being or even euphoria in a healthy animal.

Principal terms

AGONISTS: chemicals whose action reduces pain and prompts a strong addiction; an example is morphine

ANALGESIC: a pain-reducing or blocking chemical that may be taken into the body, such as aspirin, or naturally produced in the body, such as beta endorphin

ANTAGONIST: a chemical that actually intensifies the sensation of pain; an example is naloxone

BETA ENDORPHIN: a peptide made of thirty-one amino acids that acts as an opiate; it can be found in the pituitary gland but not in the brain

BETA LIPOTROPIN: a pain-regulating protein hormone found in the pituitary gland that contains enkephalin in its substructure and is a small portion of a larger molecule, ACTH

ENDORPHIN: a neuropeptide found in the pituitary gland that has an opiate analgesic effect; released when portions of the nervous system transmit messages of pain to and from the brain

ENKEPHALIN: a neuropeptide found in the brain and spinal cord that is released by nerve axons during pain impulses; it is found in the limbic, or emotion-regulating, portion of the brain

NEUROPEPTIDES: a class of compounds synthesized in neuron cell bodies that act as neurotransmitters or neuromoderators

OPIATE: any natural or synthetic drug that acts as a pain reducer via a morphinelike action; it prompts the same kind of euphoria found when the drug morphine is taken into the body

RECEPTORS: protein structures, found on the membrane surface of nerve cells in the spinal cord and brain, that are responsible for taking in chemicals carrying messages of pain or pleasure

Summary of the Phenomenon

Pain-controlling chemicals, called endorphins and enkephalins, can be found within the nervous systems of many animals. These chemicals are also classified as neuromoderators to suggest their role as regulators of the physical sensations of pain and pleasure.

Endorphins and enkephalins have been found in many animal species, including cats, camels, pigs, sheep, toads, and humans. The most important neurological trait these species have in common is their neurological design: Peripheral nerves continuously monitor the body for both internal and external signals; a spinal cord serves as the relay center for signals and responses that travel to and from the peripheral nerves and the brain; and the brain stores, interprets, learns, and responds to neural information. These three components form a sophisticated, coordinated, and highly evolved nervous system.

A neurochemical called substance P is responsible for generating the neurological signals that the brain interprets as pain. Substance P (P for pain) transmits important messages that the brain interprets as a warning of danger that threatens the life or well-being of the animal. In response, the brain then releases other neurochemicals to adjust to or respond to the message. These responses vary according to the kind of pain and its relative severity. Frequently, neurochemicals that produce a sensation of pleasure can also act to reduce a sensation of pain. In fact, during moments of extreme stress or pain, the quantity of pain-suppressing neurochemicals rises significantly as the hurt animal attempts to cope with or eliminate the source of pain or the pain itself.

Neurotransmitters and neuromoderators can frequently counteract or otherwise influence one another. For example, high levels of endorphins in the central nervous system (CNS) can inhibit the release of substance P. Conversely, high levels of substance P can prompt the release of endorphins and enkephalins. Although the statement is overly simplified, it is possible to suggest that neurological systems have a natural preference to feel pleasure, happiness, or euphoria. A certain normal level of endorphin and enkephalin activity is always present in the body. The ability of these chemicals to reduce substance P production indicates that the body is coded to prefer pleasurable sensations over feeling or enduring pain. When the body is confronted with stress or pain, levels of these neuromoderators are increased.

Produced through the body's anabolic (or synthesizing) pathways, endorphins and enkephalins work as both pain-relieving and euphoria-inducing neurochemicals. As such, these chemicals are associated with events such as a "runner's high," tolerance of pain, and the "bliss" of love. Unpleasant or even pleasant stress increases the body's production of endorphins and enkephalins. This increase is observed in all animals when exposed to various stressors.

Although they are synthesized in different parts of the CNS, both endorphins and enkephalins are made of the same building blocks—amino acids. Generally, amino acids are said to be the building blocks of very large molecules called proteins. Given the small number of amino acids required to build endorphins or enkephalins, however, coupled with their action upon the CNS, a more specific term— neuropeptide—is often used to describe these chemicals.

The discovery of endorphins and enkephalins in the laboratory occurred at about the same time, but their presence in the body had been suggested many years earlier. In 1975, many scientists were either presenting papers or publishing articles that reported nearly identical laboratory investigative designs and laboratory results. Most records give researchers at the University of Aberdeen, Scotland, credit for having not only isolated but also fully identified the constituent parts of two previously unknown neurochemicals.

In Scotland, researchers John Hughes and Hans Kosterlitz had extracted a low-molecular-mass, opiatelike neurochemical from a mixture of brains collected from guinea pigs, rabbits, pigs, and rats. The Scottish team successfully isolated the substance and recognized that a new substance had been found. Furthermore, the substance acted as a natural analgesic (a pain reducer that does not cause loss of consciousness). Hughes realized that this new chemical prompted physiological responses that are associated with the use or abuse of morphinelike substances. In other words, it acted as a natural opiate in the body. Heroin, codeine, methadone, and meperidine are all opiod analgesics, or opiates. Opiate drugs not only reduce pain but also induce sleep (act as a narcotic) and generate euphoria.

Hughes decided to name this natural, body-synthesized chemical an enkephalin. The term originates from *enkephalos*, a Greek word meaning "the head," and the English suffix -in, meaning "within." Hughes led his group into further investigations of enkephalin. Soon they found that enkephalin was composed of only five amino acids chemically linked together through peptide bonds. Furthermore, they soon came upon evidence indicating that the enkephalin material actually contained two very similar, yet different, forms of the natural opiate. With more studies, the existence of two forms of enkephalin was confirmed. The two forms differ in one of the five amino acids in their primary structures; one contains methionine, and the other has leucine. The former was named met-enkephalin, the latter, leu-enkephalin. They exhibit similar biological roles.

The thoroughness of Hughes' research design and his subsequent success were not duplicated in the history of endorphin discovery. Indeed, the discovery of endorphins could be credited to any number of researchers who achieved results in 1975. Avram Goldstein, a biochemist at Stanford University, was working with his colleagues on the isolation of what appeared to be a morphinelike substance obtained from the pituitary and hypothalamus glands of slaughtered cattle. In May of 1975, Goldstein announced that his research group had isolated this substance. Furthermore, his group knew that their material was distinctly different from those described by the Hughes group in Scotland.

In December of that year, Goldstein contacted a researcher at the University of California in San Francisco, Chao Hao Li. Goldstein and Li recognized that the five amino acid sequences of Hughes' enkephalins appeared, several times, within the last thirty-one amino acids of the ninety-one amino acid chains of beta lipotropin, a hormone that Li had previously discovered. This surprising news prompted investigations into the possibility that beta lipotropin was the molecular precursor (or parent) of the two enkephalins; Li and Goldstein worked with camel pituitary extracts. The sequence of amino acids sixty to ninety-one of beta lipotropin could be isolated from the camel pituitary gland. Soon, the term "beta endorphin" was tagged to this substance, which was found to have extremely high opiate action in living systems.

A group at the National Institute for Medical Research in London, England, was finding similar chemicals. Derek Smyth was working with a section of beta lipotropin which he called the "C fragment." His fragment contained the same amino acids being examined in the California research. In the early summer of 1975, Smyth received a tip from another biochemist, Howard Morris, who pointed out to Smyth that his C fragment contained several copies of the enkephalin sequence. Smyth and his colleagues found that the C fragment was a hundred times more potent than morphine as a drug. A powerful new opiate was discovered.

Smyth's C fragment and Li's beta endorphin were the same substance. Li's term is more descriptive and has (without the "beta") therefore been incorporated into modern scientific language. The prefix *endo* originates from endogenous, meaning "coming from within," and *orphin* originates from "morphine."

Endorphins and enkephalins are able to reduce pain because they act upon pain-blocking and euphoria-inducing receptors in the brain. These receptors are designed specifically to match the molecular geometry, or spatial configuration, of endorphins and enkephalins. This kind of structural match is often called a lock-and-key model. Because exogenous morphine can mimic the role of endorphins and dock at these receptors, they are known as opiate receptors. Surprisingly, the chemical geometries and structures of endogenous and exogenous morphinelike substances are very similar. This explains why drugs such as morphine and heroin can act much the same as endorphins and enkephalins do in the body; exogenous opiates "fool" the natural chemistry of the body.

Methods of Study

The laboratory studies of endorphin and enkephalin chemistry really originated with the work of a graduate student, Candace Pert, who devised a method for detecting opiate receptors in the brain. Working with her research adviser, Solomon Snyder, at Johns Hopkins University in Baltimore, Maryland, Pert proved that naturally occurring opiate receptors are indeed present in the brain. This theory had been proposed several decades before 1973, but the effective technique of radioactively labeling opiates and then "watching" them dock to receptors was developed by Pert. The technique was essentially Pert's proof of the existence of opiate receptors.

In her technique, radioactively labeled opiates migrated only to specific sites where the "docking" occurred. To verify that these zones were opiate-specific (that other chemicals would not dock there), a drug antagonist called naloxone was added after the opiate drug was attached to a receptor. According to Pert and Snyder's theory, the antagonist should knock the opiate out of the receptor. An antagonist is a chemical that mimics the shape of a drug, in this case an opiate; it also fails to mimic the pleasure of an opiate and, in fact, reverses the opiate effect. In the case of naloxone, the opiate-induced euphoria is rapidly lost and is quickly followed by a sense of extreme, excruciating pain when naloxone is administered. When Pert added naloxone to opiate-receptor sites, the radioactive labels (opiates) were promptly displaced. This proved the receptor theory: Opiate-specific receptors indeed exist in the brain.

The receptor theory had been previously suggested, based upon studies of opiate addicts. With the 1973 confirmation that opiate receptors exist in the brain, the logical next question was whether these receptors are present so that drugs from the outside can be introduced into living systems or whether the receptors perform an important natural role in the body. The consensus was that if sheep, rats, toads, and humans had receptors for opiates, then these species must produce natural opiates within the body. It seemed unlikely to have such receptors present if the body had no normal use for such a structure. Furthermore, if the body does produce opiates, there must be an important biological role that these chemicals could perform. The discoveries of endorphins and enkephalins in 1975 answered many of these questions. The natural opiates—endorphins and enkephalins—and the opiate receptors were all verifiable in laboratory research.

Subsequent research has explored the questions of where endorphins and enkephalins originate in the body, how they are alike and different in altering physiology, and how these chemical models can explain drug addiction. Moreover, mental illness or chronic pain can be related to excessive or limited amounts of endorphins and enkephalins. The use of radioactive labels on endogenous or exogenous opiates has evolved into the use of laboratory-grown antibodies of endorphins and enkephalins that have fluorescent chemical labels attached. The endorphin antibody will exclusively locate and attach to endorphin. The enkephalin antibody will exclusively locate and attach to enkephalin. Thus, a highly specific fluorescent probe can now be used in research to locate where and how these chemicals enter the central nervous system. Tracing the location of endorphins or enkephalins is easily accomplished simply by following the fluorescent paths. Photomicrographs can illuminate where the antibody-tagged endorphins or enkephalins are. Photomicrographs can also provide visual and permanent records of the research.

Antibody techniques and fluorescent markers provide modern probes that allow researchers to trace the separate and distinctly different paths of endorphins and enkephalins. In addition, drug antagonists and radioactive labeling continue to be important laboratory investigative tools. The results of these investigations will contribute to the increased understanding of drug addiction, chronic pain, mental illness, and pharmacology. Perhaps, through this increased understanding, cures or treatments will be developed that will be effective and nonaddictive and (because of their specific action or target location) will produce minimal side effects.

Context
Those animals whose bodies produce endorphins and enkephalins are dependent upon a normal, constant, and balanced amount of these neurochemicals in order to sustain good health. These natural opiates are vital as regulators of one's sense of

well-being and as moderators of pain. Since 1981, scientists have known that opiate-like neuropeptides occur in animals lacking a backbone, thus lacking a spinal cord. In terms of evolutionary time, the indications that early species of life may have neuropeptide functions in their relatively simple neurosystems are strong. Enkephalinlike and endorphinlike peptides have been found in certain eye structures of lobsters as well as in single-celled organisms called protozoans. Clearly, these neurochemicals are fundamental ingredients of living systems.

Several clinically significant associations between levels of endorphins and enkephalins and physical or mental health have been identified. Researchers continue to seek answers to the problems of Alzheimer's disease, drug addiction, sudden infant death syndrome (SIDS), and control of chronic pain, and some potential uses of endorphin and enkephalin research are suggested for these areas. Each of these health problems is complex and multifaceted, however, so that many factors must be considered to gather a full understanding of any of them.

In 1983, Japanese researchers identified a possible correlation between endorphin levels in cerebrospinal fluid and Alzheimer's disease. This disease is marked by a pronounced decrease in frontal and occipital activity within the brain. Lower than normal levels of endorphins have been found in Alzheimer's patients. It is possible that this is a result of the progressive death of brain cells; otherwise, it may be that low endorphin concentrations may increase the rate of dying of brain cells. Some scientists have suggested that physicians may one day be able to diagnose a patient with Alzheimer's disease in its early stages by testing the cerebrospinal fluid for endorphin levels.

In the challenging field of treating drug addicts, many psychologists and psychiatrist continue to hope for a "miracle cure" for this entrapping disease. Genetics clearly plays a role in chemical addictions. Some researchers postulate that low levels of endorphins and enkephalins may prompt some people to experiment with narcotic or opiate drugs. Low endorphin production may be genetically inherited; alternatively, some families may carry genes that improperly code how to build an opiate receptor in brain cells. Should either condition exist, a person would be overly sensitive to physical and emotional stress in a physiological sense. Many societal taboos exist concerning drug addiction and treatment; sadly, many people are predisposed to this disease because of a flaw in their body design, not because they are "bad" people or "chose" to be addicted.

One of the side effects of opiates is a depressed respiratory system. When the respiratory system is depressed, breathing slows, blood circulation decreases, and metabolic activity drops. A team of German researchers has suggested that high levels in endorphins and enkephalins may contribute to the tragedy known as SIDS. Infants are often traumatized merely by the process of being born and adapting to their new environment. It may be possible that higher endorphin and enkephalin levels, activated during the adaptation process, can cause such a great depression of the baby's respiration that breathing actually stops. The normal level of endorphins and enkephalins for infants is not well defined, but evidence has shown elevated levels in SIDS infants as compared to normal levels for human adults. Perhaps future parents will not have to suffer the loss of an infant to SIDS if research and progress continue to be made in this area.

Other clinical applications of endorphin and enkephalin research include possible treatments for some forms of mental illness; treatment or control of pain for chronic pain sufferers or terminally ill patients experiencing great pain; development of new anesthetics without side effects such as nausea, vomiting, or headaches; and the development of nonaddictive, safe, and effective pain relievers.

Bibliography

Clark, John, ed. *The Human Body—The Nervous System: Circuits of Communication*. New York: Torstar Books, 1985. Chapter 8, "Agony and Ecstasy," is a clear and concise treatment of the human body's sensory centers for pain and pleasure as well as of the neurochemicals responsible for these sensations. The gate theory of pain, the use of painkillers, and pain and its treatment are all discussed. Supplemented by photographs, diagrams, and charts, the chapter gives excellent introductory information to all readers.

Davis, Joel. *Endorphins: New Waves in Brain Chemistry*. New York: Dial Press, 1984. This book of about two hundred and fifty pages is divided into three parts. "The Stage" presents a historical account of the researchers who made endorphin discoveries, accurately describing the competitive and cooperative efforts of the scientific community. Part 2 addresses the links between endogenous opiates and mental illness, pain, stress, drug abuse, and general health. The last section addresses futuristic and optimistic applications of this basic scientific research. Accessible to mature high school readers. A historical synopsis of the end of the text and an excellent reference list provide useful information to all readers.

Julien, Robert M. *A Primer of Drug Action, 5e*. 5th ed. New York: W. H. Freeman, 1988. Although this book is authored by a physician, it is written for the layperson who seeks a deeper understanding of the pharmacological action of alcohol, street drugs, or pharmaceuticals; addresses topics ranging from psychoactive drugs to birth control. Six appendices provide additional information on drug transport, anatomy of the nervous system, and the physiology of nerve cells. Chapters that particularly relate to endorphins and enkephalins are chapter 1, "Principles of Drug Action," chapter 2, "Classification of Psychoactive Drugs," and chapter 7, "The Opiates." Includes sketches and diagrams.

Kettlekamp, Larry. *The Human Brain*. Hillside, N.J.: Enslow Publishers, 1986. For persons with little familiarity about the human brain and its chemistry, this book is an excellent resource. The six chapters cover brain messengers, the senses, chemicals and moods, and left brain/right brain characteristics. Diagrams aid in explaining how certain chemical pathways occur, and photographs show neurological structures.

Levinthal, Charles F. *Messengers of Paradise: Opiates and Brain Chemistry*. New York: Doubleday, 1988. Well written for the layperson who is curious about neuropeptide chemistry; however, a person with more background will also enjoy and perhaps better understand the material. The book is written in two segments. Part 1, "The Endorphin Story," comprises five chapters that describe the origins of opium use by humans, the history of opiate use, and the history of scientific research leading to the discovery of endorphins and enkephalins. Part 2, "Endorphins and Evolution," has four chapters that explore the potential health and medical applications of endorphin discoveries and the evolutionary origins of opiates and opiate receptors in living systems. Excellent reference notes are included at the end of the text.

Ornstein, Robert, and Richard F. Thompson. *The Amazing Brain*. Boston: Houghton Mifflin, 1984. The excellent illustrations provided by David Macauley, combined with the simple, clear, and informative writing styles of the authors, make this book a fine resource for the novice investigating the human brain. The text provides the right balance of information, theory, and sketches for the beginner. Chapter 4, "The Chemical Brain: The Molecule Is the Messenger," is devoted to the topic of neurotransmitters. The "lock and key" theory is presented along with a study of the nearly identical molecular geometries of morphine, the antagonist called naloxone, and an enkephalin. The models of opiate receptors, showing how these molecules "dock" and produce some action, are useful.

Pinchot, Roy B., ed. *The Human Body—The Brain: Mystery of Mind and Matter*. Tarrytown, N.Y.: Torstar Books, 1984. An excellent introduction to brain anatomy. The chapter "The Electrochemical Brain" is devoted to explaining how chemicals act in the brain. The function of opiate receptors and their discovery is described. In addition, enkephalins are described as painkillers and mood regulators. Contains useful, easy-to-read information about the mind, the brain, and the way memory, learning, feeling, and creating are generated. Photomicrographs, illustrations, and diagrams complete the descriptions.

Poole, Robert M., ed. *The Incredible Machine*. Washington, D.C.: National Geographic Society, 1986. This brilliantly colorful book provides excellent photographs and brief captions to describe the human body and how it functions. It includes a fascinating series of color plates. The section "Landscapes of the Mind" has two segments devoted to endorphins and enkephalins. Pages 350 to 352 contain images describing endorphins in neurons, the use of electric impulses and acupuncture to induce endorphin production, and thermograms that help trace sources of body pain. Pages 355 to 356 describe the link between endorphins and enkephalins and emotions. An excellent resource for parents or teachers who want to discuss the human body with their children. Also appropriate for the adult seeking a holistic guide to the human form.

Snyder, Solomon. *Drugs and the Brain*. New York: Scientific American Books, 1986. Contains eight chapters devoted to topics of the brain, brain activity, and biochemicals that control and regulate all aspects of the healthy or unhealthy mind. Expertly written by one of the most recognized scientists in neuropeptide research. Diagrams, photographs, photomicrographs, and schematics provide superb visual support to the written text. Chapter 2, "Opiates," is particularly pertinent to endorphin and enkephalin topics. Approximately thirty pages are devoted to this chapter, which includes a description of the chemical basis of drug addiction as well as of the body's own morphine production.

Mary C. Fields

Cross-References

Central and Peripheral Nervous System Functions, 404; The Forebrain, 1032; The Hindbrain and Midbrain, 1291; Membrane Potential, 1674; Neurotransmitters, 1936; Proteins, 2272; Synapses, 2587.

ENDOSKELETONS

Type of life science: Animal anatomy
Other fields of study: Biochemistry, biophysics, and developmental biology (embryology)

Endoskeletons are a distinctive primary feature of most of the members of the phylum Chordata. Their evolution eventually provided vertebrates with many advantages over invertebrate animals. Study of the various types of tissues that make up endoskeletons are important to the study of both medicine and evolution.

Principal terms
APPENDICULAR SKELETON: one of two main divisions of vertebrate skeletal systems, composed of the bones of the pelvic girdle, the shoulders, and the limbs
AXIAL SKELETON: the other main division of vertebrate skeletal systems, made up of the bones of the skull, the vertebral column, the ribs, and the sternum
CANCELLOUS BONE: spongy bone that is composed of an open, interlacing framework of bony tissue oriented to provide maximum strength in response to normal strains and stresses
CARTILAGE: a soft, pliable typically deep-lying tissue that constitutes the endoskeletons of primitive vertebrates, such as sharks, as well as the embryonic skeletons and jointing structures of adult higher vertebrates
CHORDATA: the animal phylum that includes all vertebrate classes as well as certain nonvertebrate protochordates
COMPACT BONE: a dense type of bone, often termed lamellar bone, formed of a calcified bone matrix having a concentric ring organization
ENDOSKELETON: the type of skeleton that is found beneath the musculature of an animal's body; it provides mechanical support for the body as a whole, some protection for vulnerable internal organs and tissues, and sites for muscle attachment
HAVERSIAN SYSTEMS: narrow tubes surrounded by rings of bone, called lamellae, that are found within compact bones of animals having endoskeletons; the tubes contain blood vessels and bone
OSTEOBLAST: a bone-secreting cell found in vertebrates that is instrumental in the process of ossification
OSTEOGENESIS: the total biological process by which bone is formed within the body; the process involves the action of osteoblasts, and is also called ossification

VERTEBRATA: a subphylum of the phylum Chordata that includes all
animals with backbones, and thus all animals possessing
endoskeletons

Summary of the Phenomenon

The study of endoskeletons can be approached in three basic ways. First, endoskeletons can be approached as gross structures—that is, as primarily mechanical
or architectural systems. Second, they can be viewed as types of tissue—bone and
cartilage—which involves study at the microscopic level. Third, endoskeletons can
be considered products of the evolution of the endoskeletal organism. This area examines such factors as the organisms' development from protochordates and the intrinsic biological advantages of the endoskeleton over the exoskeleton.

The evolution of vertebrate animals, such as fishes, reptiles, and mammals, having articulating endoskeletons represents a biological quantum leap forward for the
phylum Chordata. The development of endoskeletons permitted several significant
structural advantages that allowed the higher chordates to compete successfully with
invertebrates and eventually to become dominant in many varied ecosystems.

The evolution of endoskeletons allowed a greater degree of general body efficiency and organization. Coupled with a great increase in the rapidity, power, and
control of movement that endoskeletons and their improved musculature endowed
their possessors, endoskeletons allowed vertebrates to become the highest and fast-
est flyers, the swiftest runners and swimmers, and the widest ranging of animals.
The organizational plan of the endoskeleton of the more highly evolved vertebrates
is exemplified by that of mammals. The mammalian endoskeleton is articulated in
many ways, giving it a great degree of flexibility and great range of movement. Cartilaginous joints facilitate the articulations. The endoskeleton itself is typically
made of bone material composed of calcium phosphate. Other than the endoskeleton proper, minor externalizations can take the form of fingernails and toenails,
claws, hooves, antlers, and horn cores, as well as teeth. In these cases, materials
other than bone can sometimes originate at or near the body surface or in the skin.
These expressions can be present in the form of scales or plates, though this is the
exception rather than the rule among this vertebrate class. All these external expressions can be considered, in a way, forms of a limited exoskeleton.

Aside from such exceptions as pangolins and armadillos among mammals, and
turtles and tortoises among reptiles, exoskeletal tissue does not usually constitute an
architectural structure that the animal's other organs or structures depend on for
support or protection. The one exception among the various bones of the vertebrate
endoskeleton is the bones of the cranium, or skull. The cranial bones are a group of
hard, thick bones, usually ovoid or spheroidal in general geometry, that offer extensive protection to the brain and primary sensory organs, such as the eyes and ears.
The cranium is such a universal feature among vertebrates that the subphylum is
sometimes referred to as the craniates. Evolutionarily lower vertebrates tend to have
larger numbers of skull bones. Some fish have as many as 180 skull bones. Higher

taxonomic groups have inversely lower numbers of skull bones: Amphibians and reptiles possess between fifty and ninety-five, while mammals have thirty-five or fewer. Humans have only twenty-nine. The skull itself is a member of two fundamental divisions between which the entire endoskeleton is usually subdivided; it is part of the axial skeleton. The axial skeleton also includes the bones of the vertebral system, the ribs, and the sternum. Possession of all axial features is not universal. Some vertebrates, such as the leopard frog, do not possess ribs, while others, such as the snakes, do not have sternums.

The other endoskeletal subdivision is called the appendicular skeleton, and it is made up of the bones of the pelvic girdle, shoulders, and limbs. The components of the appendicular system exhibit a great degree of variation from vertebrate group to vertebrate group and even among species, as does the axial system, and reflect the many different environments and life-styles to which their respective possessors have adapted. A case in point are the numerous variations in form and length found among limb bones. The various lengths represent adaptations to such external environmental factors as the medium through which the animals move from place to place (air, water, ground surface, and subsurface) and speed. The lower and upper limb bones themselves are connected by joints. The jointing arrangements of limb bones are highly efficient mechanical developments. Two basic types of limb joint exist: the pulley joint and the ball-and-socket joint. Pulley joints are exemplified by finger and toe joints and represent great freedom of motion in one plane. Ball-and-socket joints are exemplified by shoulder or hip joints and represent freedom of universal motion. Still another joint type is a cross between these two. Such a combination of pulley and ball joints is exemplified by the elbow joint in humans.

Another major approach to the study of the endoskeleton is its histology, or the fine details of tissues and how these tissues develop. Bone material itself is active metabolically—that is to say, it is alive. It can be considered not only an architecture along which the vertebrate body is arranged but also a complex and specialized connective tissue. As an organic material, it possesses a number of unique properties that are derived from the fact that it has evolved to perform its various duties efficiently for the size, weight, and arrangement of the materials of which it is composed. It is engineered like structurally reinforced concrete, having fibers of collagen, a tough, fibrous binding protein that is analagous to the function of steel rods.

The mineral calcium is analogous to the concrete in a building. Bone is formed in two different ways, depending on type. One process involves a means of growth of two bone types, termed lamellar bone (compact bone) and cancellous bone (spongy bone). Lamellar bone, sometimes also called membrane bone, develops through the process of ossification when certain cells called osteoblasts become bone-secreting. The osteoblastic cells, in association with numerous fibers of connective tissue cells, form a network in which layers of calcium mineral salts, called lamellae, are deposited. This network slowly builds up a plate that expands along its margins. As the plate thickens, some osteoblasts remain alive and are incorporated into the bone growth. At this point, they begin to have irregular shapes and are termed osteocytes. Spaces in which the osteocytes are sited are termed lacunae (cavities) and develop long, omnidirectional, branching processes, termed canaliculi. Neighboring canaliculi eventually link up and create a network through which life-supporting blood containing oxygen and food can reach the growing bone tissue. The canaliculi system grows such that no bone cell is more than 0.1 millimeter from a blood-carrying capillary. This overall arrangement is termed a Haversian system.

Cartilage tissue is another endoskeletal material that forms the adult skeletons of lower vertebrates, such as mammals, when they are still in early developmental stages. In mammals, this type of tissue is not formed directly, but rather by a replacement process. In mammalian embryos, most of the skeletal structure is initially laid down in the form of cartilage and then subsequently replaced by true bone. The process does not reach completion in the higher vertebrates until the animal is full-grown; in humans, this is as late as twenty-five or twenty-six years of age. Cartilage is not as hard or rigid as bone, but it is extremely tough and is resistant to forces of compression or extension. Under microscopic examination, it appears as a clear matrix which possesses numerous, embedded cells termed chondroblasts. These chondroblasts lie in fluid-filled voids termed lacunae. Chondroblasts secrete the matrix called chondrin, which surrounds the lacunae. Both the chondrin and the fluids act in an elastic manner and are resistant to compression and external shocks. There are various types of cartilage having collagen fibers. The amounts of collagen fiber present determines the amount of extension that the cartilage can resist. The total effect of the cartilage's unique composition is to render it a good skeletal material for young, rapidly developing, vulnerable animals, such as mammal embryos.

The last basic approach to the study of endoskeletons is that of examining the evolutionary development of the phylum Chordata in general and the subphylum of vertebrates in particular. The earliest history of the chordates is only very sketchily understood; the remains of early, ancestral forms of this group made poor candidates for the fossilization process because they lacked hard body parts. A line of hypothesized evolution, therefore, has been drawn through surviving marine animals called protochordates, which presently are sessile or stationary for most of their life cycle, although before attaining this current form, they were capable of locomotion. These curious animals are considered invertebrate chordates as they possess a notochord, or flexible skeletal rod that runs up the long axis of their bodies. Among this group are such animals as the amphioxus and the so-called sea squirts or tunicates.

Further evolved along the path that eventually led to the present diversity of endoskeleton-possessing vertebrates are animals possessing bone matter, such as the agnathan (jawless) fishes. Later fishes evolved jaws and eventually true teeth and progressed from having cartilaginous skeletons (the class Chondrichthyes) to having true, bony endoskeletons (the class Osteichthyes). These more advanced fishes eventually gave rise to the land-pioneering class Amphibia and ultimately engendered the vertebrate classes of Reptilia (reptiles), Aves (birds), and Mammalia. The reason that bone tissue evolved at all in the lower vertebrates is a subject that is still open to debate. Several rival theories exist; one holds that bone evolved simply as a more improved, harder material for exoskeletons superior to such material as calcium carbonate, the most common building material for invertebrate exoskeletons. Another suggests that bone evolved as a phosphate reserve as one component for energy storage and transfer for metabolic processes within the bodies of ancestral vertebrates. Still another theory postulates that bone materials such as dentine and enamel evolved originally simply as effective insulation for the electrosensory organs found in primitive, marine vertebrates. Other theories integrate versions of the above theories in complex, interactive arrangements.

Methods of Study

Histological research of endoskeletal tissues has in the past been the most productive approach to obtaining the large body of data on bone tissues and processes that currently exists. The majority of the data accumulated with this approach has been gained in the laboratory and has involved specialized equipment and the use of techniques tailored to produce useful information on bone cells, their composition, related tissues, and the various organic processes involved. These techniques and laboratory tools and appliances were developed laboriously over the centuries. Real progress in the field had to wait until the advent of the simple microscope. Believed to be invented by the Dutch scientist Antoni van Leeuwenhoek or one of his contemporaries in the seventeenth century, the simple optical microscope—utilizing only one lens—allowed the first closeup look at living structures at or near the cellular level. Examination of Leeuwenhoek's original equipment has revealed that he was able to obtain the respectable magnification of as much as $250\times$. His lenses thus allowed humans an entry into a world that had hitherto been barred to them— the world of the very small. Subsequent development in microscopes produced compound optical microscopes with several lenses working in series and an eventual exponential increase in magnifying power. Biologists quickly recognized that the new tool underscored the relation between structure and function of organic materials at the microscopic level. It is this critical concept that has been the key to unlocking the many secrets of the organic microstructures of living things, among them endoskeletons.

Hand in hand with the development of research using optical microscopes has been the preparation of histological sections. These are extremely thin, transparent shavings of organic tissues prepared in such a way as to facilitate microscopic examination. With the increased sophistication of the use of microscopy has come the perfected use of many different types of staining and dying. The use of stains and dyes has been selectively employed to highlight the different types of tissue being observed. A further refinement in microscopy has been the use of various lens filters, such as polarizing filters, that have added additional control of the light target to emphasize or deemphasize various features.

After the advent of applied nuclear physics during World War II, a new technique called autoradiography appeared; this enhanced the resources available to histological research. Autoradiography involves the introduction of radioactive substances into animals; consequently, they are incorporated into various tissue components. The great advantage to this technique is that it can provide direct information on how long it takes for the various tissue components to be synthesized and on how long they last.

As the spectrum of isotopic labels expanded and became refined, it became possible to label and study in great detail almost every common tissue component found in animals. The study of the most intricate or delicate endoskeletal tissues thus became realistic along with the added advantage of being able to determine the durations of the metabolic processes involved in development, decay, and replacement.

A solution to the magnification limitation of the light microscope was reached when the first electron microscope (EM) was built in 1931. Further improvements were made until the 1950's saw the widespread use of more technologically advanced devices called scanning electron microscopes (SEMs), which allow observation and SEM photography, termed electron micrography, of target objects considerably less than 1 micron in diameter.

Still newer technologies, such as the use of fiber-optic probes inserted into the living bodies of animals and humans, allow benign observation of tissues in their natural state in the midst of normal processes. Fiber optics involves the transmission of light (and therefore images) through very fine, flexible glass rods by internal reflection. Fiber-optic instruments called fiberscopes allow the viewing of extremely small, and normally dark, internal structures such as skeletal tissues.

Context

The importance of the study of endoskeletal tissue cannot be overemphasized. The knowledge that must be acquired to make substantial inroads against the various bone diseases afflicting humans warrants extensive research. Cancer of the bone tissues, congenital deformities, and traumatic injuries are some of the traditional skeletal maladies that further research may alleviate or possibly eliminate.

Coupled with the older problems have come a host of new medical complications engendered by the widespread use of new technologies. These include the cumulative effect of radiation from nuclear sources, such as power plants and weapons testing, which finds its way into human and animal bone tissues. The worldwide use of pesticides and numerous other chemical pollutants and toxins as the direct and indirect by-products of rapid and uncontrolled industrialization and mass consumerism has also caused bone pathogens to enter the food chain. Because humans and the other higher vertebrates are at or near the top of the ecological food pyramid, these new problem chemicals concentrate in higher and higher doses as protein is passed on from simpler to more complex organisms. Because of these new and proliferating health hazards, there is even more reason to understand as fully as possible the skeletal tissue as well as all the tissue that together makes up the body.

Bibliography

Carroll, Robert L. *Vertebrate Paleontology and Evolution*. New York: W. H. Freeman, 1988. An extremely thorough and detailed treatment of most known types of fossil vertebrates. The great bulk of the work concerns fossil reptiles and mammals. Readers who are curious about the role of endoskeletons in evolution can read a discussion entitled, "The Origin of Skeletal Tissues," found near the conclusion of chapter 2. This book is suitable for readers with a solid foundation or keen interest in natural history.

Cosslett, V. E. *Modern Microscopy: Or, Seeing the Very Small*. Ithaca, N.Y.: Cornell University Press, 1966. A very informative paperback that explains the different types of techniques scientists use to analyze microscopic structures. Emphasis is on explaining how each technique is actually accomplished and the useful types of information that can be produced. Numerous black-and-white plates of both organic and inorganic structures greatly enhance the text. Suitable for all readers interested in the histology of endoskeletons.

Ham, Arthur W. *Histology*. 6th ed. Philadelphia: J. B. Lippincott, 1969. A meticulously written textbook clearly intended for students majoring in the life sciences at the college level. Emphasis is on examples of tissues as found in humans, but representative of vertebrates in general. Chapter 18, "Bone," is a comprehensive treatment of bone tissues. This is a useful book for those who already have a solid foundation in biology or zoology.

Hickman, Cleveland P., and Cleveland P. Hickman, Jr. *Biology of Animals*. St. Louis: C. V. Mosby, 1972. A clearly written text intended for use within introductory biology or zoology classes at the undergraduate college level. Readers should turn their attention to part 3, "Physiology of Animals," and particularly chapter 7 within that section: "Body Covering and Support," a key section for information on endoskeletal systems and tissues.

Kessel, Richard G., and Randy H. Kardon. *Tissues and Organs: A Text-Atlas of Scanning Electron Microscopy*. San Francisco: W. H. Freeman, 1979. Although intended as a textbook for advanced college biology students who are either actually learning the use of SEMs or learning to analyze various types of scanning electron micrographs, the book has numerous large-format, high quality reproductions of SEM-photographed bone tissue. These are extremely useful in understanding endoskeletons at the level of tissue. A good book for readers with a solid science foundation.

Parker, T. Jeffery, and William A. Haswell. *A Text-Book of Zoology*. 6th ed. London: Macmillan, 1956. Volume two of this two-part text series treats the various classes that make up the phylum Chordata. The second volume discusses in great detail the various anatomical characteristics of members of each vertebrate class, with discussions of the types of tissues involved. Useful for serious readers and college-level students of the life sciences.

Savage, R. J. G., and M. R. Long. *Mammal Evolution: An Illustrated Guide*. New York: Facts on File, 1986. A book intended for the general reader with some science background or enthusiasm for the subject. Contains many good color and monochrome drawings and diagrams tied in with the text. Chapter 3, "Bones and Teeth," explains the basic, overall skeletal structure of all vertebrates. Mammalian dentition, as well as the limbs and the bones of the head, is discussed at length.

Zuidema, George D., ed. *The Johns Hopkins Atlas of Human Functional Anatomy.* Baltimore: The Johns Hopkins University Press, 1977. Outstanding color drawings of great intricacy illustrate the various parts of the human body. The extensive accompanying text clearly and concisely explains the various types of tissues and structures. A good introduction to skeletal anatomy for readers at an undergraduate college level and above.

Frederick M. Surowiec

Cross-References

Animal Cell Types, 105; Bone Growth and Dissolution Processes, 286; Evolution: A Historical Perspective, 903; Exoskeletons, 945; Histological Analysis, 1299; Histology, 1307; Muscle Anatomy in Vertebrates, 1822; Muscular Calcium Release and Reuptake, 1843; Skeleton and Muscle Interactions, 2514.

ENZYMES AND RIBOZYMES

Type of life science: Biochemistry
Other fields of study: Genetics, molecular biology, and the origin of life (paleontology)

Almost all enzymes are proteins that greatly enhance the rate of specific chemical reactions without being consumed. Ribozymes are enzymes that are not proteins but instead consist of ribonucleic acid. The study of enzymes has greatly increased the understanding of basic life processes; the discovery of ribozymes has shed light on how the first genetic material was synthesized.

Principal terms

AMINO ACID: any one of twenty types of organic molecules that contain a carboxyl and an amino group; amino acids can be bonded together to form macromolecular chains called proteins

CATALYST: a substance that alters the rate of a chemical reaction and is not consumed in the process

CYTOPLASM: the material surrounding the nucleus in the interior of a cell; most enzyme-catalyzed reactions of cell metabolism occur in the cytoplasm

METABOLISM: all the processes by which complex molecules, such as carbohydrates and proteins, are formed (anabolism) or broken down (catabolism) in plants and organisms

NUCLEOTIDE: the repeating unit in ribonucleic acid; a nucleotide consists of an organic nitrogenous base bonded to a simple sugar molecule containing a phosphate group

PEPTIDE: any molecule forming a bond between the amino group of one amino acid molecule and the carboxyl group of another

PROTEIN: a macromolecule consisting of long chains of amino acids linked by peptide bonds

RIBONUCLEIC ACID (RNA): a macromolecule that consists of a chain of nucleotides linked through the phosphate groups; different types of ribonucleic acid play a major role in determining the structure of proteins that are synthesized in cells

SUBSTRATES: the substances undergoing transformation in an enzyme-catalyzed reaction

Summary of the Phenomenon

Most biological reactions occur very slowly in the absence of enzymes. An enzyme can accelerate a reaction by a factor of at least one million. Thus, an enzyme serves to increase the rate of a reaction and make it compatible with the other biochemical processes that maintain the cell. Nearly two thousand enzymes are known, and although a systematic method for naming enzymes has been developed, it is quite cumbersome. Another method is to add the suffix "-ase" to the substrate involved in the reaction that the enzyme catalyzes. Thus, urease is the enzyme that catalyzes the breakdown of urea. It should be noted, however, that many enzymes have been given names which do not indicate the substrate involved.

Pancreatic ribonuclease assists in the breakdown of ribonucleic acid (RNA) and is an example of an enzyme that consists only of polypeptides. Other enzymes often require the presence of a cofactor for activity. There are three types of cofactors: an inorganic ion, which is called a metal activator when it binds loosely to the enzyme; a loosely bound organic molecule, referred to as a coenzyme; and a prosthetic group, which is a cofactor that is firmly bound to the enzyme. Vitamins are compounds that are transformed into coenzymes. They are an essential component of food intake because the body does not synthesize vitamins, and without them enzymes are inactive.

In general, a unique enzyme is required for a defined reaction. This specificity is attributable to the folding of the constituent proteins of the enzyme, which presents the surrounding solution with a catalytic site with a certain shape and reactive groups of atoms. The specific arrangement of atoms ensures that only the substrate with a corresponding three-dimensional arrangement of atoms can be firmly attached. This is analogous to the relationship between a lock and key. The active site is the lock, and only those substrates having a specific configuration, the keys, will fit.

Some enzymes are absolute in their specificity for a given substrate. For example, aspartase catalyzes the addition of ammonia to a four-carbon acid, fumaric acid, to form the amino acid L-aspartate. No other four-carbon acid is activated by aspartase, nor is D-aspartate, the mirror-image of L-aspartate, involved. Another example is provided by thrombin, a proteolytic enzyme (that is, one that catalyzes the breakdown of proteins) that is involved in blood clotting. Thrombin assists only in the cleavage of peptide bonds in which the amino acid on the carbonyl side of the bond (the side bearing the carbon-oxygen double bond) is arginine, and the one on the amino side is glycine. Other enzymes will act on many compounds having a specific structural feature. For example, subtilisin, which occurs in certain bacteria, catalyzes the cleavage of all peptide bonds regardless of which amino acids make up the bond. Similarly, chymotrypsin catalyzes the cleavage of all peptide bonds in which the amino acid on the carbonyl side is phenylalanine, tyrosine, or tryptophan.

It is useful to consider enzymes in three general groups: monomeric enzymes, with only one polypeptide chain in which the active site resides; oligomeric enzymes, with more than two subunit polypeptides that are firmly associated to form the active enzyme protein; and multienzyme complexes, in which a number of enzymes are tightly bound and catalyze a sequential series of reactions.

All cells contain ribosomes, the large nucleoprotein particles where proteins, including enzymes, are synthesized. This might seem to present a problem, because the enzymes necessary for digestion catalyze hydrolytic processes—processes in which certain bonds are broken upon reaction with water. Because this is the same type of reaction that breaks down proteins, the presence of proteolytic (protein-cleaving) enzymes in the cell could cause severe damage. This does not occur, however: Proteolytic enzymes, which are monomeric enzymes, are synthesized as inactive precursors called zymogens. Before they become converted to their active form, zymogens are transported out of the cell and into the digestive tract.

Most enzymes are oligomeric. The enzymes that activate the glycolytic sequence, for example, in which glucose is broken down to lactic acid with production of energy, are oligomeric enzymes, each consisting of two or four subunits. Oligomeric enzymes can be subdivided into three classes. Isozymes are different forms of oligomeric enzymes that consist of different polypeptides. Each form catalyzes the same reaction. For example, lactic dehydrogenase (LDH) catalyzes the reversible transformation of pyruvic acid into lactic acid in the last stages of the glycolytic sequence and can occur in five forms.

Enzyme-activated processes have a "pacemaker," or regulatory, enzyme, which is usually the first enzyme in the sequence and which controls the rate of the entire sequence of reactions. These enzymes are also called allosteric enzymes and are the second type of oligomeric enzymes. Allosteric enzymes possess a modulator site that binds specific metabolites, with the result that an increase or decrease in the activity of the catalytic site occurs.

The third type of oligomeric enzyme is typified by tryptophan synthetase in *Escherichia coli* bacteria. This is a bifunctional enzyme; two catalytic sites are present, each of which catalyzes a different reaction. The product of one reaction is the substrate of the second reaction.

An example of a multienzyme complex is provided by the *Escherichia coli* pyruvic acid dehydrogenase. This complex actually consists of three enzymes that catalyze a sequence of reactions in the transformation of pyruvic acid, obtained from the glycolytic process, into acetyl-coenzyme A, which is further broken down in the Krebs cycle. Dissociation of any of the constituent enzymes results in complete inactivation of the complex.

Compounds that can inhibit the catalytic activity of an enzyme by either blocking the catalytic site or binding to some other site and causing a loss of activity are called reversible or irreversible inhibitors. An irreversible inhibitor forms a covalent bond at the catalytic site of the enzyme. Dissociation of such an inhibitor occurs very slowly. The nerve gas diisopropylfluorophosphate is an irreversible inhibitor that binds to acetylcholinesterase, an enzyme that catalyzes processes in the transmission of nerve impulses. Paralysis occurs because the nerve impulses can no longer be transmitted.

Reversible inhibitors can be subclassified into competitive and noncompetitive types. Competitive inhibitors bind at the catalytic site, but the bonding is weak, and the inhibitor dissociates as the substrate builds up. Succinic dehydrogenase is a competitive inhibitor that catalyzes the oxidation of succinic acid to fumaric acid in the Krebs cycle. A noncompetitive inhibitor does not block the catalytic site. Therefore, enzyme properties are affected in such a way that catalytic activity is decreased. The allosteric enzymes are subject to this type of inhibition.

Inhibitors are essential to living systems because they provide the tools by which biochemical processes are regulated. Regulation is necessary so that, for example, a muscle that is being used will be supplied with the energy required and so that when it is allowed to rest the energy-producing processes will slow down or stop. A common regulatory process is called feedback inhibition; a sequence of enzyme-catalyzed reactions is affected by a product formed in the latter stages of a sequence or at a stage where other processes branch out. If the compound is not being metabolized for energy, its concentration increases and it inhibits the first enzyme in the sequence of reactions that produces it, with the result that the production sequence slows down.

Because the synthesis of proteins is enzyme-catalyzed, the entire process is subject to the action of inhibitors. In fact, many antibiotics are inhibitors of protein synthesis in bacterial cells, thus preventing their growth. For example, puromycin has a structure similar to aminoacyl-tRNA and bonds to the polypeptide in the elongation step of protein synthesis. The protein is not completed because new amino acids cannot be added to the chain. Tetracyclines block the site of attachment of aminoacyl-tRNA to the ribosome and prevent the initiation of the bacterial protein synthesis.

Until 1981, all enzymes were generally believed to be proteins. This belief could not answer the problem of which came first, the nucleic acids or proteins. Enzymes are the proteins required in biosynthesis of deoxyribonucleic acid (DNA) and RNA, and yet DNA and RNA are required for the synthesis of enzymes. The discovery that RNA in ribosomes can catalyze reactions gave rise to the term "ribozymes" for this particular type of nonprotein catalyst and solved the puzzle.

An intervening sequence of nucleotides, called an "intron," was known to be excised from a precursor RNA molecule, which was then spliced together to form ribosomal RNA in a species of protozoa (single-celled eukaryotic organisms) known as *Tetrahymena*. It was shown that the entire process occurred in the absence of proteins or enzymes. Furthermore, the intron was shown to act as an enzyme catalyst by folding in such a way as to form a complex surface that catalyzed various other processes involving RNA molecules. Subsequently, other families of catalytic RNA, such as transfer RNA, have been discovered. Self-splicing RNA molecules with similar structures have been found in fungi and a bacterial virus.

Methods of Study

Many properties of an enzyme are revealed by a study of kinetics, in which the effect of substrate concentration, enzyme concentration, and other factors are studied in terms of their influences on the activity of an enzyme. The classical description of enzyme kinetic behavior, which provides insight into the mode of action of an enzyme, is called the Michaelis-Menten equation.

Another research technique is to "label" a compound by replacing one of its atoms with a similar atom, such as a radioactive isotope, that makes the compound easy to detect. The labeled compound is introduced into the appropriate system, and its fate is discovered. In the early 1950's, Paul Zamecnik demonstrated that ribosomes within the cell are the sites for biosynthesis of proteins, including enzymes, by injecting radioactive amino acids into a rat and analyzing its liver cells a short time later. The ribosomal fraction exhibited most of the radioactivity. Zamecnik was able to separate the various components of liver by a method called differential centrifugation. In this technique, homogenized cells are centrifuged and, because the dense components are most able to overcome the solution resistance (viscosity), they move to the bottom of the centrifuge tube. Samples at different levels in the tube can be analyzed. Proteins (including ribosomes and enzymes) are large and tend to coil, so that they are very dense and are found near the bottom of the tube.

Electrophoresis separates molecules in an applied electric field. The medium is usually a solution or gel through which proteins migrate at different rates because they have different charges. After the proteins of an enzyme have been separated, they can be analyzed by breakdown into their constituent amino acids. Enzyme-catalyzed hydrolysis is employed: Specific enzymes will cleave specific peptide bonds in the protein, with the result that different sets of polypeptide fragments are obtained from each enzyme. This provides the structure of the protein.

The analysis of mixtures can be carried out by different techniques of chromatography. For example, in paper chromatography, an amino acid mixture is spotted at one end of a strip of paper, which is then placed into a specific solvent. As the solvent moves up the paper by capillary action, the various amino acids are drawn up at different rates and separated. Comparison with known amino acids establishes the identities of the components.

Technological advances have permitted instrumental methods of study. A mass spectrometer causes the breakdown of a protein and simultaneously determines the molecular weights of the fragments. Various types of spectrophotometers are used to characterize a material in terms of its spectrum, which shows the wavelengths of light it absorbs. This method has been used to show the change in the spectrum of an enzyme when it binds with a substrate, or inhibitor. RNA can be detected by ultraviolet spectrophotometry.

Finally, X-ray analysis actually provides a detailed picture of the material being analyzed. Several enzymes have been analyzed this way, including enzyme-substrate complexes. All the methods are used to complement one another, and they provide different items of information that increase researchers' understanding of the structure of enzymes and ribozymes and their mode of function.

Context

One of the aims of science is to learn about the nature of life: how living organisms began, how they survive, and what factors control life. Biochemical discoveries often have philosophical and evolutionary implications, and they have shown that there is an underlying similarity in all living things, even at the molecular level.

As a result of learning about the factors that control the processes of life, scientists and medical researchers have been able to develop a greater ability to fight disease. The antibiotic properties of penicillin, discovered by Alexander Fleming in 1928, were later shown to be a result of irreversible inhibition of an enzyme called transpeptidase. This enzyme catalyzes the formation of crosslinks between peptidoglycans, which results in the network that constitutes bacterial cell walls. Incomplete cell walls prevent the normal growth of the bacteria. Since then, many other antibiotics have been developed as a result of the steady increase in scientific understanding of enzymes.

Knowledge of the role of vitamins and metal activators as essential cofactors of enzymes has increased human awareness of dietary intake and nutrition. Many health problems have been identified and remedied by nutritional adjustments. Beriberi is a neurological disorder attributable to a deficiency of thiamine, which is a coenzyme for pyruvic dehydrogenase. This enzyme is required to complete the metabolic breakdown of glucose to provide energy for the cells. Absence of the coenzyme therefore results in muscle weakness, apathy, and other symptoms. Scurvy, known to be a result of ascorbic acid (vitamin C) deficiency, causes blood spots or bruises under the skin, weakness, and eventual death in untreated cases. The most common vitamin deficiency is folic acid deficiency, which is manifested by anemia, weight loss, and weakness.

Many diseases are known in which an enzyme is defective or inactive as a result of a genetically inherited disorder. These diseases include albinism, alkaptonuria, galactosemia, homocystinuria, phenylketonuria, and Tay-Sachs disease. One method of counteracting these is to supply the enzyme to the patient artificially with some sort of time-release process. Genetic research is providing information regarding genetic defects responsible for a variety of diseases, however, and better methods will become available in the future.

Enzyme are also in widespread use even in such common applications as soap powders. In the chemical industry, enzymes have been used since World War I, when bacterial fermentation was used in Great Britain to increase supplies of acetone, required for the production of cordite, the propellant in bullets and shells. The study of enzymes and their mode of action has had profound beneficial effects on humanity. Many improvements in the quality of life, the treatment of disease, and the scientific basis for philosophical ideas about human existence are directly influenced by this increase in awareness and understanding.

Bibliography

Alberts, Bruce, Dennis Bray, Julian Lewis, Martin Raff, Keith Roberts, and James D. Watson. *Molecular Biology of the Cell.* 2d ed. New York: Garland, 1989. This is an excellent text and is easy to read. The illustations, particularly those relating to ribozyme action in chapter 3, are most appropriate. Pertinent sections are found throughout the book, and each chapter contains a list of references.

Baum, Rudy M. "Nobel Prize for Catalytic RNA Found Winners on Separate

Tracks." *Chemical and Engineering News* 67 (December 4, 1989): 31-34. This article provides an excellent review of the research on ribozymes that led to their discovery and that resulted in the award of the 1989 Nobel Prize in Chemistry to Thomas R. Cech and Sidney Altman. References to some of their publications are provided.

Conn, Eric E., and P. K. Stumpf. *Outlines of Biochemistry.* 3d ed. New York: John Wiley & Sons, 1972. Chapters 8, 9, and 19 are enzyme-related and are easy to read. Illustrations of enzyme and cofactor functions are clear and explanatory. Reference lists are provided at the end of each chapter. The appendices contain an excellent overview of biochemical research techniques.

Fieser, Louis F., and Mary Fieser. *Organic Chemistry.* 3d ed. Lexington, Mass.: D. C. Heath, 1956. Chapter 16, on proteins, contains a most informative account of the development of enzyme research and understanding from a historical perspective. Brief biographies of the major scientific figures are included.

Lehninger, Albert L. *Principles of Biochemistry.* New York: Worth, 1982. Chapters 1 and 2 treat the basic cell functions and contain some evolutionary comments. The chapters on enzymes, vitamins, and protein synthesis provide easy-to-read, detailed explanations of the topics. Illustrations and structures are excellent.

Noller, Carl R. *Textbook of Organic Chemistry.* 3d ed. Philadelphia: W. B. Saunders, 1966. Some information on fermentation processes in industry, which are catalyzed by yeast and yeast extracts, is provided.

Stryer, Lubert. *Biochemistry.* 2d ed. San Francisco: W. H. Freeman 1981. Various chapters contain a wealth of information on proteins, protein structure, purification techniques, enzymes, enzyme kinetics, coenzymes, and zymogens. Although this is a college-level text, it is easy to read, and the illustrations and pictures are excellent. Each chapter provides a list of further references.

Tedder, J. M., A. Nechvatal, A. W. Murray, and J. Carnduff. *Basic Organic Chemistry.* New York: John Wiley & Sons, 1972. Chapter 1 has a clear description of enzyme function, and details of enzymes and vitamins and their roles are provided throughout the text. Annotated references are included at the end of each chapter.

Massimo D. Bezoari

Cross-References

Allosteric Regulation and Covalent Modification 65; Central Metabolism Regulation, 411; Exergonic and Endergonic Reactions, 939; Glycolysis and Fermentation, 1219; The Krebs Cycle, 1520; Nutrition and Metabolic Diversity in Microbes, 2001; Proteins, 2272; Ribosomes, 2406; Translation of Messenger RNA to Form Protein, 2647.

ETHOLOGY

Type of life science: Ethology
Other fields of study: Genetics and neurobiology

Ethology is the study of animal behavior from the perspective of zoology. The information acquired through ethology has helped scientists better understand animals in all their variety and has provided the opportunity to look at human behavior from a biological point of view.

Principal terms
ADAPTATION: a structure, physiological process, or behavioral pattern that gives an organism a better chance of surviving and of reproducing
BEHAVIORAL ECOLOGY: the systematic study of the strategies animals use to overcome environmental problems and the adaptive value of those strategies
BEHAVIORISM: the school of psychology that focuses on the investigation of overt behaviors and rejects allusion to inner processes as a means of explaining behavior
COMPARATIVE PSYCHOLOGY: the branch of psychology that uses comparative studies of animals as a means of investigating phenomena such as learning and development
EVOLUTIONARILY STABLE STRATEGY: a behavioral strategy that will persist in a population because alternative strategies, in the context of that population, will be less successful
IMPRINTING: a specialized form of learning characterized by a sensitive period in which an association with an object is formed
SOCIOBIOLOGY: the scientific discipline that examines social behavior in the context of evolutionary theory

Summary of the Phenomenon

Ethology is the branch of zoology that investigates the behavior of animals. Behavior may be defined as all the observable responses an animal makes to internal or external stimuli. Responses may be either movements or secretions; however, the study of behavior is much more than a descriptive account of what an animal does in response to particular stimuli. The ethologist is interested in the how and why questions about the behaviors they observe. Answering such questions requires an understanding of the physiology and ecology of the species studied. Those who study animal behavior are also interested in the ultimate or evolutionary factors affecting behavior.

Ethology is a young science, yet it is also a science with a long history. Prior to the late nineteenth century, naturalists had accumulated an abundance of information about the behavior of animals. This knowledge, although interesting, lacked a theoretical framework. In 1859, Charles Darwin published *On the Origin of Species*, and with it provided a perspective for the scientific study of behavior. Behavior was more central to two of Darwin's later books, *The Descent of Man* (1871) and *Expression of the Emotions of Man and Animals* (1873). By 1973, the science of ethology was sufficiently well developed to be acknowledged by the presentation of the Nobel Prize for Physiology or Medicine to Niko Tinbergen, Konrad Lorenz, and Karl von Frisch for their contributions to the study of behavior. The work of these men was central to the development of modern ethology.

The experimental studies of Karl von Frisch revealed the dance language of the honeybee and ways in which the sensory perception of the bees differed from our own sensory world. An awareness of species-specific sensory abilities has provided an important research area and has emphasized a factor that must be considered in the experimental design and interpretation of many types of behavioral research.

Tinbergen studied behavior in a variety of vertebrate and invertebrate organisms. He was good both at observation of animals in their natural habitat and in the design of simple but elegant experiments. His 1951 book, *The Study of Instinct*, is a classic synthesis of the knowledge that had been gained through the scientific study of animal behavior of that time.

Konrad Lorenz is considered by many to be the founder of ethology, because he discovered and effectively publicized many of the classic phenomena of ethology. Pictures of Lorenz being followed by goslings are almost a standard feature of texts that discuss the specialized form of learning known as imprinting. In natural settings, imprinting allows young animals to identify their parents appropriately. Another contribution of Lorenz was his book *King Solomon's Ring: New Light on Animal Ways*, published in 1952. This extremely readable book raised public awareness of the scientific study of animal behavior and kindled the interest of many who eventually joined the ranks of ethologists.

Many of the features of ethological research characteristic of the work of Lorenz, Tinbergen, and von Frisch have continued to be characteristic of the field. They were concerned that the behavior of animals be understood in the context of the species' natural habitat and that both proximate and ultimate levels of explanation would be examined. Their research strategies have been supplemented by an increase in laboratory-based research and by the introduction of new types of experimental design. These developments have softened the distinctions between ethology and another field of behavioral study, comparative psychology. The focus of comparative psychology is comparative studies of the behavior of nonhuman animals. Initially, questions about learning and development were the major problems investigated in comparative psychology. Although the animals most frequently studied were primates and rodents, those doing the research were interested in gaining insight into the behavior of humans. Comparative psychology was long dominated by behaviorism, a school of thought that assumes that the ultimate basis of behavior is learning. The behaviorists employed rigorous experimental methods. Because such methods require carefully controlled conditions, behavioral research is typically laboratory based, and animals are therefore tested in surroundings remote from their natural environment. Over time, comparative psychology has broadened both the questions it asks and the organisms it studies. The boundaries between comparative psychology and ethology have been further blurred by the rising number of scientists crossing disciplinary lines in their research. Each discipline has learned from the other, and both have also profited from knowledge introduced through neurobiology and behavioral genetics.

Neurobiology investigates the structure and function of the nervous system. One area of ethology that has been directly enriched through neurobiology is the study of sensory perception in animals. The techniques developed in neurobiology allow the investigator to record the response of many individual neurons simultaneously. The neurobiologist examines phenomena such as stimulus filtering at the level of the cell. Stimulus filtering refers to the ability of nerve cells to be selective in their response to stimuli. For example, moths are highly sensitive to sounds in the pitch range of sounds made by the bats that are their chief predators. Neurobiology provides a powerful tool for understanding behavior at the proximate level.

Another source of information for the ethologist is behavioral genetics. Because of the evolutionary context of ethology, it is important to have an understanding of the genetic basis of behavior. If there were no genetic component in behavior, behavior would not be subject to natural selection. (Natural selection refers to the process by which some genes increase in frequency in a population while alternates decrease because the favored genes have contributed to the reproductive success of those organisms that have them.) While the ethological approach to behavior assumes that behavior patterns are the result of interactions between genes and environment, investigators often ask questions about the genetic programming of behavior.

Early ethologists performed isolation and cross-fostering experiments to discover whether behaviors are learned or instinctive. If a behavior appears in an individual that has been reared in isolation without the opportunity to learn, the behavior is considered instinctive. Observing the behavior of an individual reared by parents of a different species is similarly revealing. When behavior patterns of conspecifics appear in such cross-fostered individuals, such behaviors are regarded as instinctive. Instinctive behaviors typically are innate behaviors that are important for survival. For example, one very common instinctive behavior is the begging call of a newly hatched bird. Isolation and cross-fostering experiments are still a part of the experimental repertoire of ethologists, but behavioral genetics permits the asking of more complex questions. For example, a behavior may accurately be labeled instinctive, but it is more revealing to determine the developmental and physiological processes linking a gene or genes to the instinctive behavior.

The ethologist is also interested in determining whether behavior is adaptive. It is not sufficient to identify what seems to be a common-sense advantage of the behavior. It is important to show that the behavior does in fact contribute to reproductive success in those that practice the behavior and that the reasons the behavior is adaptive are those that are hypothesized. When behaviors are tested, they frequently do turn out to be adaptive in the ways hypothesized. This type of research, however, has provided many surprises. Research on the adaptive value of behaviors in coping with environmental problems that affect reproductive success is known as behavioral ecology; this is a major area of modern ethology.

Behavioral ecology addresses a variety of questions, in part because the process of evolution is opportunistic. For any environmental problem there are alternate solutions, and the solution a particular species adopts is dependent upon the possibilities inherent in its genes. Questions addressed include such things as whether a species is using the optimum strategy or how a species benefits from living in a group. Because alternate strategies are possible even within a species, behavioral ecologists are interested in "evolutionarily stable" strategies. An evolutionarily stable strategy is a set of behavioral rules that, when used by a particular proportion of a population, cannot be replaced by any alternative strategy. For example, the sex ratio present in a particular population will determine the optimum sex ratio for the offspring of any individual.

Sociobiology is another major area of modern ethology. Sociobiology examines animal social behavior within the framework of evolution. Animal species vary in the degree of social behavior they exhibit; other variables include group size and the amount of coordination of activities occurring within the group. The sociobiologist is interested in a number of questions, but prominent among them are the reasons for grouping. Hypotheses such as defense against predators or facilitation of reproduction can be tested. The particular advantage or advantages gained by grouping varies among species. Two important concepts in sociobiology are kin selection and inclusive fitness.

Kin selection refers to the differential reproduction of genes that affect the survival of offspring or closely related kin. Behavior such as the broken-wing display of the killdeer is an example. The behavior carries risk but would be promoted by selection if the offspring of individuals using the display were protected from predators often enough to compensate for the risk. Inclusive fitness is the term used to recognize the concept that fitness includes the total genotype, including those genes that may lower the individual's survival as the price of leaving more genes in surviving kin. The concepts of kin selection and inclusive fitness help to address one problem raised by Darwin, the question of altruistic behavior. Ethology is a young science but a very exciting one, because there are so many questions that can be asked about animal behavior within the context of evolution.

Methods of Study

The methods and tools of ethology cover the entire spectrum of complexity. One simple, but demanding, method is to collect normative data about a species. In its simplest form, the scientist observes what an animal does and writes it down in a field notebook. Finding and following the animal, coping with field conditions such as bad weather and rugged terrain, and keeping field equipment in operating condition add challenge and variety to this approach. The ethologist uses various techniques to get data as unbiased as possible. One of these is to choose a focal animal at random (or on a rotation) and observe the focal animal for a specific amount of time before switching observation to another member of the population. This prevents bias in which individuals and which behaviors are observed. The sampling of an individual's behavior at timed intervals is an even more effective way of avoiding bias.

When all or most of an animal's behavioral repertoire is known, a list known as an ethogram can be constructed. This catalog can be organized into appropriate categories based on function. Ethograms provide useful baseline information about the behavior of a species. For animals that are difficult or impossible to follow, radio-tracking techniques have been developed. Collars that emit radio signals have been designed for many animals. Miniaturization has made it possible for radio tracking to be used even on relatively small animals.

In field studies, animals are often marked in some way so that observers are able to follow individual animals. A number of techniques have been developed, including banding birds with colored acrylic bands. Color combinations can be varied so that each member of the population has a unique combination. Marking allows the observer to get information such as individual territory boundaries and to determine which animals interact.

Models are frequently used in experiments. For example, a model can be used to determine whether individuals in a species need to learn to identify certain classes of predators. Models were used in many of the classic experiments in ethology. Modern technology has allowed the development of much more sophisticated models. One of the most interesting is a "bee" that can perform a waggle dance (used by bees to indicate location) so effectively that its hivemates can find the food source. Whether a model is simple or sophisticated, it can provide a tool to determine the cues that trigger an animal's response.

Neurobiologists use electrodes and appropriate equipment to stimulate and record the responses of neurons. They can also stimulate specific regions of the nervous system by using tiny tubes to deliver hormones or neurotransmitters. Genetic technology has made it possible to examine the deoxyribonucleic acid (DNA) of individuals in a species. This tool can be used, for example, to determine whether females in monogamous species are completely monogamous or whether some of their offspring are fathered by males other than their mates.

Tape recorders have become very important in studies of animal vocalizations. Recorders are used in two ways. The animal's vocalizations may be recorded and the recording used to make sound spectrographs for analysis. The recordings may also be used to determine whether individuals can discriminate between the vocalizations of neighboring and non-neighboring individuals in their species. Playbacks can also be used to simulate intruders in the territory of an individual and can be applied to many other experimental situations in both the field and laboratory.

The methods used by ethologists are as varied as the problems they investigate. Because the skill of the observer is still a vital link in the investigation of animal behavior, ethology remains one of the more approachable areas of scientific investigation.

Context

The investigation of animal behavior has a number of benefits, both practical and abstract. Some animals are pests, and knowledge of their behavior can be used to manage them. For example, synthetic pheromones have been used to attract members of some insect species. The insects may then be sampled or killed, depending upon the application. To the extent that researchers develop behaviorally based pest management strategies and reduce pesticide use, they will be promoting our own safety as well as that of other species.

It is sometimes important for humans to be able to understand the communication signals of other species and the characteristics of their sensory perception. The knowledgeable individual can recognize the cues that indicate risk that a dog might bite, for example, and can also avoid behavior that the dog will regard as threatening. Understanding the behavior of the wild animals most likely to be encountered in one's neighborhood is an important factor in peaceful coexistence.

Understanding the behavioral repertoires of animals that may be selected as pets is useful in making an appropriate choice of a pet. Some animals need more care and attention than others, and if such care will not be given, a less demanding pet should be chosen. Once a pet has been selected, knowledge of its behavioral repertoire will then be useful in understanding how to provide an appropriate environment and proper care.

The study of animal behavior is providing one of the more fascinating areas of evolutionary biology. Ethology has demonstrated more effectively than most fields of study how diverse the solutions to a given problem can be and has provided insight into human behavior from a biological perspective. Knowledge of animal behavior also enriches human lives simply by satisfying some of our natural curiosity about animals.

Bibliography

Clutton-Brock, T. H., and Paul Harvey, eds. *Readings in Sociobiology*. San Francisco: W. H. Freeman, 1978. This anthology provides short selections from a number of the scientists who have made contributions to the theoretical base of sociobiology. The text is sparsely illustrated with some graphs, tables, drawings, and diagrams. References are provided at the end of each chapter. There are references for the introductory sections and an index at the end of the text.

Daly, Martin, and Margo Wilson. *Sex, Evolution and Behavior*. North Scituate, Mass.: Duxbury Press, 1978. This is a well-written synthesis that examines the phenomenon of sex and sexual strategies in an evolutionary context. Illustrations include graphs, tables, and a small number of black-and-white photographs. The book has a glossary, bibliography, and index.

Dawkins, Richard. *The Selfish Gene*. New York: Oxford University Press, 1976. An extremely well-written book. Dawkins gives a persuasive presentation of the concept of the gene as the unit of natural selection. In addition, he provides an excellent account of evolutionarily stable strategies. No glossary, but terms are well explained in the text. Index and bibliography.

Lorenz, Konrad. *King Solomon's Ring: New Light on Animal Ways.*. New York: Thomas Y. Crowell, 1952. A delightful book touching a number of different animals. Lorenz writes out of his personal experience as a keen observer of animals. He communicates good information in an informal and anecdotal style. The vocabulary is nontechnical. Illustrations consist of line drawings on page margins. Index.

Moss, Cynthia. *Portraits in the Wild*. 2d ed. Chicago: University of Chicago Press, 1982. This is a very readable anthology covering many of the mammals of eastern Africa. The book is illustrated with a number of good black-and-white photos. It also includes a map of eastern Africa. There is both a bibliography and an index.

Owen, Jennifer. *Feeding Strategy*. Chicago: University of Chicago Press, 1980. This book provides an interesting account of the various ways in which animals get their food. It is illustrated with drawings, diagrams, and both color and black-and-white photographs. There is a short glossary and an index. Includes a list of readings with short descriptions.

Wilson, Edward O. *Sociobiology*. Cambridge, Mass.: The Belknap Press of Harvard University Press, 1975. This book is a classic; it synthesizes a massive amount of information to illustrate the key concepts of sociobiology. The style is succinct. The book is challenging to read, but more because of the format and type size than the style. Illustrations include black-and-white photographs, drawings, tables, and graphs. It has a glossary, bibliography, and index.

Donna Janet Schroeder

Cross-References

THE ORIGIN OF EUKARYOTES

Types of life science: Evolutionary biology and the origin of life (paleontology)
Other fields of study: Cell biology (cytology), developmental biology (embryology),
  genetics, and microbiology

*Eukaryotes, or "true" cells, contain smaller structures called organelles, such as
the nucleus and mitochondria, which house chromosomes and special membranes.
Organelles are wrapped in two or more membranes. By contrast, prokaryote cells,
such as bacteria and cyanobacteria, contain a thread of DNA and membranes that
are naked in the cytoplasm.*

  Principal terms
  AUTOGENOUS: arising anew—in this case, resulting from structures
    synthesized for the first time because of mutations in the genetic
    code
  CHLOROPLAST: a membrane-filled sac containing chlorophyll and other
    photosynthetic pigments; chloroplasts also contain DNA, RNA, and
    ribosomes and replicate themselves
  ENDOCYTOBIONT: a remnant-organism living inside a cell that retains
    some of its original genes (DNA and RNA) and shares others with
    the nuclear chromosomes of the host
  ENDOSYMBIONT: an autonomous organism living inside a host cell;
    although the cells exchange molecules and regulate growth, they have
    independent genetic systems and may live independently
  MITOCHONDRIA: they are the cell's "power plant," where glucose is
    oxidized to carbon dioxide and the high-energy compound ATP is
    made; cells usually contain many such sacs
  ORGANELLES: structures within the cell that have specific molecular
    functions and that may have originated from an endocytobiont
  PHASED GROWTH: growth that is characteristic of eukaryotes, in which a
    cell clock governs phases of the cell cycle; the clock entrains to its
    environment so that all members of a population may experience the
    same phase simultaneously
  PHYLOGENY: a classification system that assigns an individual to a
    hierarchy of groupings; each group has features in common
  SEME: a group of genetic characters, acquired through natural selection,
    that function together and are responsible for shared features
  UNDULIPODIUM: the kind of flagellum found in eukaryotes, it is a tube
    surrounding eleven pairs of microtubules that are embedded in the
    cytoplasm

Summary of the Phenomenon
All life is composed of cells, and two major types of cells exist. "True cells," or

eukaryotes, contain smaller bodies, or organelles, within them. Each type of organelle is responsible for a different cell function. Typical organelles, in addition to the nucleus, are mitochondria, which oxidize glucose to carbon dioxide, and chloroplasts, which strip hydrogen from water and convert carbon dioxide to glucose. Organelles are enclosed in two or three membranes. Eukaryotes first appeared in the fossil record about 1.5 billion years ago.

The prokaryote cell, the second major type of cell, lacks a nucleus and other membrane-wrapped inclusions. It is more primitive, and it arose before eukaryotic cells. All bacteria are prokaryotes, including the cyanobacteria (also called bluegreen algae). Unlike other bacteria, the cyanobacteria use water as the hydrogen donor in photosynthesis. The membranes involved in photosynthesis range throughout the bacterial cell. Prokaryote cells are typically much smaller than eukaryote cells. The earliest fossil prokaryotes are believed to be 3.5 billion years old.

Eukaryotes descended from prokaryotes in an unknown way. Three alternative explanations have been championed, two of which involve symbiosis. In the serial endosymbiosis theory (SET), the eukaryote cell emerged from an archaeobacterium-like ancestor and its bacterial endocytobiont. Sequential invasions resulted in the establishment of a "cell cooperative." Each successful invasion may have become integrated through a similar pathway.

First, host and symbiont each derive value from the other. The partnership may become unstable, however, as the symbiont loses genes to the chromosomes of the host. Genes of the host and the guest guide guest function. Ultimately, the chromosome of the cytobiont produces only a part of itself. Integration of the dual function of guest and host becomes the work of the chromosome in the host nucleus. Separate invasions accounted for mitochondria, chloroplasts and other plastids, and the flagellum. Other organelles from cytobionts include microbodies and parts of the host nucleus. Another theory, the "progenote" theory, also proposes a symbiotic origin. Both eukaryote and prokaryote, however, are believed to have evolved from a common ancestor, the progenote, about 3.5 billion years ago.

The third theory favors a direct, filial or "autogenous" evolution of the eukaryote: Cell organelles evolved progressively by the usual mutations and rearrangements of DNA in the cell's nucleus. A leading proponent of the autogenous evolution theory recognizes the symbiotic origin of mitochondria and chloroplasts, but this theory claims that the organelles contain proteins from both host and symbiont.

Each theory has its strong and weak points. Serial endosymbiosis theory (SET) is supported by three lines of evidence: the similarity of chloroplasts to prokaryotes, including a common sequence of nucleic acids in the RNA of their ribosomes; the substitution of symbiotic bluegreen algae for chloroplasts in a small group of algae called the Glaucophyta; and the survival of "intermediate" and "ancestral" species in the current biota. Another organelle, the mitochondrium, also retains ancestral DNA and is similar to several different kinds of aerobic bacteria.

A weakness in SET is the presence of eukaryotes that lack, and presumably never had, chloroplasts or mitochrondria. Yet the nucleus, which is the elaborate command center of the eukaryote, is present and performs functions that have been attributed to endosymbionts. The weakness is offset by substantial, if not generally accepted, evidence that the nuclear cytoplasm was an archaeobacterium: The nucleus is partially endosymbiotic.

A major weakness with the progenote theory is the absence of fossil progenotes and early eukaryotes. Although both kinds of cells are believed to have arisen 3.5 billion years ago, the only evidence for an organism simpler than a prokaryote is a theoretical argument. The earliest fossil eukaryotes are the acritarchs. Since they appeared 1.5 billion years ago, this leaves a gap of 2 billion years.

The autogenous, or direct filiation, theory argues that organelles arose by a selective process associated with feeding. The internal discharge of enzymes to digest food inclusions creates a threat to the cell's own cytoplasm unless the inclusion can be wrapped in a resistant membrane. In other words, a cell containing a nucleus wrapped in membranes arose as the survivor in a mutation that would have released an otherwise fatal load of digestive enzymes into the body of the cell. The origin of the nucleus has not been traced to an endosymbiont, although the origin of the nuclear-cytoplasm and some of the nuclear membranes has been attributed to endosymbionts. A serious weakness of the autogenous theory is the need to account for the large number of simultaneous nonlethal mutations that would be necessary to explain the appearance of the nucleus.

An endosymbiosis is established following a particular sequence of interactions between a host and an endosymbiont. The guest seeks out its host by "tasting" the host, then enters through the host's cell membrane. The guest must avoid being digested by the lysosomes of the host. The symbiont increases in number and reaches and maintains an equilibrium density in this and subsequent generations of host cells. Such accommodation may require hundreds, even thousands, of generations. Ultimately, symbionts and hosts become mutually dependent.

Methods of Study

All the methods employed in the study of cells, the study of bacteria, and the study of fossils have probably been employed in the search for the origin of the eukaryote cell. Light and electron microscopy, in particular, are essential for the study of structure of cells and organelles.

The SET has stimulated research on the relatedness of prokaryotes and their possible relationships to certain organelles in the eukaryote cell. Many approaches help determine relatedness. Common ancestry is indicated by identical sequences of deoxyribonucleic acid (DNA) base pairs; this research is carried out by sequencing DNA and ribonucleic acid (RNA) as they occur along the chromosome. All the tools of modern genetics have been enlisted in the study of relatedness of bacteria, including classical genetic recombination. Relatedness is also measured by comparing metabolic pathways and the enzymes they involve. Another approach is to compare molecular structure. Such studies employ X-ray crystallography, spectroscopy, electrophoresis, chromatography, and antibody recognition, as well as classical biochemistry and enzymology.

The "direct approach" reveals stages in the development of a stable symbiosis. Bacteria and single-cell eukaryotes are placed together in a two-membered culture. The sequence of interactions necessary to establish internal symbiosis is determined. Potential symbionts are isolated from other hosts by procedures that include freezing and thawing, sonic disruption, and centrifugation.

Special properties of symbionts such as the ability to escape detection by the host's immune system, have been studied with the indirect fluorescent antibody test. Their ability to resist digestion has been explained as a resistance to the enzymes contained in another organelle, called the lysosome, and the ability of the vesicle containing the partner to avoid attachment by the lysosome. Structural analyses of hosts evaluate the effects of a symbiotic relationship. Nutritional studies with both stable and radioactive isotopes can trace the fate of chemical elements that are essential for growth and reproduction. Such studies show the types and amounts of materials that are exchanged between host and symbiont.

Context

Endosymbiosis explains many improbables in the evolution of the eukaryote cell. It also indirectly addresses the course of the evolution of eukaryote cells into multicellularity, communication systems among separate living systems, and even the bases on which populations and communities are organized.

Large groups of genetic traits somehow were acquired by simple organisms in such a way that no intermediate, developmental versions of the organisms appear in the fossil record. For example, features such as the nuclear membrane are common to all eukaryotes; a blastula-stage larva is present in all animals. These prominent features are found in all members of a fairly high taxonomical grouping, such as a class or phylum. According to SET, the most probable cause of this phenomenon is that the genetic characters were acquired when a large number of genes was incorporated simultaneously from an endosymbiont. The shared traits of such acquired characters are called semes. Semes that are common to all members of a kingdom or phylum are probably impossible to alter. A feature of evolutionary theory called "punctuated equilibrium" can be satisfactorily explained by the acquisition of semes through endosymbiosis. Punctuated equilibrium is part of the concept that evolution is not a constant process; rather, there are long periods when an organism does not change, then brief periods during which evolutionary changes occur.

One such seme is made possible by a "clock" that coordinates genetic transcriptions and prevents lethal interactions. The same clock that directs the phased growth and differentiation of the cell also permits the cell to recognize cyclic happenings in its environment. Through natural selection, the clock directs the twin thrusts of evolution. Two features are exposed to natural selection simultaneously: the trait and the timing of its expression.

This time control coordinates mutually beneficial traits among unrelated organisms. Two species, free-living or symbiotic, become associated as "chronobionts."

The advantages bestowed by the relationship are clock-controlled and are based as much on the timing as on the act itself.

Chronobionts exploit time relationships. Their associations may increase efficiency of resource use, reduce competition for resources, or reduce mortality. Free-living eukaryote cells, populations, and biological communities are structured by the same clock. The same clock coordinates gene expression within that multicelled cooperative of former bacteria, the eukaryote cell.

Recognition of chronobiosis simplified ecology. To understand the consequences of environmental disturbances is to understand how the disturbance may destabilize the time (and space) relationships within the biological community. For example, nutrient pollution of aquatic communities destabilizes chronobionts and promotes the growth of pathogens of the chronobionts and of man.

Upswings in waterborne diseases such as cholera may be traced to a seasonal interaction of the bacteria that spread the disease with their aquatic hosts—several species of copepod crustaceans. The bacteria seek a special kind of egg that delays development and then undergo a kind of dormancy themselves. The cell clocks of the eukaryote synchronize the release of dormant eggs. The cholera bacteria attach to the eggs and use them as a storage incubator while waiting for a new host.

Bibliography

Kwang, W. Jeon, ed. *Intracellular Symbiosis*. New York: Harcourt Brace Jovanovich, 1983. Presents a technical working account of the many facets of the symbiotic partnerships in single cells.

Lee, John J., and J. F. Fredrick, eds. *Endocytobiology III*. New York: New York Academy of Sciences, 1987. Individual papers in a symposium document the progress being made to illumine and test the theory of endosymbiotic origin of eukaryote cells. Excellent editing makes this technical volume readable at college and even advanced high school levels.

Margulis, Lynn. *Symbiosis in Cell Evolution*. New York: W. H. Freeman, 1981. A well-written and detailed essay of the evolution of eukaryote cells. It describes prokaryotes from the earliest fossil record and traces their evolution to and beyond the fossil record of eukaryotes. Presents likely scenarios of earth's environment from the dawn of life until the present. Organelles generally accepted as having originated as prokaryote endosymbionts are traced to the prokaryotes that initially invaded.

Margulis, Lynn, and David Bermudes. "Symbiosis as a Mechanism of Evolution: Status of Cell Symbiosis Theory." In their *Symbiosis*. Vol. 1. Glenside, Pa.: Balaban, 1986. A brief overview of the leading theories of eukaryote origin. Major developments in the serial endosymbiosis theory (SET) are summarized. Semes common to kingdoms and phylums are identified. The time and course of their origin is seen to parallel the fossil record and to explain the phylogeny of these groups.

Schenk, H. E. A., and W. Schwemmler, eds. *Endocytobiology II: Intracellular Space as Oligogenetic Ecosystem*. Hawthorne, N.Y.: Walter de Gruyter, 1983. This volume presents papers from a symposium on many aspects of symbiosis within cells, including theory, physical and molecular biology, and the significance of the phenomenon.

Ray Stross

Cross-References

Eukaryotic Gene Organization, 871; Positive and Negative Eukaryotic Transcriptional Control, 895; Evolution: A Historical Perspective, 903; Eukaryotic Gene Regulation, 1111; The Definition of Life, 1564; The Origin of Life, 1572; The Origin of Multicellularity, 1804; Nuclear Structure, 1972; Prokaryotic Cell Structure, 2210.

EUKARYOTIC GENE ORGANIZATION

Type of life science: Genetics
Other fields of study: Genetic regulation in eukaryotes and molecular biology

Eukaryotic organisms (that is, protists, fungi, plants, and animals) have large quantities of DNA. Eukaryotic DNA is widely diverse, consisting of repetitive noncoding DNA regions and clusters of evolutionarily related coding DNA (genes). Each gene is internally complex, consisting of control regions, coding regions, and noncoding regions.

Principal terms

C VALUE: the quantity of haploid (single copy) DNA per cell of any organism of a species; it is a distinct characteristic of that species

COEVOLUTION: evolution in which two or more genes evolve together, either from a common gene ancestor or by recombination of common DNA regions

EUCHROMATIN: true chromatin, that is, DNA which is coding for protein; a chromosome region containing active genes producing messenger RNA for protein production

EXON: a coding region within the nucleotide sequence of a gene—for example, DNA that encodes RNA for encoding protein

GENE CONVERSION: a process whereby genes having similar nucleotide sequences exchange genetic information by genetic recombination, thereby becoming more similar and coevolving

HETEROCHROMATIN: noncoding, inactive DNA regions, where there are no genes actively encoding protein; some of these regions may be active during certain developmental stages

INTRONS: noncoding nucleotide sequences within a gene; these sequences are spliced out of messenger RNA before protein translation begins

PSEUDOGENES: DNA regions on a chromosome that do not encode protein, although they are very similar to various active genes

REPETITIVE DNA: short stretches of DNA on a chromosome, usually ten to twenty nucleotides long, that are repeated thousands of times

TANDEM GENE CLUSTERS: groupings of genes whose proteins have related functions, probably because the genes have coevolved by duplication and recombination

Summary of the Phenomenon

In living organisms on earth, the inheritable genetic information is nucleic acid: either deoxyribonucleic acid (DNA) or ribonucleic acid (RNA), or both. In eukaryotes (organisms whose cells are highly compartmentalized with special structures called organelles), both nucleic acids are utilized. DNA is the storage form for genetic information; RNA is an intermediate messenger molecule between the DNA and its expressed form, protein. In cells, proteins act both as structural molecules and as catalysts, substances that control cellular chemical reactions. DNA encodes RNA which encodes protein.

Structurally, DNA is two parallel polynucleotide chains. Each chain consists of a seemingly endless series of nucleotides; each nucleotide consists of a phosphate-sugar-nitrogenous base unit. There are four nitrogenous base types: adenine, guanine, cytosine, and thymine. To hold the two DNA polynucleotide chains together, an adenine nucleotide on one polynucleotide chain pairs with a thymine nucleotide (by a hydrogen bond) on the companion polynucleotide chain, and vice versa. A guanine nucleotide on one chain hydrogen bonds to a cytosine nucleotide on the companion chain, and vice versa. Each DNA polynucleotide chain is a virtually endless series of adenines, guanines, cytosines, and thymines.

The ordering of these polynucleotide nitrogenous bases serves as the genetic code, or information content of the DNA. Approximately one thousand nucleotides are usually sufficient to encode a specific protein. Such a protein-encoding group of DNA polynucleotides is called a gene. The DNA polynucleotide chain does not end here, however; a typical DNA molecule can have between 10 million and 100 million nucleotides, which (with protein structural support) form a chromosome. Each chromosome contains enough genetic information to encode hundreds of proteins. Therefore, a chromosome (DNA) contains many genes, each of which encodes a unique type of protein.

Different eukaryotic species have varying numbers of chromosomes per cell. For example, fruit flies (*Drosophila melanogaster*) have four chromosome types, with two copies of each, giving them a total of eight chromosomes per cell. Humans (*Homo sapiens sapiens*) have twenty-three chromosome types, with two copies of each, giving a total of forty-six chromosomes per cell. Chimpanzees (*Pan troglodytes*) have two copies of twenty-four chromosome types, giving them forty-eight per cell. Because different eukaryotic species have different chromosome numbers, they have different quantities of DNA and, therefore, different numbers and types of genes.

The amount of haploid (that is, single copy) DNA per cell of a given species is called its C value. For example, most mammalian species (such as humans, bears, rats, and whales) have C values of approximately 3 billion base pairs; that is, there are 3 billion nucleotide pairs per cell. Crustaceans have approximately 2 billion base pairs per cell, worms have approximately 100 million base pairs per cell, and bacteria have approximately 1 million base pairs per cell. The basic C value pattern is one of increasing DNA content with increasingly complex organisms. This would seem reasonable, since more complex species would require more proteins for catalysis and structural organization and therefore would need more genes (DNA).

Nevertheless, certain phyla, or groups of species, have tremendous C value ranges. Such phyla include angiosperms (flowering plants such as roses, corn, and maple trees), amphibians (such as frogs, toads, and salamanders), and insects. Among the angiosperms, some plant species have as few as 400 million base pairs of DNA per cell, whereas other plant species have as many as 100 billion base pairs of DNA per cell. Certain plant, amphibian, and insect species have more DNA per cell than do humans. The question of why seemingly less complicated organisms should need more DNA per cell than highly complex organisms is known as the C value paradox.

Experiments in DNA reassociation kinetics have yielded some very unusual data. DNA that has been isolated from any given eukaryotic species can be separated into its component polynucleotide chains. Allowing the two DNA polynucleotide chains to reassemble reveals an interesting pattern: A portion of the DNA reassociates slowly, a second portion a little faster, and a third portion very quickly. These three DNA reassociation components, found in every eukaryotic species, are termed slow component, intermediate component, and fast component. The percentage of total DNA found within each component varies from species to species. For example, fruit fly DNA is approximately 17 percent fast, 12 percent intermediate, and 70 percent slow. Mouse DNA is approximately 24 percent fast, 11 percent intermediate, and 58 percent slow.

Fast-reassociating DNA has been identified as highly repetitive DNA—short stretches of nucleotides, such as ATATAT, that are repeated over and over again, up to hundreds of thousands of times. Such sequences would find one another rapidly during DNA reassociation. The intermediate component has been identified as moderately repetitive DNA, longer DNA stretches (for example, GAAAAATGT) that are repeated over and over. Moderately repetitive DNA sequences would require a little more time for reassociation. Slow-reassociating DNA has been identified as nonrepetitive DNA, long stretches of nucleotides that do not repeat. Nonrepeating DNA nucleotides would require considerable time to reassociate.

Highly and moderately repetitive DNA components are believed to contribute to DNA structure. Nonrepetitive DNA is the site of genes, regions approximately one thousand nucleotides long that encode protein. Therefore, nonrepetitive DNA is also associated with euchromatin, those chromosome regions where genes are actively producing messenger RNA (mRNA) for protein production. Highly and moderately repetitive DNA are associated with heterochromatin, inactive chromosome regions where no genes are producing RNA.

Many eukaryotic genes are bunched together into tandem gene clusters, with one gene coming right after another. Such tandem gene clusters belong to gene families, because they usually consist of genes that encode proteins having identical or similar functions during various stages of organismal development. These genes invariably have common, or consensus, nucleotide sequences within their structures. Consequently, the members of a gene cluster probably evolved from a single ancestral gene in the distant past.

The tandem gene clusters that have been most thoroughly studied include the alpha globin, beta globin, histone, and immunoglobulin gene clusters. The human alpha globin gene cluster, located on chromosome sixteen, consists of five genes. The alpha-1, alpha-2, and zeta-2 genes encode proteins that help to construct hemoglobin, a tetrameric (four-protein) enzyme that transports oxygen in the red blood cells of humans and other animals. Pseudo-alpha-1 and pseudo-zeta-1 are pseudogenes, genes having almost enough nucleotides to encode a functional protein, but failing because of mutations.

The human beta globin gene cluster, located on chromosome eleven, consists of six genes: beta, delta, pseudo-beta-1, A-gamma, G-gamma, and epsilon. The beta globin genes produce proteins that combine with the alpha globin proteins to construct hemoglobin. Two alpha globin gene proteins combine with two beta globin gene proteins to construct tetrameric hemoglobin. Different alpha and beta globins are produced during various stages of human development. Human fetal hemoglobin consists of two alpha globins and two gamma globins; human adult hemoglobin consists of two alpha globins and either two delta globins or, usually, two beta globins. Other vertebrate species have similar alpha and beta globin gene clusters.

The nucleosome is a structure that helps to fold and package DNA into a compact chromosome in eukaryotic cell nuclei. Each nucleosome is constructed from five histone gene proteins: H1, H2A, H2B, H3, and H4. In both fruit flies (*Drosophila melanogaster*) and sea urchins, the histone-encoding genes are clustered within chromosome regions that are six thousand nucleotides long. In *Drosophila*, the histone gene order is H1, H2A, H3, H2B, and H4. In sea urchins, the order is H1, H3, H4, H2A, and H2B.

The immunoglobulin (antibody) genes of vertebrates define an incredible model of gene arrangement and complexity. In immune system cells called B and T lymphocytes, immunoglobulin genes encode protein antibodies. These genes cover more than 10 million nucleotides. The immunoglobulin gene cluster consists of eight constant (C) genes covering 200,000 nucleotides, a 4,000-nucleotide-long J gene, a 10,000-nucleotide-long D gene, and countless variable (V) genes. When a lymphocyte decides to manufacture an antibody, one C, one J, one D, and one V gene combine by chromosomal rearrangement and copy a messenger RNA, which will be used to make the appropriate protein antibody. Lymphocytes can manufacture antibodies against virtually any foreign invader (such as a virus or bacterium) that enters the body. What is not understood, however, is how the lymphocyte "knows" which variable (V) gene to combine with the C, J, and D genes so that the correct antibody is made.

Such gene clusters have coevolved over millions of years, through many species, from one originator gene in some distant ancestral species. A gene many have duplicated, with its twin copy then accumulating mutations to the point that it made a slightly different protein with slightly different functions than the original gene. Such a process could repeat itself many times, resulting in an extended family of linked related genes. Some genes formed by such a process might become inactive by mutation, thus creating pseudogenes. Additionally, two genes of different origin might evolve together into similar genes by exchanging nucleotides having similar sequences, a process called gene conversion.

Outside the eukaryotic chromosome, a few genes are located in small, circular, cytoplasmic chromosomes called plasmids and within certain organelles, such as the mitochondria and chloroplasts. Lynn Margulis has proposed that mitochondria, the organelles where cellular respiration occurs, are the evolutionary remains of a formerly independent cellular life-form that began a symbiotic relationship inside a host cell. The fact that mitochondria have their own DNA and that this DNA replicates independently of the cell support Margulis' hypothesis.

The genes of eukaryotic chromosomes are not necessarily stable. Transposable elements, also called transposons and "jumping genes," are blocks of genes that can copy themselves and move to a different chromosomal location. Transposons, discovered by Barbara McClintock, the recipient of the 1983 Nobel Prize in Physiology or Medicine, probably have some role in eukaryotic gene regulation. Some transposons may have evolved into the viruses that parasitize all cellular life.

In eukaryotic cells, the thousand or so nucleotides that compose each gene usually are sectioned into coding regions (exons) that encode protein and noncoding regions (introns) that do not encode protein. The introns are interspersed between the exons. When a gene is active, or expressed, a molecule called RNA polymerase transcribes the gene, reading the nucleotide sequence for the gene and manufacturing a complementary messenger RNA molecule. Before the ribosome translates protein from this messenger RNA, the introns are spliced out of the messenger RNA, and the remaining exons are joined together in the correct order. Thus, the proper protein can be manufactured by the ribosome. Some genes can encode more than one protein simply by splicing out different introns each time a particular protein is needed. Therefore, an intron can sometimes serve as an exon, and vice versa.

Immediately preceding each gene's coding region is a sequence of several hundred nucleotides that serves as the gene's control region. This region is activated or inactivated by the actions of various hormones. If a gene is activated, RNA polymerase enters the control region, identifies the nucleotides GGTCAATCT at about eighty nucleotides before the coding region and TATAAT at about ten nucleotides before the coding region; it then starts making messenger RNA. If a repressor hormone blocks these sequences, however, the RNA polymerase cannot make messenger RNA, and the gene becomes inactive.

Methods of Study

The organization of eukaryotic genes has been studied by a variety of very sophisticated experimental techniques, including cytogenetics, DNA kinetic reassociation, cloning, radioactive probes, DNA sequencing, and mutagenesis. The explosive growth of molecular biology and biotechnology in the 1970's and 1980's has greatly enhanced understanding of how eukaryotic genes are arranged and promises to reveal many further breakthroughs.

Cytogenetics is the study of chromosome structure and chromosomal abnormalities at the cellular level. Essentially, the process involves removing specified cells from an organism (for example, human fetal amniotic cells or fruit fly larval salivary glands), extracting the nuclear material (chromosomes) of these cells, and appropriately staining the chromosomes for subsequent microscopic analysis. For a given staining procedure, all chromosomes of a species will stain in exactly the same pattern. Darkly staining chromosome regions are considered to be inactive heterochromatin; lightly staining regions are euchromatin. In various developmental stages of some species, certain very active euchromatic regions will expand, or "puff." Comparisons of chromosomal staining patterns between different species is useful in evolutionary studies; the patterns of human and chimpanzee chromosomes, for example, are amazingly similar.

DNA reassociation kinetic experiments involve separating the two polynucleotide strands of the DNA molecule by heating the molecule and applying a combination of various chemicals. The DNA then is allowed to reassociate over time as it cools. At various times, however, the reassociation is stopped by the addition of chemical inhibitors. Addition of an enzyme called a restriction exonuclease digests and removes any DNA that has not reassociated. The remaining double-stranded reassociated DNA can be measured by methods such as spectrophotometry. In this way, the rate of DNA reassociation can be measured, and specific reassociating DNA regions can be identified.

Gene cloning is a very important method in biotechnology. A specific gene that encodes a specific protein can be isolated from the cells of an organism. This gene can be inserted into the DNA of a plasmid or a virus. The plasmid or viral vector is then used to get the cloned gene into the cells of a convenient host organism such as the bacterium *Escherichia coli*. The host organism can be grown in the laboratory in mass quantities; the cloned gene can be preserved, and the protein made by the gene can be harvested in large quantities for medical, research, or agricultural uses.

Once a gene is cloned, it can be grown in the presence of a radioactive isotope such as phosphorus 32. The isotope is incorporated into the DNA of the gene so that the gene becomes radioactively labeled. Its precise location can then be traced in experiments. Radioactively labeled cloned genes have been used to probe chromosomes; they bind to active euchromatin. Radioactively labeled short DNA repeat sequences, such as AGAGAG, bind to heterochromatin.

Once a gene is cloned, it can be nucleotide-sequenced by a very elaborate and tedious series of experiments. The exact order of nucleotides can be determined for the gene so that control regions, exons, and introns can be identified. Furthermore, the amino acid sequence of the encoded protein can be predicted. Mutagenized genes, in which changes have occurred in the gene nucleotide sequence, can also be studied to determine important control regions in the gene.

Context

An understanding of the organization of eukaryotic genes is critical to a scientific comprehension of life and how it operates. Genes are the code for all aspects of cells—in fact, for all aspects of all living organisms. DNA encodes RNA, which encodes protein. If it is known where genes are located, how they are organized, and how their nucleotide sequences are constituted, then the discovering of how genes are controlled and how they interact with one another can begin. The implications of this work may be enormous: eradicating cancer, extending longevity, and treating many diseases.

Eukaryotic gene organization has attracted so much attention that the governments of the United States, Soviet Union, Japan, and several European countries have committed large budgets to the Human Genome Project, which is attempting to determine the polynucleotide sequence of every human chromosome by the first decade of the twenty-first century. Heterochromatic and euchromatic regions will be mapped so that scientists will have a much more comprehensive view of human genes, where they are, what they encode, and when they act during development.

Any given gene is a small segment of a long DNA molecule called a chromosome. A gene's polynucleotide sequence consists of an arrangement of four types of nucleotide bases: adenine, guanine, cytosine, and thymine. A given gene consists of approximately one thousand nucleotides. Although the four types of nucleotide bases seem to be in a totally random order, it is the order of these bases (for example, AGCCTCGAAT . . .) that determines the genetic code: the code for every protein made by every cell of every living organism. The DNA of a gene encodes a messenger RNA, which encodes a specific protein. In cells, proteins are both catalysts for speeding chemical reactions and structural molecules; proteins determine everything about every living organism, from the organism's development to its shape.

Each gene has a control region preceding its coding region. Chemical messengers called hormones act at the control region in such a way that protein is either made or not made, depending upon the type of hormone controlling the gene. Other regions of DNA do not encode protein; instead, they consist of repeated nucleotides that may help to provide structure for the chromosome or may help to regulate the activities of genes. Additional genes are located outside the cell nucleus in mitochondrial DNA and plasmid DNA, collectively known as extrachromosomal DNA.

Bibliography

Alberts, Bruce, Dennis Bray, Julian Lewis, Martin Raff, Keith Roberts, and James D. Watson. *Molecular Biology of the Cell*. New York: Garland, 1983. This massive work is an excellent advanced undergraduate/graduate textbook in cell biology and developmental genetics, written by several of the major scientists in these fields. The book is clearly written, with excellent photographs and diagrams. Chapter 8, "The Cell Nucleus," is a comprehensive discussion of prokaryotic and eukaryotic gene organization.

Eisen, Herman N. *Immunology: An Introduction to Molecular and Cellular Principles of the Immune Responses*. 2d ed. Philadelphia: J. B. Lippincott, 1980. This graduate-level textbook, originally derived from Davis, Dulbecco, Eisen, Ginsberg, and Wood's *Microbiology*, is an extremely detailed, well illustrated, extensively referenced discussion of the human immune system. Chapter 17, "Immunoglobulin Molecules and Genes," is an excellent discussion of the immunoglobulin gene cluster.

Felsenfeld, Gary. "DNA." *Scientific American* 253 (October, 1985): 58-67. As part of a special *Scientific American* issue devoted to "The Molecules of Life," this article clearly describes the structure of DNA, how it is organized into genes, and how DNA folds up to form a chromosome. The article includes excellent diagrams, relevant experiments, and a summary of gene regulation mechanisms.

Lewin, Benjamin. *Genes II*. New York: John Wiley & Sons, 1985. A sequel to *Genes*, this advanced undergraduate/graduate textbook is a comprehensive yet very readable summary of current advances in molecular biology. The text includes numerous chapters on gene organization and regulation, including chapter 18, "Eukaryotic Genomes: A Continuum of Sequences," and chapter 21, "Structural Genes Belong to Families."

Raven, Peter H., and George B. Johnson. *Biology*. 2d ed. St. Louis: Times Mirror/ Mosby, 1989. This beautifully illustrated textbook is for beginning biology majors. It is very clearly written and is understandable to the layperson. Chapter 14, "DNA: The Genetic Material," and chapter 15, "Genes and How They Work," are excellent introductions to the organization and functions of genes.

Roberts, Leslie. "Plan for Genome Centers Sparks a Controversy." *Science* 246 (October 13, 1989): 204-205. This news commentary article is a discussion of the political and research strategies involved in the Human Genome Project, an attempt by the United States National Institutes of Health (NIH) to map every gene of every human chromosome. Several major scientists are quoted, including Nobel laureate James D. Watson.

Sang, James H. *Genetics and Development*. London: Longman, 1984. This textbook is suitable both as a graduate-level text and as a reference source for developmental geneticists. Chapter 2, "The Molecular Organization of the Genome," is a thorough discussion of chromatin, C values, reassociation kinetics, and gene organization. Several hundred references are cited.

Swanson, Carl P., Timothy Merz, and William J. Young. *Cytogenetics: The Chromosome in Division, Inheritance, and Evolution*. 2d ed. Englewood Cliffs, N.J.: Prentice-Hall, 1981. An outstanding discussion of cytogenetics, this textbook is a detailed description of chromosome structure and gene organization for graduate-level students. Chapter 3, "Architecture of the Chromosome: II. Eukaryotic Chromosomes," is an excellent summary of C values, reassociation kinetics, and histone genes.

Wallace, Robert A., Jack L. King, and Gerald P. Sanders. *Biosphere: The Realm of Life*. 2d ed. Glenview, Ill.: Scott, Foresman, 1988. This is an excellent beginning biology textbook both for biology majors and for nonmajors. Excellent diagrams, photographs, and writing make it very understandable to the layperson. Chapter 13, "Genes and Chromosomes," and chapter 14, "What is DNA?" are very basic descriptions of DNA structure and chromosomal organization.

David Wason Hollar, Jr.

Cross-References

Chromatin Structure for Active Genes, 445; DNA Sequencing, 698; DNA's Molecular Structure, 706; Eukaryotic Transcriptional Control: Steroid Hormones, 887; Extranuclear Inheritance, 960; Gene Amplification and Deletion, 1090; Genes and Nucleic Acids, 1134; Genes and Polypeptide Chains, 1141; In Situ Hybridization, 1408; Transposable Elements, 2654.

EUKARYOTIC POST-TRANSCRIPTIONAL CONTROL

Type of life science: Genetic regulation in eukaryotes
Other fields of study: Animal physiology, biochemistry, developmental biology (embryology), and plant physiology

Post-transcriptional controls influence the way proteins are made inside cells. They ensure that proteins appear in the correct amounts and at the proper times so that cells can function normally.

Principal terms
EXON: the part of the primary transcript that contains the language to make a protein
INTRON: the part of the primary transcript that is removed because it is not needed to make a protein
PRIMARY TRANSCRIPT: the ribonucleic acid (RNA) molecule that is copied from genes in the deoxyribonucleic acid (DNA)
RIBONUCLEOPROTEIN (RNP): a particle containing RNA and protein
RNA PROCESSING: the modification of the primary transcript to create a messenger RNA (mRNA)
SNURP: a "small nuclear ribonucleoprotein" that helps to remove introns from the primary transcript
SPLICING: the stitching together of exons after introns are removed to make an mRNA
TRANSCRIPTION: the production of RNA and DNA
TRANSLATION: the production of proteins

Summary of the Phenomenon

A cell contains a particular collection of proteins that helps it to function normally. These proteins must be present in the proper amounts, and they must be made at the proper time during the life of that cell. Proteins are manufactured following instructions that are found in the deoxyribonucleic acid (DNA). These instructional regions, called genes, are unique for each different protein in the cell. When a particular gene is "turned on," eventually its protein appears in the cell. When the gene is "turned off," the protein does not appear. This turning on and off of genes is referred to as the regulation of gene expression, and it is a highly complicated process.

The regulation of gene expression can be broken down into two main categories, called transcriptional controls and post-transcriptional controls. The earliest to come into play are the transcriptional controls. They determine which genes are to be turned on and therefore which proteins are to be made. Each gene is copied into an intermediate ribonucleic acid (RNA) molecule by a process called transcription. The control of transcription—that is, the choice of which genes are to be copied—

is responsible for the appearance of the particular set of proteins that defines the cell type. Specialized cell types (such as muscle or nerve cells) contain a unique array of proteins and therefore can carry out unique functions.

Once transcription has occurred, then post-transcriptional controls become important. Beginning with the appearance of new RNA, and ending with the production of new protein, these controls precisely regulate how much of a protein is made and when it appears. The production of RNA and protein takes place in different regions of eukaryotic cells (the cells of plants and animals, for example). Such cells are divided into two main compartments, the nucleus and the cytoplasm. Transcription is limited to the nucleus, since that is where nearly all the cell's DNA resides. The machinery for protein synthesis is found in the cytoplasm. This separation means that the cell must have some way to regulate not only which RNAs enter the cytoplasm but also how rapidly each enters and when each becomes involved in making a protein.

Post-transcriptional controls are imposed at a number of different places between the time the RNA is produced and the time the protein appears in the cell. The first of these involves a change in the structure of new RNAs by a sequence of events called RNA processing. Once modified in this fashion, the RNAs are ready for transport into the cytoplasm. This process is thought to be controlled in some way to ensure a smooth transfer of RNAs between the two cell compartments. Once the RNAs are in the cytoplasm, the rate at which proteins are made is regulated. Thus, controls are built in at each step so that the proper amount of each protein appears when it is needed by the cell.

Translation is the process by which proteins are synthesized. In order for translation to proceed normally, three different kinds of RNAs are required. Messenger RNA (mRNA) contains the information that is used to make a particular protein. Ribosomal RNA (rRNA) forms part of the ribosome, an organelle that is the physical site at which proteins are manufactured. Transfer RNA (tRNA) carries the building blocks of proteins, called amino acids, to the ribosome, where they are assembled according to the instructions found in RNA.

The first place that post-transcriptional controls become important is in RNA processing. The tRNAs, rRNAs, and mRNAs are synthesized as parts of larger RNA molecules called primary transcripts. Each primary transcript is "processed" in order to create the final tRNA, rRNA, or mRNA molecule. This end is achieved by giving a unique chemical tag to those parts of the primary transcript that will end up in tRNA, rRNA, or mRNA. The untagged regions are broken down into small building blocks, the nucleotides, that can be reused to make more RNAs.

The sequence of events that unfolds as an mRNA is created from its primary transcript provides an illustration of how RNA processing works. As the primary transcript is synthesized, it gradually peels off the DNA, creating a dangling end. This end, which contains a nucleotide called guanosine, is chemically modified to yield a region called a "cap." When transcription is complete, the other end of the primary transcript falls away from the DNA and is tagged with a "tail" containing a group of adenosine nucleotides referred to as poly A. This capped and tailed molecule, which is about five times longer than the mRNA to which it will give rise, is now ready for further processing.

The next steps in processing are collectively referred to as splicing reactions. The primary transcript is made up of stretches of nucleotides called exons, which are needed to make a protein, intermixed with other stretches of nucleotides called introns, which have nothing to do with the protein to be made. The next job is to remove the introns and stitch the exons back together to produce an mRNA molecule containing both cap and tail. This process demands precision because, if any part of an intron is mistakenly stitched in with the exons, the resulting protein will not be normal and cell function may be disrupted.

Splicing is accomplished by a unique group of RNAs that that are found only in the nucleus. These small nuclear RNAs (snRNAs) are associated with proteins to form small nuclear ribonucleoproteins (snRNPs), or "snurps." The snurps are able to recognize the boundary between intron and exon, since it is defined by particular groups of nucleotides. Acting as "molecular scissors," they snip out the introns and connect the exons together in the same order to make an mRNA. Some primary transcripts may contain as few as two or three exons, while others may be made up of as many as fifty of these regions. Thus, splicing can be a very complicated process. Some primary transcripts even contain the information for several different mRNAs. Thus, by linking together different combinations of exons, different mRNAs can be made, which permits additional flexibility in the kinds of proteins made in the cell.

RNAs that have been correctly processed in the nucleus are transported into the cytoplasm. Regardless of the type of RNA that is involved, at some point during processing proteins bind to the RNA to form ribonucleoproteins (RNPs). In the case of rRNAs, these RNPs make up the small and large subunits of the ribosome. Proteins also associate with tRNAs before they leave the nucleus, and a similar process leads to the formation of messenger ribonucleoproteins (mRNPs). The RNPs are large, and they must somehow cross the barrier that separates the nucleus from the cytoplasm. This boundary, called the nuclear envelope, is composed of two membranes that are perforated by areas called nuclear pores. It is likely that movement of RNP complexes into the cytoplasm takes place through these pores, but it is not known how this process occurs. Perhaps nuclear pores regulate molecular traffic, limiting the entry of RNPs into the cytoplasm. Alternatively, these regions could simply serve as channels, permitting unrestricted travel.

Once in the cytoplasm, the three kinds of RNAs, along with their bound proteins, become part of the protein-synthesizing machinery. Other small molecules are also engaged in regulating translation, so that the rate at which a particular protein is manufactured is the product of a wide variety of controlling factors. The post-transcriptional controls that have been studied most thoroughly focus on the regulation of mRNA stability in the cytoplasm. The half-life of an RNA—that is, how long it is available for translation—affects the time that a protein is made, how much of the protein is made, and when the synthesis of that protein stops. For example, some mRNAs are translated immediately upon entry into the cytoplasm. In other cases, the mRNP remains dormant in the cytoplasm until some signal arrives that releases it for translation. Once translation begins, the mRNA can be translated a few times or many times, thereby generating different amounts of protein.

The turnover rate of the mRNA, that is, how rapidly or slowly it is broken down, is regulated to some extent by the structure of the molecule. An mRNA is composed of a linear sequence of nucleotides. Centrally located in the sequence is the region containing the information for a protein. On either side of the coding region are noncoding regions that serve other purposes. Both the noncoding and coding sequences are important in defining the stability of the mRNA. For example, the poly A tail may have to be intact if the mRNA is to be continually translated. Removal of this region signals breakdown of the mRNA, thereby stopping the synthesis of that specific protein.

The breakdown of cytoplasmic RNAs is accomplished by enzymes called ribonucleases. These proteins specifically attack the RNA, causing it to fragment into individual nucleotides. How the RNA becomes available for such attack, and whether the proteins bound to each mRNA protect it from breakdown, are subjects of intense investigation. Proteins have a definite lifetime in the cell. The final step in controlling the amount of protein in the cell is determined by regulating the half-life of individual proteins. Proteins with a short half-life will be broken down quickly, while those with a longer half-life will be active much longer in the cell. These differences can have profound effects on cell function.

Methods of Study

One of the first investigations of post-transcriptional control processes began in the 1960's and focused on the relationship between nuclear RNA and cytoplasmic RNA. The question was whether all the RNA made in the nucleus eventually ended up in the cytoplasm. Two basic techniques can be used to answer this question. In the first, called subcellular fractionation, cells are broken open and the mixture is placed in a centrifuge. Since the nucleus is a large particle, it separates easily from the more liquid-like cytoplasm, so that relatively pure fractions of nucleus and cytoplasm can be obtained. The second, termed radioactive labeling, is achieved by incubating cells with radioactive nucleotides that are needed to make new RNA. The new RNA becomes labeled and can easily be located and identified in the cell. When the radioactivity present in RNAs within the nucleus was followed to determine how much of it appeared in the cytoplasm, it became evident that only a small fraction of the radioactive RNA left the nucleus.

The next step was to determine the sizes of the RNAs found in the cytoplasm. That can be accomplished using a method called gel electrophoresis. In this technique, RNAs are separated from one another on the basis of difference in size. RNAs are separated by running them through a gel-like material. The results demonstrated that primary transcripts are cleaved to produce smaller mRNAs, tRNAs, and rRNAs. To determine if the primary transcripts were manufactured at particular sites in the DNA, the process of autoradiography can be used. This technique permits the visualization of radioactively labeled molecules, in this case RNA, using photographic film. Sites of radioactivity expose the film, leaving a clearly visible blotch. If cells are radioactively labeled and then placed under film, the site at which RNA synthesis has occurred can be seen. Using this method, it was found that the primary transcript for rRNA is localized to a special part of the nucleus called the nucleolus, while the synthesis of other primary transcripts is spread out over the remainder of the DNA.

The electron microscope has also played a valuable role in studies of post-transcriptional control mechanisms. This instrument can magnify objects thousands of times, making it possible to see parts of the cell clearly. The technique of molecular hybridization can be used in concert with the electron microscope to show that introns are removed from the primary transcript, leaving only exons. In this procedure, the mRNA for a particular protein is mixed with the DNA containing the gene for that protein. Similar regions in the DNA and mRNA form a match with each other, creating a two-stranded structure called a hybrid. One half of the hybrid is made up of DNA, and the other half is made up of mRNA. The DNA-RNA hybrid can be observed with the electron microscope. When it was done, however, it was found that the DNA and mRNA did not match up exactly. Rather, some parts of the DNA were looped out and away from the mRNA; these represented unmatched DNA regions. The unmatched parts of the DNA corresponded to the introns that had been removed during processing of the primary transcript. The matched-up regions corresponded to the exons making up the mRNA.

The electron microscope has also been useful in examining the transfer of RNPs from the nucleus to the cytoplasm. While in the nucleus, the RNPs are rounded in shape. As they begin to move through the nuclear pores, however, they become cigar-shaped. This change may be required in order to fit through the small channel in the center of the nuclear pore. When the RNPs enter the cytoplasm, they regain their original shape.

A variety of methods have played an important part in advancing understanding of how post-transcriptional controls are coordinated. Each method defines a particular step into this complex process, and together they reveal how the controls as a whole influence the proteins made in the eukaryotic cell.

Context

Cells must execute specific functions in order to remain alive. For example, they must reproduce, grow, and react to the environment around them. Of all the cell's components, the proteins are most responsible for cell function. Thus, an understanding of how protein synthesis is controlled has significant impact on understanding how cells function. The study of post-transcriptional controls has led to a deepening understanding of both normal and abnormal functions. For example, an understanding of how RNAs are processed before leaving the nucleus has important implications for health and disease. Normal function of the immune system leads to the production of antibodies. These proteins protect the body against invasion by foreign substances. The production of antibodies is dependent on proper splicing reactions, so that if this process is impeded in any way, the immune system does not function the way it should. In another example, defects in the splicing of the primary transcript containing the information for the protein hemoglobin can occur. When this happens, a defective hemoglobin protein is made, which can lead to a disease of the blood called thalassemia. In this case, not enough oxygen is carried in the blood because the oxygen-carrying hemoglobin molecule is not normal.

The importance of post-transcriptional controls becomes evident when one considers how cells become specialized. For example, a heart muscle cell becomes specialized for one function, which is contraction, while a red blood cell becomes specialized to carry oxygen throughout the body. These different functions reflect the control of synthesis of particular proteins in each cell type. When scientists understand how to manipulate the controlling factors, it might be possible to make normal proteins in a cell that contains defective proteins. This knowledge may be important in the treatment of certain diseases, such as cancer.

For the first time in history, it is possible to program changes in the genes. The methods that make this possible, called recombinant DNA technology, were developed in the 1970's, and they have made a significant contribution to the understanding of transcriptional controls. Genes can now be inserted into the DNA, and the factors that cause the genes to be turned on or off can be studied in some detail. This approach can be extended to post-transcriptional controls as well. The implications of these studies are far-reaching. For example, in agriculture, the ability to insert genes for a particular protein into certain crop plants will have enormous impact on the types and amounts of food that can be grown to feed an increasingly hungry world.

Bibliography

Darnell, James. "RNA." *Scientific American* 253 (October, 1985): 68-78. This general article describes the kinds of RNA and what role each plays in the cell. RNA processing is treated in a clear manner and is complemented by illustrations that are instructive and easy to follow. Some electron micrographs are also included. The article is written for the reader with no scientific background. A bibliography is included.

Freifelder, David. *Essentials of Molecular Biology.* Boston: Jones and Bartlett, 1985. This primer of molecular biology is written for the college student with some background in biology. It describes the control of gene activity in an abbreviated yet lucid fashion. Chapter 9, "Transcription," and chapter 16, "Regulation of Gene Activity in Eukaryotic Cells," are useful in gaining a more profound understanding of post-transcriptional controls. Clear discussions of the methods used in studies of RNAs are an added feature of these chapters.

Ross, Jeffrey. "The Turnover of Messenger RNA." *Scientific American* 260 (April,

1989): 48-55. This article discusses the structure of messenger RNA (mRNA) and relates that structure to mRNA stability in the cytoplasm. The role of ribonucleases is described, and examples of autoradiography and gel electrophoresis are presented in illustration format. Some information on RNA processing is presented. Written for the reader with no knowledge of biology. Bibliography.

Steitz, Joan Argetsinger. "Snurps." *Scientific American* 258 (June, 1988): 56-63. This discussion of small nuclear ribonucleoproteins (snurps) illustrates the importance of these cell components in the controlled removal of intron sequences necessary to produce a biologically viable messenger RNA. Details of the variety of types of snurps and the precise role each plays in RNA processing are clearly illustrated and discussed. For the reader with no knowledge of biology. Bibliography.

Villee, Claude A., Eldra Pearl Solomon, Charles E. Martin, Diana W. Martin, Linda R. Berg, and P. William Davis. *Biology.* 2d ed. Philadelphia: Saunders College Publishing, 1989. This college-level textbook of introductory biology describes the fundamentals of post-transcriptional control. Chapter 13, "RNA and Protein Synthesis," discusses the processing phenomena. Other post-transcriptional controls are covered in chapter 14, "Gene Regulation." A glossary of terms appears in the back matter of the book.

Zubay, Geoffrey. *Genetics.* Menlo Park, Calif.: Benjamin/Cummings, 1987. This college-level textbook of basic genetics presents a succinct view of post-transcriptional modifications of RNA in chapter 5, "Transcription: Synthesis of RNA." Processing of ribosomal RNAs and messenger RNAs is described, and an electron micrograph showing molecular hybridization is presented, as well as other illustrations. The glossary of terms is useful.

Valerie M. Kish

Cross-References

Eukaryotic Gene Organization, 871; Positive and Negative Eukaryotic Transcriptional Control, 895; Eukaryotic Gene Regulation, 1111; Genes and Nucleic Acids, 1134; Protein Synthesis: Locational Specificity and Targeting, 2266; Transcription of DNA to Form RNA, 2632; Translation of Messenger RNA to Form Protein, 2647.

EUKARYOTIC TRANSCRIPTIONAL CONTROL:
STEROID HORMONES

Type of life science: Animal physiology
Other fields of study: Biochemistry, genetic regulation in eukaryotes, and molecular
biology

*Cell-to-cell communication in eukaryotic organisms (such as animals and plants)
is mediated by chemical messengers called hormones, of which there are two principal types: protein and steroid. In animals, steroid hormones, which are derivatives
of cholesterol, switch genes on or off in target cells, thereby controlling the production of proteins and how the cell functions.*

Principal terms

ADRENAL CORTEX: an endocrine gland, located above each kidney in
most vertebrate animals, that produces and secretes steroid
hormones

ALARMONE: a hormone (such as as cyclic adenosine monophosphate, or
cyclic AMP) that triggers molecule-to-molecule interactions within a
cell, eventually leading to control of certain genes

CHOLESTEROL: a type of steroid that is prevalent in animal tissues and
that assists in steroid hormone production

ENDOCRINE SYSTEM: a system of ductless glands in vertebrate animals
that produces and releases hormones into the bloodstream for
transport to various target tissues

GENE: a sequence of several thousand deoxyribonucleic acid (DNA)
nucleotide pairs in a chromosome that encodes a messenger
ribonucleic acid (RNA), usually for encoding a protein

HOMEOSTASIS: the maintenance of constant conditions within an
organism's internal environment; usually it is regulated by
hormones

HORMONE: a chemical messenger, usually protein or steroid in content,
that controls cell function by regulating the activities of the cell's
genes

PROTEIN: a long chain of amino acids encoded by the DNA nucleotide
sequence of a gene; proteins can provide cell structure, control
chemical reactions, and act as hormones

RECEPTOR: a molecule, usually a protein, found in the membrane of a
hormone's target cell; the hormone must activate the receptor to
effect changes in the cell

STEROID: a type of lipid, found in plants and animals, that produces
many changes in living organisms by controlling genes

Summary of the Phenomenon

Multicellular eukaryotes, such as fungi, plants, and animals, must have efficient cell-to-cell communications in order to coordinate the activities of all the cells constituting the organism. These organismal activities include basic cellular metabolism, cell and organismal growth, cell differentiation, tissue development, regeneration, and aging. Homeostasis, the maintenance of constant controlled conditions within the organism, is a central theme of cell-to-cell communication. For animals, communication among all parts of the organism is mediated by elaborate nervous systems in which electrical impulses are transmitted along nerve cells called neurons. In chordates, animals having nerve cords, these nerve systems can extend for hundreds, even thousands of miles within a single individual, as well as encompassing organized structures (the brain, in particular) containing billions of cells.

In addition to elaborate nervous systems, animals use chemical messengers for communication throughout the individual and between individuals. These chemical messengers, called hormones, are the principal means of communication in primitive animals and in nonanimal species, ranging from multicellular eukaryotes (fungi and plants) to single-celled eukaryotes (protists) to single-celled prokaryotes (bacteria). All cellular life-forms use hormones to some extent in cell-to-cell interactions. The nervous systems of higher animals are intricately connected with hormonal systems. Animal nervous systems, in fact, probably evolved from hormonal systems.

Hormones are chemical messengers that are produced and released by one cell to provide information to another cell. Such information may include instructions for the recipient cell to produce certain substances, to orient itself into a specific position, or to become inactive. Hormones produce these changes by controlling specific genes, or molecules of deoxyribonucleic acid (DNA), in the target cells, the cells which are receiving the hormone. The hormone penetrates the target cell and either acts directly on specific genes or triggers a series of chemical reactions that ultimately act on specific genes.

The hormonally controlled genes in the target cells are sequences of several thousand DNA nucleotide base pairs. The majority of these nucleotide base pairs encode a specific protein. The enzyme RNA polymerase reads the DNA nucleotide sequence to manufacture a ribonucleic acid (RNA) molecule. Subsequently, the nucleotide sequence of the RNA molecule is read by the multienzyme ribosome to make a protein. Therefore, a gene (that is, a DNA molecule) encodes RNA, which encodes protein.

Not all of the DNA nucleotide sequence of a gene encodes protein. Usually, the first few hundred DNA nucleotide base pairs of a gene serve as a control region that can be switched on or off. If the gene's control region is switched on, then RNA polymerase can read the protein-coding region of the gene and thus manufacture an RNA, which then will be used to make a protein. If the gene's control region is switched off, then RNA polymerase cannot read the coding region, preventing the RNA and protein from being made. The gene control region is the point of action for hormones. Some hormones (activators) will turn on a specific gene, thus causing a particular protein to be manufactured, whereas other hormones (repressors) turn off a gene, thus preventing the manufacture of a particular protein. A particular hormone may be an activator for some genes but a repressor for others. This system is very valuable in cellular differentiation. For example, blood cells must make the protein hemoglobin in order to transport oxygen; these blood cells must receive the correct hormonal signals to make hemoglobin and not some other protein, such as keratin (hair protein).

Hormones generally fall into two major structural classes: proteins and steroids. Protein hormones are composed of protein, long chains of amino acids that are encoded by genes in the hormone producer cells. Steroid hormones are derivatives of cholesterol, a type of steroid lipid, or fat. Cholesterol is found in most animal tissues and has significant effects upon cellular metabolism.

Chemical messengers are not necessarily limited to proteins and steroids. Many cells use other chemicals, such as cyclic adenosine monophosphate (cyclic AMP) and sugars to help control genes. When cells are stressed, chemical messengers such as cyclic AMP trigger a cascade of enzyme reactions that switch genes on or off to help the cells survive. Such hormones are appropriately called alarmones. A system of this type exists in the cellular slime mold *Dictyostelium discoideum*, which normally exists as single amoebalike cells. When these cells are starved, they release cyclic AMP, which attracts the cells along a concentration gradient until they clump together as a multicellular mass. The multicellular mass migrates to a new food source, whereupon some cells differentiate, leading to the production and release of spores, each of which becomes a single amoebalike cell. The alarmone cyclic AMP has a distinct role in cellular communication during this process.

In animals, protein and steroid hormones play important roles in cellular growth, differentiation, and development. They are both gene regulators, although their mechanisms of action are slightly different. Both are produced and secreted by endocrine glands, small ductless organs in the body that secrete substances directly into the bloodstream. The blood transports the hormones to various target tissues. Like *Dictyostelium* cyclic AMP, however, hormones follow a concentration gradient in the bloodstream: They are distributed throughout the bloodstream and could affect any tissue. Nevertheless, they will concentrate heavily at particular target tissues because the target tissue cells contain receptor molecules to attract and chemically bind to the hormones. Thus, the receptor molecules, usually protein, act as signals on the target cell to guide the hormone into the target cell.

When a protein hormone reaches its target tissue, it chemically binds to a receptor protein located in the cell membrane. Once the binding reaction occurs, the receptor triggers the molecule adenylate cyclase to produce the alarmone cyclic AMP. Cyclic AMP triggers a series of enzymes to activate other enzymes that eventually turn on or turn off certain genes, thus controlling the production of proteins by these specific genes. Therefore, protein hormones, the products of genes, control the production of other proteins by other genes.

When a steroid hormone reaches its target tissue, it also chemically binds to a protein receptor resting in the cell membrane. Unlike a protein hormone, however, it is believed that the steroid-receptor complex penetrates the cell membane to the cell nucleus, where it binds to the control regions of certain genes, thereby switching those genes on or off. Therefore, both protein and steroid hormones control genes, but steroid hormones appear to do so more directly than do protein hormones. Neither protein nor steroid hormones can enter or control the genes of a target cell if that cell does not have the appropriate receptor in its membrane. The receptor identifies a cell as a hormone target.

The endocrine system consists of numerous glands located throughout the animal body, including the hypothalamus and pituitary gland in the brain, the thyroid and parathyroid glands in the neck, the thymus gland above the heart, the pancreas in the abdomen, the adrenal glands above the kidneys, and the gonads, or reproductive organs (the male testes and the female ovaries).

The endocrine system works primarily by cause and effect, one cell producing hormones that instruct other cells' genes to produce hormones to control still other cells. For example, if the body needs to convert fat into glucose, the hypothalamus will secrete a protein hormone that instructs cells of the pituitary gland to secrete the protein hormone adrenocorticotropic hormone (ACTH). ACTH travels via the bloodstream to the adrenal cortex, where it instructs genes of certain cells to produce and secrete the steroid hormone cortisol, which instructs various body cells to convert fat into glucose. Once the body has an adequate glucose supply, the hypothalamus stops releasing its hormone, which results in the pituitary stopping ACTH, which results in the adrenal cortex stopping cortisol. This type of on/off system based upon the body's needs is termed negative feedback; once everything is properly balanced, the system shuts off. Negative feedback is central to homeostasis.

The principal steroid hormone-secreting endocrine glands are the adrenal cortex (the outermost part of the adrenal gland) and the gonads. The adrenal cortex, situated just above each kidney, secretes three major classes of steroids: the mineralocorticoids, the glucocorticoids, and the androgens. The primary mineralocorticoid is aldosterone, which increases the retention of sodium by the kidneys. The primary glucocorticoid is cortisol, which instructs body cells to convert fats and proteins into glucose. The androgens are male sex steroid hormones.

In males, the testes secrete the steroid hormone testosterone, which stimulates the development of male sexual organs, sperm development (spermatogenesis), and the development of male secondary sex characteristics, such as a deeper voice, increased musculature, and increased body hair. In females, the ovaries secrete estrogen and progesterone. Estrogen stimulates the development of female sexual organs and the development of female secondary sex characteristics (such as increased body fat and increased skin vascularization), and it plays an important role in the menstrual cycle. Progesterone maintains the stability of the uterus during pregnancy and stimulates breast development.

In animals, steroid hormones are derived from cholesterol, a steroid found in many body tissues. While evidence indicates that excessive body cholesterol contributes to heart disease, a small amount of body cholesterol is needed to produce all required steroid hormones. In addition to serving as hormones, steroids have other useful bodily functions. Exposure of the skin steroid ergosterol to ultraviolet light (present in sunlight) converts the molecule into another steroid, Vitamin D_2, which is important for proper bone growth. The steroid cholic acid is a principal ingredient for bile, a chemical released from the liver into the small intestine to assist fat digestion.

Methods of Study

Studies of hormonal structure and function have been primarily biochemical in nature, although recent studies of homeotic genes in organismal pattern development indicates that molecular genetics will become an important tool for studying hormone action at the genetic level. Protein hormone synthesis is well understood, based upon scientists' knowledge of protein biochemistry (for example, DNA encodes RNA, which encodes protein). Steroid biosynthesis was first understood by Konrad Bloch of Harvard University in the 1940's. Bloch demonstrated that the steroid cholesterol could be derived from acetic acid.

Various hormones have been traced to their producer endocrine glands by a combination of biochemical tests on dissected gland extracts and the study of various diseases affecting endocrine gland function, such as goiter, dwarfism, and diabetes. Some hormones have been identified based upon nutritional deficiencies (a low level of vitamin D, for example, causes rickets).

Hormone-receptor interactions have been studied using a technique called affinity chromatography. Affinity chromatography involves the use of a glass tube column that has been packed with a semisolid chemical containing a specific target cell receptor molecule. A buffer containing the purified hormone is washed through the column. If the hormone binds to this specific receptor, then it will remain in the column, stuck to the receptor molecules. If the hormone does not bind to this specific receptor, it will simply wash through and exit the column. This simple technique establishes which hormones will bind to which receptors, and therefore which hormones will control which target cells in the organism.

Hormonal interactions with DNA have been studied using a combination of radioactive isotope labeling and biochemical kinetic studies (that is, studying the rates of reaction). Protein hormones contain sulfur; therefore, the radioactive isotope sulfur 35 "labels" the protein, enabling the experimenter to determine precisely where the molecule goes within the organism—and even within individual cells. Similarly, steroid hormones can be traced using the radioactive isotope tritium (hydrogen 3), a hydrogen atom having two neutrons. Experiments involving radioactive isotopes have verified that protein hormones do not directly interact with the genes they control; instead, protein hormones activate the receptor to stimulate a series of other molecules to control certain genes. Steroid hormones interact directly with the genes they control.

Experimenting with the fruit fly *Drosophila melanogaster*, Michael Ashburner and colleagues demonstrated that the steroid hormone ecdysterone controls genes in a specified pattern during larval development. In *Drosophila* larvae, the salivary glands contain polytene chromosomes, DNA molecules which have multiplied up to one thousand times without separating. These polytene chromosomes are easily visible under the microscope. Furthermore, active genes (that is, those producing proteins) on the polytene chromosomes "puff": They are visible as expanded regions of the chromosome. Ashburner showed that ecdysterone causes the puffs in a predictable order.

Steroids were demonstrated to act specifically at gene control regions in experiments involving the antibiotic rifampicin, which inactivates the enzyme RNA polymerase. RNA polymerase reads the nucleotide sequence of DNA to manufacture RNA, leading to protein production. Rifampicin inactivates RNA polymerase, resulting in no RNA and no protein. Subsequent addition of steroid hormones, however, reactivates the gene, and new RNA polymerase begins making RNA again.

Synthetic steroid hormones can be manufactured in the laboratory, including steroids involved in birth control. The steroid progesterone maintains pregnancy by controlling target cells in the female uterus. A synthetic antiprogesterone known as RU 486, also a steroid, competes with progesterone for receptors on the uterine target cells, eventually beating progesterone, deactivating the uterine cells, and terminating conditions needed for a fetus to survive. The use of RU 486 has created controversy, but it has successfully induced abortions in women tested worldwide.

Context

The study of both protein and steroid hormones is very important for improving knowledge of gene regulation and cell-to-cell communication as well as for developing medicines to treat various diseases and disorders. Hormones play a critical role in communication and control among cells of all living organisms. Hormones control genes, which encode proteins, which affect every cellular activity, including cellular metabolism, growth, differentiation, development, regeneration, and aging. Hormones called pheromones enable cellular communication between different organisms and affect activities such as mating and territoriality. For many years, the extent of hormonal influence in living organisms had been grossly underestimated.

Steroid hormones are useful for treating certain diseases, such as rheumatoid arthritis, although in controlled doses. Excessive steroid use can severely disrupt the body's physiological balance, resulting in possible damage to the heart, liver, and kidneys. Many athletes have used steroids as rapid muscle builders; the short-term competitive edge is often accompanied by physical damage and even death. Steroids also are administered to beef cattle for the same purpose: rapid muscle building. The steroids remain in the beef, however, when it is consumed by humans. In some countries, excessively high beef steroid levels have produced sexual organ abnormalities in children whose diets included such beef.

Medical applications include the treatment of physical conditions such as kidney disease, skin disorders, and shock. These treatments are currently limited because scientists lack a proper understanding of which genes are being controlled in which target cells. Until knowledge of hormones improves, the use of steroid hormones in medicine will produce various side effects, resulting in the need for limited dosages. Nevertheless, athletes abuse steroids, and the introduction of steroids into cattle is allowed. Controversy surrounds the proper and improper uses of steroids, including their role in birth control. The pregnancy-ending steroid RU 486, for example, is banned in the United States, although it has been used elsewhere in the world.

Bibliography

Alberts, Bruce, Dennis Bray, Julian Lewis, Martin Raff, Keith Roberts, and James D. Watson. *Molecular Biology of the Cell*. New York: Garland, 1983. As an intermediate-level undergraduate textbook, this outstanding work is a comprehensive, clear discussion of molecular and developmental biology. It contains excellent photographs and diagrams. Chapter 13, "Chemical Signaling Between Cells," provides detailed information concerning hormones and neurotransmitters.

Ashburner, Michael, Carol Chihara, Paul Meltzer, and Geoff Richards. "Temporal Control of Puffing Activity in Polytene Chromosomes." *Cold Spring Harbor Symposia on Quantitative Biology* 38 (1973): 655-662. This review article is a comprehensive summary of Ashburner's experiments showing that the steroid hormone ecdysterone activates genes, and therefore "puffing," in polytene chromosomes of *Drosophila melanogaster*. The article is clearly written, with presentations of several important hypotheses and some very elegant experiments.

Barrack, Evelyn R., and Donald S. Coffey. "Hormone Receptors and the Nuclear Matrix." In *Gene Regulation by Steroid Hormones II*, edited by A. K. Roy and J. H. Clark. New York: Springer-Verlag, 1983. This article is a very detailed scientific discussion of steroid hormone action. While it is very technical, the introduction is clearly written, numerous experiments are described, and an extensive reference list is provided.

Baulieu, Étienne-Émile. "Contragestion and Other Clinical Applications of RU 486, an Antiprogesterone at the Receptor." *Science* 245 (September 22, 1989): 1351-1357. This review article, written by the French biochemist who developed RU 486, is a discussion of how this synthetic steroid works and its applications. RU 486, coined the "morning-after pill," has generated a storm of controversy because of its ability to induce abortions chemically.

Berridge, Michael J. "The Molecular Basis of Communication Within the Cell." *Scientific American* 253 (October, 1985): 142-152. As part of a special *Scientific American* issue devoted to "The Molecules of Life," this article is a discussion of what happens within a cell after a hormone contacts the cell's receptors. The article includes a very clear description of intracellular communication molecules, including alarmones such as cyclic AMP. The illustrations are excellent.

Dworniczak, B., S. Kobus, K. Schaltmann-Eiteljorge, and O. Pongs. "Ecdysterone, Ecdysterone Receptor, and Chromosome Puffs." In *Gene Regulation by Steroid Hormones II*, edited by A. K. Roy and J. H. Clark. New York: Springer-Verlag, 1983. This review article discusses the activation of polytene chromosome puffing in *Drosophila melanogaster* caused by the steroid hormone ecydsterone. The authors present a modified version of Ashburner's hypotheses concerning steroid hormonal control of genes.

O'Malley, Bert W., and William T. Schrader. "The Receptors of Steroid Hormones." *Scientific American* 234 (February, 1976): 32-43. This clearly written, well-illustrated review article is an excellent discussion of steroid hormones for the layperson. The article discusses steroid structure, function, and interactions with receptor molecules, and it notes important experiments.

Raven, Peter H., and George B. Johnson. *Biology*. 2d ed. St. Louis: Times Mirror/ Mosby, 1989. This clearly written textbook is for beginning biology majors, although it is very understandable for the layperson. Chapter 48, "Hormones," is a concise discussion of protein and steroid hormones with excellent tables and graphs containing all important human endocrine glands and hormones.

Solomons, T. W. Graham. *Organic Chemistry*. Rev. printing. New York: John Wiley & Sons, 1978. An outstanding introductory organic chemistry textbook for undergraduate chemistry majors. Chapter 23, "Special Topics IV: Lipids," is a thorough discussion of lipid chemistry, including a good discussion of steroid biochemistry.

Zubay, Geoffrey. *Biochemistry*. Reading, Mass.: Addison-Wesley, 1983. A graduate biochemistry textbook, this work is very detailed, and the illustrations and tables are excellent. Chapter 29, "Hormone Action," provides considerable information on protein and steroid hormone structures and actions, including a good discussion of negative feedback homeostasis.

David Wason Hollar, Jr.

Cross-References

Endocrine Functions of the Kidneys and Heart, 780; Endocrine Functions of the Pancreas, 787; Endocrine Systems in Invertebrates, 793; Endocrinology of the Adrenal Glands, 800; Endocrinology of the Pituitary Gland, 807; Endocrinology of the Thyroid and Parathyroid Glands, 814; Genes and Polypeptide Chains, 1141; Hormone Mechanisms and Second Messengers, 1361; Hormones and Behavior, 1377; Pheromones, 2051; Transcription of DNA to Form RNA, 2632.

MAGILL'S
SURVEY
OF
SCIENCE

ALPHABETICAL LIST

CATEGORY LIST